# PHOTO-OFFSET

## FUNDAMENTALS

Large Six-Color Offset Press Used to Print Folding Cartons (Courtesy Harris-Seybold Company)

JOHN E. COGOLI

Hartford Public High School

Hartford, Connecticut

# PHOTO-OFFSET

# FUNDAMENTALS

McKNIGHT & McKNIGHT

Publishing Company

Bloomington, Illinois

SECOND EDITION

COPYRIGHT 1967

by McKnight & McKnight Publishing Company

*Lithographed in U. S. A.*

First Edition, 1960

Library of Congress
Card Catalog Number: 67-11871

# Foreword

This book is a basic manual for the beginner in the field of photo-offset lithography — a division of the graphic arts more popularly known as offset printing. Worker, student, teacher, apprentice, salesman, buyer and other interested persons will gain a fundamental working knowledge of the offset printing method by a careful study of these pages.

The wide acceptance of the first edition of this book, especially by schools and the industry, has prompted the preparation of this revised edition. This edition contains practically all that was in the first edition, plus greatly expanded treatments, especially in methods of type composition, copy preparation, reproduction photography (line, halftone, and color), platemaking and presswork (including duplicator sizes).

No attempt has been made to include *all* the various special fields of the offset method. Such an ambitious work would defeat the very purpose of this book. However, the topics which *are* included are covered by sufficient description, hints, diagrams and illustrations so that the serious beginner (or learner) may proceed doing practical work with little assistance or direction.

Having worked for more than three decades instructing beginners, the author deeply appreciates the difficulties besetting the learner. To this end, he has constantly attempted to present this material in as self-teaching a manner as possible. It would be a serious mistake to do otherwise.

Manufacturers and sources of supply for much of the equipment, supplies and materials mentioned in the text are purposely identified in the Acknowledgments, in captions beneath the illustrations, and in credit notes where applicable. These firms and individuals have a wealth of information, experience and resources with which they are pleased to assist learners and workers in the field.

Any suggestions which will improve future revisions will be appreciated by the author.

J. E. C.
Wethersfield, Connecticut

# Acknowledgments

All Typefaces Begin with the Designer (Harris-Intertype)

This writer extends his most sincere and grateful appreciation to the large number of organizations whose technical and administrative personnel have aided tremendously to the writing and illustrating of this book — both the first edition and this revision. If through error, he has omitted any from the following list, he humbly apologizes and will seek to include them in future printings.

In addition, special gratitude is owed Mr. Wesley D. Stephens, of McKnight & McKnight Publishing Company, for his cooperation and encouragement in the preparation of the first edition of this book, and to Dr. Raymond L. Cornwell, of McKnight & McKnight Publishing Company, for his suggestions and his work with this second edition.

J. E. C.

Abbeon Supply Co.
Acme Staple Co.
Addressograph Multigraph Corp.
Agfa Inc.
American Type Founders Co., Inc.
American Wood Type Mfg. Co.
Amsterdam Continental Types
   and Graphic Equipment, Inc.
Paul Anderson Manufacturing Co.
Russell Ernest Baum, Inc.
The Biddle Co.
ByChrome Co.
The Challenge Machinery Co.
The Chandler & Price Co.
Chart-Pak, Inc.
The Clipper Creative Art Service
   — Dynamic Graphics, Inc.
The Consolidated International
   Equipment and Graphic Supply Co.
Craftsman Line-Up Table Corp.
A.B. Dick Co.
Eugene Dietzgen Co., Inc.
Ditto, Inc.
E.I. DuPont de Nemours & Co.
George Eastman House
Eastman Kodak Co.
Engineering Instruments, Inc.
Fairchild Camera & Instrument Corp.
   — Fairchild-Davidson Div.
   — Fairchild Graphic Equip. Div.
Filmotype Corp.
Fototype, Inc.
Friden, Inc.
Arthur H. Gaebel, Inc.
Gazette Offset Americana
General Binding Corp.
General Printing Ink Co.
   — Division of Sun Chemical Corp.

C. P. Goerz — American Optical Co.
Graphic Arts Publishing Co.
Graphic Arts Technical Foundation
Hammermill Paper Co.
John Hancock Mutual
   Life Insurance Co.
Milo Harding Co.
Harris-Intertype Corp.
   — Harris-Seybold Co., Div.
   — Intertype Co., Div.
HCM Corp.
Heidelberg Eastern, Inc.
C. Howard Hunt Pen Co.
Ilford, Inc.
Interchemical Corp.
   — Printing Ink Div.
International Business Machines Corp.
Itek Business Products
Kenro Corp.
Keuffel & Esser Co.
Kimberly-Clark Corp.
Lanston Monotype Co.
Lawrence Engineering Service
Letterguide Co.
Max Levy & Co.
Litho Chemical and Supply Co., Inc.
Ludlow Typograph Co.
   — and the Brightype Div.
Lufkin Rule Co.
Robert A. McCoy
Mechanical Enterprises, Inc.
Mergenthaler Linotype Co.
Metropolitan Museum of Art
Micro Essential Laboratory, Inc.
Miehle Co.
   — Div. of Miehle-Goss-Dexter, Inc.
Miller Printing Machinery Co.
Minnesota Mining and Mfg. (3M) Co.

Munsell Co.
Museum of the City of New York
NuArc Co., Inc.
Paillard Inc.
Pelouze Manufacturing Co.
Photo Typositor, Inc.
Polychrome Corp.
Printing Arts Research Laboratories
Printing Production Magazine
Protype Div. of Electrographic Corp.
Quillo Advertising Aids Co.
Remington Office Machines
   — Div. of Sperry Rand Corp.
Roberts & Porter, Inc.
Robertson Photo-Mechanix, Inc.
Royal Zenith Corp.
Rutherford Machinery Co.
   — Div. of Sun Chemical Corp.
Ilya Scheinker, Inc.
The Senefelder Co., Inc.
Separon Co.
Stouffer Graphic Arts Equipment Co.
StripPrinter, Inc.
Olivetti Underwood, Inc.
U.S. Department of Commerce
U.S. Government Printing Office
U.S. Library of Congress
U.S. National Archives
U.S. National Park Service
U.S. Treasury Department
Van Son Holland Ink Corp. of America
Varigraph, Inc.
VariTyper Corp.
S.D. Warren Co.
Welch Scientific Co.
Western Printing & Lithographing Co.
Whitin Machine Works
Wild & Stevens, Inc.

# Contents

Electronic Phototypesetter Prints 1200 Char./Min. (Intertype)

FOREWORD v                                    ACKNOWLEDGMENTS VI

*Chapter 1.* INTRODUCTION TO PHOTO-OFFSET PRINTING . . . . . . . . . . . . . . *1*

Major Printing Processes, **1**; Net Value of Printed Products by Processes, **3**; Basic Theory of Offset Printing, **3**; Demonstrations, **6**; Questions, **7**; Problems and Projects, **7**; New Words, **7**.

*Chapter 2.* A BRIEF HISTORY OF PHOTO-OFFSET PRINTING . . . . . . . . . . . *8*

The Invention of Lithography, **8**; The First Lithographic Presses, **10**; Applications of the Lithographic (Stone-Printing) Processes, **11**; Use of Metal Plates on Cylinder Presses, **12**; Advent of Offset, **12**; Introduction of Photography, **12**; The Halftone Screen, **16**; Photo-Offset Lithography, **16**; Questions, **18**; Problems and Projects, **19**; New Words, **19**.

*Chapter 3.* THE OFFSET PRINTING INDUSTRY . . . . . . . . . . . . . . . . . . . . . . *20*

Divisions of Work, **20**; Special Services to the Trade, **23**; The Office Offset Unit, **24**; Questions, **24**; Problems and Projects, **24**; New Words, **25**.

*Chapter 4.* JOB PLANNING AND LAYOUT . . . . . . . . . . . . . . . . . . . . . . . . *26*

Equipment and Materials, **27**; Thumb-Nail Sketches, **27**; Rough Layouts, **28**; Comprehensive Layouts, **28**; Copyfitting, **29**; Illustrations, **30**; The Dummy, **31**; Questions, **31**; Problems and Projects, **32**; New Words, **32**.

*Chapter 5.*   Type Composition for Reproduction ............... 33

*Hot Type Composition*
Metal Type, **33**; Wood Type, **43**; Relief Form-to-Film Conversion, **43**; Questions, **47**; Problems and Projects, **48**; New Words, **48**.

*Cold Type Composition — Mechanical*
Copying Existing Printed Work (For Reprinting), **48**; Hand Lettering and Art, **49**; Clip Art, **50**; Pre-Printed Type, **51**; Typewriter (Impact) Composition, **54**; Questions, **70**; Problems and Projects, **70**; New Words, **71**.

*Cold Type Composition — Photographic*
Photographic Display Composition, **71**; Questions, **76**; Problems and Projects, **76**; New Words, **77**; Photographic Text Composition, **77**; Composition Summary, **90**; Questions, **92**; Problems and Projects, **92**; New Words, **93**.

*Chapter 6.*   Proofreading ........................................ 94

Kinds of Proofs, **94**; Proofreaders' Marks, **94**; Reading and Marking the Proof, **94**; Questions, **97**; Problems and Projects, **98**; New Words, **98**.

*Chapter 7.*   Preparing Camera Copy for Reproduction ........... 99

Kinds of Camera Copy, **99**; Scaling Reductions and Enlargements, **99**; Specifying Reductions or Enlargements, **101**; Preparation of Line Copy, **101**; Preparation of Halftone Copy, **102**; Combinations, **104**; Screen Tints, **104**; Questions, **106**; Problems and Projects, **107**; New Words, **108**.

*Chapter 8.*   Line Photography ................................. 109

Theory of Photography, **109**; The Film, **111**; Process Cameras, **111**; Basic Parts of the Camera, **113**; Setting the Camera for "Same Size", **119**; Determining A Basic Exposure, **120**; Determining the "Best *f*-Number" of the Lens, **121**; Basic Camera Settings, **122**; Reductions and Enlargements, **122**; An Example in Setting the Camera, **123**; Corrections Based on the Sensitivity Guide, **124**; Procedure for Shooting Line Copy, **124**; Colored Line Copy and Paper, **126**; Questions, **127**; Problems and Projects, **128**; New Words, **128**.

*Chapter 9.* HALFTONE PHOTOGRAPHY ........................... *129*

Gradation of Tone, **129**; Theory of Halftone Reproduction, **131**; Screening Methods, **132**; Understanding Densitometry, **135**; Making a Single-Color Halftone Negative, **143**; Making A Negative from A Halftone Print, **149**; Making Halftones with Prescreened Film, **150**; Duotones, **152**; Questions, **152**; Problems and Projects, **153**; New Words, **153**.

*Chapter 10.* COLOR REPRODUCTION ............................. *155*

Color, **155**; How We See Color, **159**; Color Mixing, **160**; How Inks Reproduce Color, **162**; Films to Record Colors of Light, **166**; Process Color Reproduction, **170**.

*How-To Procedures for Color Printing*
Procedures for Flat Color, **175**; Procedures for Process Color, **180**; A Demonstration Project, **185**; Color Separation Proofs, **186**; Questions, **187**; Problems and Projects, **188**; New Words, **188**.

*Chapter 11.* FILM DEVELOPING AND DARKROOM PROCEDURES ........ *189*

Layout of the Darkroom, **189**; Order of Trays, **190**; Theory of Negatives, **190**; Preparation of Tray Solutions, **191**; Developing Procedure for Negatives, **192**; Three Methods of Developing Film, **193**; Darkroom Printing Operations, **194**; Proofing Methods, **202**; Supplies, **203**; Questions, **205**; Problems and Projects, **206**; New Words, **206**.

*Chapter 12.* LAYING OUT AND STRIPPING THE FLAT .............. *208*

Goldenrod Paper, **208**; Equipment and Supplies, **208**; Layout Table, **209**; Preparation for Stripping, **210**; Laying Out the Flat, **210**; Stripping-In the Negatives, **211**; Reference Marks Cut Into the Flat, **213**; Additional Layouts for Imposition, **214**; Step-and-Repeat Work, **215**; Combinations, **215**; Stripping for Two Colors, **216**; Questions, **216**; Problems and Projects, **217**; New Words, **217**.

Making Adjustments at Back of a Process Camera (Courtesy Printing Production Magazine — Separations by Seidel-Farris-Clark, Toledo — Transparency by Wilbar Photo Engraving Co.)

Stripper Scribes a Line on a Negative Which Has Been Mounted in a Goldenrod Flat for Exposure to Offset Plates (Courtesy Graphic Arts Monthly)

**Chapter 13. PLATEMAKING** ..................................... 218

Plate Characteristics, **218**; General Care of Offset Plates, **219**; Gum Arabic, **220**; Main Types of Plates, **221**; Plate Exposure Devices, **223**.

*Surface Plates*
Direct-Image Plates, **226**; Presensitized Plates, **228**; Albumin Plates, **237**; Wipe-On Plates, **238**; Transfer Plates, **239**; Electrostatic Plates, **245**; Minor Surface Plate Corrections, **249**.

*Deep-Etch Plates*
How To Prepare a Deep-Etch Plate, **250**; Multimetal Plates, **252**.

*Relief Plates For Offset*
Metal Dry-Offset Plate, **252**; Kodak Relief Plate, **252**; Dycril Photopolymer Relief Plates, **253**; Questions, **254**; Problems and Projects, **255**; New Words, **255**.

**Chapter 14. OFFSET INKS** ..................................... 256

Requirements, **256**; Composition, **256**; Manufacture, **257**; Color Mixing of Inks, **257**; Ink Terminology, **258**; Storing Inks, **258**; Questions, **259**; Problems and Projects, **259**; New Words, **259**.

**Chapter 15. PAPERS AND BINDERY WORK** ..................... 260

Requirements, **260**; Papermaking Pulps, **260**; Papermaking, **262**; Some Common Paper Terms, **266**; Papercutting, **267**; Figuring Number of Pieces from a Sheet, **268**; Controlling the Stretching and Shrinking of Paper, **270**; Bindery Operations, **270**; Questions, **272**; Problems and Projects, **273**; New Words, **273**.

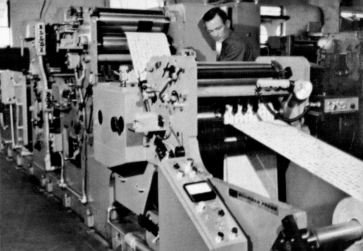

Book Press Operator Checks Webs of Paper as They Flow from the Printing Cylinders to the Folding Unit of an Offset Press (Courtesy Cottrell Company of Harris-Intertype)

Continuous Business Forms Rolling off of a Specialized Web-Fed Offset Press Are a Part of the "Paper-Work Explosion" Ignited by Computers (Courtesy Schriber Company of Harris-Intertype)

*Chapter 16.* OFFSET PRESS FUNDAMENTALS . . . . . . . . . . . . . . . . . . . . . . *274*

Operation and General Nomenclature, **274**; Paper Feeding to Delivery, **278**; Some Basic Arrangements, **278**; The Dampening System, **281**; Fountain (Dampening) Solution, **284**; The Inking System, **286**; The Plate Cylinder, **288**; The Blanket Cylinder, **290**; The Impression Cylinder, **292**; Pressure Checks (Settings), **292**; Undercut-Cylinder Packings, **294**; Questions, **294**; Problems and Projects, **295**; New Words, **295**.

*Chapter 17.* OFFSET PRESSWORK OPERATIONS . . . . . . . . . . . . . . . . . . . . . *296*

Preliminary Preparation, **296**; Setting Up for Operation, **297**; Operating the Press, **303**; Press Wash-Up, **305**; Questions, **307**; Problems and Projects, **308**; New Words, **308**.

*Chapter 18.* OFFSET PRESSES AND DUPLICATORS . . . . . . . . . . . . . . . . . . *309*

Multilith 1250, **308**; Heidelberg Model KOR, **314**; ATF Chief 20A, **316**; Whitin-Manufactured Offset Duplicators — Ditto 215, ATF Chief 15, Itek 11.15, **317**; A. B. Dick and Related Presses, **320**; Fairchild-Davidson Dualiths, **321**; Selected Other Models, **321**.

*Chapter 19.* OFFSET PRESSWORK TROUBLESHOOTING . . . . . . . . . . . . . . . . *323*

Scumming, **326**; Tinting, **327**; Filling Up, **327**; Piling, **327**; Set-Off, **328**; Vanishing, **328**; Sticking, **328**; Picking, **328**; Roller Stripping, **329**; Spraying, **329**; Mottling, **329**; Gray Type, **329**; Chalking, **329**; Running, **330**; Questions, **330**; Problems and Projects, **330**; New Words, **330**.

*Chapter 20.*  SHOP SAFETY ...................................... *331*

General Safety Precautions, **331**; Fire Safety, **333**; Electrical, **334**; Operating Equipment, **335**; Small Tools, **337**; Safeguard, **338**; Questions, **338**; Problems and Projects, **339**; New Words, **339**.


*Chapter 21.*  LEGAL RESTRICTIONS ON COPYING ................... *340*

Copyrighted Materials, **340**; Photographs for Advertising, **341**; Counterfeiting, **341**; U. S. Savings Bonds, **342**; U. S. Coins, **342**; U. S. and Foreign Postage Stamps, **342**; Miscellaneous Documents, **343**; Offensive and Obscene Material, **343**; Questions, **343**; Problems and Projects, **344**; New Words, **344**.


*Appendix 1.*  THE USE AND CARE OF DRAWING INSTRUMENTS ...... *346*

Fastening Paper Squarely, **346**; Drawing Pencils, **346**; T Square, **347**; Triangles, **347**; Protractor, **348**; Rules and Scales, **348**; Compasses, **349**; Dividers, **350**; Bow Instruments, **350**; Ruling Pen, **351**; Sharpening a Ruling Pen (or Pen Part), **352**.


*Appendix 2.*  CONVERTING FRACTIONS, DECIMALS, AND PERCENTAGES . *353*


*Appendix 3.*  DECIMAL EQUIVALENTS — PARTS OF AN INCH,
POINT SYSTEM ...................................... *354*


*Appendix 4.*  HOW TO READ THE MICROMETER CALIPERS ........... *356*

Reading Thousandths, **356**; Testing Your "Feel" or "Touch", **357**; Reading to Ten-Thousandths, **357**; Recording Measurements, **357**; Paper Gage Micrometers, **358**.


*Appendix 5.*  WEIGHTS AND MEASURES ........................... *359*


*Appendix 6.*  CONVERSION FACTORS ............................. *360*

*Appendix 7.* HUMIDITY ........................................ *361*

100% Humidity, **361**; Relative Humidity, **361**; Measuring Relative Humidity, **361**; Control of Relative Humidity, **362**.

*Appendix 8.* ALBUMIN PLATE COATING ......................... *363*

How to Make an Albumin Plate-Coating Solution, **363**; How to Prepare an Albumin Metal Plate Using a Whirler, **364**; How to Prepare a Wipe-On Albumin Paper Plate, **369**.

BIBLIOGRAPHY ................................................ *373*

INDEX ....................................................... *375*

COLOPHON ................................................... *385*

LIST OF TABLES

*1.* Exposure-Time for Various Degrees of
Enlargement and Reduction ................................. *123*

*2.* Critical Step on a 12-Step Scale for Various Types
of Copy and Its Reduction or Enlargement ..................... *124*

*3.* Film and Filter Combinations for Copying or
Dropping Various Colors .................................... *127*

*4.* Equivalent Density Factors ............................... *137*

*5.* Determining the Shadow Flash Exposure ..................... *145*

*6.* Color Temperatures (°K) of Common Light Sources ............. *159*

*7.* Screen Sizes Needed for Making Angled Screens ............... *182*

*8.* Some Useful Paper Information ............................ *269*

*9.* Amount of Albumin Solution to Use in Preparing
the Coating Solution ...................................... *365*

(GATF)

(Harris-Intertype)

(Harris-Intertype)

**The current revolution** in printing techniques is being brought about by extensive research programs. Several examples are given here. Research in paper and ink, and an automatic dampening control by Graphic Arts Technical Foundation are shown at top left. The 4-color web offset press directly above is run by the American Newspaper Publishers Association to study offset for daily papers. The experimental 5-color electrostatic printer at the left, prints large maps for the Army directly from 70mm microfilm without plates, at 2000 per hour. The color separation enlarger below is part of the research program at Rochester Institute of Technology devoted to offset color inserts for newspapers.

(Courtesy Printing Production Magazine — Separations by Seidel-Farris-Clark, Toledo — Transparency by Eastman Kodak Company)

# Introduction to Photo-Offset Printing

# CHAPTER 1

The printing industry in the United States turns out an annual volume of printed products valued in the billions of dollars. In addition to the usual printing on paper, printing is also done on wood, glass, cloth, rubber, metal, plastic and leather.

The constant improvement of machines, methods and processes has transformed the printing procedure from the essentially slow, laborious hand methods of early days. The printer of today is still a craftsman, but a craftsman aided by swiftly-operating automatic or semi-automatic machinery.

## Major Printing Processes

To be able to produce the needed quantities of printed products as speedily and as economically as possible, the printing industry utilizes a number of different printing processes. The five major processes by which most of today's printing is done are: (1) *letterpress*, (2) *gravure*, (3) *screen*, (4) *engraving*, and (5) *offset*. (NOTE: These are not arranged in order of dollar volume.)

### Letterpress

In the letterpress process of printing, raised (relief) type characters and lines and dots of illustration plates are inked and then pressed against the paper to be printed, thus transferring the ink from the type face to the paper. The type characters and the illustration plates for letterpress printing are always made in reverse (mirrored image) so that, when printed, they read correctly from left to right. Flat forms of the original type characters may be used on the press — or duplicate plates, either flat or curved, may be made from the original type matter and used on the press.

### Gravure

In the gravure process, original proofs of type matter and illustrations are photographed through a gravure screen. The screened negatives are placed into contact with the photographically sensitive surface of a copper gravure plate (flat or cylindrical). After exposure, a chemical process etches the printing design *into* the plate. The dots which are etched *into* the plate are tiny cup-shaped cavities below the surface of the plate.

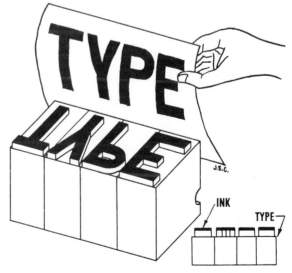

Fig. 1. Letterpress Printing

On the gravure press, ink is applied to the plate surface, filling the cavities caused by the etching process. A scraper blade (doctor)

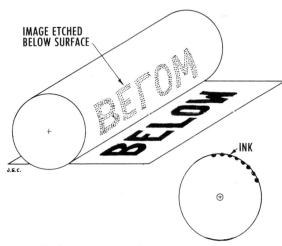

Fig. 2.  Gravure (Rotogravure) Process

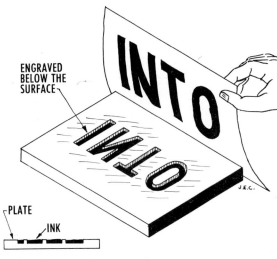

Fig. 4.  Printing by Engraving

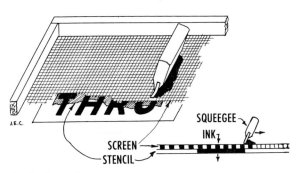

Fig. 3.  Screen Process

removes all ink from the plate except the ink in the etched-image cavities. Pressure of the plate against the paper to be printed transfers ink from the cavities to the paper, resulting in a finished printed product.

When the printing is done from an etched cylinder, instead of a flat plate, the process is called "rotogravure." Any method which prints from below the plate surface is known as an intaglio (in-tal'-yo) method.

### Plate Engraving

This is another intaglio printing process. In the engraving process of printing, the design or lettering to be reproduced on paper must be engraved, or *cut into,* the surface of a copper or a steel plate. This engraving may be done by hand, using a tool called a *graver,* or it may be outlined by a graver and then etched with acid. In either case the work is done in mirrored image. If very small lettering is to be done, a pantograph engraving machine may be used to simultaneously trace large master letters and cut them the desired size into the plate.

The plate on the engraving press is inked and wiped clean. The engraved lines retain ink because they are below the surrounding surface. The plate is then forced against the printing paper, with sufficient pressure to cause the ink to adhere to the paper.

### Screen Process

In the screen process of printing, a finely-woven cloth is stretched tightly and fastened to a frame. A stencil bearing the desired design or printing message is adhered to the bottom side of the cloth. This stencil may be prepared photographically, or it may be prepared by cutting out the desired image or message with a knife.

After the screen stencil is prepared, paper (or any other object to be printed) is placed beneath the stencil frame, and the stencil is lowered into contact with it. A paint-like ink is poured into the frame. Then a rubber-blade squeegee is scraped across the stencil, forcing ink through the open areas of the stencil onto the object beneath it.

### Offset

In the offset process, the printing image is drawn by hand, typed or prepared photographically on the surface of a thin, flat offset plate. This offset plate is then mounted on the plate cylinder of the offset press. During operation of the offset press, the inked image of the offset plate is printed onto the rubber-covered surface of a blanket cylinder. In turn, the blanket cylinder transfers (or "offsets") its printed image onto the paper which is fed between the blanket cylinder and the impression cylinder.

### Net Value of Printed Products by Processes

Bureau of Census figures show that offset printed (lithographed) products with a total value of $1,895,707,000 were produced in 1963.* This represents a 46% gain over the value of these products in 1958, and also indicates the tremendous growth in importance of the offset process.

Letterpress printing, in the same period, made a gain of 10.4%. It produced, in 1963, products having a value of $2,380,560,000.

These figures indicate that letterpress printing is still the "giant" of the industry, but that offset printing is second in production importance, and is growing rapidly.

The third most important process, dollar-wise, is gravure, with a value of $287,187,000 in the year 1963.

That same year, engraving and silk screen accounted for values of $87,392,000 and $69,225,000, respectively. It may be observed that the value of products printed by each of these processes has been growing.

### Basic Theory of Offset Printing

In this book our study will be confined to the offset process of printing. It should be noted that there are several additional names by which the offset process is known: *photo-offset, lithography, photo-lithography, photo-offset lithography,* and *offset lithography.* As generally used, the above names refer to one and the same process. This writer prefers the

*The latest government data at this printing.

more descriptive term *photo-offset lithography,* but has for convenience used the shorter term *offset* throughout the greater part of this book.

Offset printing is a *planographic method* of printing; that is, it employs a *flat* printing plate on which the image (or printing area) is level with the non-printing area. In other words, the part of the plate which does the printing is neither raised above, nor cut below, the surface of the plate.

### Theory

Offset printing can be done from a flat plate because of a fundamental chemical fact: "grease and water do not readily mix."

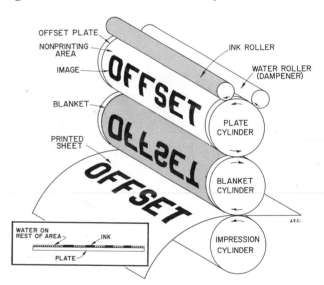

Fig. 5. Offset Printing

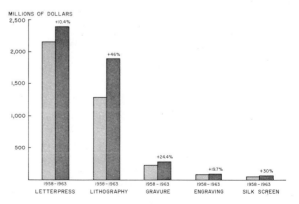

Fig. 6. Commercial Printing — Value of Receipts by Process

*The plate.* As purchased or prepared in the shop, the offset plate is a thin sheet of paper or metal, so treated chemically and mechanically that its surface will readily retain a thin film of applied moisture.

The message to be printed (the image) is placed on this plate by a photographic-chemical process, employing in its final steps the

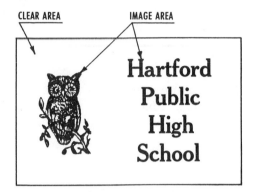

Fig. 7.  An Offset Plate Has Two Areas

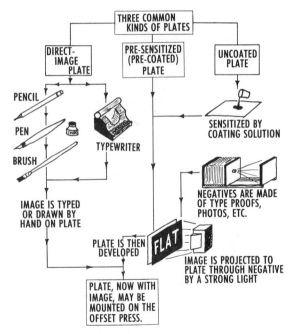

Fig. 8.  Producing a Printing Image on the Surface of Three Kinds of Offset Plates. The pencil, ink and typewriter ribbon used for preparing the direct-image plate are especially made for lithographic purposes. In developing the presensitized and uncoated plates which are coated in the shop, a greasy lithographic developing ink is used to make the image ink-receptive.

developing of the image by use of a greasy or "fatty" ink. The image may also be created directly on the plate by typing, hand lettering, or drawing, in each case using special lithographic typewriter ribbons, pencils, tusche or ink which will cause a "greasy" image on the plate. (Platemaking is discussed in more detail in Chapter 12.)

A completely prepared offset plate, then, actually contains two separate and distinct areas on its flat surface: (1) the *image* (printing) area, which is composed of greasy or fatty ink, and (2) the *clear* (non-printing) area. (See Fig. 7.)

*Water repellent and ink receptive.* If a water-saturated cloth pad is passed over the entire surface of a completed offset plate, it will be observed that a thin film of moisture will adhere to the clear areas of the plate. Moisture will not adhere to the inked image area — instead, it actually will be seen to run off and pull away from the greasy-inked image.

If, now, a brayer charged with greasy lithographic ink is passed over the entire plate, it will be observed that a deposit of ink is added to the greasy-ink image, and that no ink adheres to the moisture-dampened clear areas of the plate.

The following conclusions are then evident:

(1) The greasy-inked image is *receptive* to ink, but will *repel* water.
(2) The dampened clear area of the plate is *receptive* to water, but will *repel* ink.

However, if an ink-charged brayer is passed over an offset plate which *has not* been moistened, the ink will adhere to the entire surface of the plate — image and clear areas alike.

*Water and ink balance.* On commercial offset presses, the water and ink are fed automatically to the offset plate. The press operator maintains and controls a judicial balance between the amounts of ink and water which are allowed to reach the plate. This balance insures that only the image portions of the plate will print.

### The Offset Press

A schematic drawing of an offset press is shown in Fig. 9. This drawing shows only the basic, fundamental parts of an offset press. Actual offset presses have a great many more parts.

Note that the offset press has three large cylinders:

(1) the *plate cylinder,* on which is mounted the offset plate

(2) the *blanket cylinder,* which is covered with a rubber blanket

(3) the *impression cylinder,* which has a smooth metal surface.

There are two *fountains* (reservoirs):

(1) the *ink fountain,* which carries a supply of ink

(2) the *water fountain,* which contains the plate-dampening solution.

Two series of rollers, one from the ink fountain and one from the water fountain, furnish ink and water to the plate.

Paper is fed automatically through the press and is stacked neatly after printing.

### Inking the Plate

When the press is started in motion, the water fountain roller is brought into contact with the plate, coating it with a film of moisture. The water adheres only to the clear area of the plate because the developed image repels the water.

The ink roller next contacts the plate. The ink adheres to the developed image, but is repelled by the water-covered clear area. By a carefully controlled feeding of water and ink, the offset plate is successfully inked in only the desired image areas.

### Printing

When the rubber-covered blanket cylinder is brought into contact with the plate cylinder, the *readable** inked image of the plate

---

*Type matter which can be read normally from left to right is referred to as "readable", or "right reading"; if type matter is reproduced so it must be read from right to left on the page, it is called "unreadable", or "wrong-reading".

prints onto the blanket. The image printed on the blanket is a wrong-reading or mirrored image of the plate image.

Finally, the paper is passed through the press between the blanket and impression cylinders and is printed upon by the blanket

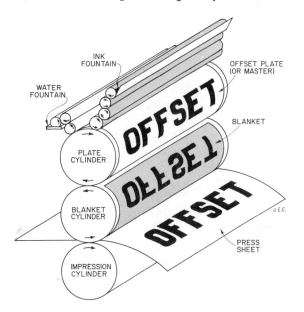

Fig. 9. Schematic Drawing of an Offset Press; from Plate, to Blanket, to Paper.

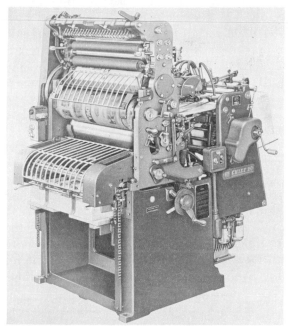

Fig. 10. ATF Chief 20A Offset Press
(Courtesy American Type Founders Co., Inc.)

— the image being mirrored again, and appearing *readable* on the paper.

Note that the plate does not print on the paper. Instead, the plate prints on the blanket, and then the blanket image is transferred (or *offset*) to the paper, thus the term *offset printing*.

## Demonstrations

In addition to a study and discussion of the foregoing text material, the student will gain a deeper and fuller understanding of the theory and practice of fundamental offset principles if the instructor will actually demonstrate the principles involved.

### Platemaking and Presswork

The finest demonstration of offset principles would require that platemaking equipment and a simple offset press (such as a duplicator) be available.

Expose and develop a presensitized paper or metal plate, using an available stripped-up flat. Explain each step and the materials used.

Mount the plate on the press (which has been prepared for the printing operation). Show how the plate is dampened and how the plate image picks up a coverage of ink. Stop the press and allow the students to examine the plate.

Transfer the plate image to the blanket, and again stop the press. Point out how the blanket image is a "mirror image" of the plate image.

Take a few impressions and pass out the printed sheets to the students.

Close the demonstration by showing the students how the plate is preserved and stored for future use.

If preparations are made beforehand, the complete demonstration should not take more than twenty minutes, allowing ample time for the lively discussion which is sure to follow.

### Plate and Proof Press

If it is neither desirable nor convenient to demonstrate with an offset duplicator or off-set press, much the same principles can be demonstrated with an offset plate and a letterpress proof press.

For this demonstration, build up the proof press bed with a block of wood and several sheets of thin cardboard so that the press gives a slight squeeze impression. Also ink up a hand brayer and an ink slab with offset ink.

Demonstrate the exposure and developing of an offset plate (as above) or take from storage a previously-used offset plate.

Place the plate, image side up, on the built-up bed of the proof press. Wash the preservative from the plate surface with sponge and water, and roll up the image with the hand brayer. It may require several passes with the brayer to build up the image with sufficient ink. If so, sponge off the plate with water between inkings. If water accumulates on the brayer, remove it by rolling the brayer on clean newsprint.

Place a sheet of printing paper on the inked plate, and pull an impression. Additional impressions may be taken if, before each additional impression, the plate is moistened and then inked.

This demonstration will show the "grease and water" theory, and also the "mirror reversal" of the plate image when it prints on the paper.

Conclude by showing how to prepare the plate for storage. Then hold a discussion on what has been demonstrated.

### Plate, Blanket and Proof Press

A third demonstration which may be made involves the same set-up of offset plate and proof press. In addition, an offset-press blanket, or a portion of one, is needed.

After washing off and rolling up the plate with ink, place the blanket over the plate and pull an impression on the proof press.

Remove the printed-upon blanket, and show that its image is a "mirror image" of the plate image.

Now, remove the offset plate from the proof press, and place the blanket (image side up) on the built-up proof press bed.

Place a sheet of printing paper on the blanket and pull an impression. Show that the impression printed on the paper is a "right-reading" duplicate of the plate image.

In this demonstration, additional sheets may not be printed unless the blanket is washed between impressions. However, the inclusion of the blanket makes this a convincing demonstration.

Conclude, as before, with plate preservation and class discussion.

## Questions

1. Name eight materials on which printing is commonly done. Are there others?
2. What are the five major printing processes?
3. Describe the process of letterpress printing.
4. Why is screen printing so called?
5. Which of the five major printing processes is commonly used for printing on glass bottles? Why?
6. Which two of the major printing processes employ printing plates which do their printing from lines or dots below the surface of the plates?
7. What is meant by offset printing?
8. Why is the name "offset" used to describe this process?
9. What is the "grease and water" theory as applied to offset printing?
10. Why is a greasy (or fatty) ink used in offset printing?
11. With a dry offset plate on the press, which is applied first — water or ink? Why? What would happen if the other were applied first?
12. Give another name for the image portion of the offset plate.
13. Give at least two names for that portion of the offset plate which carries no image.
14. Suppose the plate image in Fig. 9 were reversed, left to right; would the image on the blanket then be readable or wrong reading? Would the resulting image appear on the paper in unreadable or readable form?

15. Define the following terms as they apply to offset printing:
a. Water receptive
b. Water repellent
c. Ink receptive
d. Ink repellent
e. Image area
f. Clear area
g. Printing area
h. Non-printing area
i. Blanket
j. Ink fountain
k. Water fountain
l. Water rollers
m. Ink rollers
n. Impression cylinder
o. Readable image
p. Wrong-reading image
q. Right-reading
r. Unreadable
s. Mirrored image

## Problems and Projects

1. Examine an offset press in the shop. Locate each of the basic parts shown in the schematic drawing in Fig. 9.
2. Examine a used offset plate in the shop. Ask if you may touch, and rub, the image with a fingertip. What can you say about the image?
3. Closely inspect two printed samples — one printed by letterpress, and the other printed by offset. Notice the outlines of the magnified letters of each sample. Describe what you see. Why is it so?
4. Clip and mount on a notebook page, five samples of printed matter, each printed by a different major process. Identify and label each according to the printing process used.

## New Words

1. adhere
2. aluminum
3. billions
4. characterized
5. characters
6. combination
7. controlled
8. cylinder
9. duplicate
10. economically
11. engraving
12. essentially
13. etching
14. fountain
15. fundamental
16. greasy
17. illustration
18. importance
19. industry
20. letterpress
21. lithographic
22. lithography
23. mirrored
24. original
25. pantograph
26. pressure
27. processes
28. production
29. rotogravure
30. schematic

Portrait of Senefelder by Guaglio (1818)

(Courtesy Metropolitan Museum of Art)

CHAPTER

2

# A Brief History of
# Photo-Offset Printing

Offset printing derives its present form from several adaptations of an earlier printing method — stone lithography, in which stone slabs served as the printing plates.

## The Invention of Lithography

Alois Senefelder (Nov. 6, 1771 - Feb. 26, 1834), a Bohemian by birth, invented the lithographic process of printing in the year 1798. Because he used a flat stone plate from which to print on paper, the process was called "lithography". The term "lithography" comes from two Greek words: "lithos", meaning *stone* and "graphein", meaning *to write*. Combined, the term may be understood to mean *writing from stone,* or *stone writing.*

Because of his extensive experiments, his perfection of the lithographic process, and his development of the necessary materials and methods of execution, Senefelder is regarded as the "father" of lithography.

### Early Attempts

During his youth in Munich, young Senefelder aspired to become an actor, as was his father before him. His father compelled him to study law, but his love for the theater won out.

Senefelder found that he was more successful at writing plays than in acting, and had several of his plays published. The profits from his publications were so small that Senefelder decided to try to print them himself and thus save part of the cost of publication. Lacking funds to purchase the necessary type, press and paper, young Senefelder experimented to find a less expensive printing method.

In his early attempts, Senefelder borrowed an idea from the copperplate printers of the time. Taking a copper plate, he cleaned its surface and covered the surface with etcher's ground. On this surface he then wrote his type characters *in reverse*, cutting through the protective coating of ground, and exposing the bare metal. When the copper plate was treated with acid, the exposed lines of copper were etched below the surface of the plate. The etched plates could then be printed on the engraver's press.

Senefelder had one great difficulty with his "reverse writing" on copper — his frequent mistakes were difficult to correct. What he needed was a thin, quick-drying varnish which he could use to paint over his errors, and which would yield satisfactory pen corrections. For this he finally found a mixture of three parts of wax, one part of soap, some lampblack and rainwater to be satisfactory. (Although he didn't realize it at the time, the formula for this "correction fluid" was to become the greasy or fatty lithographic ink he was to use in his future work on stone.)

The expensive copper plates proved too much for Senefelder's slim purse. Consequently he turned to experimenting with a flat piece of Bavarian limestone which he had been using for grinding inks. This stone was cheap, and it was easier to grind flat than were the copper plates.

8

One day, after he had ground a stone plate smooth and flat for experimenting, his mother asked him to write down a laundry list. Having exhausted all his paper and writing ink, Senefelder took some of his "correction fluid" and wrote the list on the stone. Later, being curious, he poured a dilute solution of aqua fortis (nitric acid) over the stone. In a few minutes, the acid etched the un-inked portion of the stone surface, leaving the inked letters in slight relief (raised), much like type characters.

By carefully inking the raised letters, Senefelder obtained excellent proofs, and, for a time, used this method for successful printing. After finishing an edition, the printing stones were easily ground smooth and flat again, and could be used over and over. It was a relatively cheap and easy method of printing.

## Chemical Printing

It was while Senefelder was experimenting to find a method of reproducing illustrations by stone printing without redrawing the pictures on the stone that he invented his chemical process of printing. (He personally preferred to call his process "chemical printing", rather than "lithography".)

He had an order to reprint a book, the original of which had been illustrated with copperplate engravings. Instead of laboriously copying the illustrations onto the stone by hand, Senefelder inked an original etched copper plate with his fatty ink. Then he pulled a proof of the etching. Placing the proof carefully on a clean lithographic stone, he pulled a wood scraper across the proof with considerable pressure. Amazingly, the design on the proof was transferred to the stone!

Now, placing the stone plate in his press, he wet the entire surface of the stone with a solution of water and gum. The stone was naturally porous and retained a thin film of moisture on those parts of the surface not covered with the design. The design, being composed of fatty ink, repelled the water.

Over the entire stone plate he then passed a leather roller charged with his fatty ink.

The design accepted the ink beautifully, whereas the wet portion of the stone plate remained clean. Placing a sheet of paper over the stone, he found that the resulting press impression yielded results as good, or better, than could be obtained from the original copperplate.

Additional impressions were easily made from the stone — by alternately first wetting the plate with water and gum, then inking the plate. Thus was "chemical printing" born — based on a fundamental of chemistry, that "grease and water do not mix."

Senefelder's success with transferring a design, or image, from the proof paper to the stone showed him that printing could be done from stones without laborious reverse writing. If the original work were drawn on transfer paper reading normally from left to right, it could be transferred under pressure to the stone where it would appear in reverse. This reverse image on the stone would then appear in readable form when the stone plate transferred its image to the paper in the printing process.

Naturally, if the original work were to be drawn directly on the stone, it would necessarily have to be drawn in reverse. Only a reversed image on the stone would produce a readable impression on the paper.

## Lithographic Stones

The stones used for lithographic printing are a natural Bavarian limestone. When un-

Fig. 25.  Inking a Lithographic Stone Prior to Printing from It
(Courtesy of The Metropolitan Museum of Art)

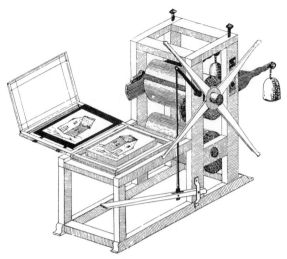

Fig. 26. Copperplate Cylinder Press Modified for Lithographic Printing by Senefelder (About 1798) (Courtesy General Printing Ink Co., Division of Sun Chemical Corp.)

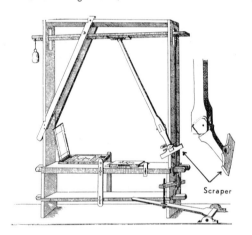

Fig. 27. Lever-scraper Lithographic Printing Press Invented by Senefelder in 1802 (Courtesy General Printing Ink Co., Division of Sun Chemical Corp.)

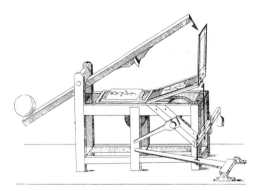

Fig. 28. Cylinder-scraper Lithographic Press Invented by Prof. Mitterer (About 1806-1817) (Courtesy General Printing Ink. Co., Division of Sun Chemical Corp.)

covered in the earth at the quarries, the stones are in the form of layers, ranging from paper-thin sheets to slabs more than several inches in thickness, and many times in great blocks which can be split to make thinner stones. In general, stones from one and one-half to three and one-half inches in thickness are strong enough to withstand impressions without cracking.

Above all, the properties of Bavarian limestone which make it ideally suited for lithography are:

(1) the natural affinity of its finely-grained surface for water (its ability to retain a thin film of applied moisture on its surface)

(2) its affinity for greasy ink

(3) the ease with which one stone may be used to grind another stone flat.

### The First Lithographic Presses

The press which Senefelder used for his first stone printing was a modified etcher's press. The stone plate, together with the printing paper on it, was drawn between two wooden cylinders under pressure. It was powered manually by a crank. The wetting and inking of the plate were also performed by hand.

The cumbersome operation of this cylinder press prompted Senefelder to design and construct, in 1802, a lithographic "lever-scraper press". The flat stone plate was placed on the press bed, wet, then inked and covered with the printing paper. Over this was placed a cloth blanket and a leather impression pad. An impression blade, suspended from above, was forced against the leather pad and scraped across it, causing the inked image to transfer to the paper. In this press, inking, wetting and power were also applied by hand; however, since the stone plate was stationary, printing was less laborious, and therefore faster.

Professor Mitterer, an associate of Senefelder, developed a cylinder-scraper press (about 1806-1817) in which the stone plate was carried horizontally underneath a stationary scraper blade which pressed the paper against the inked stone. Inking and

Fig. 29. ACROSS THE CONTINENT. "Westward the Course of Empire Takes Its Way." Lithograph: Currier and Ives, 1868. (Courtesy the Museum of the City of New York, the Harry T. Peters Collection)

dampening were done by hand, and power was applied manually by a crank. This cylinder-scraper press was regarded by both Senefelder and Mitterer as an improvement over the lever-scraper press.

In 1813, Senefelder demonstrated the use of a flat *metal* plate on his lever press for lithographic printing. In addition, he showed that cloth, paper and wood could each be coated with an artificial stone composition to successfully replace the weighty limestone slabs then in use for printing by lithography.

A few years later, in 1817, Senefelder exhibited a water-powered press which mechanically dampened and inked the flat stone or metal plates. As yet, no curved plates were used for printing.

## Applications of the Lithographic (Stone-Printing) Process

The printed work which Senefelder produced by the lithographic (stone-printing) process consisted of circulars, statistical tables, charts, prayer books, music sheets, portraits, landscapes and textbooks.

The advantages of the new process were quickly appreciated by printers everywhere, and the process was readily adopted in the United States.

Nathaniel Currier, who began his apprenticeship in the lithographic trade at 15 years of age (in 1825), was perhaps the most famous of all American lithographers. His realistic lithographic print of the sinking of the S.S. Lexington in Long Island Sound on January 13, 1840, was published three days after the tragedy and sold so many thousands of copies that he decided to specialize exclusively in lithographic scenes depicting life in America. Some of his editions ran to more than 70,000 copies.

James Ives, an assistant of Nathaniel Currier, became a partner in the firm in 1857. From that time on, the firm was known as Currier & Ives. More than 7,000 different Currier & Ives lithographic prints are still in existence today.

*11*

A number of graphic arts supply houses today carry lithographic stones, crayons, presses and other supplies for artists who wish to express themselves in this medium. Portraits, landscapes, still life and other forms of artwork produced by crayon or pen and ink on stone are referred to as "lithographic prints", much prized for framing or for reproduction as illustrations in publications.

## Use of Metal Plates on Cylinder Presses

Senefelder's original introduction of the flat metal plate for lithographic printing led to extensive experimentation and research concerning its use. It was discovered that thin sheets of aluminum were flexible enough to be wrapped around and fastened to a cylinder. This plate-covered revolving cylinder could then print onto the paper.

Although aluminum was light, easily formed into thin sheets and could be grained satisfactorily to retain the film of water necessary, it was at that time too expensive for general use. Zinc was cheaper, and was therefore substituted for the first metal plates. Modern manufacturing methods have lowered the cost of aluminum so that today both zinc and aluminum are commonly used for lithographic plates.

It should be noted that when metal plates were first used, the plate *printed directly onto the paper*. Although this was an improvement over the flat stone and metal plates, the images on the plate had a relatively short life.

## Advent of Offset

The introduction of the "offset" principle in the lithographic press — the addition of the blanket cylinder which received the inked image from the plate and, in turn, *offsetted* that image to the paper — is credited to the ingenuity and awareness of Ira Rubel, an American lithographic pressman.

While Mr. Rubel was operating a lithographic press — one which printed directly from the plate — one sheet of paper failed to feed through, and so the plate printed its image onto the surface of the impression cylinder.

The next sheet was printed normally, but it *also* picked up an "offset" image on its reverse side from the impression cylinder.

Instantly intrigued by the clarity of this "offset" image, Ira Rubel decided to put it to practical use. In 1905, he built the first lithographic press employing an "offset", rubber-covered cylinder, which today we call the "blanket" cylinder. No longer did the plate touch the paper. All modern offset presses still are constructed on this same principle: plate to blanket to paper.

This "offsetting" of the image gave rise to the term "offset printing". Since the process included the same lithographic principles as formerly, the new term was soon enlarged to "offset lithography".

## Introduction of Photography

Photography is one of our newer arts. Prior to the invention of practical photography, much of our knowledge of the cultures of the past was derived through the existing artwork of those periods which was executed as designs, pictures or statues. The mediums employed were pottery, tapestries, stone, bronze, stained-glass windows, tile mosaics, canvas paintings, building surfaces, and, more recently, woodcuts, copperplate engravings and etchings, and stone lithographs. In most of these, the artist strove for, and achieved, a remarkable degree of minuteness and clarity of detail.

In spite of the excellence of the available methods of hand-executed art, scientific minds were intrigued by such natural phenomena as reflected images in mirrors and pools of water — and by the shadows cast by the sun. These phenomena suggested the possibility of capturing and recording permanently exact images or pictures on paper.

### Silhouette-Outline Pictures

The earliest attempts at photography were successful in producing only a silhouette outline of the subject. In about 1802, two Englishmen, Sir Humphry Davy and Thomas Wedgwood, used paper coated with silver chloride in their photographic experiments. The person to be photographed (or silhouetted) sat before a vertically-mounted sheet of this paper. A light was used to project the sitter's shadow onto the paper. Since no method had yet been invented to reduce the unexposed silver chloride coating, subsequent exposure of the paper to the sunlight also darkened the unexposed portions of the photographic paper. Thus these early silhouette pictures were not long-lasting.

## Daguerreotype Pictures

The first practical process which produced lasting pictures in great detail was the Daguerreotype process — known as *Daguerreotypy*. It was invented by Louis Jacques Mendé Daguerre, a Frenchman, in 1839.

In the Daguerreotype process, a silver-coated copper plate was placed in the camera. Then the exposure (sometimes as long as several minutes) was made. The plate was developed with mercury vapors, resulting in a positive picture of the subject. One drawback to this process was that there was no way to make additional prints or copies — the plate itself was the picture.

On one of his trips abroad, Samuel F. B. Morse (the inventor of telegraphy) met Daguerre who instructed Morse in the art of Daguerreotypy. Morse, at that time, was a portrait artist in New York City, and hoped that this new process would be useful in cap-

turing poses of his subjects which he could later paint at his leisure.

In turn, Morse taught the new art to a young man, Mathew Brady, who was quick to see the economic possibilities of the new process. Brady opened a Daguerreotypy studio in New York, and the excellence of his work did much to make Daguerreotypes popular. In fact, at that time, prior to the Civil War, it was the fashionable thing to have one's portrait made by Daguerreotypy, especially by Brady. Many beautiful Daguerreotypes made during that era are yet in existence.

## The First Negatives

In 1840, William Talbot (an Englishman), discovered the first practical process for producing photographic negatives from which any number of permanent positive prints could be made. He used a paper coated with

Fig. 32. Daguerreotype Portrait of President Abraham Lincoln. (Believed to be the earliest-known portrait of Lincoln. Photographer: N. H. Shepherd, Springfield, Ohio, about 1846) (Courtesy National Park Service)

Fig. 31. Daguerreotype Camera (Courtesy George Eastman House)

silver iodide for his negative plate. Before exposure, the coated paper was dampened with silver nitrate and gallic acid. A camera exposure of about thirty seconds was required.

Fig. 33.  Collodion Wet-plate Camera for Making Cartes-de-visite (Courtesy George Eastman House)

Fig. 34.  Portrait of General Ulysses S. Grant, from a Wet-Collodion Negative (Courtesy National Archives)

A most important point in Talbot's process was his method of developing the negative. He used a developing solution of the same silver nitrate and gallic acid — and then immersed the negatives in a fixing bath of sodium thiosulphate (hypo) to remove the unexposed silver salts. This fixing bath, by removing the unexposed silver salts, preserved the negatives against fading when subsequently exposed to light.

Talbot made permanent positive prints from his negatives by coating print paper with silver chloride, placing the negative in contact over the print paper, and then exposing the combination to light. Developing and fixing were done in a manner similar to that employed for the negatives.

Despite the importance of Talbot's contributions, experimenters continued to seek improvements. The paper negatives which Talbot employed, when projected onto the photographic print paper, imparted to the finished print a lack of clarity caused by the grain structure of the paper fibers.

To gain clarity of detail in the finished prints, Claude Felix Niepce, in 1847, substituted glass for the paper negatives. He coated his glass plates with albumin and potassium iodide. Just before exposure in the camera, the plate was wet with a solution of silver nitrate. Development and fixing of these negatives, and the making of the positive prints, were carried on in the same manner as for the paper negatives described above. The finished prints were of excellent quality, but required exposures of much longer duration than for Talbot's paper negatives.

### Wet-Collodion Negatives

In 1851, the wet-collodion negative was introduced by Frederick Scott Archer, an Englishman. In this process, glass plates were first treated with an albumin (egg white) solution, and allowed to dry. When the photographer wished to use a plate, he entered a darkroom, coated the plate with collodion, and then with silver nitrate and finally placed the plate in a plateholder. While still wet, the plate (in its plateholder) had to be inserted into the camera, exposed for about five seconds, and then rushed back to the darkroom for developing.

In spite of the handicap and discomfort in handling the glass plates and the coating of them in total darkness, the wet-collodion process, which required only a relatively short exposure time, was phenomenally successful. Photographers of the day achieved such clarity of detail that photographs made at that time are still acclaimed as masterpieces of the art.

Mathew Brady (mentioned previously), who in 1852 was operating a Daguerreotypy studio, was quick to employ the new wet-collodion process in his studio. His results were of such excellence that, again, to be photographed by Brady was a mark of distinction in society.

At the start of the Civil War, Brady saw the historical importance and the possibilities of photography in warfare. He set himself the task of making a photographic record of the War Between the States. This was the first time in history that photography was used in warfare. To do this, he obtained permission to accompany the Union troops into battle to get his on-the-spot pictures.

Brady outfitted two horse-drawn, van-type wagons as photographic darkrooms, and became a familiar sight as he set up his cameras for his scenes, shielding the lens from the sun with his hat, and removing and replacing the lens cap to make his exposures.

Despite the great difficulties in coating and developing his negatives in his portable darkrooms amid battle conditions, Brady achieved spectacular success in portraying the war history in thousands of clear photographs.

## Dry Negatives

Photography, as we know it today, never would have achieved its popularity without the introduction of a "dry" plate — one which could be prepared well in advance of exposure.

In 1878, Charles Bennett, an English photographer, introduced a dry plate. Its emulsion (coating) consisted of gelatin and silver bromide. Bennett's dry plates required such

a short length of exposure time that a snapshot was now possible.

George Eastman, an American (and founder of the Eastman Kodak Company), experimented to find a substitute for the bulky

Fig. 35.  Mathew Brady Shooting a War Scene. Exposure was made by removing the lens cap. Notice, in the background, one of his photographic darkroom wagons. (Courtesy John Hancock Mutual Life Insurance Co.)

Fig. 36.  George Eastman (Courtesy George Eastman House)

and breakable glass plates, and in 1884 he patented the first flexible film. His first films were of a paper base. Later, in 1889, he introduced a thin, flexible cellulose-nitrate (celluloid) base for his film.

This flexible film made possible the roll-film camera which is so popular today. The

Fig. 37.   Early Roll-Film Camera, Kodak No. 1
(Courtesy George Eastman House)

Fig. 38.   Multilith 2024-1, Single-Color Offset Press
(Courtesy Addressograph Multigraph Corp.)

ease with which a prepared roll of film can be loaded into and removed from the camera has brought photography within the reach and experience of all.

Today, most of our photographs, both professional and amateur, are taken on flexible film, either in roll or sheet form.

### The Halftone Screen

The first halftone screen for the reproduction of photographs was used by Henry Talbot, an Englishman, about the year 1852. He employed a loosely-woven, gauze-like cloth as a screen. In 1885, an American, Frederick Ives, made the first cross-line halftone screen by taking two exposed (glass) negatives, scribing equally-spaced lines on them through the emulsion, and then cementing them together, face to face, with the lines at right angles. With the halftone screen it was now possible to print photographs and type on the same sheet.

Modern halftone screens are made of glass. Two sheets of glass, each with finely engraved horizontal lines, are cemented face to face with the lines at right angles. Screens for process color work are circular, set in square frames arranged so that the circular screens may be rotated to the angle required for each color.

Contact halftone screens, which are made of a flexible plastic material, are also widely used today.

### Photo-Offset Lithography

The development of photography, and along with it the halftone screen, gave offset lithography a fresh boost. With these aids, it was now possible to reproduce both line and halftone work on plates without resorting to manual artwork. The process now carried the name *photo-offset lithography*, and the first metal plates employing photographically-prepared negatives for their image preparation were used in the period between 1910 to 1920.

Improvements in offset presses followed in rapid succession. Four-color press units and web-fed presses which printed from rolls of

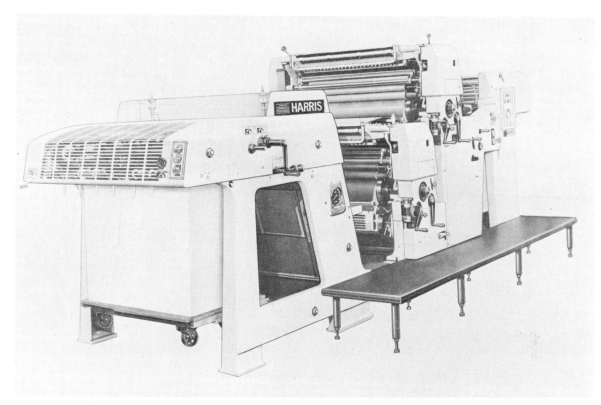

Fig. 39.  Harris Two-Color 25" x 38" Offset Press (Courtesy Harris-Intertype Corp.)

Fig. 40.  Four-Color Sheet-Fed Offset Press (Courtesy Western Printing & Lithographing Co.)

Fig. 41.  Harris-Cottrell 4-over-4 Web-Fed Offset Press (Courtesy Harris-Intertype Corp.)

paper were designed and manufactured. Many letterpress shops began adding offset presses, or offset departments. Other plants turned wholly to offset production of magazines, newspapers, and job work.

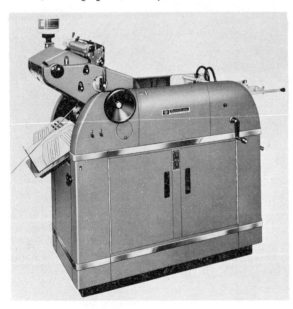

Fig. 42.  Multilith 1250 Offset Duplicator
(Courtesy Addressograph Multigraph Corp.)

Smaller machines, sometimes called "offset duplicators" were developed for producing forms and sales literature in business offices. These have been improved to the point where they do some work which is comparable, in many respects, to that of the larger offset presses.

Today, high-quality chemicals, fine plates, precision presses and highly-refined photographic processes enable skilled workmen to produce a large volume of beautifully printed advertising, books, packaging materials and other products.

## Questions

1. From what words is the term "lithography" derived?
2. How is lithographic stone printing done?
3. Describe the nature of lithographic stone.
4. Why does the applied moisture (water) adhere only to the clear portion of the stone? What helps the water to adhere to the stone?
5. Why does the ink repel the water?

6. Who is generally regarded as the "father" of lithography?
7. Describe briefly the work of the inventor of lithography printing.
8. Describe the transfer process (or method).
9. What two metals are commonly used for lithographic plates today?
10. Describe Ira Rubel's contribution to modern offset printing. How does it differ from stone lithography?
11. Why was the rubber blanket added to the lithographic press?
12. What did Daguerre perfect?
13. Describe how photographers utilized the wet-collodion process.
14. What were Eastman's contributions to photography?
15. What contribution did the halftone screen make to the printing industry?
16. What does the term "photo-offset lithography" mean?

## Problems and Projects

1. Prepare an outline map of Europe, locating the areas where the principal events in this chapter took place.
2. Prepare a lithographic stone for printing. Take an impression. Make a transfer of this image to another stone, or to a paper or metal plate. Use words and drawings in the image.
3. Obtain information on the production of aluminum and zinc. Make a display of samples of the raw materials that go into the manufacture of aluminum and zinc offset plates.
4. Try to locate and borrow an old Daguerreotype picture to show to the class. Make a report on the camera used for making Daguerreotypes, and tell how these pictures were developed.
5. Obtain information on the manufacture of rubber. Obtain samples of the raw materials used, and make a display.
6. Examine a black-and-white photograph in a newspaper using a strong magnifying glass. Examine the black-and-white cartoons and the color cartoons in the newspaper using the same glass. Now, again with the glass, examine a full-color reproduction of a photograph in a magazine or book which was printed on high-gloss paper. Ask your instructor to suggest some sources for information to answer the questions you surely must have. Make a report to the class.
7. Secure an opaque projector, and project the illustrations (in 6, above) on a screen, greatly enlarged. Ask your instructor to lead the class discussion.

## New Words

| | |
|---|---|
| 1. adaptations | 36. lithographer |
| 2. affinity | 37. mechanically |
| 3. Alois Senefelder | 38. medium |
| 4. artificial | 39. moisture |
| 5. associate | 40. negatives |
| 6. Bohemian | 41. nitrate |
| 7. cellulose | 42. obviously |
| 8. characters | 43. original |
| 9. chemical | 44. phenomena |
| 10. circulars | 45. photographic |
| 11. combination | 46. photography |
| 12. compelled | 47. porous |
| 13. consequently | 48. principles |
| 14. copperplate | 49. process |
| 15. corrections | 50. projected |
| 16. cylinder | 51. protected |
| 17. Daguerreotype | 52. publications |
| 18. demonstrated | 53. published |
| 19. depicting | 54. readable |
| 20. development | 55. relatively |
| 21. dilute | 56. relief |
| 22. directly | 57. repelled |
| 23. duplicators | 58. silhouette |
| 24. emulsion | 59. silver chloride |
| 25. exhausted | 60. sodium thiosulphate |
| 26. experiments | 61. solution |
| 27. exposed | 62. specialize |
| 28. flexible | 63. stationary |
| 29. formula | 64. statistical |
| 30. gelatin | 65. successful |
| 31. halftone | 66. transferred |
| 32. improvement | 67. vertically |
| 33. invention | 68. wet-collodion |
| 34. laborious | 69. withstand |
| 35. limestone | |

# The Offset
# Printing Industry

The complete, modern offset printing plant is equipped and staffed to handle all phases of the production of the printed piece from its planning and writing to the shipping of the finished product. In the smaller plants, each worker may perform a variety of operations, but in the larger plants, workers tend to specialize in one operation, or even one type of work within an operation.

## Divisions of Work

In general, the work performed by each department or worker is as follows:

### Management and Service Workers

*Executives* plan and direct the company operation. They plan for necessary equipment and financing, are responsible for employment and operating policies of the plant, and supervise all employees.

The *sales staff* works with customers, determining their requirements and furnishing information about the work to be done in the plant. To be successful in securing enough work to keep the plant active, they must know printing procedures, what the plant can do, and how much it will cost.

*Estimators* analyze each piece to be printed, determine the time required for each production step, compute the value of materials used, and give the sales department the total cost of the job to "quote" to the customer.

The *office staff* maintains correspondence and records of purchases, billings, payrolls, work performed, and taxes and also performs general accounting.

*Maintenance workers* are charged with keeping the plant clean and well-lighted. In addition they maintain the heating and air conditioning, and sometimes the lubrication, adjustment, and repair of equipment and machinery.

Sales promotional literature and campaigns are planned by *copywriters and advertising men* specially trained in sales methods and informed about production techniques.

*Layout men* make the detailed layouts, which actually are the "blueprints" from which the production workers proceed to do the necessary work for the printing of the finished product. On the layouts are indicated the type to be set and the artwork to be used — all in their respective positions and in the size and color they will appear when printed.

A staff of *photographers, retouchers, artists and draftsmen* provides all the original photographic and hand art for the illustrations which will appear in the finished pieces. Sometimes the customer furnishes part, or all, of the artwork.

### Composing Room

A staff of *compositors* sets type from the copy. This may be metal type, set by hand or machine, or it may be photographic type.

After a trial printing (proof) of composed type is made on a proof press, *proofreaders* carefully read it to be sure there are no errors. If any errors are found, they are corrected by the compositors, and verified for correction by the proofreaders. When the type is completely accurate, a *reproduction or etch proof* is taken, which will be used for camera copy.

*Copy preparation* workers assemble the etch proofs and prepare them in desired page layouts for the camera.

### Lithographic Preparation

*Cameramen* make negatives of the desired size for all the type proofs, photographs and other illustrations or hand artwork.

The *strippers* arrange and tape all the negatives on a sheet of goldenrod paper, according to a ruled-out layout for the plate to be made. This "stripped-up" arrangement of negatives is called a "flat". "Windows" are cut out of the other side of the flat to enable the images on the negatives to be exposed.

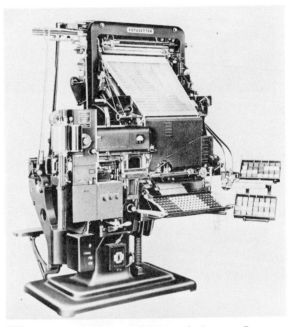

Fig. 58. Photo Composition of Type on the Intertype Fotosetter (Courtesy Intertype Co.)

Fig. 56. Setting (Composing) Metal Type by Hand

Fig. 57. Machine Composition of Metal Type on the Linotype (Courtesy Mergenthaler Linotype Co.)

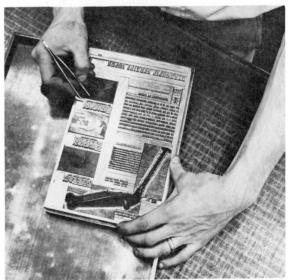

Fig. 59. Hand Composition, Checking a Page after Make Up from Metal Type and Cuts (Courtesy Western Printing and Lithographing Co.)

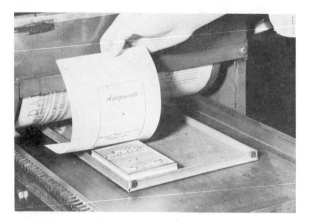

Fig. 60.  Pulling a Proof from a Galley of Type

Fig. 63.  Stripping Up a Flat (Courtesy Xerox Corp.)

Fig. 61.  Photo-Lithographer's Camera, Robertson 320
(Courtesy Robertson Photo-Mechanix, Inc.)

Fig. 64.  Graining Offset Plates
(Courtesy U.S. Government Printing Office)

Fig. 62.  Photographing the Copy, Xerox Camera No. 4
(Courtesy Xerox Corp.)

Fig. 65.  View in Platemaking Room
(Courtesy U.S. Government Printing Office)

*Platemakers* clean the surface of the offset plates, prepare coating solutions and coat the plates with the sensitizing solution. They place each flat over a sensitized plate, expose it to a strong light source and then develop the exposed plate. The plate is then sent to the pressroom.

Very often, a single-page negative for a job may be exposed many times on different parts of a large plate so as to be able to print many copies of the job on one sheet — then these printed sheets are cut apart into separate job-size pieces. These multiple exposures are made on a "step-and-repeat" machine.

### Printing and Binding

*Storekeepers* maintain stocks of paper, ink, and other supplies in anticipation of the regular run of work. Before paper is sent to the pressroom or to the *papercutters* to be cut to press size, it is conditioned to adjust the moisture content of the paper in relation to the moisture content of the air in the pressroom.

Paper stock is selected to fit the specifications for the job or is ordered specially for the job.

*Pressmen* ready the press for operation. They attach the plate to the press, adjust the ink, water, paper feed and other mechanisms, and take trial impressions. When all is in order, the job is run. *Feeders* and *helpers* assist the pressmen on large presses.

The printed sheets are sent to the *bindery* where they may be cut, folded, punched, perforated, assembled, stitched, padded or otherwise finished as may be required.

### Shipping and Receiving

The *shipping department* wraps or packages the finished work and ships or delivers it to the customer. It also *receives*, from suppliers, incoming stock and materials which are sent to the stockroom.

### Special Services to the Trade

Not all the workers or facilities mentioned above are to be found in every offset shop. Some shops do only the presswork or the presswork plus some of the other operations,

Fig. 66.   Platemaking on the Step-and-Repeat Machine
(Courtesy Western Printing & Lithographing Co.)

Fig. 67.   Cutting Paper Stock to Size
(Courtesy Harris-Seybold Co.)

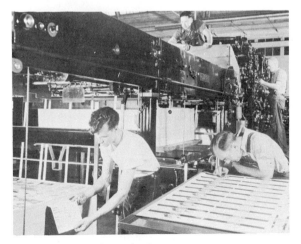

Fig. 68.   View in Lithographic Pressroom
(Courtesy Harris-Seybold Co.)

and work with special service, or "trade" shops for the other phases of production.

*Lithographic, chemical and graphic arts supply houses* furnish plates, presensitized plates, films and photographic processing chemicals, platemaking and pressroom solutions and chemicals, press blankets and numerous other items for offset work.

*Composition houses* furnish type set to copy in either metal type or photographic type. They also furnish reproduction proofs.

*Special artwork* for which facilities are not available is prepared by firms specializing in finished art and photography.

Fig. 69.  Cutting Apart the Printed Sheets
(Courtesy Harris-Seybold Co.)

Fig. 70.  Folding Machine, 39" x 52" Baumfolder
(Courtesy Russell E. Baum, Inc.)

A layout, with the necessary proofs and photo copy, may be sent to a firm which *specializes in making a completed "flat,"* or in some cases supplying only the negatives for the job.

Some shops regularly send their flats out for *platemaking;* other shops have trade shops make special plates for which facilities are not available in the shop.

## The Office Offset Unit

Many small offset "duplicators" are found in offices, schools and factories and these machines turn out a great deal of printed work. The addition of a small camera and platemaking unit, together with the use of the presensitized plates, has made many of these units fairly complete.

## Questions

1. Describe the flow of work in a complete offset shop.
2. Who sets the type for a job?
3. What two general classes of type are used?
4. Who would take the photograph of a vacuum cleaner which is to appear in a printed job?
5. Which worker would make the negative for the illustration of the vacuum cleaner?
6. How could a shop get along without a camera, if it didn't have enough camera work to justify it?
7. Study each of the divisions of work discussed.  Is every one of them really necessary?  State your reasons.
8. In a one-man shop, who would be the foreman? the pressman? the shipper? the salesman?  Who could he blame for poor work results?  What should be his qualifications?  List them.

## Problems and Projects

1. Arrange, well in advance, for several field trips to offset plants.  Visit a small one first, then larger ones.  Plan, with a representative of the plant, what you would

like to see. Use the standard procedure in your school for going on a field trip.

2. Arrange for the showing of one or more films on the offset process. Show the same film twice, with several days intervening, to give a chance for class discussion.

3. Invite a man from an offset plant to come to the school and talk to the class about offset printing, new techniques in offset, offset occupations or some other related topic.

4. Interview one or more representative craftsmen employed in the offset industry. Ask about advantages and disadvantages of the work, wages, hours, opportunities for training and entrance into the occupation.

5. Secure information about training for lithographic employment and where it may be obtained, such as apprenticeship, technical schools (public and private) and colleges. Report to the class on the requirements, locations, costs, courses and variety of training available.

6. Get facts and figures on employment locally, regionally and nationally. Find the number of plants, the number of workers, wages and hours.

7. Arrange a bulletin board display of pictures of offset presses, cameras, plate-making equipment and other tools and equipment used in offset work. Label each one.

8. Post a large world map on the board. Pinpoint locations of sources of raw materials going into the offset industry and locations of historical significance in offset work. A row of identification tags along the bottom can be connected to appropriate pins on the map with strings or yarn.

9. If you are interested in a career in offset printing, try to get a job, part time or in the summer. Be willing to accept any type of work that will give you an opportunity to get acquainted with the methods, workers and working conditions.

## New Words

| | |
|---|---|
| 1. accounting | 21. lithographic |
| 2. advertising | 22. lubrication |
| 3. anticipation | 23. maintenance |
| 4. arrangement | 24. mechanisms |
| 5. chemicals | 25. multiple |
| 6. commercial | 26. negatives |
| 7. compositors | 27. operation |
| 8. conditioning | 28. papercutters |
| 9. copywriters | 29. perforated |
| 10. correspondence | 30. photographers |
| 11. customers | 31. platemakers |
| 12. department | 32. presensitized |
| 13. duplicators | 33. processing |
| 14. equipping | 34. production |
| 15. executives | 35. promotional |
| 16. facilities | 36. proofreaders |
| 17. financing | 37. reproduction |
| 18. goldenrod | 38. respective |
| 19. illustrations | 39. specialize |
| 20. impressions | 40. specifications |

# CHAPTER 4

# Job Planning
# and Layout

In order that the finished printed job may be exactly what the customer desires, a full-sized plan or "layout" of the contemplated work must be drawn up in as detailed a form as possible before the actual production work begins. In addition, this layout must contain all necessary instructions so that each worker knows exactly what is to be done.

It is vitally important that the customer approve the layout before the printing proc-ess starts since he alone knows exactly what he wants.

In an offset shop which employs few workers, the owner of the shop, the foreman, or the compositor may make the layouts. In large shops, specialists in layout are employed. Again, customers may have their

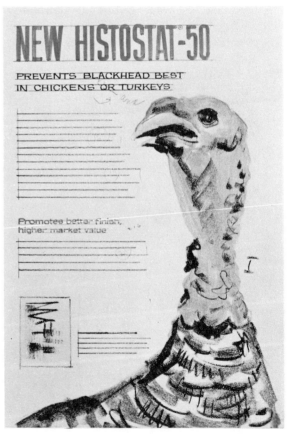

Fig. 85. Copywriter's Rough Layout Shows Areas Needed for Type (Courtesy The Biddle Co.)

Fig. 86. Artist's Layout Provides Copy Space, Shows Art Needed (Courtesy The Biddle Co.)

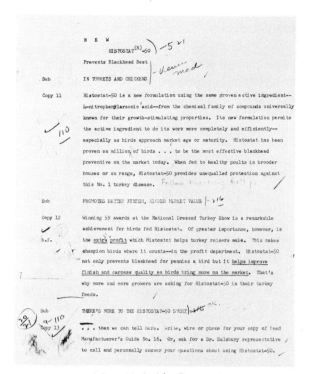

Fig. 87. Prepared Copy Marked for Composition
(Courtesy The Biddle Co.)

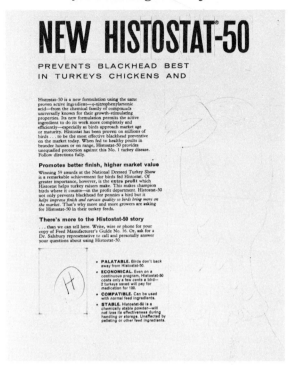

Fig. 88. Etch Proofs Pasted in Position for Camera
(Courtesy The Biddle Co.)

work planned and laid out by commercial advertising agencies who specialize in this work, or they may employ layout men on their own advertising staff.

## Equipment and Materials

The layout man may work at a draftsman's table, or at an artist's table. His usual equipment includes type specimen books and sheets, copyfitting tables, proportional rule, paper catalogs, ink charts, drawing board, T square, triangles, French curves, scales (rulers), various grades and colors of pencils, drawing inks, draftsman's tools or instruments, erasers, airbrush and crayons. He has a supply of various grades of layout paper and tracing paper for making the layouts and for tracing large letters and illustrations.

## Thumb-Nail Sketches

Before attempting a full-size layout, a number of small "thumb-nail" sketches are made, exploring various arrangements until both the layout man and the customer or account executive are pleased.

Fig. 89. Printed Piece (Courtesy The Biddle Co.)

Fig. 90. A Type Tracing Card. Vertical lines at ends of lines show vertical space occupied by type face plus shoulder. (Reduced)

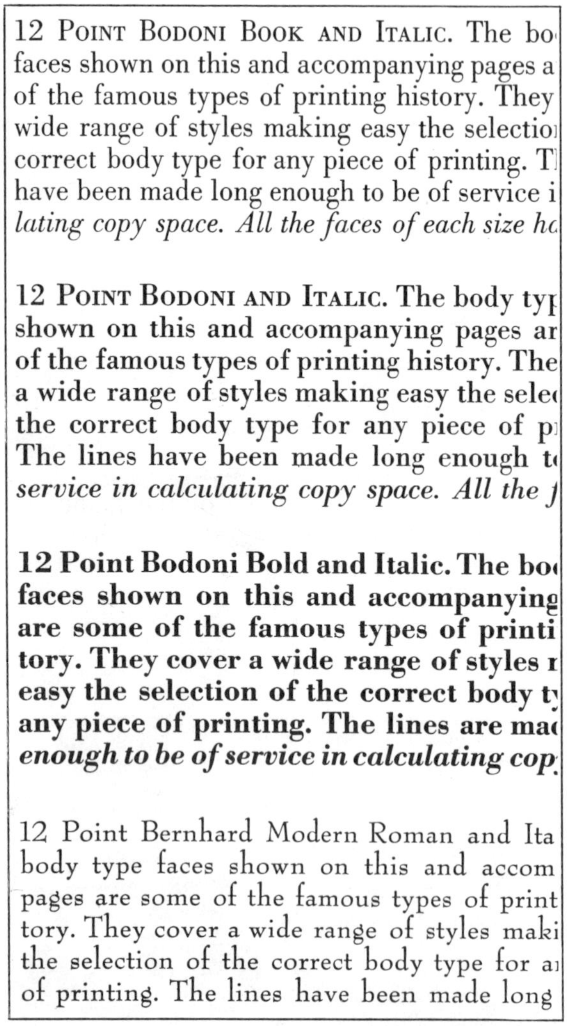

12 POINT BODONI BOOK AND ITALIC. The bo faces shown on this and accompanying pages a of the famous types of printing history. They wide range of styles making easy the selectio correct body type for any piece of printing. T have been made long enough to be of service i *lating copy space. All the faces of each size h*

12 POINT BODONI AND ITALIC. The body typ shown on this and accompanying pages ar of the famous types of printing history. The a wide range of styles making easy the selec the correct body type for any piece of p The lines have been made long enough t *service in calculating copy space. All the f*

**12 Point Bodoni Bold and Italic. The bo faces shown on this and accompanying are some of the famous types of printi tory. They cover a wide range of styles r easy the selection of the correct body ty any piece of printing. The lines are mac *enough to be of service in calculating cop*

12 Point Bernhard Modern Roman and Ita body type faces shown on this and accom pages are some of the famous types of print tory. They cover a wide range of styles maki the selection of the correct body type for a of printing. The lines have been made long

Fig. 91. Legible Body Types (Part of a Specimen Sheet) (Courtesy American Type Founders Co., Inc.)

## Rough Layouts

Working from the selected thumb-nail sketch, a full-size "rough" layout is made to show how the finished job may look in full size. The full-size rough also gives some idea of the proper sizes of type to use, and the required sizes of the illustrations.

## Comprehensive Layouts

When the rough layout seems promising, a "comprehensive" layout is made. This layout will resemble, as closely as is possible, the desired finished job.

A sheet of the stock to be used is marked off to the exact finished (trimmed) size. The layout is made on this sheet, indicating the display lines of type, the body type, any hand art and illustrations. Spaces in which mounted proofs may be placed are left in the layout sheet for these illustrations.

### Display Lines of Type

Type, 14 point and larger, is generally referred to as display type. It is drawn on the comprehensive layout in actual size and form — or it can be traced from specimen sheets (or type tracing cards) and pasted in place. Spacing (leading) between lines is allowed for. A notation is made to the side of the layout, indicating the size, face, and catalog number of the type face. It is good practice to indicate also the manufacturer of the type, whether it is hand or machine set, the length of the line and the position of the words in the line. For example, the copy notation (marking) for a display line may read:

"18 pt. No. 2 Stymie Medium Italic, ATF, 30 picas, flush left."

If a type size is specified as "72/60", or "72 on 60", it indicates that the type face is a 72-point face and the body size is 60 points.

If the type size is specified as "14/16," or "14 on 16", it indicates a 14-point face on a 16-point body. The extra shoulder width, as above, eliminates the need for inserting a 2-point lead between lines. The type can be set "solid", and yet appear as though leaded. This is a real time-saver.

### Text (or Body) Type

Type faces 12 points and smaller are called "text" or "body" types. These are the sizes which are used for newspaper columns, book pages, and general reading matter. It is generally agreed that the most legible body type composition consists of 10- to 12-point type, set in lines which are equal in length to 1½ to 2½ times the length of the lower-case alphabet of that particular type face.

Text (or body) matter is generally indicated on the layout by a rectangle the exact width and depth (in picas) which the type matter will occupy when set. Individual lines of text type may be indicated by parallel lines to show the height of the lower-case and capital letters.

Notations (as described for display lines) on the typewritten copy or the layout tell the compositor what face, leading and line length are to be used. A "key" (reference) marking in the text-matter rectangle identifies the typewritten copy to set for that space.

### Copyfitting

It is time- and labor-saving to know, in advance of setting the type, whether or not the type will fit in the available space, and exactly how many lines of type must be set at a given width to accommodate the typewritten copy.

### Display Type

To find out how much space a word or group of words will require if set in display type, take a strip of paper and mark off on it the exact widths of each letter and space in the line, taking your measurements from a type specimen sheet.

### Body (Text) Type

To find out, in advance, how many lines of body type must be set, use the following method:

1. *Number of characters in the copy.* Determine how many typewritten characters there are in the total copy.
    a. Find the number of typewriter characters in *one inch* of the typewritten copy. (Pica typewriter type is 10 characters per inch; elite typewriter type is 12 characters per inch.)
    b. Multiply the *average length* of copy lines (in inches) by the number of typewriter characters per inch. The result is "the number of typewriter characters per line of copy".
    c. Multiply the number of typewriter characters per line by the number of typewritten lines in the copy to arrive at the number of typewriter characters on the page.

NOTE: In computing typewriter characters per inch, per line and per page, *punctuation marks and spaces are included.*

    d. Multiply the number of typewriter characters per page by the number of pages of copy to find the total number of typewriter characters in the job. In counting the number of pages in the copy, make allowance for partial pages of copy, and spaces left for illustrations on the copy pages.

NOTE: It will aid greatly if the typist types all lines the same width and an equal number of lines per page.

2. *Number of lines of type required.* Determine how many lines of type must be set for the total amount of copy. Of course, one must know the size and face of the type, the name of the manufacturer, whether it is hand or machine set and the *length of line in picas* to which the type will be set.

Fig. 92. Using a Strip of Paper to Copyfit a Display Line from Type Tracing Card.

a. Measure (compare) the length of type line required, *in picas,* against an actual printed specimen of the type to be used. Count the number of *type* characters contained in this number of picas. This is the number of type characters required to set one line of type at the given length.

NOTE: It is best to check the number of characters in several lines of the required length (or of a much longer line) and divide to obtain an average number of characters per line of type.

In counting type characters, again include punctuation marks and spaces.

b. Divide the total number of *typewritten* characters in the job by the number of *type* characters required for one line of the desired length. The result is the *total number of lines of type,* for the required length of line.

Type founders and manufacturers of typecasting and slug-casting machines furnish character counts per pica for their type faces. These are preferred by some for copyfitting.

### Leading Between Lines

The amount of vertical space which will be occupied in a column by *one line* of type is the body size of that type plus the thickness of the leading used between lines of type in the column.

For example, if 10-point type is used, and 2-point leading is used between lines, each line of type will actually account for 12 points of vertical measure in the column. Thus, 12 lines of 10-point type, set leaded 2 points, would actually equal 12 lines of 12-point type (measured vertically on the page), or 144 points, which is equal to 12 picas.

If the type is set "solid" (no leading between lines), the depth of the column or page would be equal to the body size of the type multiplied by the number of lines of type in the column.

To determine how many lines of a certain size type will fit in a given depth of page, divide the depth of the page in points (picas × 12) by the size of the type plus the amount of leading between lines. For example: How many lines of 10-point type will fit on a page 28 picas deep, if the type is to be set leaded 4 points?

10-pt. body + 4-pt. leading = 14 pts. per line
28-pica depth × 12 pts. per pica = 336 pts. depth.
336 pts. ÷ 14 = 24 lines.

NOTE: Slug-casting machines produce slugs which are slightly thicker than the nominal size (12-pt. slug is about 12¼ pt.), so check actual printed samples for exact spacing.

### Typing Line-for-Line

If there are to be several pages of typed copy, instruct the typist to type the copy so that each line of typing will occupy a line of type when the type is set; also, type each page to contain the same number of lines as there will be lines of type on the page.

Find out from the type specimen book how many type characters will be contained in a type line of the planned length. Set the typewriter carriage for this number of characters. Try to maintain this average number of typewriter characters on each line.

Typewriter paper can be pre-printed with faint vertical lines showing the desired width of the lines to be typed. This will indicate if the typist is overrunning the line, so it can be balanced by underrunning the next line.

### Illustrations

The exact space to be occupied by an illustration should be indicated on the layout by a rectangle of the desired size, or by a profile outline. Mark each space reserved on the layout for an illustration by a "key" letter, number or title, corresponding to the marking on the illustration. This will help to insure that the correct illustration will be used.

To improve the layout, the illustration may be sketched in the allotted space, or a proof of it may be pasted in the space.

A more convincing layout is achieved if color is used to simulate the job as it will appear when printed.

## The Dummy

For a printed piece of work involving a number of pages, a dummy is compulsory. To prepare a dummy, secure a number of pieces of the stock to be used. Cut these to a size that, after folding once, will be the untrimmed-page size of the booklet. Prepare a piece of cover stock of the same size (after folding).

Assemble the cover and sufficient folded sheets, and staple them once through the fold, near the top. Number the pages in the lower outside corners consecutively, beginning with "1" on the first right-hand page.

Cut a number of pieces of stock, each the final untrimmed-page size of the booklet page. These page-size pieces will serve as layout sheets for the pages of the booklet. (Page proofs may be used, instead.) When laid out, these single pages will be attached to the dummy pages — the outside cover will be clipped to the outside cover of the dummy; the title page clipped to page 1, if it is desired there; and remaining pages clipped where desired in the dummy. On each single page, indicate the actual page number it will carry when printed.

Each page should be laid out completely for the job. Ruled lines should be drawn to indicate the space to be occupied by the body type. Display type, ornaments and illustrations should be indicated in their actual size, and in the exact position. Dimensions must be given for the width and depth of the printed page and the location of the page numbers and running heads. If the page has more than one column, the width of the columns and the spacing between columns must be specified.

Type faces, sizes and length of line must be indicated.

Trim lines should be drawn on the cover (and pages) to indicate the appearance after trimming head, foot and outside edge of the printed and folded booklet.

Indicate all margins to show how much white space will remain at the head, gutter (next to the fold), foot, and fore-edge.

In short, the dummy must be made to look as much like the finished work as possible.

Yet, while still in the planning stage, individual pages can be shifted about, added, or eliminated without much trouble. Once the dummy is approved, the pages can be made up, and production can start.

## Questions

1. What is a layout?
2. What tools, equipment, and materials does the layout man use?
3. What are thumb-nail sketches?
4. What is a rough layout?
5. What is a comprehensive layout?
6. How is display type indicated on the comprehensive layout?
7. How is body type indicated on the comprehensive layout?
8. What does each item in the following copy markings indicate?
   a. 18 pt. Baskerville Italic No. 2, American, caps, 25 picas.
   b. 24/30 Spartan Bold, Linotype 154, caps & l.c., 28 picas, center.
   c. 24 pt. Baskerville 1B24, Intertype, 30 picas, flush left, all caps.
   d. 6 pt. Adtype, Monotype 163J, caps & l.c., 13 picas, solid.
   e. 14 pt. Bodoni Bold Condensed, Ludlow 3-BC, caps, 15 picas, leaded 4 points, flush right.
   f. 48 pt. Scotch Roman, ATF, caps, 45 picas, centered, letter-spaced.
8. What is the difference in size between body type and display type? Answer in point sizes.
9. Make a list of the display type in your shop, listing the faces of type, and the body sizes of each.
10. Make a list of the body (text) type in the shop, listing the faces of type, and the body sizes of each.
11. How are illustrations indicated on the comprehensive layout?
12. How is keying done?
13. Of what value is a dummy?
14. What is copyfitting?
15. Tell how to copyfit display type.
16. Tell how to copyfit text (or body) type.
17. What qualifications should the layout man have?

## Problems and Projects

1. Make a list of the tools, materials and equipment for layout work which the shop is lacking. Consult current catalogs and make out a requisition for ordering this material. Use company names, catalog numbers, catalog date, item name as used in catalog and include size, finish, color, price and other information needed to describe specifically the items desired.

2. Make layouts — thumb-nails, roughs, then comprehensives — for the following:
   a. Personal card, imprinted note paper and return envelope.
   b. Greeting card — single sheet, folded sheet or French fold.
   c. Matched set of business card, letterhead, envelope corner, check and stub, and billhead.
   d. Menu.
   e. Four-page program (for a graduation, musicale, school play, etc.)
   f. Poster or show card.

3. Mount a collection of printed samples of one of the above-mentioned items on full-size sheets of heavy board.

4. Redesign a printed job which is used in your school shop, or business. Make a comprehensive layout. See if your new design will more economically utilize a stock size of paper.

5. Plan a job which will require a dummy and copyfitting of both display and text type, and which when printed will be of practical use in the shop. Consult with your instructor.

## New Words

| | |
|---|---|
| 1. accommodate | 24. indicated |
| 2. advertising | 25. instructions |
| 3. allotted | 26. instruments |
| 4. allowance | 27. lower-case |
| 5. alphabet | 28. manufacturer |
| 6. arrangements | 29. multiply |
| 7. carriage | 30. notation |
| 8. catalogs | 31. occupy |
| 9. characters | 32. ornaments |
| 10. compensated | 33. production |
| 11. completely | 34. profile |
| 12. composition | 35. proportional |
| 13. compositor | 36. punctuation |
| 14. comprehensive | 37. rectangle |
| 15. compulsory | 38. reference |
| 16. computing | 39. reserved |
| 17. contemplated | 40. shoulder |
| 18. copyfitting | 41. simulate |
| 19. determine | 42. specialists |
| 20. dimensions | 43. specified |
| 21. draftsman's | 44. specimen |
| 22. dummy | 45. typewritten |
| 23. generally | 46. vertical |

# Type Composition
# for Reproduction

Any of the available methods of type composition may be used for setting copy which is to be printed by photo-offset lithography. Indeed, the possibilities of the offset process have inspired the invention and development of several of the newer methods of type composition.

In general, the various methods of type composition may be classified as:

1. Hot type (three-dimensional) composition*:
   a. Metal type, which includes hand-set foundry type, Monotype, Linotype and Intertype, Ludlow.
   b. Wood type.
   c. Letterpress printing plates, both line and halftone.
2. Cold type (two-dimensional) composition*:
   a. Photo-copying existing printed work, in whole or in part.
   b. Mechanical composition.
      (1) Clip art, such as borders, pictures, logotypes, words, etc.
      (2) Hand-drawn lettering (free-hand or with various guides), graphs, forms, charts, diagrams, etc.

*The present usage is to refer to solid-metal, letter-press type and letterpress relief plates as "hot type" composition, because of the melting and casting procedures usually inherent. The term "three-dimensional type" is also common. "Cold type" composition refers to the several methods of producing type composition on paper or film without resorting to the use of "hot type" materials. The various forms of cold type can be called "two-dimensional type" because they all are on essentially flat surfaces.

(3) Stencil scribing, with strip stencil or stencil device.
(4) Pre-printed type, including hand-assembled tab type, adhesive type and transfer type.
(5) Typewriting, on standard typewriters or on special typewriter-keyboard-actuated machines (sometimes called "strike-on" or "impact type").
c. Photo-typesetting.
   (1) Photographic display lines (usually hand-set).
   (2) Photographic page-composed type (usually machine-set).

This chapter does not attempt to explain in detail how to perform the actual operation of setting type; rather, it describes these methods. For detailed instructions in the actual composition of type, the reader is advised to consult standard reference books and manufacturers' manuals on the subject.

## HOT TYPE COMPOSITION

### Metal Type

Metal type is set (composed) by hand or machine to form the lines of type for the intended pages. After proofreading and correction of errors, reproduction proofs (also called "repros" or "etch proofs") are taken on dull, coated, white paper with black ink. These reproduction proofs, which must be clean and sharp, are then photographed (with possible reductions or enlargements in size) to produce a film negative (or, where necessary, a film positive for platemaking. Repro proofs may also be "pulled" on cellophane or acetate. These may be used as film postives — or they may be contact-printed photographically on film to produce film negatives.

Reproduction proofs (proofs to be photographed for platemaking) should be pulled from newly-cast type or from type reserved only for proofs. Worn and battered type may not produce clean, sharp proofs. The proof press used should be reserved only for repro-

duction proofs, and, if possible, should be equipped with grippers and a good inking mechanism.

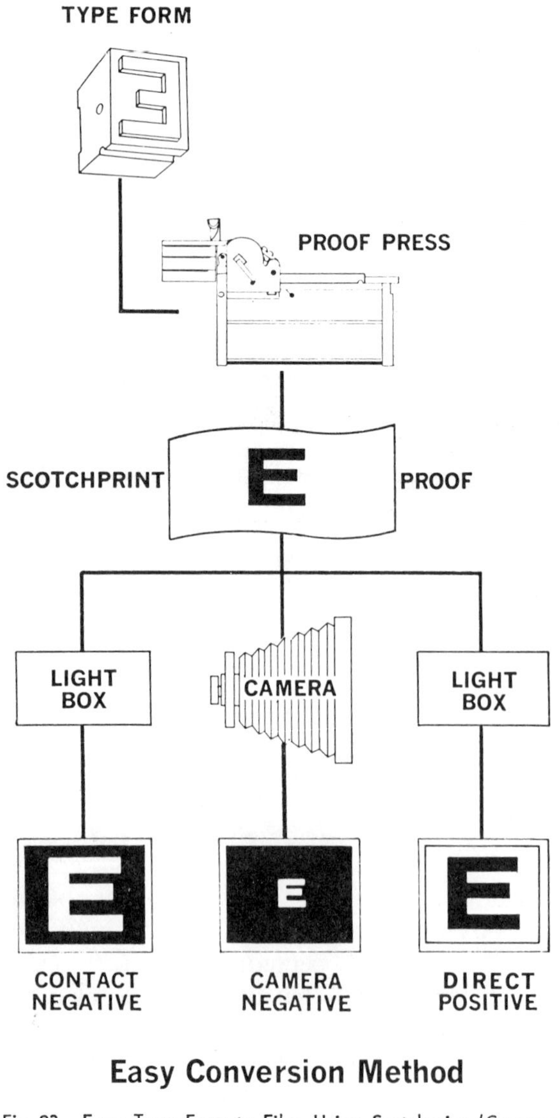

Cellophane reproduction proofs are best made on a proof press equipped with a rubber tympan sheet (blanket). The inked type is first run through the proof press with no paper over the type, thus printing directly on the blanket. Then the cellophane sheet is laid over the type, and the proof is pulled. This results in printing on both sides of the cellophane and makes the image more dense.

Reproduction proofs may be made without special preparation on a grainless, translucent, plastic sheet (Scotchprint, Fig. 93), using a standard proof press and regular ink. This produces a positive transparency which can be mounted on the layout, or used by itself as camera copy to yield a film negative. A film negative or reverse print also may be produced by contact printing the Scotchprint, using standard developing procedures. A film positive is possible by directly contact printing the Scotchprint onto auto-positive materials, or by reversal developing.

Letterpress type forms, including line and halftone plates, may be converted directly to images on film (and paper) by several conversion methods — Brightype, Instant Negative and Cronapress conversion film. These are described beginning on page 43.

It should be remembered when enlarging or reducing type that the beauty of the original type design must not be sacrificed. Too great a reduction in size may weaken or obliterate the finer lines of the type; conversely, too great an enlargement may coarsen or excessively darken those same fine lines. When originally designed, the individual letters of each size of a type face are proportioned in the weight of lines for that size of type.

Current practice in the industry is to send reproduction proofs to the cameraman all "made up" in page form, with headings in place, necessary spacing between lines and paragraphs and all lines ruled in for ruled forms. In this way, the resulting negative of a complete page is ready for the stripping operation.

**Easy Conversion Method**

Fig. 93.  From Type Form to Film, Using Scotchprint (Courtesy 3M Co.)

Composition (typesetting) houses and type founders furnish type specimen books in which they illustrate the faces and sizes of the type they have available. Sample pages of type specimen books are shown in Figs. 94A and 94B. Type sizes are determined by the measurement (in points) of the entire body from the back to the belly, as shown in Fig. 95A. Metal types have a space beneath most characters, called the "shoulder," which allows for descending strokes (as "y" or "p" in Fig. 95B) and for space between lines. This shoulder is included when measuring the body size of the type, and it varies with different faces. So, it is necessary to see the type in actual printed form to determine how large it will appear. For example, 12-point Century Expanded (with short descenders) appears much larger than 12-point Garamond (which has long descenders).

A printer's line gauge is used to measure sizes of type. Note in Fig. 95A that six picas equals approximately an inch. Although not shown, each pica is divided into 12 points. Thus, a type character which measures two picas across its body, from belly to back, would be 24-point type; if it measured six picas, it would be 72-point type. All metal type used in the United States is cast to be .918 inches high (commonly called "point nine one eight"), measured from the feet to the face of the type. This measurement is referred to as "type-high."

The several kinds of metal type in use are described below.

## Foundry Type

Foundry type is cast (produced) by a type foundry in individual oblong units called "types", or "characters," each having on one end a "wrong-reading"* letter in relief. Printers purchase foundry type in *fonts*, which are complete collections or assortments of letters, figures and punctuation marks of one size and type-face style. The quantities of each letter in a font are supplied according to the fre-

---

*Note: "Wrong-reading": laterally reversed, or reading from right to left.

14, 18, 24, 30, 36, 48, 60 PT.

## Stymie Medium Condensed   1234

24, 30, 36, 48 60 PT.

## Stymie Bold   1234

8, 10, 12, 14, 18, 24, 30, 36, 48 PT.

## *Stymie Bold Ital.   12*

8, 10, 12, 14, 18, 24, 30, 36, 48 PT.

## Stymie Ex. Bold 12

8, 10, 12, 14, 18, 24, 30, 36, 48 PT.

## *Stymie Ex. Bold It.*

14, 18, 24, 30, 36, 48, 60 PT.

## Stymie Extra Bold Cond.   1

24, 30, 36, 48 PT.

## STYMIE OPEN 1

24, 30, 42, 48 PT.

## Trylon Bold          1234567890

14, 18, 24, 30, 36, 48 PT.                    (36 pt. shown)

## *Typo Script   1234567890*

12, 14, 18, 24, 30, 36, 48 PT.

## Ultra Bodoni   12

14, 18, 24, 30, 36 PT.

## *Ultra Bodoni Ita.*

12, 14, 18, 24, 30, 36, 48, 60 PT.

## Ultra Bodoni Ex. Cond.   1

14, 18, 24, 30, 36 PT.

## Valiant          1234567890

Fig. 94A. Page from a Composition House Type Specimen Book.

## Standard Bold

6 point  no. 38 24 77 a                    22×A 41×a 21×1

**A spot of colour here and there will double the value of printing. Many new and beautiful types are displayed in this new catalogue. Pleasingly AN IMPORTANT NOTICE FOR PRINTERS 12345**

8 point  no. 38 24 78                    21×A 39×a 20×1

**Experience has immensely broadened ideas governing the management and development of business. During these productive periods EXHIBITION AND SALE IN FEBRUARY 1958**

10 point  no. 38 24 80                    19×A 34×a 13×1

**En las imprentas y sobre todo en los talleres de composicion, la estabilidad del personal presenta ventajas NUESTRO FAVORECEDOR 567890**

12 point  no. 38 24 82                    16×A 28×a 11×1

**Typography sends knowledge abroad as heaven sends rain. The one fructifies the soil, the ASK FOR NEWEST SPECIMEN**

14 point  no. 38 24 83                    13×A 24×a 10×1

**Gaceta oficial de Valencia Nuevos tipos de reclame MANUAL DEL FUNDIDOR**

18 point  no. 38 24 85                    8×A 16×a 8×1

**Furniture Catalogue A VERY NICE HOME**

24 point small  no. 38 24 86                    6×A 11×a 7×1

**España y Portugal BURGOS/LISBOA**

24 point large  no. 38 24 87                    5×A 10×a 5×1

**Steel Company BRANCH LINES**

30 point  no. 38 24 88                    5×A 8×a 4×1

**Type Writers REMINGTON**

42 point  no. 38 24 89                    4×A 7×a 3×1

**Sol y Luna**

60 point  no. 38 24 90                    3×A 5×a 3×1

**GUARD**

72 point  no. 38 24 91                    3×A 5×a 3×1

**Month**

**A B C D E F G H I J K L M N O P Q R S T U V W X Y Z**
**a b c d e f g h i j k l m n o p q r s t u v w x y z 1 2 3 4 5 6 7 8 9 0**

Fig. 94B.  Page of a Type Catalog Showing the Available Sizes of One Face of Type. Several different sizes of the same type face are known as a "series of type." This is the "Standard Bold" series. (Courtesy Amsterdam Continental Types and Graphic Equipment, Inc.)

quency of its normal use in printing. Blank units of various widths, called spaces, are used to provide the spacing between words and where needed at other points in the composition. By changing the width, weight of line, or slant of a particular type face design, manufacturers create variations in type faces. Variations of any one type face design are known as a "family." Part of the Spartan family is shown in Fig. 96B.

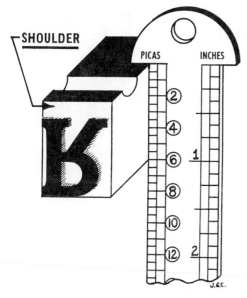

Fig. 95A. Measuring Body Size of Foundry Type with a Line Gauge. This is 72-point type.

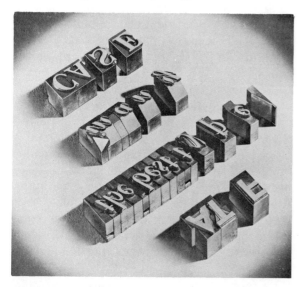

Fig. 95B. Foundry Type (Courtesy American Type Founders Co., Inc.)

AAAAAAAABBBBBBBBCCCCCCCCCCCEEEEEEEE''''
DDDDDFFFFFGGGGGGHHHHHJJJJJJJJJJJJJJJJJK
KKLLLLLMMMMMMMNNNNNNOOOOOO!!PPP
PPPPPPQQRRRRRRSSSSSSSSSSSSTTTTTTTTTTU
UUUUUWWWWWWWXXYYYYZZ&&GGGGGG..........:..::........---??

aaaaaaaaaaaaaaaaaaaabbbbbbbbcccccccccccc.......dddddddddddd
ddeeeeeeeeeeeeeeeeeeeeeeeeeefffffffffgggggggggghhhhhhhhhhhh
hhhiiiiiiiiiiiiiiiiiiiiiiijjjjjkkkkkklllllllllllll---mmmmmmmmmmm
mmmmmmmmmmmmmmmmmmmnnnoooooooooooooooooooo??pppp
ppppqqqqrrrrrrrrrrrrrrrrrrrrssssssssssssssssssss!!ttttttt
tttttttttttttuuuuuuuuuuuuuuvvvvvwwwwwwwyyyyyyyyyyzzzz
xxxxfififfffffflflflffifffffifffflffffaaaaoaoaoa..........::;;..........''''

1111111111222222222333333344444445555555566666666---
...............77777778888888899999999000000000000000$$$$$$$$

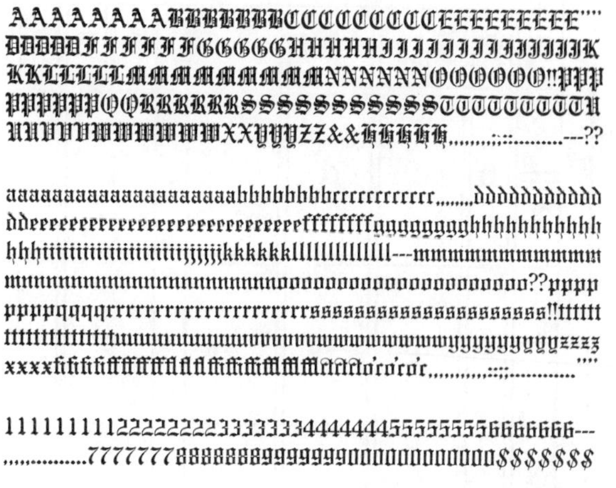

Fig. 96A. A Font of Type as Received from the Foundry, 18-point Engravers Old English (148) (Reduced) (Courtesy American Type Founders Co., Inc.)

18, 24, 30, 36, 48 PT.

# Spartan Medium   12345

18, 24, 30, 36, 48 PT.

# Spartan Med. Italic   1234

10, 12, 14, 18, 24, 30, 36, 48, 60 PT.

# Spartan Medium Condensed   123456

18, 24, 30, 36, 48, 60 PT.

# Spartan Heavy   123456

18, 24, 30, 36 48 PT.

# Spartan Heavy Italic   12

6, 8, 10, 12, 14, 18, 24, 30, 36, 48, 60 PT.

# Spartan Black   12345

6, 8, 10, 12, 14, 18, 24, 30, 36, 48 PT.

# Spartan Black Ital.   12

8, 10, 12, 14, 18, 24, 30, 36, 48, 60, 72 PT.

# Spartan Black Condensed   123

8, 10, 12, 14, 18, 24, 30, 36, 48, 60 PT.

Fig. 96B. Several Variations of the Same Basic Face Is Called a Type "Family." This is part of the "Spartan" family.

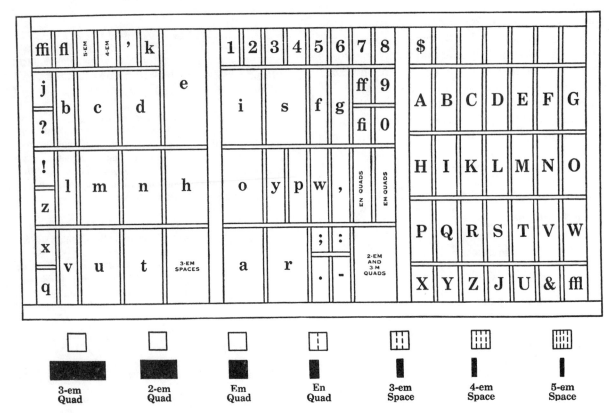

| | | | | | | | | | | | | | | |
|---|---|---|---|---|---|---|---|---|---|---|---|---|---|---|
| ffi | fl | 5-EM | 4-EM | ' | k | | 1 | 2 | 3 | 4 | 5 | 6 | 7 | 8 | $ | |
| j | | | | | e | | | | | | | | | ff | 9 | A B C D E F G |
| ? | b | c | d | | | | i | s | f | g | fi | 0 | |
| ! | | | | | | | | | | | EN QUADS | EM QUADS | H I K L M N O |
| z | l | m | n | h | | | o | y p w | , | | |
| x | | | | | | | | | ; : | | P Q R S T V W |
| q | v | u | t | 3-EM SPACES | | | a | r | . - | 2-EM AND 3-M QUADS | X Y Z J U & ffl |

| 3-em Quad | 2-em Quad | Em Quad | En Quad | 3-em Space | 4-em Space | 5-em Space |

Fig. 97A. California Job Case Layout. Usual arrangement of letters in a case for metal type. Below the case is shown the names and relative widths of spaces and quads. These blank pieces of type are inserted in the line for spacing.

Foundry type is stored in type cases from which the compositor (typesetter) picks out individual characters, putting them in order in a composing stick which has been set to the desired length of line. The compositor inserts spaces or quads\* between words to make the lines of equal length (justifying), or to provide indentions and to fill out the last line of a paragraph.

Space between lines of foundry type is provided by inserting thin, 2-point strips of lead called "leads" (pronounced *leds*). Strips 6 points or more in thickness are called "slugs."

Composed type is then placed on a tray-like "galley" which is placed on the bed of a proof press. The type is inked with a brayer, covered with a clean sheet of paper, and a proof is taken (Fig. 60, page 22). The galley proof is read for mistakes, and any mistakes discovered are corrected in the type form. After use, the type is cleaned of ink, and is then distributed back into the proper compartments of its original type case to be available for use again when next needed. Today,

\*Quads are wide spaces. The various quads used with foundry type are shown below the type case layout, in Fig. 97A.

Fig. 97B. Setting Type by Hand from the Case

because of expense, handset type has largely been replaced by machine methods except where only a few lines of display are involved.

### Monotype

Monotype is similar to foundry type in that it, too, is individual pieces of type. Unlike foundry type, however, Monotype is cast in the shop, when needed, in complete lines of individual letters and spaces according to copy. Lines of single letters can also be cast for hand setting from type cases.

The Monotype system employs two machines: the keyboard machine and the caster.

An operator sits at the keyboard of the Monotype keyboard machine with the copy before him. He manipulates the keys, selecting the desired letters and spacing combinations. In response, the machine perforates little holes in a controller ribbon (roll of paper 4¼″ wide), making a record of what is desired.

Fig. 98A.   Monotype Keyboard
(Courtesy Lanston Monotype Co.)

Fig. 98C.   Paper Controller Ribbon Placed on Monotype Caster
(Courtesy Lanston Monotype Co.)

Fig. 98B.   Monotype Caster
(Courtesy Lanston Monotype Co.)

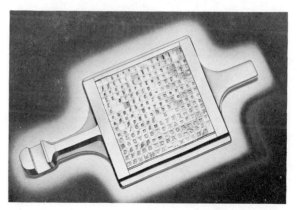

Fig. 98D.   Monotype Matrix Case with 225 Letter Molds
(Courtesy Lanston Monotype Co.)

Fig. 99. Linotype Slugs (Courtesy Mergenthaler Linotype Co.)

Fig. 100. Intertype Slug (Courtesy Intertype Co.)

Fig. 101 Linotype "Elektron II," Manually Operated, Line-Casting Machine (Courtesy Mergenthaler Linotype Co.)

The ribbon is then removed from the keyboard machine and is placed on the Monotype caster. On the caster machine, air is forced through the variously-placed holes in the ribbon, causing the caster machine automatically to position the called-for matrix (mold) in place for the casting of the individual characters and spaces.

Complete lines of characters and spaces (as set from copy) are produced by the machine. Additional spacing between lines is provided by inserting leads and slugs.

After use, the Monotype characters may be remelted, and the metal used for casting more type. Since Monotype lines are composed of individual letters or characters, alterations or corrections may be made in a line without recasting the whole line. Monotype composition costs about 50 percent more than Linotype straight matter, but it is preferred for complicated tables, formulas, and especially fine work.

### Linotype and Intertype

The Linotype and the Intertype machines, although manufactured by different companies, are similar in appearance, operation and final product. Each machine casts solid pieces of metal with the characters for an entire line in relief on one narrow edge. These lines of type are the required length for the job as predetermined, with the proper spacing allowed between the words and elsewhere in the line. In the following description of these line-casting machines, no distinction is made between Linotype and Intertype machines.

Fig. 102. Linotype Keyboard
(Courtesy Mergenthaler Linotype Co.)

The line-casting machine carries, at the top, several magazines divided into channels (90 usually). Each channel holds a number of identical matrices of one character. In sizes of 14 point and less, each matrix has two molds for its character — a "regular" and an "auxiliary" position giving, for example, an italic or bold face version on the second mold. See Figs. 103A and 103C.

The operator sits before the machine and manipulates the particular keys on the keyboard to select the letters or characters in the sequence of the copy.

Each time a key is depressed, the escapement mechanism allows a corresponding matrix to drop from its channel onto a moving belt which assembles it with other matrices into a line. Between words, the operator depresses the spaceband key, allowing a two-piece wedge-shaped spaceband to fall into proper place between the lined-up matrices.

After setting a line of matrices and spacebands, the operator sends that line on its way and commences setting another line.

Once composed, the line of "mats" (matrices) and spacebands is automatically taken over by the machine. Upward pressure on the wedge-shaped spacebands between the words causes the line to be justified to length. The line of mats is then moved before a mold opening, molten metal is forced into the mold, resulting in a cast line of type, called a "slug." The slug is then automatically trimmed and ejected onto a galley.

The used mats are elevated to the top side of the magazine, and fed onto the distributor bar where the distributor screws push them along by the "ears" on the sides of the mats. On the distributor bar, the mats

Fig. 103B. Linotype Spaceband Showing the Ribs at "A" and the Clearance Cut at "B" (Courtesy Mergenthaler Linotype Co.)

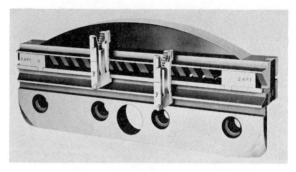

Fig. 103C. Mold with Matrices in Regular and Auxiliary Positions (Courtesy Mergenthaler Linotype Co.)

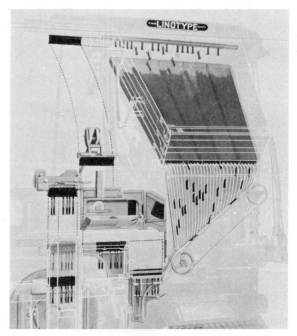

Fig. 103D. Phantom View of Linotype Machine Showing Travel of Mats and Spacebands (Courtesy Mergenthaler Linotype Co.)

Fig. 103A. Linotype Matrix Shown in Various Views (Courtesy Mergenthaler Linotype Co.)

are suspended by "teeth" which engage in corresponding slots in the distributor bar. The combinations of mat teeth and length of bar slots are such that, upon arriving above their

respective magazine channels, each matrix is released to fall back where it originated so it may be ready for reuse.

After the slugs have been used, they are melted down so that the metal may be used for casting other slugs.

Usually, an error in a slug-cast line requires that the entire line be cast again, since it is one solid piece of metal.

### Ludlow

The Ludlow machine produces a solid line of type (or slug) similar to the slug produced on the Linotype and Intertype machines, but it is hand-set. While not as fast as the Monotype, Intertype or Linotype for straight body composition, it finds great use in display composition, especially for headings, advertisements, forms work and wherever larger sizes of type are needed. It is faster than hand setting foundry type and gives the advantage of type which is always new and which needs only remelting after use.

In the Ludlow system, the compositor gathers the character matrices (molds) from the matrix case, and assembles them, together with the space units, into the Ludlow matrix composing stick. The matrix stick is then inserted into the Ludlow machine and locked into position for casting. Operation of the casting lever causes molten metal to be forced through the mouthpiece, against the matrices. The finished slug is then delivered on the galley at the front of the machine. By automatic recasting, any number of identical slugs can be cast from the same stickful of mats. The mats are then returned (distributed) back into their case. Thus, fewer individual characters are needed than with foundry type.

Fig. 104. Ludlow Machine and Matrix Cabinets (Courtesy Ludlow Typograph Co.)

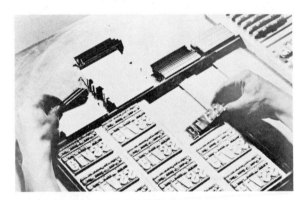

Fig. 105A. Ludlow Slugs (Courtesy Ludlow Typograph Co.)

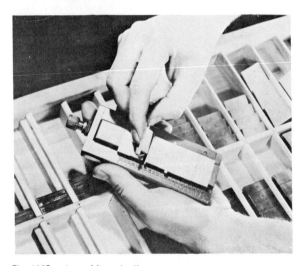

Fig. 105B. Assembling Ludlow Matrices in Composing Stick (Courtesy Ludlow Typograph Co.)

Fig. 105C. Close-Up View of Ludlow Matrices in Composing Stick (Courtesy Ludlow Typograph Co.)

## Wood Type

Wood type is employed instead of metal type for very large sizes of type, generally in sizes 72 points and larger. It is used in exactly the same manner as metal foundry type: it is set by hand, proofs are taken, and after use, it is returned to its type cases.

Wood type is generally made of end-grain maple. The faces (characters) are cut by machine and then trimmed by hand to final form. A special sealer-type impregnation on the printing face of the wood type tends to prevent checking and shrinkage, and imparts a smooth printing face to the letters.

Sizes of wood type are designated in "lines"; a line is equal to a pica, or 12 points. Thus, 12-line wood type would measure 12 picas (144 points) across the body from the belly to the back, Fig. 106.

## Relief Form - to - Film Conversion

Several simplified methods or systems are available for converting letterpress type forms (including halftone and line plates) to images on film for use in offset platemaking. These are in addition to the traditional photographic techniques which use a camera. (These are covered in Chapters 8, 9, and 10.)

Fig. 105D. Casting Ludlow Slugs (Courtesy Ludlow Typograph Co.)

## 3M Orange Color-Key

The 3M Orange Color-Key is a thin, flexible, presensitized polyester-base material which, when contact printed to a positive original copy, yields a film negative at 100% (same

Fig. 106. Specimen of 12-Line Wood Type (Courtesy American Wood Type Manufacturing Co.)

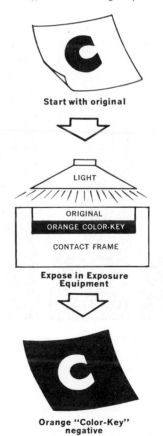

Fig. 107A. Steps in Producing an Orange Color-Key Negative (Courtesy 3M Co.)

size). The Orange Color-Key film negative is then used as a film negative intermediary for exposing presensitized offset plates. See Fig. 107A.

The film also can be used to prepare reverses of existing negative or positive films.

No darkroom is needed; this material can be handled in ordinary room light. The usual plate-exposure equipment can be used, or a simple contact-printing frame and an ultraviolet light source will do.

*Originals.* Originals for reproduction by this method can be proofs of type matter, or any printed, drawn or typed original on one side of a lightweight paper or other material that is suitable for diazo reproduction.

*Determining Coated Side.* The coated side of negative Orange Color-Key will be up when the notch is in the upper right-hand corner of the film.

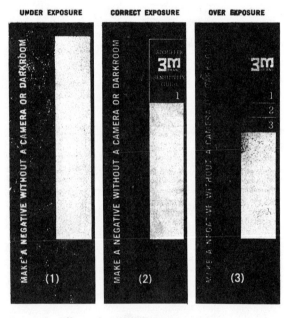

Fig. 107B. Effect of Different Orange Color-Key Exposures
(Courtesy 3M Co.)
   (1) Lack of reading on the sensitivity guide, broken background and type — sure sign of underexposure;
   (2) Solid background, sharp type and a reading of Step 1 on the sensitivity guide — exposure is correct;
   (3) Sharpened, broken type and a reading of Step 3 on the sensitivity guide — a case of overexposure.

*Exposing.* Lay the Color-Key *coated side down* on a black or yellow masking paper. (The paper prevents "light bounce".)

Place the original, image side down (or the photographic film emulsion-side down) on the Color-Key. Expose in any standard exposure unit to ultraviolet light through the original.

Expose to at least a solid Step 1 on a Stouffer 21-step platemaker's sensitivity guide (or 3M 10-step sensitivity guide) placed *under the original* (Fig. 107B).

Correct exposure is very important. If the image area cannot be held open at a Step 1 exposure, then that imaging material cannot be used. (To change the guide indication two steps, either double or halve the exposure time. To change it one step, multiply or divide the exposure time by one-fourth.)

*Developing.* Lay the exposed Color-Key on a smooth, flat surface (preferably glass), with the coated side up.

Pour a liberal amount of negative Color-Key developer on the center of the sheet, and swab the entire surface with a cotton wipe wrapped around a small cushioned block or applicator. Use enough developer to cover the entire sheet.

Rub lightly with the wipe, removing the color coating from the image areas. Keep the applicator flat against the sheet. Dry the sheet before using it.

*Scribing and Opaquing.* Color-Key can be scribed on the coated side with conventional scribing tools to add any desired lines, forms or original art. It can also be opaqued on the coated side with turpentine-based opaquing solutions.

### Instant Negative

In the Instant Negative process, a reproduction proof is made on paper in the usual manner, using special ink on the proof press. This proof is then covered with a sheet of instant negative film (in full daylight), and both are placed in a vacuum-contact heater (135° to 145°F.) for 30 seconds. The heat transfers the image-forming substance from the ink to the film. The film is then swabbed with the clearing solution and is ready for stripping into the flat, or for direct exposure to an offset plate. See Fig. 108.

## Cronapress Conversion Method

The DuPont Cronapress Conversion method utilizes a translucent, non-photographic, pressure-clarifiable film on .002″ polyester film base, Fig. 109A. In the lithographic field, it is used for producing same-size film conversions from type, engravings, electrotypes and other kinds of relief plates without the use of a camera.

The type form (or other letterpress relief plate) to be converted is placed in the Clarifier, Fig. 109B, and over it is placed the Cronapress conversion film with its coated side down. Vacuum is applied, drawing the film snugly against the form surface.

The ball-retainer frame of the Clarifier is then lowered in place over the film, the timer is set, and the vibrator is turned on.

Vibration (of 6 to 8 minutes duration) causes the thousands of tiny lead balls to bounce repeatedly against the film, pressing it

against the type form, Fig. 109A. Where pressure has been applied to the film against the raised (relief) portions of the type form, the film becomes transparent or "clarified". This converted film is now a low-density right-reading negative.

Cronapress densifier dye is then applied by brush or in a tray to the coated side of the film, Fig. 109C. The non-image areas of the film absorb the dye, while the transparent image areas repel it.

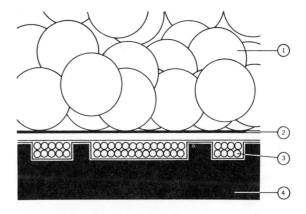

Fig. 109A. Effect of Pressure on Cronapress Conversion Film:
(1) Vibrating metal balls,
(2) Vacuum cover sheet,
(3) Cronapress conversion film,
(4) Type form, or letterpress line or halftone plate.
(Courtesy E. I. DuPont de Nemours & Co.)

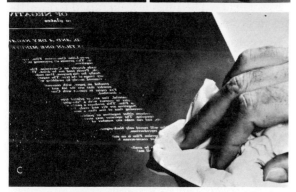

Fig. 108. Instant Negative — In Three Steps:
(A.) Repro Proof,
(B.) Vacuum Heat,
(C.) And Wipe to Clear. (Courtesy Printing Arts Research Laboratories, Inc.)

Fig. 109B. Sheet of Cronapress Conversion Film Peeled Off Electrotype Plate Following Clarification. Type-high furniture surrounds the electro. (Courtesy E. I. DuPont de Nemours & Co.)

Fig. 109C. Special Dye Applied to Clarified Cronapress Conversion Film Negative. The absorbed dye provides the contrast and density range necessary for subsequent film or platemaking steps. (Courtesy E. I. DuPont de Nemours & Co.)

Fig. 110. Brightype Camera, Showing Rotating Lighting System (Courtesy Brightype Division of Ludlow Typograph Co.)

After an application of stabilizer to make the dye insoluble, the film is rinsed and dried. It is then ready for use in platemaking.

### Brightype Method

Brightype is a production method which converts any kind of letterpress material (including halftone plates) directly to a photographic image on film or paper. It consists of form preparation equipment; a special camera (Fig. 110) with a patented rotating lighting system, which creates a controlled shadowless illumination of the copy; and complete darkroom equipment required for processing the photographic material. A description of the Brightype process follows:

*Spraying.* The form to be reproduced is placed in the spray booth, and the printing surface is rubbed with a large eraser, which creates a diffuse, reflective surface.

The entire form is then sprayed with an instantaneous-drying solution containing lampblack, which is light-absorbent. See Fig. 111A.

*Erasing.* Another large eraser is rubbed over the surface of the form, removing the lampblack and leaving the surface relatively bright. The form is now essentially a negative image (Fig. 111B).

*Copyboard Preparation.* The form is centered on the copyboard and clamped in position, Fig. 111C. Edges and gutters are then masked with velour and magnets, so that no part of the background will appear on the film (Fig. 111D). The form is then raised to a vertical position, and is ready to be photographed.

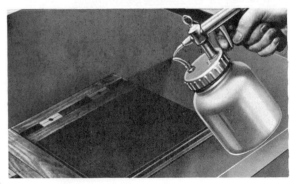

Fig. 111A. Brightype Method. Form is sprayed with negative spray. (Courtesy Brightype Division of Ludlow Typograph Co.)

*Preparing Darkroom End of Camera.* Sensitized material is placed on either a vertical or horizontal stay-flat plate, according to whether a right- or wrong-reading film or paper print is desired. Usually the vertical position is used for paper prints and material for offset surface plates, and the horizontal position is used for deep-etch offset, letterpress and rotogravure processes. A large front-surface mirror is used to reflect the image to a horizontal position and is lowered when the vertical position is used.

*Final Steps.* The timer is set for the sensitized material in use, and the button which controls the lighting and exposure is pressed. After the exposure, the sensitized material is developed according to a fixed schedule of time and temperature.

The end product is usually a positive. A negative may be made by contact printing from the film positive, or by chemical reversal. Also, the use of direct-duplicating film will produce negatives directly.

## Questions

1. What are "repros"? To what use are they put?
2. Of what advantage is it to the cameraman to have a reproduction proof all "made up" in page form?
3. Of what use are type specimen books?
4. What is the height (in thousandths of an inch) of metal type used in the United States?
5. How many picas equal one inch?
6. How many points equal one pica? Two and one-half picas? One inch?
7. What is a "font" of type?
8. What is a type "series"?
9. What is a "family" of type?
10. Describe foundry type.
11. Briefly describe the method of producing (composing) type on the Monotype machine.
12. How does the product of the Monotype differ from that of the Linotype and the Intertype?
13. What are line-casting machines?
14. How is justification of line achieved on the Linotype and the Intertype?

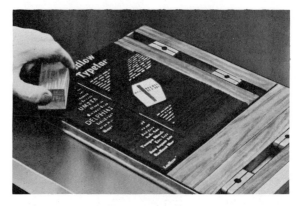

Fig. 111B. Brightype Method. Negative spray is removed from printing surface with soft rubber eraser. (Courtesy Brightype Division of Ludlow Typograph Co.)

Fig. 111C. Brightype Method. Magnetic clamps for locking form on galleys on copyboard. (Courtesy Brightype Division of Ludlow Typograph Co.)

Fig. 111D. Brightype Method. Form on copyboard, background masked out. (Courtesy Brightype Division of Ludlow Typograph Co.)

15. How are the "mats" distributed on the Intertype and the Linotype?
16. Describe the procedure of producing a slug by the Ludlow process.
17. How is an image produced on film in the Cronapress Conversion method?
18. Describe the Brightype method of producing a photographic image on film from a form of type.

## Problems and Projects

1. Memorize the layout of the California Job Case.
2. Secure, for your shop library, type specimen books from nearby printers or type composition houses.
3. Observe the action and operation of typecasting machines in your shop, or arrange for observation of these machines in other shops. Work with your instructor in making arrangements for visits.
4. Secure, for inspection and permanent display, discarded matrices employed on typecasting machines.
5. Arrange a display of individual types and slugs produced by the various typecasting machines.
6. Make a class report on the vocational aspects of the occupations of typecasting machine operator. Include:
   a. Where employed
   b. Duties
   c. Training required
   d. Where training is available
   e. Prerequisites for training
   f. Wages, hours, working conditions.

## New Words

1. advertisements
2. auto-positive
3. auxiliary
4. cellophane
5. characters
6. clarification
7. clarify
8. composition
9. compositor
10. controller ribbon
11. conversion
12. enlargement
13. escapement
14. font
15. gauge
16. illumination
17. impregnation
18. justification
19. justified
20. letterpress
21. light-absorbent
22. manipulate
23. matrices
24. matrix
25. mechanical
26. page-composed
27. perforate
28. photo-copying
29. photo-typesetting
30. platemaking
31. relief
32. reproduction
33. sensitized
34. spaceband
35. stencil
36. translucent
37. tympan
38. velour

## COLD TYPE COMPOSITION — MECHANICAL

### Copying Existing Printed Work
### (For Reprinting)

Sample copies of existing printed work are often used as camera copy. Entire pages may be used, or "clips" (parts) of an entire sheet may be pasted up on the "mechanical" (layout) with repro proofs, original art, or any form of cold type to form a page of camera copy.

For additional information on copying, see Chapter 7, "Preparing Camera Copy for Reproduction".

It is preferred that the sample of existing printed work be "black-on-white", clean, and of good quality printing. Copying printed halftones dot-for-dot will coarsen their dot structure, and a reduction of a printed halftone may lose the dot structure.

Any reduction of type characters or line drawings should anticipate a general sharpening of bold designs — but also a probable loss of fine detail. Enlargement usually blurs most details and may add a grainy appearance. Pre-inspection with a magnifying glass, reducing glass, or the camera's ground glass will aid in predicting the end result.

When jobs are run off on the press, some of the best copies always should be saved for possible future use as camera copy.

*A word of caution:* Copyrighted materials require authorization, see Chapter 20.

Fig. 112A.  Rapidograph Technical Fountain Pen  (Courtesy Keuffel & Esser Co.)

MUSIC SYMBOLS

_____  00

_____  0

_____  1

_____  2

_____  2 ½

_____  3

Fig. 112B.  Rapidograph Pen Line Widths — Actual Size (Courtesy Keuffel & Esser Co.)

OUTLINE SHADOW

ABCDEFG WXYZ 567890

OLD ENGLISH

ABCDEFGHI $1234567

HEBREW

אבגדהוזחטיככלמ
םנןסעפףצץקרשת

ELECTRONIC TUBE SYMBOLS

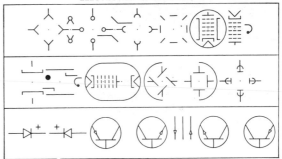

Photo-direct offset plates may be made directly from pages of original work or pasted-up "mechanicals". (See page 237.)

## Hand Lettering and Art

Depending upon the ability of the artist, special lettering, maps, cover designs, graphs, cartoons, borders, and other artwork may be produced by hand for use as camera copy. Hand lettering is especially useful for display lines or for single words in the larger sizes.

Usually, originals prepared with pencil, airbrush, crayon, watercolors or oil paints must be reproduced through the halftone process. (See page 129.)

When hand art is to be incorporated into the mechanical with other items such as clip art or repro proofs, generally a pen or brush is used with India black ink on a white, semigloss or dull paper stock. Such artwork can be reproduced through the simpler line process. (See page 109.)

Fig. 113.  Some Typical Leroy Lettering and Symbol Templates (Reduced) (Courtesy Keuffel & Esser Co.)

To keep the work clean, the triangles, templates and T square should be washed occasionally with soap and water, and the ink bottle should be kept in a wide-base holder *off* the drawing board. Preparatory lines should be drawn lightly (or a non-reproducing blue pencil should be used), and the ink should dry thoroughly before these pencil lines are erased. The hands should be kept clean, and all pens and brushes should be washed after use.

Errors may be cancelled either by painting over them with a white opaque or China white

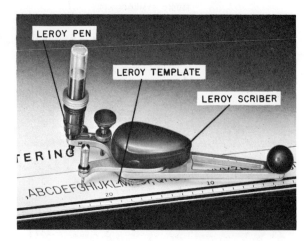

Fig. 114A. Leroy Lettering Instrument (Courtesy Keuffel & Esser Co.)

Fig. 114C. Varigraph, Italic Model "Headwriter" (Courtesy Varigraph, Inc.)

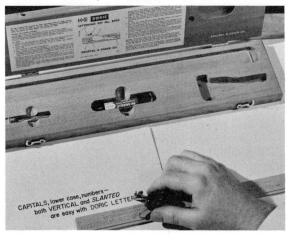

Fig. 114B. Doric® Lettering Set (Courtesy Keuffel & Esser Co.)

Fig. 114D. Letterguide Scriber (Courtesy Letterguide Co.)

paint or by re-drawing the copy on a separate piece of the same paper stock and pasting this over the original error. All edges of the patch then should be painted to avoid shadows on the negative when it is photographed.

Numerous special lettering pens, templates (stencils), and lettering devices are available to aid the hand-letterer in producing work of commercial quality.

By using the reservoir pen, Fig. 112A, with any one of several available tips, lines and letters of varying widths can be drawn. (See Fig. 112B.) The use of the ruling pen and drafting instruments for drawing lines and circles is explained and illustrated beginning on page 346.

Templates may be used in combination with a technical lettering (reservoir) pen for producing lettering, symbols, or even sheets of music, Fig. 113.

Figs. 114A through 114D show several different lettering devices which utilize templates and lettering pens to produce attractive and accurate lettering and special effects.

Speedball pens in an ordinary penholder are used for freehand lettering of highly artistic design, depending upon the skill of the user. (See Figs. 115A through 115C.)

## Clip Art

Commercially-prepared "clip art" may be purchased in sheets or books containing a variety of line and halftone illustrations, symbols, slogans, words, borders, decorations,

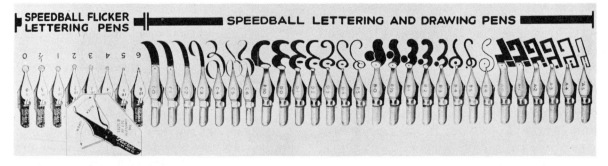

Fig. 115A.  Speedball Pens (Courtesy C. Howard Hunt Pen Co.)

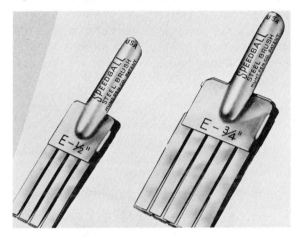

Fig. 115B.  Speedball Steel Lettering Brush (Courtesy C. Howard Hunt Pen Co.)

Fig. 115C.  Hand Lettering Done with Speedball Pens (Courtesy C. Howard Hunt Pen Co.)

etc. Although these generally are printed in black and white, various colors are available. See Fig. 116. Sometimes illustrations are furnished in several different sizes, so that enlargements or reductions need not be made.

To use clip art, simply cut out the desired artwork and mount it in place on the mechanical, together with the other elements of the job for copying on the camera.

The purchase (or subscription) price for the clip art includes the right to reproduce any of the included pieces.

## Pre-Printed Type

Pre-printed type is available in several forms — individual letters in tab form; pressure-sensitive (self-adhesive) letters, words, symbols, borders, decorations, etc., in sheet or roll form; and transfer type. These are described in the next three sections.

Fig. 116.  Clip Art (Courtesy The Clipper Creative Art Service, Dynamic Graphics, Inc.)

### Tab-Type Individual Letters

Display lines may be composed by selecting and assembling printed characters. These are supplied on tabs of paper pads, such as illustrated in Figs. 117A and 117B. The letters are selected as desired, aligned in a composing stick and fastened together with transparent tape. As the dense black reproducing print is on the reverse side, the taped line is turned over and it is mounted on the layout whereever desired. The complete page is then photographed as a unit.

Many different sizes and faces are available, including reverse characters (black background with white letters) and transparencies (black letters on a transparent background).

### Adhesive Type

Pre-printed letters on clear acetate (with a self-adhesive back coating) may be cut out, lifted from their backing sheet, and placed on the mechanical where desired. Guide lines on the letters and on the layout aid in alignment. Fig. 118 shows these steps.

Borders and symbols in roll or sheet form are available in a wide variety of sizes and designs, Fig. 119A. They are simply pressed into position on the mechanical, and their self-adhesive backing holds them in place. See Fig. 119B. Caution must be taken not to stretch the strips as they are applied; otherwise, the mechanical may curl.

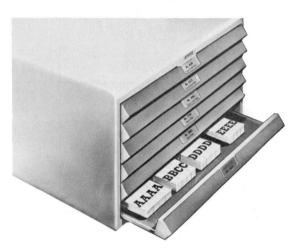

Fig. 117A. Fototype Stored in Cabinet (Courtesy Fototype, Inc.)

Fig. 117B. Setting Fototype (Courtesy Fototype, Inc.)

(1) Draw a guide line with the aid of a ruler or T-square (with a sharpened light blue pencil) on your paper or illustration board. The light blue pencil will not reproduce in photographic reproduction.

(2) Cut around selected letter and guide line with razor blade or sharp knife, cutting through acetate only. Be sure you are cutting guide line under letter you are cutting out. Place the point of your knife under the edge of the cut out letter and lift away.

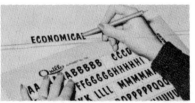

(3) Line up guide line on the bottom of cut out letter with your blue line already drawn on paper. A slight rubbing pressure on cut out letter will hold it in place. When letters are in final position, burnish them firmly, but not the guide line. Then cut off the printed guide line. Your lettering is now ready for reproduction.

Fig. 118. Three Steps in the Application of Adhesive Type to a Mechanical (Courtesy Quillo Advertising Aids Co.)

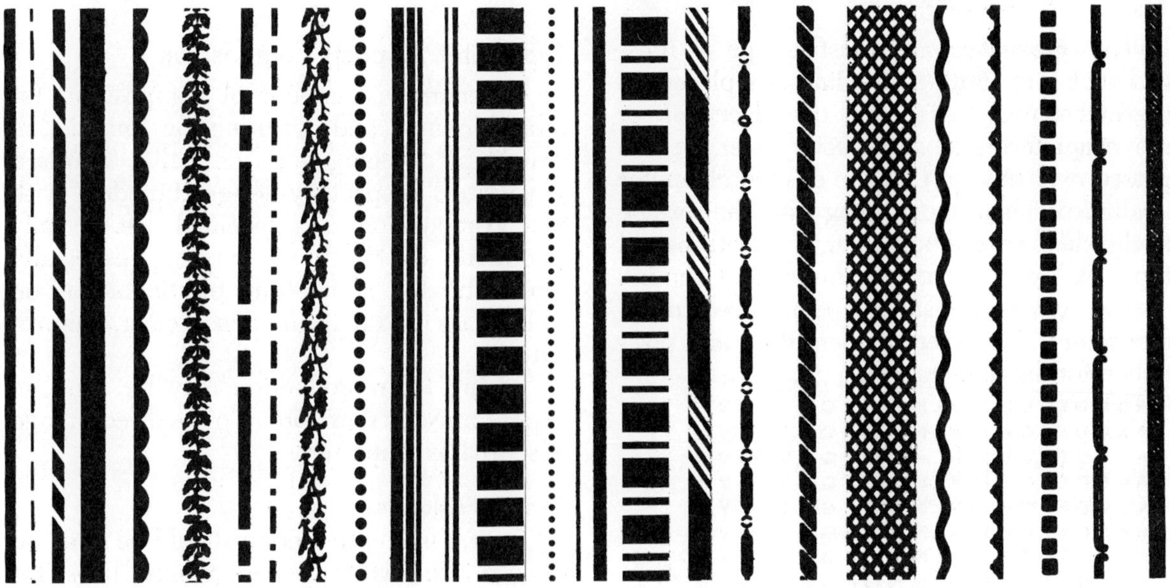

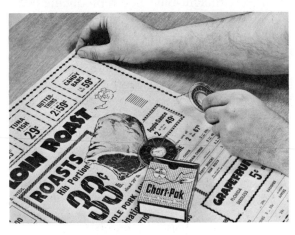

Fig. 119A. Some Samples of Pre-Printed, Self-Adhesive Borders Available in Roll Form (Courtesy Chart-Pak, Inc.)

ROASTS
Rib Portion
Chart-Pak

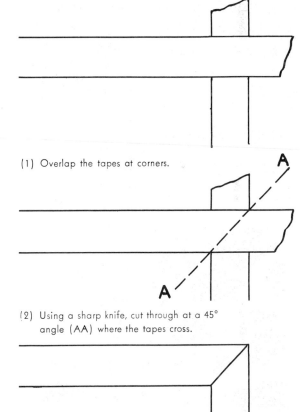

Fig. 119B. Applying Self-Adhesive Border to Mechanical Layout (Courtesy Chart-Pak, Inc.)

(1) Overlap the tapes at corners.
A
A
(2) Using a sharp knife, cut through at a 45° angle (AA) where the tapes cross.
(3) Peel away the scraps, and press down ends.

Fig. 119C. Forming Perfectly-Joined Mitered Borders with Self-Adhesive Tape.

Perfectly mitered corners may be formed as shown in Fig. 119C. Cut the overlapping pieces, peel away the scrap and burnish the joint. Folding a little bit of the roll tape onto itself after use makes it easier to unroll the tape later.

### Transfer Type

Transfer type consists of plastic transparent sheets, on the back of which has been printed (in a transferable ink) letters, borders, symbols, illustrations, etc., in a wide variety of stock designs and special forms. Note Fig. 120A.

The application of transfer type is illustrated in Fig. 120B. Guide lines are placed on the mechanical to indicate the placement of the character. The sheet of transfer type is placed over this, so that the desired character is aligned. Then, by rubbing over the surface of the sheet with a burnisher, a smooth pencil top, a ball point pen, or a similar tool, the ink on the back of the sheet is transferred to the mechanical. The sheet is then lifted and positioned for the next transfer.

ABCDEFGHIJKLMNOPQRSTUVW
ABCDEFGHIJKLMNOPQRSTUVW
ABCDEFGHIJKLMNOPQRSTUVW
ABCDEFGHIJKLMNOPQRSTUVW
ABCDEFGHIJKLMNOPQRSTUVW
ABCDEFGHIJKLMNOPQRSTUVW
ABCDEFGHIJKLMNOPQRSTUVWXYZ
ABCDEFGHIJKLMNOPQRSTUVWXYZ
ABCDEFGHIJKLMNOPQRSTUVWXYZ

INSTANTYPE

Fig. 120A.  A Few of the Many Available Stock Sheets of Instantype (Courtesy Van Son Holland Ink Corp. of America)

## Typewriter (Impact) Composition

An enormous amount of composition for reproduction (and lettering on production drawings) is being done on either standard typewriters or specially-designed models, with type composition as a specified use. Usually electrically-operated typewriters, especially those utilizing a one-time plastic or carbon ribbon, are used to insure dense, clear, uniform letters.

Typing for reproduction may be done on paper for use as repro proofs or on direct-image offset plates or masters.

### General Procedures

Typing for reproduction should be done on smooth, dull-white paper. Guide lines for width of columns (or other positioning) may be ruled with light-blue, non-reproducing pencil or may be pre-printed on the press with a light-blue ink. This color will not be picked up by the camera.

On most standard typewriters, both letters and spaces are of equal width. However, *proportional spacing* is being provided on many models. This feature provides a choice of spacing widths between words and also has individual characters of varying widths as in foundry type. In Fig. 121 for example, a typed "i" is equal to two spacing units; an "o," three units; a "w," four units; and an "m," five units. (Unit values range from 1/45" to 1/32".) Spaces between words may be selected to equal one, two, three, four, or five units.

To manually align the right-hand margin (*i.e.*, to justify or space each line to the desired

Fig. 120B.  Tranferring Instantype from Sheet to Artwork (Courtesy Van Son Holland Ink Corp. of America)

length), it is necessary to type a first draft, mark each line with the number of spacing units needed for justification, and then type a second copy, adding the necessary spaces between words. As an aid, two sheets of paper may be placed side-by-side in a wide-carriage typewriter, (or one wide sheet which is later cut in half). A line is typed on the left, the needed spacing for justification is noted, and the corrected line is typed on the right. This process is continued for the entire job. (See Fig. 122.)

Since the manual justification procedures for typewriters equipped with proportional spacing vary from one model to another, these are detailed later in this chapter as each specific model is described. These models include the Hermes "Ambassador," the IBM "Executive" and "Selectric Composer," the Underwood "Raphael," the Remington "Statesman," and the tape-operated Friden "Justowriter."

Currently available also is an attachment (called a "Marginator") which can be added to many kinds of typewriters to justify the margins in a second typing without manual calculation.

Methods of copyfitting and typing line-for-line are explained beginning on page 29.

Before a reproduction copy is made, the typewriter keys should be cleaned, and the ribbon should be tested to see that it will produce dense, black letters. A plastic, one-time carbon ribbon is a decided advantage in eliminating fabric ribbon pattern in the typed letters and in producing consistently sharp and dense letters. Typing without a ribbon through a sheet of fresh carbon paper gives a similar result.

Uniform pressure should be used in typing. However, care should be taken not to punch through the paper or the master. A thin, plastic backing sheet may be placed between the typewriter platen and the master to help avoid this. Light letters also should be avoided. An electrically-operated typewriter will give uniformity to the typing stroke.

Typewritten copy can be enlarged or reduced, either in whole or in part, to vary the types sizes, especially for headings. See Fig. 123. Standard typing can be dressed up by using decorative headings from other cold type methods. Also, bold typing can be achieved by several typings in the same position. Italics and distinctive headings can be obtained by using copy from typewriters having different type faces. All the elements of a job should be pasted up and photographed as one unit.

Typing errors may be changed by using white opaque correction fluid, by erasing, or by pasting a corrected patch over the error. Also, the entire line may be retyped and pasted over the original line. Some prefer to *cut in* corrections. This is done by placing the correction over the error and making a rectangular cut through both layers. The error then is removed,

**ORDINARY SPACING**

iiiii

ooooo       As the representative o

wwwww       letter should convey an

mmmmm       sincerity and warmth.

**EXECUTIVE" SPACING**

iiiii

ooooo       As the representative o

wwwww       letter should convey an

mmmmm       sincerity and warmth.

Fig. 121.  Typed Characters of IBM "Executive" Occupy Different Widths (Courtesy International Business Machines Corp.)

| This is an example of manual justification performed on a standard typewriter which is not equipped with proportional letters or spacing. All the letters and spaces are the same width. | 1  2  2  1  4 | This is an example of manual justification performed on a standard typewriter which is not equipped with proportional letters or spacing. All the letters and spaces are the same width. |

Fig. 122.  Manual Justification of Composition Produced on a Typewriter Which Has Equal Widths of Letters and Spaces
(Left) Rough Draft. The figures at the end of each line indicate the number of spaces (as marked with checks) which must be added to that line to bring it flush with the ruled vertical line.
(Right) Justified Draft. The needed spacing has been inserted between the words.

THIS IS HOW A VARIETY OF TYPE-
FACE EFFECTS CAN BE CREATED ON
A TYPEWRITER EQUIPPED WITH ONE
TYPE FACE.

THIS IS HOW A VARIETY OF TYPE-
FACE EFFECTS CAN BE CREATED ON
A TYPEWRITER EQUIPPED WITH ONE
TYPE FACE.

THIS IS HOW A VARIETY OF TYPE-
FACE EFFECTS CAN BE CREATED ON
A TYPEWRITER EQUIPPED WITH ONE
TYPE FACE.

This is how a variety of type-
face effects can be created on
a typewriter equipped with one
type face.

This is how a variety of type-
face effects can be created on
a typewriter equipped with one
type face.

This is how a variety of type-
face effects can be created on
a typewriter equipped with one
type face.

THIS IS HOW A VARIET
FACE EFFECTS CAN BE
A TYPEWRITER EQUIPPI
TYPE FACE.

THIS IS HOW A VARIET
FACE EFFECTS CAN BE
A TYPEWRITER EQUIPPI
TYPE FACE.

THIS IS HOW A VARIETY OF TYP
FACE EFFECTS CAN BE CREATED
A TYPEWRITER EQUIPPED WITH C
TYPE FACE.

THIS IS HOW A VARIETY OF TYP
FACE EFFECTS CAN BE CREATED
A TYPEWRITER EQUIPPED WITH O
TYPE FACE.

THIS IS HOW A VARIETY OF TYP
FACE EFFECTS CAN BE CREATED
A TYPEWRITER EQUIPPED WITH O
TYPE FACE.

This is hc
face effec
a typewrit
type face.

This is how a variety of typ
face effects can be created
a typewriter equipped with o
type face.

This is hc
face effec
a typewrit
type face.

This is how a variety of typ
face effects can be created
a typewriter equipped with o:
type face.

This is how a variety of typ
face effects can be created
a typewriter equipped with o:
type face.

Fig. 123.  Varying Typewritten Copy of Same Type Face. Enlargement is at 150% and Reduction is to 50%. Line
spacing is on 1, 1½, and 2 spaces.

and tape is placed across the back of the opening; the correction is positioned in the opening and pressed onto the tape.

### Direct-Image Plates (Paper Masters)

The simplest method of duplicating typewriting (or handwork) is to type (or draw) directly onto a paper master — also called a direct-image offset plate. This is a piece of plastic or paper especially treated to receive the greasy typed image (which will hold the printing ink on the press). It is also treated to hold the ink-repelling dampening solution without growing limp or tearing. The master must fit the plate cylinder of a specific press, and a special waterproof typewriter ribbon is used.

The procedures for preparing direct-image plates is given in Chapter 13, "Platemaking."

### Mechanical Negatives (Light Stencils)

A mechanical negative is similar in appearance and construction to a mimeograph stencil. It has a wax-like coating on a tissue-like base. The coating is opaque and will not transmit light rays.

The image is prepared by typing directly on the stencil without a ribbon, drawing with a stylus or printing by letterpress with sharp rules. Each of these methods cuts through the waxy coating of the mechanical negative. If the negative is held to the light after this cutting, it will be seen that the letters and lines are transparent and will pass light rays just like a film negative.

If a whole page is being prepared on a mechanical negative, film negatives may be taped in place in cut-out portions of the mechanical negative to provide desired display lines and illustrations.

The mechanical negative is then exposed to a light-sensitive plate. This procedure eliminates camera work, yet it allows the use of a photographic plate and its long runs. Direct-image plates are used for a few copies to perhaps 5000, but mechanical negatives allow runs of hundreds of thousands.

### Care of Typewriter Machines

Machines should be covered when not in use to keep off dust. Keys should be cleaned periodically with a stiff brush and alcohol, and the excess wiped off with a clean cloth.

Erasures should be done with the carriage moved all the way to the left or right, so that eraser grit will not drop into the mechanism.

Machines should be serviced periodically. On the more intricate machines, a service contract is advisable. Repairs and adjustments should be attempted only by experienced and qualified persons.

Operators should be proficient in touch-typing methods and should be taught, if possible, by a factory-sponsored instructor or someone trained in these methods. In any event, a thorough mastery of the operator's manual is a necessity.

### Remington "25" Electric Typewriter

The Remington "25" is an electric typewriter, equipped with both a fabric and a one-time carbon ribbon. It is available in carriage widths from 13" to 27". See Fig. 124A.

The "25" is factory-equipped with the buyer's selection of a type style, chosen from an extensive range of sizes and styles. In addition, one type bar (or more, if desired) is equipped with an interchangeable head, so constructed that the operator easily can re-

Fig. 124A. Remington "25" Electric Typewriter (Courtesy Remington Office Machines, Division of Sperry Rand Corp.)

move the *type face* of that bar and replace it with any one of a large number of other characters, such as mathematical symbols or accent marks for a foreign language. See Fig. 124B. Striking the INT (Interchangeable) key operates the interchangeable type bar, in the same manner as for usual typing.

Spacing is standard, and justification of line length is manual.

### Hermes "Ambassador" Electric Typewriter

The Hermes "Ambassador," an electric typewriter, may be obtained with any one of

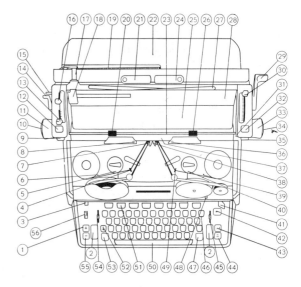

Fig. 125B.  Operating Controls of Hermes "Ambassador" (Courtesy Paillard, Inc.)

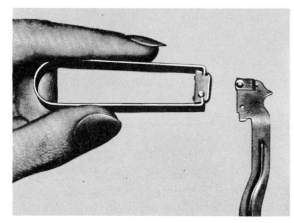

Fig. 124B.  Magnetic Tweezers Used to Install Desired Type Character on Interchangeable Type Bar Head (Courtesy Remington Office Machines, Division of Sperry Rand Corp.)

Fig. 125A.  Hermes "Ambassador" Electric Typewriter (Courtesy Paillard, Inc.)

1.  Key to set stops
2.  Automatic carriage return and line spacing
3.  Button to free jammed type bars.
4.  Lateral ribbon guide
5.  Left card holder adjusting knob
6.  Lateral ribbon guide
7.  Ribbon carrier
8.  Left card holder
9.  Left margin button
10.  Center part of left platen knob
11.  Left platen knob
12.  Left carriage release button
13.  Knob for regulating the line spacing
14.  Paper release lever
15.  Lever to clear all stops
16.  Platen release knob
17.  Arm of automatic carriage return
18.  Graduated paper guide
19.  Traction cord
20.  Left paper bail roller
21.  Left stencil support
22.  Rear protection plate
23.  Ruled paper bail
24.  Right stencil support
25.  Intermediate paper table
26.  Right paper bail roller
27.  Extending paper support
28.  Paper table
29.  Handle for paper introduction
30.  Knob to set the introduction of paper
31.  Right carriage end plate
32.  Right carriage release button
33.  Right platen knob
34.  Center part of right platen knob
35.  Right margin button
36.  Right card holder
37.  Platen
38.  Type guide
32.  Right carriage release button
40.  Right card holder adjusting knob
41.  Ribbon selector
42.  Back space key
43.  Indent key
44.  Margin release key
45.  Touch regulator lever
46.  Repeat key
47.  Right shift key
48.  Ribbon reversing lever
49.  Lateral ribbon guide
50.  Space bar
51.  First decimal tabulator key
52.  Shift lock
53.  Left shift key
54.  Impression control lever
55.  Key to clear stops
56.  Motor switch
57.  Front protection plate
58.  Notebook holder

several type faces. Some of these are proportional spacing, *i.e.*, characters and spaces of varying widths. Justification of line length is performed manually.

Additional features are line spacing varying by half-lines; a repeat key for all 92 keyboard characters (including space bar and carriage return); control for switching to either fabric or one-time carbon ribbon; and operator-interchangeable carriages (optional) for accommodating different widths of paper. See Figs. 125A and 125B.

### IBM "Executive" Electric Typewriter

The IBM "Executive" electric typewriter, Fig. 126A, is proportional spacing and may be equipped with either a fabric or carbon ribbon (or both).

The purchaser may select his type face from the wide variety of those offered. A few are shown in Fig. 126B.

Wide carriages are available to permit the typing of two sheets side-by-side for line-by-line justification and also to permit typing lengthwise on some direct-image plates, or typing directly on large drawings to be blueprinted.

Fig. 126A. IBM "Executive" Electric Typewriter (Cover Raised) (Courtesy International Business Machines Corp.)

Newest member of the type style library, Arcadia brings beauty and simplicity to your letters.

ARCADIA TYPE

One of the most expressive IBM types Mid-Century will make your Executive letters inviting to read.

MID-CENTURY TYPE

The crisp lines of Documentary type give a businesslike dignity to this popular type style.

DOCUMENTARY TYPE

*Latest addition to the Bold Face Family is Italic. It adds a personal touch to all letters.*

BOLD FACE ITALIC TYPE

DEPEND ON COPPERPLATE TO WIN ATTENTION. THIS TYPE IS EXCELLENT FOR YOUR ADVERTISING MATERIAL.

COPPERPLATE GOTHIC NO. 1 TYPE

Build company prestige with Modern type. This attractive face creates striking first impressions.

MODERN TYPE

Fig. 126B. A Few of the Many Available Type Faces of the IBM "Executive" (Courtesy International Business Machines Corp.)

This ✓is ✓an example ✓of ✓manual    4

justification´ performed´ on a´ ma-   -3

chine´ which´ is´ equipped´ with´ pro-   -5

portional ᴠᴠletters´ and ᴠᴠspacing.     5

Fig. 127A. Manual Justification of Composition on the IBM
"Executive" Proportional-Spacing Typewriter
(Left) Rough Draft. The figure 4, for the first line,
indicates that the line is four spacing increments
short of reaching justification; the check marks in

This is an example of manual

justification performed on a ma-

chine which is equipped with pro-

portional letters and spacing.

that line show where the additional spaces are to
be added. The —3 for the second line indicates
that this line needs to be shortened by three
spacing increments — at the slash marks.
(Right) Justified Draft.

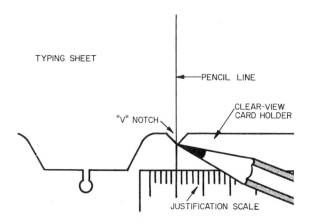

Fig. 127B. Drawing the Vertical Pencil Line.

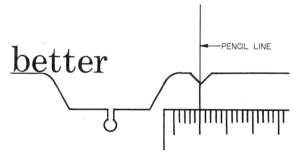

Fig. 127C. Pencil Line Exactly on Notch — Typed Line Needs
No Change.

*Justification details.* See Fig. 127A. The following procedure is recommended for manually justifying composition on the IBM "Executive" proportional spacing typewriter:

1. Insert the paper in the typewriter.
2. Set the desired margins for the width of the copy.
3. With the carriage positioned at the right-hand margin, insert a sharp-pointed pencil in the "V" notch of the justification scale, and draw a vertical line down the paper by turning the platen knob upward, Fig. 127B.
4. Set a tab stop several markings to the right of this line.
5. Begin typing the rough draft, always using the 2-unit space bar (large right-hand segment) between words. Try to end each line with a complete word or the correct word division. *Do not space after the*

*last word. If the line ends with a period or comma, backspace once before reading your scale.*
6. As you type, listen for the margin bell, and try to end each line so that the pencil marking is as near the V notch as possible. It is easier to add space than to subtract space when using 2 units for the basic word space.
7. When the pencil line ends right on the notch, the typed line requires no change. Tab and type "O" (or omit any indication for justification). See Fig. 127C.
8. When the pencil line rests to the right of the notch, the typed line must be increased. Each mark to the right of the notch means 1 unit. Tab and type the number of units to be added. (See Fig. 127D.)
9. When the pencil line rests to the left of the notch, the typed line must be *decreased.* Tab and type the number of units to be omitted. (See Fig. 127E.)

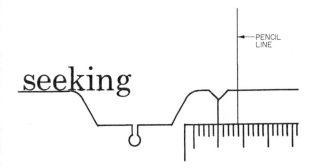

Fig. 127D. Pencil Line is Four Marks to Right of Notch — Four Spacing Increments Must Be Added.

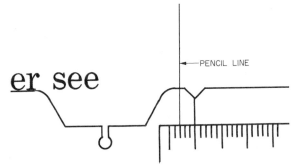

Fig. 127E. Pencil Line is Three Marks to Left of Notch — Three Spacing Increments Must Be Eliminated.

10. After typing the rough draft, remove the paper, and indicate with check marks where space units are to be increased; use diagonal marks to indicate where spaces are to be decreased. Refer again to Fig. 127A.

11. When typing the justified copy, remember that to add one space unit between words, the 3-unit space bar must be used; to omit one space unit, it is necessary to backspace once, after using the 2-unit space bar.

12. When justified, the line should appear equally spaced between words. Where one word ends with a tall letter and the next begins with a tall letter (a sequence such as *tall letter*), an extra space unit is not noticeable and may even improve the appearance; where one word ends with a short (or round) letter and the next word begins with a short letter (such as *one wing*), a decrease of a spacing unit is not noticed appreciably. Space may be either added or subtracted between one word ending with a tall or short letter and the next word starting with a letter of the opposite height (such as *the letter*).

The use of the two-increment space for the rough typing will produce tightly spaced composition with a minimum of ugly gaps between words (forming "lakes" and "rivers" of white space). Some operators use the three-unit space for the rough, leaving two units for shortening lines and a double two-unit space (four increments) for spacing out lines. This requires

Fig. 128. Underwood "Raphael" Electric Typewriter (Courtesy Olivetti Underwood Corp.)

less backspacing and so may be faster, but greater care must be used to prevent loose spacing and gaps between words. It is also possible to use a single increment (2 units with a backspace) in a very tight line, and 5 increments (a 2 plus a 3) for a very short line.

### Underwood "Raphael" Electric Typewriter

The Underwood "Raphael" electric typewriter is proportional spacing and is equipped with a polyethylene carbon ribbon. See Fig. 128. It is available with one of several type faces such as shown in Fig. 129A. The relative widths of individual characters and spaces are listed in Fig. 129B.

Justification of lines is achieved manually on the "Raphael", using the "i" method, as follows:

1. Establish the left margin where desired.
2. Line up the position desired for the right margin with the type guide.
3. Type a lower-case "i" on the rough-draft paper.
4. Use the pen holder to draw a vertical pencil line on the entire sheet, through the i.
5. Type the rough draft, ending each line as close as possible to the pencil line.
6. When the typed line ends *before* the pencil line, fill in (without spacing) with i's until an i falls on the pencil line. Count the number of i's, including the one on the line, and enter that figure with a plus sign in the right margin. This is the number of half spaces which must be added to the typed line to achieve justification.
7. When the typed line ends *past* the pencil line, backspace to this line, release the Memory Line Finder and roll the platen back half a line. Type i's until the last i is even with the right side of the last character in the line. (Restore the Memory Line Finder, and roll the platen up half a line.) Count the number of i's beyond the vertical line (not including the i on the line), and enter that figure with a minus sign in the right margin. This is the number of half spaces which must be omitted.
8. Upon the completion of the rough draft, use a / mark to indicate where to add a half space and a \ mark to indicate where to omit a half space, as shown in Fig. 130.
9. Now, type the justified draft or the duplicating master. To add a half space, backspace once after using the space bar *twice*. To omit a half space, backspace once after using the space bar *once*.

### Kent

The elements which make th important, impressive and comp recipient have been identified a the UNDERWOOD RAPHAEL writer.

### Raphael

*The elements which make the important, impressive and compl recipient have been identified a the UNDERWOOD RAPHAEL writer.*

### Windsor

The elements which make the important, impressive and compl recipient have been identified a the UNDERWOOD RAPHAEL writer.

Fig. 129A.  Several Type Styles Available for the Underwood "Raphael" (Courtesy Olivetti Underwood Corp.)

| | | |
|---|---|---|
| All small letters, numbers, symbols, punctuation and space bar | = I | space |
| EXCEPT  j i l f t ' | = ½ | space |
| w m | = I½ | spaces |
| All capitals | = I½ | spaces |
| EXCEPT  I J | = I | space |
| I (Kent and Windsor only) | = ½ | space |
| Backspacer | = ½ | space |

Fig. 129B.  Relative Widths of Characters and Spaces on the Underwood "Raphael" (Courtesy Olivetti Underwood Corp.)

The\contents\of\the letter will be framed on the page    iii  –
with/balanced/margins/on the left, right, top, and  iii  +
bottom/as carefully as/though it were an expensive  ii  +
painting.  /Any/titles/or/headings will be centered  iii  +
exactly\in\the center of the sheet.  Every character  ii  –
will appear sharp, clear, and uniform.

The contents of the letter will be framed on the page with balanced margins on the left, right, top, and bottom as carefully as though it were an expensive painting.    Any titles or headings will be centered exactly in the center of the sheet.  Every character will appear sharp, clear, and uniform.

Fig. 130.  Manual Justification on the Underwood "Raphael" Electric Typewriter.
(above) Rough draft, marked for justification. (below), Justified draft. (Courtesy Olivetti Underwood Corp.)

### IBM "Selectric" Electric Typewriter

The IBM "Selectric" electric typewriter may be obtained with either a reusable fabric ribbon or a one-time, film-carbon ribbon. See Fig. 131A.

Instead of the conventional type bars and moving carriage, the "Selectric" features a small, spherical typing element, which looks like a golf ball, containing all the type characters in relief (raised). See Fig. 131B. The printing element skims along the page, typing out the characters and storing the second of two rapidly-typed characters until the first is printed. Being removable, it may be replaced by any one of a number of other elements, each with a different type face, Fig. 132A. By having available a number of elements, a wide variety of type faces (each having the same spacing) can be used with the one machine. Each machine is built only for 10-pitch (elite) type and spacing or for 12-pitch (pica size).

*Caution:* When element is removed and replaced, typewriter must be turned *off* and must be in the *lower-case* position. Any force exerted in rotating or tilting the element may result in loosening or breaking the tape which controls the element.

*To Remove an Element.* Turn the typewriter "off," and lift the front cover. The arrow on the element cap should point toward the platen when the typewriter is in this lower-case position.

Press the spring levers together, and lift up to release the element from the notch on the element post, Fig. 132B. Holding one of the spring levers, lift the element off the post.

*To Replace an Element.* Grasp the spring lever and place the element on the post with the arrow on the element cap facing the platen. Squeeze the spring levers together and gently press down until the element slips into place with a click.

Fig. 131A. IBM "Selectric" Electric Typewriter (Courtesy International Business Machines Corp.)

Fig. 131B. IBM "Selectric" Printing Element (Type Sphere) (Courtesy International Business Machines Corp.)

*This is 12 pitch Script type. You may use it interchangeably with all the type styles on this page. Each typing element snaps on the IBM SEL so quickly, so easily that your typ can change type without ever losing place on the typing line.*

This is 12 pitch Adjutant type. You may use it interchangeably with all the type styles on this page. Each typing element snaps on the IBM SEL so quickly, so easily that your typ can change type without ever losing place on the typing line.

This is 12 pitch Scribe type. You may use it interchangeably with all the type styles on this page. Each typing element snaps on the IBM SEL so quickly, so easily that your typ

Fig. 132A. A Few of the Many Type Faces Available on Separate Printing Elements for the IBM "Selectric" (Courtesy International Business Machines Corp.)

## IBM "Selectric" Composer

The IBM "Selectric" Composer, Fig. 133A, is keyboard operated, electrically actuated, has proportional spacing, and uses a one-time ribbon. Like the "Selectric", the composer uses a spherical typing element instead of conventional type bars. At present, more than fifty type faces are available, ranging from 7 to 12 points in height. See Fig. 133B for a sample of its composition. "Leading" (spacing between lines) is adjustable.

Justification on the illustrated model of the "Composer" is semi-automatic. The operator types the first line of the rough draft, stopping

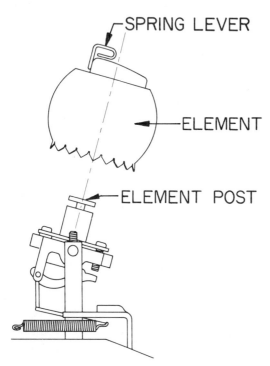

Fig. 132B. IBM "Selectric" Element Removed from Post (Courtesy International Business Machines Corp.)

Fig. 133A. IBM "Selectric" Composer, With Interchangeable Typing Element and Proportional-Spacing Type (Courtesy International Business Machines Corp.)

Through the innovation of a new system of type de has raised the standards of direct impression typogra type is designed in a nine-unit system that permits ferent character widths to assure graceful proportio letter fit. Classic type faces, proven popular over have been adapted to the nine-unit system by maste signers. Strict quality control is maintained throu stage of design and production. The IBM Compo Fonts, which are completely interchangeable with "Selectric" Composers, are assembled by skilled cra assure uniform and precise reproduction. Therefore, select type fonts from the wide range of type faces. weights that are offered, you can be sure of crisp an production day after day, even under the most h

Fig. 133B. Sample of Type Set on the IBM "Selectric" Composer (Courtesy International Business Machines Corp.)

Fig. 133C. IBM Magnetic-Tape "Selectric" Composer Installation (Courtesy International Business Machines Corp.)

The unmanned tape reader and its reproducing Composer (foreground) can keep ahead of the output of the two typewriter recording units in the background with their attached computers for determining justification. The Composer in the foreground has a keyboard so it can also be operated manually.

short of the right-hand margin. The needed justification for that line is indicated automatically on the justification control (dial at the right of the keyboard); the operator then sets the control, aided by a color code. In a second typing, the machine automatically justifies the line.

Magnetic-tape versions of the "Composer" are also available. See Fig. 133C. This system requires only one keyboarding of the copy in long lines without taking time to make any decisions for line length or justification. This produces magnetic coded tape which is fed to the captive computer which divides the words into lines of the desired length (at 20 characters per second), determines the justification, spacing, and operates the reproduction units shown in the foreground of Fig. 133C. The typist can backspace and strike over an error to correct it automatically and to provide a copy for proofreading. Output per hour is several times the number of lines produced on a typical slugcasting hot-metal machine, yet the cost of the total installation is similar to a manually operated Linotype, and regular typists require but little training to operate the equipment.

### Typit Interchangeable Type System

A simple modification to many manual or electric typewriters permits the use of the "Typit" symbol system for typing many hundreds of special characters, symbols, accents,

etc., as desired, without affecting the normal use of the typewriter.

A special Typit modified type guide is installed (and remains) on the typewriter to replace the original type guide (Fig. 134A). When a special character is needed, the typist inserts the Typit symbol unit into the Typit type guide and strikes any one of the typewriter keys. See Fig. 134B. The rising type bar, in striking the Typit unit, forces a small character slide into the platen, thus printing that special character.

Fig. 134C illustrates a few of the many hundreds of available Typit symbols.

### VariTyper Composition Machine

The VariTyper composing machine is used extensively for type composition, either on paper (for photographing) or directly on off-

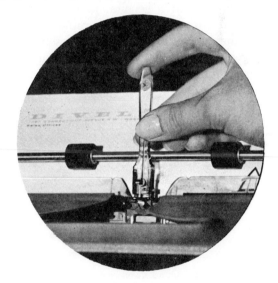

Fig. 134B. Inserting Selected Typit Symbol Unit into Modified Type Guide (Courtesy Mechanical Enterprises, Inc.)

Fig. 134A. Installing Modified Type Guide to Permit Use of Typit Symbols (Courtesy Mechanical Enterprises, Inc.)

Fig. 134C. Some of the Available Typit Symbols — Shown Half Size (Courtesy Mechanical Enterprises, Inc.)

set plates. See Fig. 135A. The VariTyper machine uses a one-time carbon ribbon, has a near-standard typewriter keyboard (arranged in three banks instead of four and with two shift positions instead of one). Some models may be obtained with differential letterspacing and automatic line justification.

On the differential-spacing models, various letters (as typed) occupy differing widths on the paper, Fig. 135B. These variations produce close to a true "foundry-type" printed effect in the typed copy. Through the use of hundreds of instantly changeable type fonts (Fig. 136A), the VariTyper can produce an infinite variety of composition. Special ruling attachments produce ruled forms, as shown in Fig. 136B.

A typical type font segment is shown being installed on the VariTyper anvil in Fig. 137. Note that the anvil accommodates *two* fonts at the same time, so that, for example, a matching italic or bold face may be used interchangeably when typing. A major feature of some VariTyper machines is line spacing,

which is adjustable by points. This allows type to be set solid or leaded 1 point, 2 points, or more, as desired.

Unlike many electric machines, the keys must be depressed firmly, fully, and in a regular rhythm, because this manual key action trips several mechanisms during each

Fig. 135A. VariTyper Office Composing Machine, Model 660 (Courtesy VariTyper Corp.)

Fig. 135B. Variation in Widths of Typed VariTyper Letters (Courtesy VariTyper Corp.)

12 pt. Alexandria Medium (880-12A)

ABCDEFGHIJKLMNOPQRSTUVWXYZ&
abcdefghijklmnopqrstuvwxyz abcdefghijl

10 pt. Alexandria Light (650-10B)

ABCDEFGHIJKLMNOPQRSTUVWXYZ& AB
abcdefghijklmnopqrstuvwxyz abcdefghijklmr

10 pt. Bell Gothic Light (FL950-10B)

ABCDEFGHIJKLMNOPQRSTUVWXYZ& AB
abcdefghijklmnopqrstuvwxyz abcdefghijklmr

10 pt. Bell Gothic Bold (FL980-10B)

ABCDEFGHIJKLMNOPQRSTUVWXYZ& AB
abcdefghijklmnopqrstuvwxyz abcdefghijklmr

10 pt. Gothic Bold Condensed (FL970-10B)

ABCDEFGHIJKLMNOPQRSTUVWXYZ& AB
abcdefghijklmnopqrstuvwxyz abcdefghijklmr

10 pt. Bodoni Book (600-10B)

ABCDEFGHIJKLMNOPQRSTUVWXYZ& AB
abcdefghijklmnopqrstuvwxyz abcdefghijklmr

10 pt. Bodoni Bold (780-10B)

ABCDEFGHIJKLMNOPQRSTUVWXYZ& AB
abcdefghijklmnopqrstuvwxyz abcdefghijklmr

10 pt. Bookman (630-10B)

ABCDEFGHIJKLMNOPQRSTUVWXYZ& AE
abcdefghijklmnopqrstuvwxyz abcdefghijklm:

10 pt. Cartoon Type (940-10A)

A B C D E F G H I J K L M N O P Q R S T U V W X Y Z
ABCDEFGHIJKLMNOPQRSTUVWXYZ ABCDEFGI

10 pt. Caslon (830-10B)

ABCDEFGHIJKLMNOPQRSTUVWXYZ& AF
abcdefghijklmnopqrstuvwxyz abcdefghijklm

8 pt. Caslon Bold (890-8C)

ABCDEFGHIJKLMNOPQRSTUVWXYZ& ABCDI
abcdefghijklmnopqrstuvwxyz abcdefghijklmnopq

Fig. 136A. A Few of the Hundreds of Instantly Changeable Type Faces for the VariTyper Machine (Courtesy VariTyper Corp.)

stroke. As the typist depresses the desired key: 1. the type font segment is rotated, bringing the desired type character into position before the hammer; 2. the hammer (at the rear) strikes forward, making the impression through the paper and ribbon against the type character (Fig. 138); 3. the paper carriage is advanced the width of the character. If a key is not *fully* depressed, erratic spacing is possible, so some practice is recommended before attempting to produce final clean copy. A uniform impression of each character is produced,

as the power for the hammer comes from a large spring which is kept wound by an electric motor.

Manual justification procedure is shown in Fig. 139. For automatic justification (on models so equipped), it is strongly recommended that the operator study the manual for the particular model, and, if possible he should be taught by a factory-trained instructor.

Briefly, automatic justification requires that the operator first set the stops for the desired widths of columns; then he must type a line on the left side of the sheet, employing a margin dial pointer and a justifier dial pointer to guide in beginning and ending the typed line. After this, he tabs to the right and repeats the typing; the machine inserts the required spacing during this second typing, justifying the line automatically (if no mistakes were made in either keyboarding).

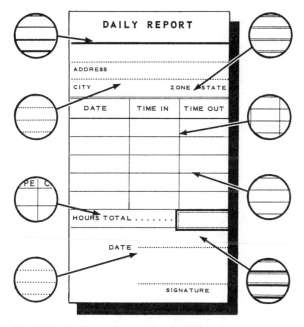

Fig. 136B. VariTyper Composition Specimen Involving Rules and Type Matter (Courtesy VariTyper Corp.)

Fig. 137. Installing VariTyper Type Font on Anvil. Note the second font to the left rear. (Courtesy VariTyper Corp.)

Fig. 138. Fundamental Parts of VariTyper (Courtesy VariTyper Corp.)

**Sample of Rough Copy for Manual Justification**

llllllll llllllll llllllll llllllll llllllll llllllll llllllll llllllll llln

Picture Writing began 5,000 years ago, and gradually developed into symbols which represented words instead of objects. A further development, about 1,500 years later, was the alphabet. This alphabet was created by the Semites, near Egypt about the second century.

5
4
−1
−2

**Sample of Copy Justified Manually**

Picture Writing began 5,000 years ago, and gradually developed into symbols which represented words instead of objects. A further development, about 1,500 years later, was the alphabet. This alphabet was created by the Semites, near Egypt about the second century.

Fig. 139. Sample of Manual Justification on the VariTyper (Reduced for Illustrative Purposes) (Courtesy VariTyper Corp.)

## Friden Justowriter

The Friden Justowriter is a tape-operated, proportional-spacing, copysetting machine for producing automatically-justified composition with one keyboarding of the type. It can be used for camera copy, or even for typing directly onto direct-image plates.

The Justowriter is composed of two main units — a recorder and a reproducer, shown in Fig. 140A. Each of the units has a typewriter keyboard and an electrically powered basic

Fig. 140A. Friden Justowriter. (Left) Recorder unit, (Right) Reproducer unit. (Courtesy Friden, Inc.)

mechanism very similar to the IBM Executive typewriters. Each also can be operated manually.

To produce composition, the operator first inserts proof paper into each of the two units. Then he types the copy on the recorder, ending each line as a panel light signals that the justification zone has been reached. This initial typing produces an unjustified, visible copy on the paper and simultaneously produces a punched paper tape. If an error is noted in a line, that line immediately can be cancelled and retyped. The combinations of punched holes in the tape record by code all of the typing and needed line justification. See Fig. 140B.

The punched tape is fed into the reproducer unit, which then automatically sets justified repro proofs (or direct-image plates) at the rate of 100 words per minute. Obviously, it is important that the operator note most of the errors, since these will be reproduced in the second automatic typing.

A motorized tape punch may be connected electrically to the reproducer unit. See Fig. 140C. This will simultaneously produce a punched tape as the reproducer is setting justified copy. This second tape may be fed into a recorder unit to set automatically justified copy

| Lower Case & Unit Width | Code Position 7654 321 | Upper Case & Unit Width | Lower Case & Unit Width | Code Position 7654 321 | Upper Case & Unit Width |
|---|---|---|---|---|---|
| a  3 | | A  4 | 6  3 | | ¢  3 |
| b  3 | | B  4 | 7  3 | | &  4 |
| c  3 | | C  4 | 8  3 | | *  3 |
| d  3 | | D  4 | 9  3 | | (  2 |
| e  3 | | E  4 | 0  3 | | )  2 |
| f  2 | | F  4 | –  3 | | –  3 |
| g  3 | | G  4 | ;  2 | | :  2 |
| h  3 | | H  4 | '  2 | | '  2 |
| i  2 | | I  2 | ,  2 | | .  2 |
| j  2 | | J  3 | .  2 | | .  2 |
| k  3 | | K  4 | /  3 | | ?  3 |
| l  2 | | L  4 | | | |
| m  5 | | M  5 | | | |
| n  3 | | N  4 | | | |
| o  3 | | O  4 | | | Function Codes |
| p  3 | | P  4 | | | |
| q  3 | | Q  4 | | | Upper Case |
| r  3 | | R  4 | | | Lower Case |
| s  3 | | S  3 | | | Back Space |
| t  2 | | T  4 | | | One Unit |
| u  3 | | U  4 | | | Three Units |
| v  3 | | V  4 | | | Space |
| w  4 | | W  5 | | | Tab |
| x  3 | | X  4 | | | Line Space |
| y  3 | | Y  4 | | | Code Delete |
| z  3 | | Z  4 | | | Stop Code |
| 1  3 | | !  2 | | | |
| 2  3 | | @  4 | | | Line Delete Code |
| 3  3 | | #  3 | | | |
| 4  3 | | $  3 | | | Justification |
| 5  3 | | %  4 | | | Code (Basis) |

Fig. 140B. Schematic Code and Unit Width Chart of the 7-Channel Punched Paper Tape for the Justowriter. The vertical row of closely-spaced holes near the center is for the tape feed. With variations of the number and positions of the horizontal punched holes, tape allows for 128 possible code combinations for upper-case and lower-case letters, punctuation marks, and function codes. (Courtesy Friden, Inc.)

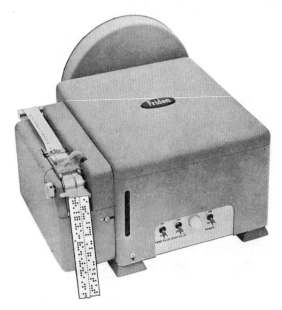

Fig. 140C. Friden Motorized Tape Punch (Courtesy Friden, Inc.)

in the size and style of type face with which the recorder unit is equipped. Thus, if the recorder unit is factory-equipped with a different type face than that of the reproducer unit, automatically justified copy can be reproduced in two different type faces, even though the operator types the copy only once.

## Summary of Impact Composition

We have seen that there are a number of typewriters and typewriter-keyboard-actuated machines available for producing cold-type composition for use as camera copy.

*Standard typewriters* offer even the smallest shops a means of cold-type composition. Uniform impression and density of typed characters are improved by using machines that are electrically-actuated and are equipped with one-time carbon ribbons. *Manual justification* of line length is achieved by typing the work twice — *first* the operator types a rough draft, carefully counting at each line the number of spacing increments needed to justify the line; then a *second* typing follows, in which the needed spacing increments are added to each line, producing a finished justified copy.

On the IBM Selectric, different type elements may be used to vary type face characters.

Machines equipped with proportional-width type characters and differential spacing produce a typed effect closely resembling that of printer's type. On these machines, manual justification is aided by a built-in gauge, and other optional devices are available.

The VariTyper and IBM Selectric Composer offer interchangeable type font segments and automatic justification of lines, achieved by the operator retyping line-for-line, while the machines automatically insert the required spacing between words.

The Justowriter produces automatically-justified type composition with a single typing of the original copy. The operator types the copy on the recorder unit, which produces a visual copy and a punched paper tape; the tape then is fed through the reproducer unit, which automatically produces a justified copy.

Special characters (called "sorts" in hot type composition), such as accents, mathe-matical symbols, etc., may be typed on some machines, either with a changeable type bar or with a Typit accessory. Sorts may also be added by drawing or by adding various kinds of preprinted characters.

Limitations of variety in type faces on available typewriters can be extended in many ways, such as:

1. Combining copy from different machines.
2. Varying spacing (leading) between lines.
3. Varying the reproduction size on the camera for all or portions of the copy.
4. Letterspacing (*i.e.*, leaving extra space between each letter of a word).
5. Using capital letters for entire words, using underscoring, and using strikeover bold face.

Thus, it can be seen that there are degrees of refinement in the typewriters and strike-on composing devices. They may vary in price from $75 for a rebuilt standard typewriter to perhaps $15,000 for an IBM Composer. These main stages of refinement are as follows:

1. Fabric ribbon *to* carbon ribbon.
2. Constant width of letters and spaces *to* proportional spacing.
3. Line spacing in whole units (single-space, double-space) *to* more variations (line and a half, 2-point leading).
4. Justification by keyboarding each line twice and manually computing extra spacing between words (office typewriters) *to*
5. Justification by keyboarding each line twice with spacing added automatically the second time (VariTyper and manual version of Selectric Composer) *to*
6. Justification by keyboarding each line only once, with final copy typed and lines spaced automatically by means of coded tape. (Justowriter and tape-operated Selectric Composer).

Such composition becomes somewhat competitive (where larger amounts of composition are needed) with traditional line-casting machines which require only a single keyboarding. Line-casting requires perhaps twice the investment for the machine, a higher hourly wage for the operator, and is a little slower line for line. But line-casting produces a cleaner, sharper image, and its type is faster and easier to correct or to space out into complex pages with illustrations. So line-casting and repro proofs are still commonly used for highly illustrated books such as this one.

7. *Finally,* typing of copy with a single keyboarding in long or continuous lines without determining where lines end (making a "rough" or "idiot" tape). This is much faster than having the operator decide where to end each line, as this takes nearly as much time as the keyboarding. Coded tape thus produced is fed to a computer to automatically determine lines, hyphenation, and justification at fantastic speeds. Computer output is a coded, justified tape which can be fed to various high-speed composing machines (either strike-on, line-casting, photographic, or electronic).

## Questions

1. What are the desirable characteristics of existing printed work which is to be used as camera copy?
2. What kinds of ink and paper generally are used for hand-prepared art that is to be camera copied?
3. How are corrections made on hand-prepared art (black and white line work) so they will reproduce well when photographed?
4. What tools and devices are available to the hand letterer?
5. What is "clip art"? Where is it obtained?
6. How is a heading composed from tab-type individual letters?
7. Describe the procedure in using adhesive type.
8. How is a mitered border formed with strips or a roll of adhesive border material?
9. How is transfer type applied to the mechanical?
10. In producing cold type composition for camera copy, what advantage is there in using a one-time carbon ribbon? An electric typewriter?
11. What general precautions and procedures shall be observed in producing typewriter composition for reproduction?
12. Describe what is meant by the term "proportional spacing" when that term is used to describe typewriter type faces.
13. Explain how manual justification of lines is achieved on typewriters which have no means for automatic justification.
14. How is justification of line achieved on the IBM "Executive" electric typewriter? Explain.
15. How does the IBM "Selectric" differ from a conventional typewriter?
16. Describe the action of the printing element (sphere) on the IBM "Selectric" typewriter.
17. Describe a VariTyper type font segment.
18. How is a VariTyper type font segment installed and removed?
19. Describe, in some detail, how the VariTyper produces its typed impressions on the paper.
20. Describe how justification of lines is achieved on a VariTyper equipped for automatic justification.
21. How does the Justowriter achieve justified copy through only a single typing of the original copy?
22. Describe the function of the Justowriter motorized tape punch.
23. Study the illustration of the Justowriter punched tape. How does the machine know whether a letter is a capital or a lower-case one, as the tape passes through?

## Problems and Projects

1. With the help of your instructor, arrange to have sales representatives demonstrate (in your shop) any of the "typewriter" composing machines you do not have.
2. Plan and execute projects which involve typewriter composition — justified lines, ruled forms, same-size, enlarged and reduced.
3. Under guidance of your instructor, replace one-time carbon ribbons on the

typewriters your shop has. Learn about (and do) the necessary maintenance involved in cleaning the keys and inserting and removing type fonts.

4. Arrange with your instructor and school administrators to take a formal course in touch typing.
5. Start a "clip file" of printed items which you feel may be handy as clip art for projects.
6. Using cold type methods exclusively, plan and execute a calendar having a pad approximately 8½ x 11 inches.
7. Redesign and reset school forms, using cold type methods.
8. Produce wallet-size school sports schedules, using cold type methods, and reducing the type to about six points in size.
9. Plan and produce a poster, using hand lettering and clip art.
10. Ask to have a touch-typing course added to the curriculum for graphic arts students.
11. Send to manufacturers for operators' manuals for each impact typesetting machine in the shop, if not on hand.

## New Words

1. accurate
2. alignment
3. automatically
4. cancelled
5. consistently
6. conversely
7. copyrighted
8. differential
9. interchangeably
10. impact type
11. justification
12. keyboarding
13. magnifying
14. mitered
15. non-reproducing
16. photo-direct
17. photographed
18. platen
19. preparatory
20. pre-printed
21. pressure-sensitive
22. proportional
23. reduction
24. reproduced
25. self-adhesive
26. semi-gloss
27. template
28. transferable
29. transparent
30. typewriter
31. uniformity

# COLD TYPE COMPOSITION — PHOTOGRAPHIC

## Photographic Display Composition

Photographic display type is composed on machines that, in addition to setting display lines, sometimes are capable of setting limited text matter. Details are reproduced photographically in very fine detail, and extreme enlargements without blurring are often possible. Reproduction proofs of hot metal type usually have a characteristic ridge of ink around each detail, and this tends to blur fine lines and make the letter seem a bit bolder. Photo composition eliminates this problem.

Finished photographic work usually is possible on either film or paper, as positives or negatives, and either directly from the machine, by photographic contact printing, or by reversal developing.

In use, the display typesetter is fitted with a selected type font, usually a form of film negative containing the complete font of transparent letters and characters.

The font is positioned in the machine above the printing location and between the exposure lamp and the photographic sensitized film or paper. An exposure of the desired character is made through the film font. Each succeeding letter is then positioned and exposed, the spacing being controlled by a spacing device and reference lines on the machine and type font.

The photo paper (or film) is then developed, fixed and dried, and is ready for mounting in place on the mechanical or for use in contact printing.

For some machines, the range of type sizes, in addition to the fonts available for each machine, may be extended by a built-in lens arrangement or by subsequent enlarging or reducing of the finished product photographically after it has been removed from the machine.

### The Photostabilization Process

The developing, fixing, and drying of photographic prints (and especially phototype) has been simplified by using *photostabilization* processing rather than normal photographic processing. The print is produced in seconds after the exposure is completed (by contacting or enlarging in the usual way) on a special photostabilization paper. This paper incorporates the developing agent in the emulsion. The paper is available in a range of contrasts, making it suitable for normal continuous-tone photographs as well.

The exposed paper is fed into a processing unit, Fig. 141. Here a measured amount of "activator" fluid is applied to the exposed surface, releasing the developing agents in the emulsion of the paper. Complete development

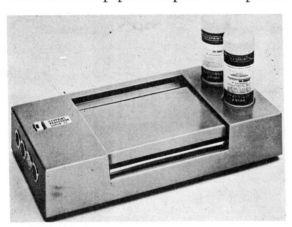

Fig. 141.   12-inch Photostabilization Processor (Courtesy Ilford, Inc.)

of the silver image takes but a second or two. The paper is then fed by the rollers to the second chemical bath, the "stabilizer", to set the image so that heat, light, and air cannot cause it to fade or the paper to yellow. The result is a stable photographic print of excellent quality which is delivered dry enough to paste up almost immediately.

### Protype

The "Protype" is primarily a display phototypesetting machine for setting single lines and also blocks of type on paper as wide as 17", Fig. 142A. A large variety of sizes and styles of type faces (ProFonts) is available, usually from 18 points to 90 points, although smaller sizes are available for some type faces. See Fig. 142B.

In operation, the desired ProFont is placed in position and the calibrated spacing wheel and light mask are adjusted for the size selected.

Exposure of each desired character is made through the ProFont. Positioning is done visually by means of guide lines below each character, advancing its position for each character. Justified spacing is controlled by use of the spacer wheel. After a trial run through the letters in a line, the spacer is set to extend the line to the desired length. This is done by gauging from the wider (lower) part of the guide lines, which leaves some extra space between each letter. Finished copies are developed after removal from the machine.

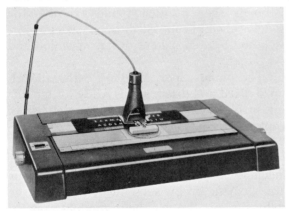

Fig. 142A.   Protype Model "816" (Courtesy Protype Division of Electrographic Corp.)

Fig. 142B.   Some Protype ProFonts (Courtesy Protype Division of Electrographic Corp.)

## StripPrinter

The "StripPrinter" is an economical photo-typesetting machine for display lines on 35mm film or paper (which is 2″ wide overall), as negatives or positives, in sizes from 6 points to 96 points. See Fig. 143.

The StripPrinter utilizes a filmstrip font — one font for each size of type desired.

In operation, the photo paper or film is loaded in the machine, and the selected type font is threaded through the exposure unit. The first letter is positioned and an exposure made. Succeeding letters are exposed by first positioning the type font and then transporting both the type font and the film or paper a preselected and indexed distance for correct spacing.

The exposed paper or film is developed, fixed, washed, and dried. It then may be mounted on the mechanical.

Another model, the StripPrinter "90", sets display letters up to 2½″ high.

## Headliner

Several models of the VariTyper "Head-liner" are available as table-top photo-composing machines, for composing lines of type 6 points to 84 points in size. The Model "800" delivers single lines of type, and the Model "840" composes as many as five lines of type — each machine using 35mm print paper or film. See Figs. 144A and 144B. The Model "880" page-composes on rolls of paper (8½″ wide) in finished page format, Fig. 144C. It can pro-

Fig. 144A. Inserting Typemaster into Model "800" Headliner (Courtesy VariTyper Corp.)

Fig. 144B. Model "840" Headliner (Courtesy VariTyper Corp.)

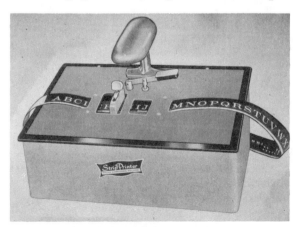

Fig. 143. StripPrinter (Courtesy StripPrinter, Inc.)

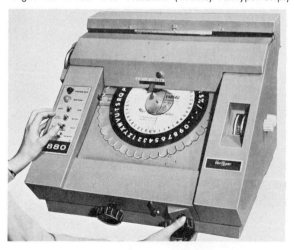

Fig. 144C. Turning Typemaster to Select a Character on Model "880" Headliner (Courtesy VariTyper Corp.)

duce large advertisements, posters, and other material having a number of consecutive lines of larger type, with fewer sections to piece together.

The Headliner employs for its type font a circular disc about the size of a phonograph record, on which are laminated the film negatives of the type characters. See Fig. 145A. This disc, called a "Typemaster," fits between the film exposure light (Light House) and the threaded roll of either photographic print paper or film. Refer again to Fig. 144A.

Each of the many available Typemasters contains one size and style of type face. The composed photographic type, however, may be enlarged or reduced from its original size.

Composition is done by rotating the selector knob in either direction until the desired character appears in the selector window. The operator then depresses the print key which automatically centers the selected character, advances the print paper or film and makes the photographic exposure of that character on the print paper or film. This process is repeated for each successive letter. Spacing between words is provided by depressing the space key.

Fig. 145A.  Headliner Typemaster (Courtesy VariTyper Corp.)

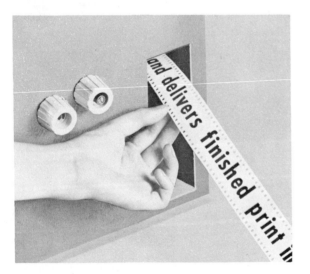

Fig. 145B.  Headliner "800" Finished Composition (Courtesy VariTyper Corp.)

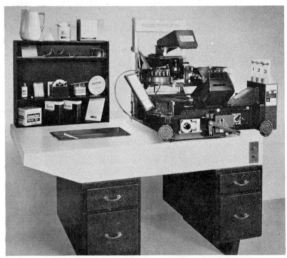

Fig. 146.  Typical Photo-Typositor Installation (Courtesy Photo-Typositor, Inc.)

Fig. 147.  A Few of the Many Variations in Composition with the Photo-Typositor (Courtesy Photo-Typositor, Inc.)

Separate adjustments may be made for providing desired letterspacing or for varying the spacing between words to justify the line.

When the desired amount of composition has been accomplished, the strip of paper or film is cut, and is then automatically sprocketed through the machine's developing, fixing and washing tanks. It emerges as a finished print ready for paste-up or as a developed film, Fig. 145B.

### Photo-Typositor

The Photo-Typositor is a projection-type photographic machine for display typesetting,

Fig. 148A. Morisawa Photo Typesetter (Courtesy Fairchild Graphic Equipment, Division of Fairchild Camera and Instrument Corp.)

Fig.148B. Photo Typesetter, Font Slide. Pins of varying heights determine letterspacing. (Courtesy Fairchild Graphic Equipment, Division of Fairchild Camera and Instrument Corp.)

Fig. 146. It utilizes a filmstrip font, 2″ in width. The projection principle permits enlarging (to 2 times) and reducing (to ¼) to 175 different point sizes from a single font. In addition, it will condense, expand, slant, interlock, overlap, distort, angle and letterspace, as shown in Fig. 147.

### Morisawa Photo Typesetter

The Morisawa "Photo Typesetter" is designed specifically for setting headlines and borders in sizes from 5½ points to 60 points, as a 10″ x 12″ paper positive or film positive (which can be used to make a negative). See Figs. 148A through 148C. By use of supplementary lenses, the letters or characters on each type font slide can be enlarged or reduced, condensed, italicized or extended (Fig. 149).

Fig. 148C. Photo Typesetter, Recording Drum. This indicates position of character on sensitized material. (Courtesy Fairchild Graphic Equipment, Division of Fairchild Camera and Instrument Corp.)

MORISAWA MORISAWA
MORISAWA MORISAWA
MORISAWA MORISAWA
MORISAWA MORISAWA
MORISAWA MORISAWA
MORISAWA MORISAWA

Fig. 149. A Few Variations Possible with One Size of Many Available Type Faces for Photo Typesetter (Courtesy Fairchild Graphic Equipment, Division of Fairchild Camera and Instrument Corp.)

### Friden Typro

The Friden "Typro" is a cold type, photo-composing machine for producing one or more lines of display type composition in sizes from 6 points to 144 points on a 2″ strip of paper or film, Figs. 150 and 151.

The Typro utilizes a filmstrip type font, with one face and size of type on each font; however, fonts may be spliced together and placed on the same reel. See Fig. 152. Composition is achieved by manually positioning each type font character and then depressing the exposure lever. The "Filmotype" is another machine using a similar system.

A choice of equipment allows the finished strip composition to be either hand-developed, continuous-developed, or automatically-developed. Fig. 153 shows a continuous-developer unit.

Fig. 150. Typro Cold Type Photo-Composing Machine (Courtesy Friden, Inc.)

Fig. 151. A Few of Many Variations of Composition Possible on Typro (Courtesy Friden, Inc.)

### Questions

1. Describe the functioning of a typical photographic display-type composing machine.
2. Describe a "ProFont".
3. How is spacing between letters and words controlled on the StripPrinter?
4. Describe a Headliner "Typemaster".
5. How is composition accomplished on the Headliner?
6. How is the resulting size of type accomplished on the Photo-Typositor?
7. What are some typical uses for a photographic display-type composing machine?
8. Which of the display-type machines described in this section would probably cost the most and which the least? Explain the reasons for your answers.

### Problems and Projects

1. Make a type specimen book of all available type faces on the photographic display-type composing machines in your shop.
2. Prepare copy for a large calendar, using photographic display type.

Fig. 152. Installing a Type Font Reel on the Typro (Courtesy Friden, Inc.)

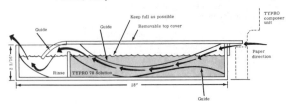

Fig. 153. Cross-section View of the Typro Continuous Developer Unit (Courtesy Friden, Inc.)

3. Prepare copy for a large poster, using photographic display type.
4. With the assistance and approval of your instructor, plan a class field trip to a local type composition house to see photographic type composition being done for commercial printers.
5. What is one advantage of a photographic display-type composing machine over tab type or transfer type?
6. Request a catalog of type faces from the manufacturer of each of the photographic display-type composing machines in your shop. Select those you feel would be a welcome addition to your shop.

## New Words

1. automatically
2. calibrated
3. condensed
4. exposure
5. interlock
6. italicized
7. laminated
8. millimeter
9. photo-composing
10. photographic
11. photostabilization
12. photo-typesetting
13. projection
14. sensitized
15. specifically
16. supplementary
17. transparent

## Photographic Text Composition

A number of machines are available which photo-compose entire pages or galleys of type matter on film, either as positives or negatives. These photographic page-composing machines are much used in the production of books, newspapers, magazines, etc. Type produced photographically is somewhat sharper and may appear a little lighter than repros of hot metal. On the other hand, it is somewhat more difficult to add special spacing (such as an extra lead between a few paragraphs, to space out a column) than with metal type. Several makes of photographic machines producing text matter are described here.

### Monophoto

The Monophoto produces exposed photographic film ready for developing. It operates at the rate of 165 characters per minute and will produce photo-composed type matter from 6 points to 24 points in size. The maximum film size is 11 inches wide by 24 inches in length. See Fig. 154A.

The master negative case (Fig. 154B) contains 255 characters. Each character is an individual film matrix that provides the same inherent flexibility for film setting on Monophoto that cellular matrices provide for type-

Fig. 154A. Monophoto (Courtesy Lanston Monotype Co.)

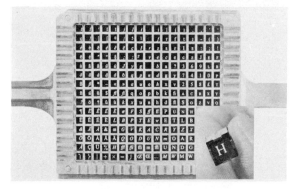

Fig. 154B. Monophoto Master Negative Case and Individual Film Matrix (Courtesy Lanston Monotype Co.)

setting on Monotype. Right-reading or reverse-reading (emulsion side up) copy can be produced on film or photographic paper.

The Monophoto is actuated by a perforated paper "controller ribbon," 4½ inches wide, that is prepared on the same Monotype keyboard used for "hot metal" composition. All classifications of copy — straight matter, tabular mat-

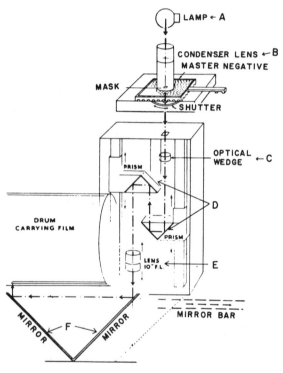

Fig. 155A. Monophoto Optical System

| B-1-57 | ADMIRAL—Page 5 | | |
|---|---|---|---|
| sis | Sheet No. | PHOTOFACT Set No. | ADMIRAL Models |
| | 5 | 118, 144† | 221K45 |
| | 6 | 103, 114† | 221K45A |
| | 5 | 118, 144† | 221K46 |
| | 6 | 103, 114† | 221K46A |
| | 5 | 118, 144† | 221K47 |
| | 5 | 118, 144† | 221K47A |
| | 9 | 177 | 221M26/27 |
| | 9 | 177 | 221UDX15L |
| | 9 | 177 | 221UDX16L/17L |
| | 9 | 177 | 221UDX26L |

Fig. 155B. Reproduced from a Film Positive Produced on the Monophoto

ter, foreign language, mathematical formulae, etc. — are set identically the same as for Monotype. Maximum line length is 60 picas regardless of type size.

In operation, the perforated paper ribbon is placed on the paper tower of the Monophoto machine. The desired negative case is placed in the machine, along with the required set-change gear and unit selector. The optical system is made ready by positioning the focusing bars for the point-size of type desired, and setting the lens diaphragm for the size of type and speed of the film being used. The film drum containing a sheet of film cut to the size needed for the specific job is put on the machine. The light is switched on and the machine started.

As the controller ribbon feeds through the Monophoto machine, compressed air passes through the ribbon perforations and automatically controls the positioning mechanism for the negative case to bring the proper character into position for exposure. See Fig. 155A. Light from the exposure lamp 'A' is concentrated by condenser lens 'B' to give intense illumination over the area of the character on the master negative. Light rays from the negative character pass downward and are aligned on the left-hand side by optical wedge 'C'. Passing through the wedge, the light rays are reflected by the two prisms 'D' and directed through the lens 'E' to produce the desired point size. Emerging from the lens, the light ray is reflected by two 45-degree mirrors to the film on the drum, where the light ray exposes the image on the film.

The single lens with the focusing bars, in the Monophoto optical system, will produce identical end-product from multiple-machine installations.

Spacing between words and justification of line length are controlled by the perforated controller ribbon. Spacing (leading) between lines is determined after the copy has been keyboarded and can be changed at will, while the machine is in operation.

After exposure, the film is removed and developed, using normal darkroom procedures for film positives, Fig. 155B. Negatives are produced by chemical reversal of the original exposed film.

A correction device is supplied that removes only the emulsion containing the errors from the film base, and corrections set on stripping film are substituted in accurate position.

### Intertype Fotosetter and Fotomatic

*Intertype Fotosetter.* This is a keyboard-operated, photographic line-composing machine, Fig. 156A. Like other photographic composing machines, the copy produced is especially sharp, Fig. 156B.

A magazine at the top of the machine contains 117 channels, each of which holds a number of identical Fotomats (matrices). Each of these Fotomats has an opening in which is mounted a "character object" (negative) of a single letter or other character. Blank Fotomats are provided for quads and spaces. See Fig. 157A.

The operator manipulates selected keys on the keyboard, and the magazine escapement mechanism releases a corresponding Fotomat for each key depressed. The Fotomats drop by gravity onto a belt which carries them to the assembling elevator where they are visible as a composed line of Fotomats. This is much like an Intertype setting hot metal slugs, except that word spaces are produced by a blank mat rather than a sliding wedge.

The Fotosetter justifies lines by inserting the needed space between each character rather than just between the words. For example, if a line having 25 characters in 4 words is 12 points short of the desired length, the Fotosetter will add ½ point between each character rather than 4 points between each word.

L'Espérance partit de Nantes un vendredi, comme le remar
des gens superstitieux. Les inspecteurs quivisitèrent scrup
brick ne découvrirent pas six grandes caisses remplies de chaine
et de ces fers que l'on nomme, je ne sais pourquoi, barres
ne furent point étonnés non plus de l'énorme provision d'e
porter l'Espérance, qui, d'après ses papiers, n'allait qu'au S
faire le commerce de bois et d'ivoire. La traversée n'est pas
vrai, mais enfin le trop de précautions ne peut nuire. Si l'o
par un calme, que deviendrait-on sans eau?

L'Espérance partit donc un vendredi, bien gréée et bien éc
Ledoux aurait voulu peut-être des mâts un peu plus solide

Fig. 156B. Reproduced from a Film Positive Produced on the Fotosetter (Courtesy Intertype Co.)

Fig. 156A. Intertype Fotosetter (Courtesy Intertype Co.)

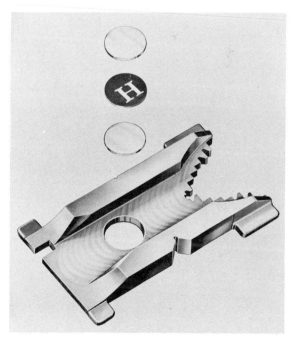

Fig. 157A. Exploded Fotomat (Courtesy Intertype Co.)

The line of assembled Fotomats is delivered to the camera unit of the Fotosetter which exposes (photographs) one letter at a time. The Fotomats are lifted, one at a time, to a position in line with a light beam which travels from the lamp through the negative (or character object) of the Fotomat, through a lens and then to the film or photographic paper in the film carriage, Fig. 157B and C.

Fig. 157B.  Phantom View of Intertype Fotosetter Showing Letter-by-Letter Exposure (Courtesy Intertype Co.)

When a matrix is lifted out of the line for photographing, the horizontal matrix rack is moved to the left a distance equal to the thickness of the matrix being photographed; a built-in gear-and-rack arrangement moves the film carriage downward a corresponding distance to provide unexposed film for the Fotomat. The justifying mechanism increases this spacing as needed to spread the line to the desired length. Spacing (leading) between lines is pre-selected and automatically provided.

As in metal composition, when the operator has sent a line of Fotomats to the camera unit of the machine, he proceeds to set the next line.

After photographing, the Fotomats are elevated to the distributor bar where they are moved along by their lugs, suspended by the notched "teeth" in their V-section which engage in matched grooves and ridges of the distributor bar. Each Fotomat is released from the distributor bar when it reaches the proper notch combination on the distributor bar, dropping directly into its proper magazine channel, in the same manner as with hot metal.

The exposed film or sensitized photographic paper is removed (with its container) from the machine and is developed in a darkroom. Since either film or paper can be used, the resulting product can be: (1) a right-reading film positive, (2) a right-reading film negative, (3) a wrong-reading film negative, (4) a wrong-reading film positive, or (5) a photographic-paper positive. See Fig. 158A.

Corrections in Fotosetter composition, either on film or photographic paper, are made possible through use of a line-correcting device, Fig. 159. The faulty lines are

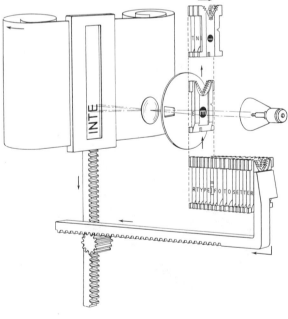

Fig. 157C.  Fotosetter Letter-by-Letter Exposure (Courtesy Intertype Co.)

Fig. 158A.  Negatives and Positives Produced by the Fotosetter Process (Courtesy Intertype Co.)

reset on the Fotosetter and then developed in the darkroom. The correct line is superimposed over the faulty line in the original film, with both galleys positioned on the line-correcting device. A precision die cuts out both the faulty line and the new line in the same operation. The correct line is then fastened in place with transparent tape.

All Fotosetters have eight lenses in the lens turret, and as many as fourteen lenses can be used on each machine to produce from 3- through 54-point type from four basic sizes of Fotomats. As many as 14 type sizes can be set from one basic font if necessary.

*Intertype Fotomatic.* This machine is much like the Fotosetter, but it can be operated indirectly through coded tape. It operates from locally-perforated tape, from transmission-wire tape, or from its own keyboard. It will produce text matter and display type in film form for books, newspapers, periodicals, etc. See Fig. 160.

The Fotomatic uses either single-letter Fotomats (Fig. 157A), or two-letter Fotomats, setting a maximum line length of 42 picas.

### Linofilm

The Linofilm is a complete photo-composition system embracing make-up as well as typesetting and correction. The system is comprised of the following four units: the keyboard unit, the photographic unit, the corrector, and the composer.

*The Keyboard Unit.* The keyboard unit produces a punched tape and a typewritten record. This tape contains all information necessary for the fully automatic operation

Fig. 159. Intertype Fotosetter Correction Box (Vacuum) (Courtesy Intertype Co.)

Fig. 158B. Full-Page Ad Set on the Intertype Fotosetter. (Note the comments at the top and side.) (Courtesy Intertype Co.)

Fig. 160. Operator Setting Up the Intertype Fotomatic for Tape Operation (Courtesy Intertype Co.)

of the photographic unit. The machine's keyboard is the same as a standard 44-key electric typewriter. With a shift and unshift key, the operator has available 88 characters in each font.

To the right of the keyboard is an auxiliary panel, which provides for the selection of point size and leading by turning appropriate dials. The operator can select any one of 18 different font grids by depressing one of several buttons.

Each font is available in six different point sizes, making a total of up to 108 different faces and sizes available as desired. Font grids are approximately 4½ inches square, and weigh only eight ounces.

To the left of the keyboard is a second auxiliary panel which controls the machine's functions. Five end-of-line functions are provided (quad right, center, quad left, justify, and line erase). A buzzer sounds when a line has been filled to within four ems* of the end, and the "justify" button then lights up. To end a line, the operator simply depresses the "justify" button. With this operation, the typewriter carriage is automatically returned and the typed script is moved up. This auxiliary panel also contains switches to turn the

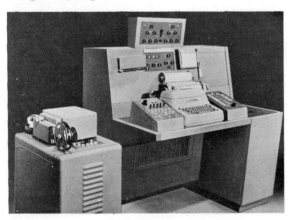

Fig. 161A.  Linofilm Keyboard Unit (Courtesy Mergenthaler Linotype Co.)

Fig. 161C.  Linofilm, Keyboard and Right-hand Control Panel (Courtesy Mergenthaler Linotype Co.)

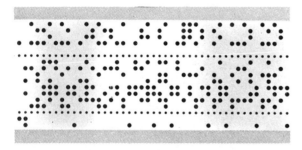

Fig.161B.  Perforated Linofilm Tape. This product of the keyboard unit contains all the information necessary for the fully automatic operation of the photographic unit. Codes in the tape record character selection, character width, and machine function information.

\*An em is a variable unit of horizontal measure. An em in any given type size is as wide as the type is high.

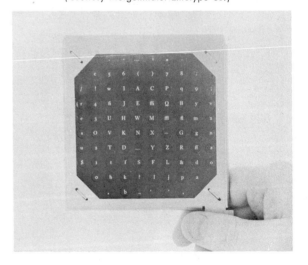

Fig. 161D.  Linofilm Font Grid (Courtesy Mergenthaler Linotype Co.)

machine on or off, enabling a line to be tried without perforating the tape. The eye-level scales above the typewriter carriage enable the operator to determine at a glance his exact location in a line, thus simplifying the setting of tabular matter and run-arounds.

The Linofilm system provides for kerning, and all characters are given their true values. Letterspacing is accomplished by unit spacing keys which can subtract from or add to the width of individual characters as may be typographically desirable. For example, if a cap 'T' is followed by a lower case 'o', the

space allotted to the lower case 'o' can be decreased so that it will fall under the cross bar of the cap 'T'. Letterspacing is entirely under the control of the operator, and the justification system does not introduce any automatic letterspacing. A wide selection of fixed spaces is available for indention, figure spacing, and so on.

When the operator starts a new job, the typewriter keyboard is locked until point size, leading, and font information have been recorded in the tape. On the typewritten record, the characters composed from the basic font selected are recorded in black, while characters drawn from other fonts appear in red. Also, an italic or bold word in a Roman line is indicated in red in the typed record.

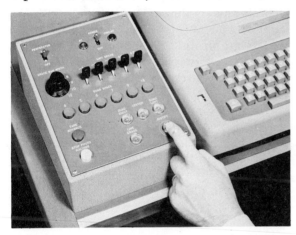

Fig. 161E. Linofilm, Keyboard and Left-hand Control Panel (Courtesy Mergenthaler Linotype Co.)

Fig. 162B. Inserting Cassette into Photographic Unit (Courtesy Mergenthaler Linotype Co.)

Fig. 162A. Linofilm Photographic Unit (Courtesy Mergenthaler Linotype Co.)

Fig. 163. Inserting Font Grid in Font Turret (Courtesy Mergenthaler Linotype Co.)

*The Photographic Unit.* The product of the photographic unit is an exposed, undeveloped photographic film positive, or positive photographic print if paper is being used.

Fig. 164A. Linofilm Corrector (Courtesy Mergenthaler Linotype Co.)

Fig. 164B. Linofilm Composer (Courtesy Mergenthaler Linotype Co.)

The operator feeds the punched tape from the keyboard unit into a reading head, and pushes a starter button. The machine will then set the material as recorded on the tape, changing point size, leading, font, etc., in accordance with the punched codes. Lines up to 30 ems in length can be set in sizes from 5 points to 18 points, at the rate of 15 newspaper lines a minute.

Upon completion of the tape, the film or paper will be automatically advanced into a removal container (cassette), and the operator will be signalled by a light and a bell that the job is done. The cassette, with the exposed film or paper, is then taken to the darkroom for processing. The operator inserts an empty cassette and a new tape, pushes the starter button, and the machine again proceeds.

Linofilm font grids are held in a turret containing a maximum of 18 font grids at one time. With 88 characters on each grid, a total of 1,584 characters are automatically available in six different point sizes, making 9,504 characters in all. Any one of the 18 fonts can be replaced within a matter of seconds.

The optical system has been designed so that the character grid remains entirely stationary. The lens system projects all character images to a common point, and selection is obtained by a shutter system. The positioning of the character in a set-wise direction is done by mirror reflection.

*The Corrector.* The film requiring correction is placed in one galley, and the film containing the corrected lines is placed in an adjoining galley. A dial is set to the desired type of correction: line for line, substitution of a complete paragraph or the replacing of one line by three or four.

Point size is set on a dial. The operator then presses the start button, and the machine automatically removes the incorrect lines and welds the correct ones in place. Up to three lines per minute can be corrected.

Many corrections can be eliminated before the composition is photographed by use of the "line erase" key at the keyboard, and by corrections spliced into the punched tape.

*The Composer.* The Linofilm composer performs two basic functions: make-up and enlarging. It produces positive type on film or paper in sizes from 3 to 108 points, to a maximum width of 96 picas. It has a working surface about the size of a full-size newspaper page.

The composer re-photographs the galley, line by line, altering its position to conform to a layout, and, if necessary, enlarging or reducing its size within certain limits. A series of dials and controls enables the operator — who sees every operation before the photographing takes place — to make up into a single photographic film positive any type film material fed into the composer. This, with the addition of artwork, is ready for platemaking operations.

*Related Machines.* The *Linotron* is a newer system growing out of Linofilm research. It makes use of magnetic tape (much as in sound recording) rather than punched paper tape, as well as extensive electronic components which allow the photo unit to operate at speeds up to 1000 characters per second. Another related fully electronic typesetter operating at similar speeds is the *RCA Videocomp.* More details for this type of electronic machine are given in the summary at the end of this chapter.

Another popular typesetter which competes with the Linofilm is the *Photon.* Because this is somewhat similar in operation to the Linofilm, it is not described in detail here.

## ATF Typesetters

*The ATF Typesetter Model B-8.* This is a photo-mechanical system for the composition of text matter on film or sensitized paper. The B-8 will set type from 5 points to 14 points in size, in line lengths of 7⅜″ maximum, on rolls of paper or film in lengths of 25 or 40 feet. Special versions having some of the type characters replaced by electronic symbols (wire connections, parts symbols, tube symbols, etc.) can produce wiring diagrams neater and much faster than draftsmen. In addition, the coded tape can be used to operate a computer to analyze such things as the number of wires needed and where they are connected.

The B-8 consists of two units — a keyboard unit and a photographic unit.

The keyboard unit is the control center, Fig. 166A. It is keyboard operated, punching a coded tape that carries all control data, and simultaneously delivering a typed proof (on paper and always in the same typewriter face) for detection and correction of errors before photosetting.

The photographic unit, controlled by the coded tape, produces the finished type com-

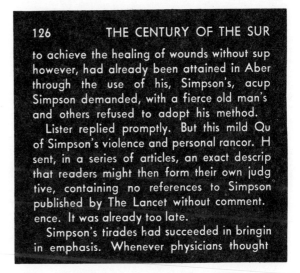

Fig. 165. Reproduced from a Film Positive Produced by Linofilm

Fig. 166A. Keyboard Unit For ATF Photographic Typesetter Model B-8 (Courtesy American Type Founders Co., Inc.)

position on a roll of film or sensitized paper, ready for developing. See Fig. 166B.

Five steps in the production of photographic composition on the Model B-8 are illustrated in Figs. 167A through 167E.

Fig. 168 illustrates, in schematic form, the functioning parts of the Model B-8, from the tape reader (upper right) to the film (upper left).

*ATF Typesetter Model KD-84T.* This model is a self-contained, photographic type-

Fig. 166B.   Photographic Unit For ATF Typesetter Model B-8 (Courtesy American Type Founders Co., Inc.)

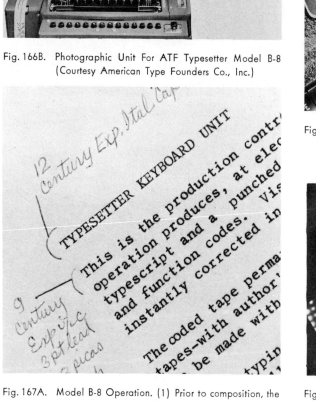

Fig. 167A.   Model B-8 Operation. (1) Prior to composition, the manuscript is marked for type styles and sizes, line widths, necessary leading, and other instructions. (Courtesy American Type Founders Co., Inc.)

Fig. 167B.   Model B-8 Operation. (2) After setting the measures, the operator types until a panel light warns that the justification zone has been reached. A switch justifies the line and returns the keyboard carriage. (Courtesy American Type Founders Co., Inc.)

Fig. 167C.   Model B-8 Operation. (3) Errors caught at once are immediately corrected by deleting either the wrong codes or the whole line. (Courtesy American Type Founders Co., Inc.)

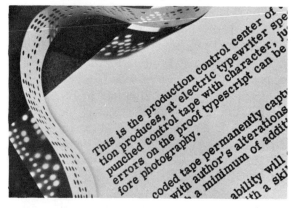

Fig. 167D.   Model B-8 Operation. (4) Errors noted after proofreading the typed proof can be corrected on the control tape before the composition is photoset. (Courtesy American Type Founders Co., Inc.)

Fig. 167E. Model B-8 Operation. (5) On the photographic unit, the control tape automatically produces sharp, smear-proof type images on photographic paper or on film. The light-proof film/paper receiver can be removed at any time for development. (Courtesy American Type Founders Co., Inc.)

setter which can be keyboarded directly or operated automatically from a coded punched tape prepared on other ATF keyboard machines (or other tape-punching equipment having compatible code arrangements). See Fig. 169A.

The Model KD-84T will produce unjustified headlines and display type, on film or sensitized paper, in sizes from 10 points to 84 points. Although this is a display machine, it is included here to simplify the description.

The *Model KD-84M* is the same as the Model KD-84T, except that it is operated by direct keyboarding only. Speed depends upon proficiency of the operator.

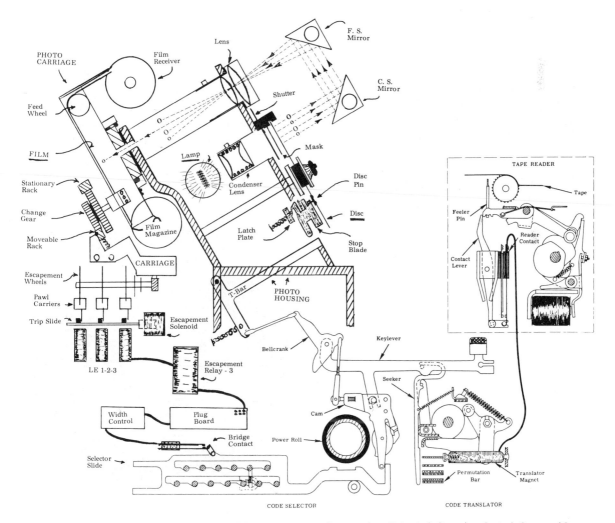

Fig. 168. Schematic Diagram of the ATF Model B-8 Typesetter Photographic Unit, Including the Optical System (Courtesy American Type Founders Co., Inc.)

Fig. 169A. ATF Typesetter Model KD-84T, Tape-Operated Headline and Display Unit (Courtesy American Type Founders Co., Inc.)

Fig. 169B. ATF Photographic Typesetter Model CS (Computer Slave) (Courtesy American Type Founders Co., Inc.)

Fig. 170. Standard Newspaper Keyboard Arrangement (One of Many Available) of the ATF Photographic Typesetter Model CS (Courtesy American Type Founders Co., Inc.)

*ATF Typesetter Model CS (Computer Slave).* This model is a photographic text matter unit and is designed exclusively for use in computerized typesetting. It is a "computer slave unit" — its composition is controlled automatically by tape from a computer (although unjustified composition can be keyboarded directly on the machine itself). See Figs. 169B and 170.

In operation, the Model CS reads the function and alphabetic codes contained in the computer-produced tape and performs the necessary composition, word spacing, justification, quadding, leading, hyphenation, and other operations called for in text composition for books, newspapers and other periodicals. In addition, it will mix sizes and styles of type for work such as classified advertisements.

As in other ATF photo-typesetters, the finished product is on film or sensitized paper, and a similar type disc is employed.

*ATF Typesetter Discs.* The film fonts are in negative form on a disc which looks much like a slightly large 45 rpm phonograph record. For text matter (Model B), there are two related fonts (such as Roman and Italic, or Light and Bold) arranged in four rings and shown in Fig. 171A. On type discs for display type

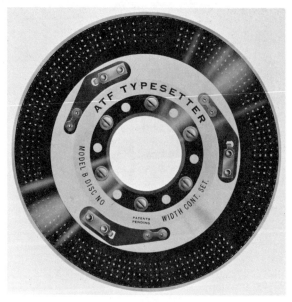

Fig. 171A. ATF Photographic Typesetter Disc for Text Machines (Courtesy American Type Founders Co., Inc.)

(Model KD-84) in sizes up to 36 points, there are four faces per disc in one of these combinations:

| | | |
|---|---|---|
| 10-pt. Roman | 14-pt. Roman | |
| 10-pt. Italic or | 14-pt. Italic | or |
| 24-pt. Roman | 30-pt. Roman | |
| 24-pt. Italic | 30-pt. Italic | |

| | |
|---|---|
| 18-pt. Roman | 12-pt. Roman |
| 18-pt. Italic or | 12-pt. Bold |
| 36-pt. Roman | 36-pt. Roman |
| 36-pt. Italic | 36-pt. Bold |

Discs for display type from 42 point to 84 point are single-font discs, each with 84 characters. See Fig. 171B. Enlargements and reductions are made from each of the nominal sizes on a disc, but (as with all photo type) if for more than a size or two, there is a slight darkening of the character in enlargement and a lightening in reduction.

### Alphatype

The Alphatype is an electronic photo-typesetter for text composition. It utilizes a standard electric typewriter as its keyboard. This is electrically connected to the Alphatype Recorder unit which transmits a ten-channel binary signal to *magnetic* tape. See Fig. 172A. These signals identify each character and its

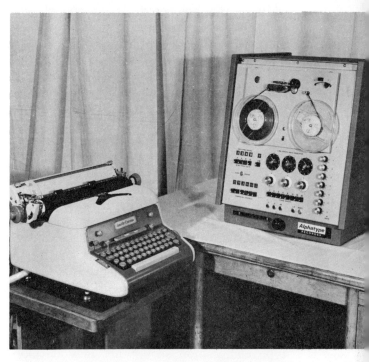

Fig. 172A. Alphatype Keyboard Unit and Recorder Unit (Courtesy Filmotype Corp.)

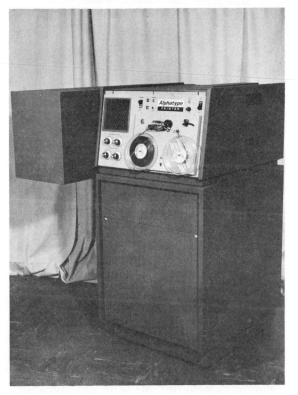

Fig. 172B. Alphatype Printer Unit (Courtesy Filmotype Corp.)

Fig. 171B. ATF Photographic Typesetter Disc for Display Machines (Courtesy American Type Founders Co., Inc.)

width as it is composed. At the end of each line, the carriage return automatically transmits the necessary justification information. After the job is recorded on the magnetic tape, the reel is fed into the Printer unit (Fig. 172B). The desired font is inserted into the exposure unit, and the leading is selected, Fig. 173. Sensitized paper (or film) is then mounted on the carrier, and the exposure unit "reads" the magnetic tape and photographically composes. Upon completion, a buzzer sounds. The sensitized paper (or film) is removed and processed in the usual manner.

Keyboard speed is 600 characters per minute. The exposure unit can accommodate a page 11″ x 12″. Maximum justified line length is 60 picas, and maximum galley depth is 11½″.

## COMPOSITION SUMMARY

A brief survey of the various methods of type composition shows that new developments are coming ever more rapidly. At the same time, it should be pointed out that none of the newer methods has ever completely replaced earlier and simpler ways of setting type (or ways of *generating characters*, to use a more modern term).

In general, there have been perhaps eight significant stages in the development of methods for generating pages of printed characters.

### 1.  Handset Foundry Type

This most basic method was invented about 1450, probably by Johann Gutenberg. Within thirty years such type was used in a number of shops in Europe, and this remained the only method of composition for about 400 years.

### 2.  Machine-Set Metal Type

The Linotype was invented in 1886 by Ottmar Mergenthaler, and the Monotype in 1887 by Tolbert Lanston, both in the United States. Within fifteen years, both had come into common usage. Typesetting was speeded up to about 5 or 6 newspaper lines per minute, but type makeup and its utilization remained essentially unchanged.

Fig. 173. An Alphatype Font Negative Containing Two Complete Fonts. This one has 16-point Clarendon and 16-point Clarendon Bold. (Courtesy Filmotype Corp.)

### 3.  Tape-Operated Line Casting

The Teletypesetter (TTS) was invented about 1930, and by the 1940's it was commonly used in daily newspapers. Paper tape was perforated automatically in justified lines as news stories came in over the teletype wire services. This tape then could be put on a special high-speed Linotype or Intertype to cast about 12 lines per minute. One operator could keep several such tape-operated machines running. TTS keyboard units also could be used to perforate tape faster and more economically than it could be keyboarded directly.

### 4.  Photo-Typesetting

The Intertype Fotosetter was first made about 1947, and by 1954 a number of machines were being used — primarily for setting type for display ads and for text matter in books having a limited number of illustrations. This adapted traditional line-casting matrices and the related mechanical mechanisms to the photographic processes prompted by the growth of photo-offset printing and photoengraving. The Monophoto similarly is an adaptation of Monotype principles. The ATF typesetters and many simple photographic units for producing headlines and display type can also be classified here.

### 5. Impact Composition

By this time, office typewriters had been used to produce duplicated materials for many years. But during the late 1940's, special models (such as the VariTyper and various machines developed from proportional-spacing typewriters) were produced especially for printing purposes. Within a few years, these were in common use, largely in small, weekly papers and in in-plant duplicating departments (rather than in commercial printing plants or large daily newspapers, both of which continued to use more complex methods). Impact bars strike a proof to check keyboarding in tape and computer operations. Pre-printed type often has been teamed with typewriter composition for headings and display lines.

### 6. Electrically-Controlled Typesetting

Machines such as the Linofilm and the Photon emerged about 1954. The Fotosetter is controlled by gears, cams, levers, combination teeth and other mechanical devices. The newer electrically-controlled devices make extensive use of contact points on perforated tape, relays, and solenoids to control the optical and the few necessary mechanical units. Some newer models (such as the Linotron or the simpler Alphatype) use magnetic tape and more electronic (vacuum tube or transistorized) controls for even more speed.

### 7. Computerized Typesetting

About 1962, the computer began to be used in the graphic arts to determine how much type fits into each line and for the hyphenation of words at the end of the line when necessary. This allows an operator to keyboard copy rapidly as if it were in one long, continuous line. The output of the keyboard unit is punched cards, perforated tape, or magnetic tape. (Each of these can be processed somewhat faster than the preceding type). The coded keyboard output becomes the input of the computer which operates at fantastic speeds (up to 1000 characters per second). The computer adds up the width of each character and subtracts this running total from the space available in each line; it then determines how the line should be spaced for justification. If corrections are needed after the type has been divided into lines, a computer can merge a correction tape (coded for changes only) with the original full-length tape to produce a new revised tape. The high speed produces justified tape for entire pages in a few seconds and entire books in minutes or a few hours. As computer time is very expensive, this speed is important economically. The electric typesetters described in Stage 6 may incorporate special-purpose computers for limited uses, but the role of the computer is expanding to ever broader uses including such possibilities as page makeup, indexing, some editorial uses, and even in operating equipment in several locations by high-speed data transmission over long-distance telephone lines.

### 8. Full Electronic Character Generation

The RCA Videocomp 70/820, teamed with an RCA Spectra 70/45 computer, was announced in June of 1966, with a number of installations then already in progress. This was one of the first systems designed to take full advantage of possible computer speeds. It prints out as fast as 600 characters per second (and even faster speeds may be possible), so that more than 1000 lines per minute of newspaper copy can be set. No matrices or photomasters are used. Characters and symbols are stored as electronic impulses which will flash the character on a small TV picture tube for exposure on film. With this technique, the basic letter form can be adapted in a number of ways: enlarged or reduced, expanded or condensed, italicized, underscored, etc. Accent marks can be added, and even Chinese ideographs can be used. Original keyboarding can be done without operator decisions for justification or word division, and a number of makeup details can be programmed. Speed is such that revised printouts from merged tapes often may be economically feasible.

## Summary

The developments in these eight stages have taken place in a little over 500 years. The first stage lasted more than 400 years, the second, perhaps 40 years. In these first two eras, changes came slowly enough that all the skills and knowledge of typesetting could be passed onto the younger generation by the practicing craftsmen. Then, note that the remaining six stages have all taken place since the time when many of today's workers received their initial training. And even greater changes can be expected. Today, to keep fully abreast of new techniques and machines, it is necessary to be a life-long student — taking refresher courses, studying current articles and advertising literature, visiting new installations, attending equipment shows and organization programs, talking with technical representatives (the "tech reps") of leading companies, etc.

Remember, however, that any one of these methods of setting type can serve as the media for learning *typography* — the art of carefully using type, illustrations, and white space so as to communicate a desired feeling and the needed information. When this ability has been developed using one of the simple processes, the transfer to using the newer complex processes comes easier.

## Questions

1. How does photographic page-composed type differ from photographic display-line type?
2. What are some of the main uses for photographic page-composed type?
3. How is the Monophoto actuated?
4. What is the function of the Monophoto negative case?
5. On the Monophoto, what controls the spacing between words and the justification of lines?
6. What is an Intertype "Fotomat"?
7. Describe the Fotosetter "letter-by-letter exposure" system.
8. How are Fotomats returned to their magazine?
9. The Intertype Fotomatic is capable of operation by what three methods?
10. Of what four main units is the Linofilm system composed?
11. What is the function of the Linofilm Keyboard unit?
12. What is the function of the Linofilm Photographic unit?
13. How does the Linofilm Composer contribute to the Linofilm system?
14. Describe the functioning of the ATF Photographic Typesetter Model B-8.
15. Describe the finished product of the B-8.
16. How is the Model CS controlled?
17. Describe a type disc used on ATF photo-typesetters.
18. Describe an Alphatype font.
19. Briefly describe how type is set on the Alphatype.

## Problems and Projects

1. Plan a field trip to a commercial shop which uses photographic page-composing machines. Enlist your instructor's assistance in the planning.
2. Make a bulletin board display of photographically-composed pages of type matter from samples obtained on your field trip or from visits to, or correspondence with, composition houses.
3. Make a permanent (wall case) display of all the methods of type composition described in this chapter. Gather your materials from your own shop, from contributions from trade shops, and from literature supplied by the manufacturers of this equipment.
4. Plan and execute projects involving the use entirely of hand art and cold type methods described in this chapter.
5. From catalogs and trade literature, replan your shop to include your ideas of what additional type composing equipment would be desirable. Make the drawing to scale, and write up specifications for each item of equipment, including prices.
6. The machines described are merely representative of the various models available.

Check articles and advertisements in the trade journals to locate other machines. Describe their operation.

7. Locate a copy of the coding system for a tape-operated machine. Try to code a sentence, or read one already coded.

## New Words

1. advertisements
2. Alphatype
3. automatically
4. binary
5. character generation
6. concentrated
7. consistently
8. controller
9. conversely
10. corresponding
11. diaphragm
12. emulsion
13. focusing
14. formulas
15. Fotomatic
16. Fotosetter
17. hyphenation
18. illumination
19. inherent
20. Linofilm
21. Linotron
22. magnetic tape
23. Monophoto
24. optical
25. perforated
26. perforations
27. photo-compose
28. Photon
29. Videocomp
30. simultaneously
31. superimposed

# Proofreading

Proofs of all composition must be carefully read for errors, and the errors corrected, before the proofs are made for reproduction, or before the preparations for camera work and platemaking can begin.

## Kinds of Proofs
Since many methods of type composition are employed for offset reproduction, proofs of the type matter, as received for reading, may be of several kinds.

### Metal and Wood Type Composition
Forms of metal and wood type are inked, and then a proof is pulled (printed) on a proof press. Generally the proof is pulled on paper which is quite a bit larger than the type form, to allow space for making corrections.

### Photographically-Composed Type
The photographic composing machines deliver either negatives or positives, on film or photo print paper, depending on the method employed and the product requested.

Proofs of the film positives and film negatives are both submitted to the proofroom as *positives* — brown on Vandyke paper, blue on blueline or diazo paper, or black on photoprint or electrostatic paper. These paper proofs are used for reading and marking.

### Typewritten and Pasted-Up Type
If the camera copy is typewritten, pasted up or even hand-lettered, naturally only the final camera copy can and must be proofread. Normally, only the one copy is avail-

able. On work such as these, corrections can only be noted in the extreme margins, if at all, or only on the letters or words which will be cut out and replaced. Many times the errors must be indicated on a separate sheet of paper. Great pains must be taken not to mar the finished copy.

## Proofreaders' Marks
Proofreaders' marks are really a printer's "shorthand." Figures 180, 181, 182 show the proofreaders' marks with an explanation of what each means, and how it is used in the margin and the text.

Figures 183, 184, 185, 186 illustrate the use of the proofreaders' marks. Normally, a good compositor would not make this many errors. Can you find any errors which have not been marked and corrected?

## Reading and Marking the Proof
The "reader" reads aloud from the original typewritten copy to the "marker" who follows along on the proof, detecting each error, and marking each error.

The marked proof is returned, together with the original copy, to the compositor for correction of the type matter. After the compositor has corrected the errors, a *revised proof* (second proof) is taken. The proofreader and proofmarker read the revised proof against the original copy and first proof to be certain that no new errors have been made in correcting the old errors. If necessary, a *second revised proof* is taken and read.

## Size and Style of Type

|  |  |
|---|---|
| *wf* // | Wrong font (size or style of type) |
| | Repeat stop mark for each additional identical error in same line |
| *lc* // | Lower Case Letter |
| *lc* | Set in (LOWER CASE) or LOWER CASE |
| ⸗ | Capital letter |
| *caps* | SET IN capitals |
| *caps + lc* | Lower case with initial caps   *u+lc* |
| *sm. caps* | SET IN small capitals |
| *caps + s.c.* | Small caps with initial caps |
| *rom.* | Set in (roman) (or regular) type |
| *ital* | Set in italic (or oblique) type |
| *L.F.* | Set in (lightface) type |
| *bf* | Set in boldface type |
| *bf ital* | **Bold italic** |
| ♭ | Superior letter or figure[b] |
| /2 | Inferior letter or figure[2] |

*A marginal correction of lower case matter should NOT be written in CAPITALS*

## Position

|  |  |
|---|---|
| ⌐| Move to right      ⌐ | ⅛ Ragged |
| ⌐ | Move to left    ⌐ |   ⅛ margin |
| *center*    ⌐ | Put in center of line or page ⌐ *ctr* |
| ⌐⌐ | Lower (letters or words) |
| ⌐ | Elevate (letters or words) |
| ═ | Straighten line (horizontally) |
| *fl* L or // | Align type (vertically) |
| *tr* # | Transpose space (transfer) |
| *tr* | Transpose enclosed in ring (matter) |
| *tr* // | Transpose (order letters of or words) |
| *tr* | Rearrange words of order numbers in |
| *run over* | Run over to next line. (A two-letter (di- over vision should be avoided) |
| *run back* | Run back to preceding line. (This div- ision is incorrect) |
| *reset* *up* *up* *up* | A syllable or short word stand- ing) alone on a line is called a "widow"; it should be eliminat- ed) |

Square up justify — flush right and left

## Spacing

|  |  |
|---|---|
| *solid* | Means "not leaded" (Pron. "ledded") |
| *leaded* | Additional space between lines |
| *lead* | Insert lead between lines |
| ϑ *ld* | Take out lead  or  *tr lead* |
| ⌣ | Close up entirely; take out space |
| # | Close up partly; leave some space |
| ⌣ or ⌣ | Less space between words |
| ⋉ or *eq#* | Equalize space between words |
| *thin #* | Thin space where indicated *hair #* |
| *l/s* | LETTER-SPACE |
| # | Insert space (or more space) |
| *space out* | More space between words |
| *en quad* | ½-em (nut) space or indention |
| ☐ | Em quad (mutton) space or indention |
| ☐☐☐ | Insert number of em quadrats shown |

## Insertion and Deletion

|  |  |
|---|---|
| *OUT* *see copy* | Insert matter omitted; refer to copy (Mark copy *Out*, see proof, galley 0) |
| *the / l* | Insert marginal additions |
| ϑ or ϑ | Dele—take out (delete) (Orig. δ) |
| ϑ | Delete and close up |
| *stet* | Let it stand—(all matter above dots) |

## Diacritical Marks; Signs; Symbols

|  |  |
|---|---|
| ü | Diaeresis or umlaut |
| é | Accent acute    è  Accent grave |
| â | Circumflex accent or "doghouse" |
| ç | Cedilla or French c |
| ñ | Tilde (Spanish); til (Portuguese) |
| *use lig* ⌢ | Use ligature (affix—ffi)   Logotype—Qu |
| / | Virgule; separatrix; solidus; stop mark; shill mark |
| ✳ | Asterisk *    ⅋ Ampersand  & |
| ✳✳ | Asterism *✲* |
| ⊙☐⊙☐ | Ellipsis . . . or ✳ ✳ ✳ or____ |

Leaders . . . . . . . .

Order of symbols: * † ‡ § ‖ ¶ #; then double

seldom used

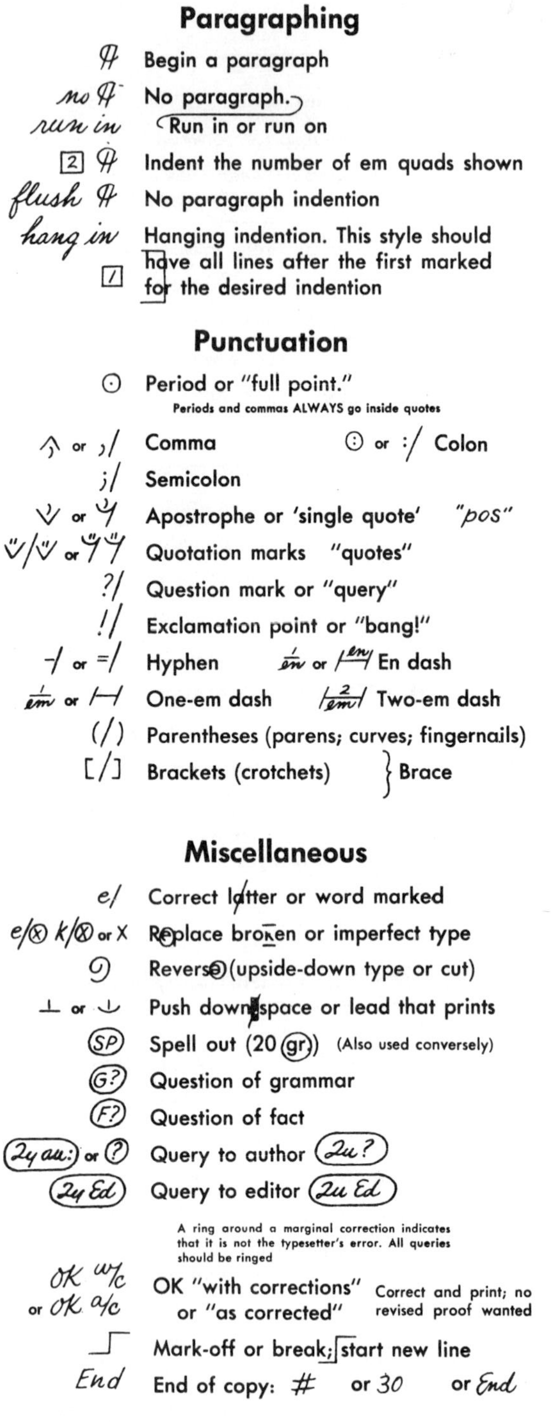

## Paragraphing

| | |
|---|---|
| ¶ | Begin a paragraph |
| *no* ¶ | No paragraph. |
| *run in* | Run in or run on |
| [2] ¶ | Indent the number of em quads shown |
| *flush* ¶ | No paragraph indention |
| *hang in* | Hanging indention. This style should have all lines after the first marked for the desired indention |

## Punctuation

| | |
|---|---|
| ⊙ | Period or "full point." |

**Periods and commas ALWAYS go inside quotes**

| | | | |
|---|---|---|---|
| ∧ or ,/ | Comma | ⊙ or :/ | Colon |
| ;/ | Semicolon | | |
| ∨ or ∀ | Apostrophe or 'single quote' | "pos" | |
| ∨/∨ or ∀∀ | Quotation marks "quotes" | | |
| ?/ | Question mark or "query" | | |
| !/ | Exclamation point or "bang!" | | |
| ⌐/ or =/ | Hyphen | *en/* or /*en* En dash | |
| /*em* or ⊢⊣ | One-em dash | /*²/em* Two-em dash | |
| (/) | Parentheses (parens; curves; fingernails) | | |
| [/] | Brackets (crotchets) } Brace | | |

## Miscellaneous

| | |
|---|---|
| *e*/ | Correct letter or word marked |
| *e*/⊗ *k*/⊗ or × | Replace broken or imperfect type |
| ℊ | Reverse (upside-down type or cut) |
| ⊥ or ↓ | Push down space or lead that prints |
| ⓈⓅ | Spell out (20 ⓖⓡ) (Also used conversely) |
| Ⓖ? | Question of grammar |
| Ⓕ? | Question of fact |
| ⟨*?u au:*⟩ or ⦿ | Query to author ⟨*?u ?*⟩ |
| ⟨*?u Ed*⟩ | Query to editor ⟨*?u Ed*⟩ |

A ring around a marginal correction indicates that it is not the typesetter's error. All queries should be ringed

| | | |
|---|---|---|
| *OK* ʷ/c or *OK* ᵃ/c | OK "with corrections" or "as corrected" | Correct and print; no revised proof wanted |
| ⌐ | Mark-off or break; start new line | |
| *End* | End of copy: # or *30* or *End* | |

Fig. 182. Roundup of Editors' and Proofreaders' Marks (Courtesy Mergenthaler Linotype Co., Copyright, 1955.)

## Reading the Proof

The reader reads the copy aloud to the marker. He reads the mark-up instructions, spells out doubtful words and names, tells which letters are caps, mentions each item of punctuation, repeats special indentions, paragraphs, etc., and tells whether dates and amounts are indicated by figures or words. He stops when requested by the marker, and repeats when necessary.

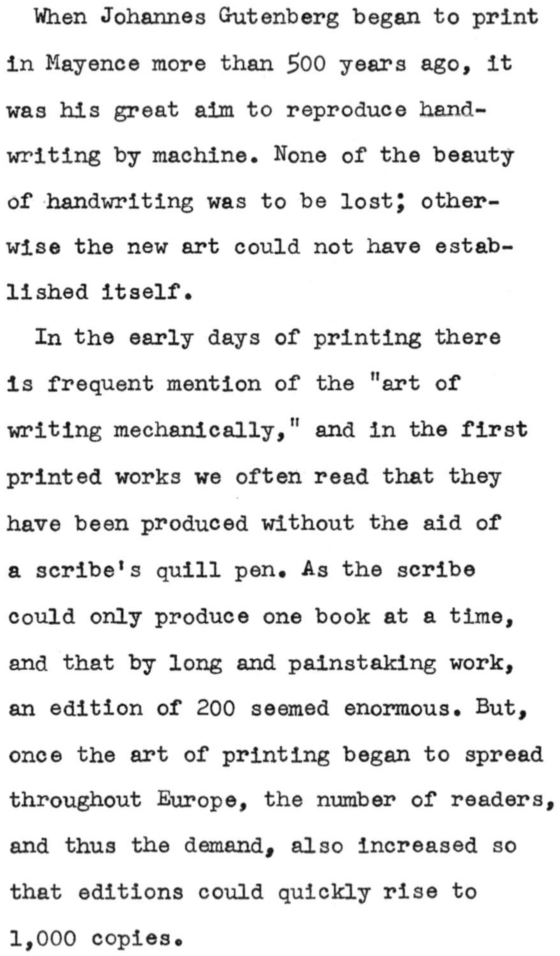

When Johannes Gutenberg began to print in Mayence more than 500 years ago, it was his great aim to reproduce handwriting by machine. None of the beauty of handwriting was to be lost; otherwise the new art could not have established itself.

In the early days of printing there is frequent mention of the "art of writing mechanically," and in the first printed works we often read that they have been produced without the aid of a scribe's quill pen. As the scribe could only produce one book at a time, and that by long and painstaking work, an edition of 200 seemed enormous. But, once the art of printing began to spread throughout Europe, the number of readers, and thus the demand, also increased so that editions could quickly rise to 1,000 copies.

Fig. 183. Original Copy

When johannes Gutenberg began to print in Mayence more than 500 years ago, it was his gerat aim to reproduce handwriting by machir e. None off the beauty of handwriting was to be lost; otherwise the new art conld not have established itself. In the early days of printing there is frequent mention of the "art of writing mechanically," and in the first printed works we often read that they have been produced without the aid ofa scribe's quill pen. As the scribe could only produce one book at a time, and that by long and painstaking work an edition of 200 seemed enormous. But, once the art of printing began to spread tɥrough-out Europe, the number of readers, and thous the demand, also increased, so that editions could quickly rise to 1,000 copies

Fig. 184.  First Proof

When johannes Gutenberg began to print in Mayence more than 500 years ago, it was his grat aim to reproduce handwriting by machiᵣe. None off the beauty of handwriting was to be lost; otherwise the new art could not have established itself. / In the early days of printing there is frequent mention of the "art of writing mechanically," and in the first printed works we often read that they have been produced without the aid ofₐ scribe's quill pen. As the scribe could only produce one book at a time, and that by long and painstaking work an edition of 200 seemed enormous. But, once the art of printing began to spread through-out Europe, the number of readers, and thous the demand, also increased, so that editions could quickly rise to 1,000 copies

Fig. 185.  Proof after Marking

When Johannes Gutenberg began to print in Mayence more than 500 years ago, it was his great aim to reproduce handwriting by machine. None of the beauty of handwriting was to be lost; otherwise the new art could not have established itself.

In the early days of printing there is frequent mention of the "art of writing mechanically," and in the first printed works we often read that they have been produced without the aid of a scribe's quill pen. As the scribe could only produce one book at a time, and that by long and painstaking work, an edition of 200 seemed enormous. But, once the art of printing began to spread throughout Europe, the number of readers, and thus the demand, also increased so that editions could quickly rise to 1,000 copies.

Fig. 186.  Revised Proof

## Marking the Proof

The marker follows along on the proof as the reader reads along. He marks each error on the proof where it occurs. In the margin, opposite the line, he indicates the necessary correction, using a system of symbols known as proofreaders' marks (Figs. 180, 181 and 182.)

Errors found in the left-hand half of the line are marked in the left-hand margin on a level with the line in which they occur; corrections for errors in the right half of the line are marked to the right of the line. If more than one proofreaders' mark is needed in either margin, it is placed to either the left or the right of the first marginal mark and separated from the first mark by a / (stop mark or "virgule"). Successive identical errors are indicated in the margin by one additional stop mark.

For great accuracy, some printing firms follow the policy of having the same proofs read as many as three separate times, each time by a different pair of markers and readers.

In addition, as an extra precaution, the proofreading may also be done by reversing the usual procedure — the marker reads aloud from the proof, and the reader follows the original copy.

In some instances, one person may perform the functions of both reader and marker.

In proofreading and marking, it is not enough that the proof be corrected to exactly match the copy. An alert and responsible proofreader or marker will catch any errors in the copy which may appear therein. Sometimes the grammar of the copy may be improved. Suspected errors in the copy, and suggested improvements in the copy, should be circled as queries in the proof margins, so they will be called to the attention of the author of the copy. When the author reads the proofs, he indicates whether or not these suspected errors actually occurred and whether or not he accepts suggested improvements or changes. Only then can these be corrected in the copy.

## Questions

1. What is the duty of the proofreader?
2. What is the duty of the proofmarker?
3. What might happen with one person both reading and marking?
4. What is a revised proof?
5. What should be guarded against in correcting an error?

6. How should successive marks on the same side of a line be separated?

7. After all errors are corrected, why is it a wise practice to submit the proof to the customer to read and approve?

8. Is the printer totally free from blame if an obvious error in the copy escapes the customers' attention on the proof and appears in the final printing of the job?

9. Where are proofreaders' marks for errors in the left-hand half of a line placed?

10. What advice should be offered a hand-compositor to have error-free proofs?

## Problems and Projects

1. Study the proofreaders' system of marks. Memorize as many as you can. Each day, try to learn a few more.

2. Prepare a bulletin board of typographical errors found in newspapers and other printed work. Paste each clipping on a larger piece of plain paper, and mark the errors and needed corrections.

3. Assume the duty of shop proofreader, and then proofmarker, for a week each.

4. Compile a list of books on proofreading, editing, and type faces (including type face specimen books) which should be in your school and shop library. Make out a requisition reminder for your instructor to order them.

## New Words

1. available
2. corrections
3. detecting
4. doubtful
5. grammar
6. impression
7. indentions
8. instructions
9. margins
10. negatives
11. paragraphs
12. photographed
13. positives
14. proofreader
15. proofreading
16. proofroom
17. punctuation
18. queries
19. received
20. reproduction
21. revised
22. separate
23. symbols
24. typewritten
25. Vandyke

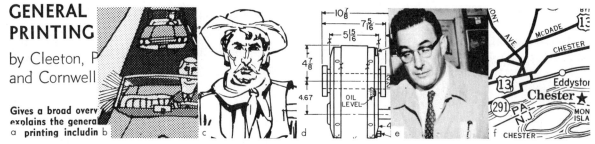

Fig. 198. Several of Many Possible Examples of Camera Line Copy: (a) type composition; (b) mechanical shading; (c) pen-and-ink line drawing; (d) pen-and-ink line drawing and template lettering; (e) halftone print; (f) pen-and-ink line drawing, transfer symbols and type matter.

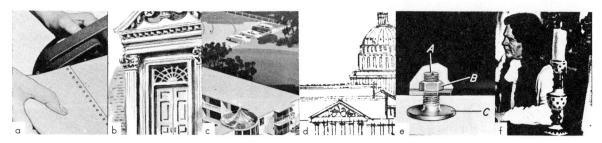

Fig. 199. Some Examples of Halftone Camera Copy. Each has gradation of tone: (a) original photograph; (b) pencil drawing; (c) wash rendering; (d) water-color line drawing; (e) line drawing with airbrush shading; (f) opaque watercolor painting.

# Preparing Camera Copy
# for Reproduction

Illustrations and type matter which are to be photographed are called "camera copy," or "copy."

Camera copy should be covered with a tissue overlay paper, and kept covered except when being photographed. Do not use paper clips on the copy. Avoid writing on the surface or the back as the indentations may show up in the finished work. Store flat. Very large illustrations may be rolled.

## Kinds of Camera Copy

Camera copy is divided into three kinds:
(1) Line copy, Fig. 198 on page 98.
(2) Halftone copy, Fig. 199 on page 98.
(3) Color copy (line or halftone), Ch. 10.

### Line Copy

Line copy includes all work which is composed entirely of lines and areas of single tones. No shadow areas, or gradations of tone may be present. Good examples of line copy are:
(1) Proofs of printed type matter.
(2) Pen-and-ink drawings, maps and cartoons.
(3) Hand-lettering with pen or brush and ink.
(4) Printed photographs which have already been screened by the halftone process and are to be reproduced the same size.

### Halftone Copy

Halftone copy includes all work which has gradations or variations in tone. Some examples of halftone copy would be:

(1) Photographs of persons, buildings, landscapes, machines, processes, etc., (all photographs except photographs of line copy).

(2) Artistic oil paintings, such as portraits, landscapes, etc.

(3) Airbrush renderings.

NOTE: If solids (line copy) are photographed by the halftone process, the screen which is used in the halftone process (before the film in the camera) will result in the solid image areas being "screened", i.e., reproduced as areas of "halftone dots", Fig. 200.

## Scaling Reductions and Enlargements

*The diagonal-line method.* The resulting height and width of a desired enlargement may be figured by the diagonal line method (Fig. 201). Assuming a given drawing is to be enlarged to a certain width, proceed as follows:

Draw rectangle ABCD the original size of the illustration. Extend lines AB, AC, and AD. Extend line AB to the desired height; at this point (E), draw a line across to the diagonal (point F), and then down to the horizontal (at G). The distance from E to F will be the width of the desired enlargement.

TYPE
AFTER
SCREENING

Fig. 200.  Result of Shooting Line Copy as Halftone Copy

99

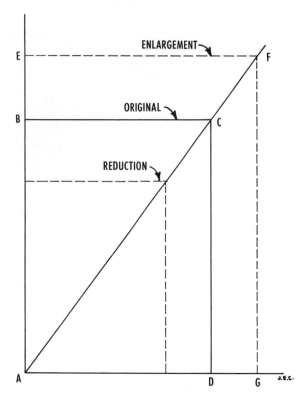

Fig. 201. Figuring Enlargements and Reductions by the Diagonal-Line Method

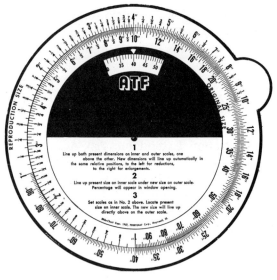

Fig. 202. Proportional Scale

Fig. 203. Proportional Rule
(Courtesy Engineering Instruments, Inc.)

To figure the resulting *height* when the illustration is to be enlarged to a certain width, first mark off the width desired on the horizontal line, extend it to the diagonal, then over to the vertical.

Reductions are figured in a similar manner.

*The formula method.* The size of an enlargement or a reduction may be computed by the formula:

$$\frac{W}{H} = \frac{w}{h}$$

in which:

W = original width in inches

w = width of enlargement or reduction in inches

H = original height in inches

h = height of enlargement or reduction in inches

For example: A space 6″ x 10″ is available for an illustration. The artist decides to make the original 9″ wide. How high should it be?

Solution:

(1) $\dfrac{W}{H} = \dfrac{w}{h}$

substituting,

(2) $\dfrac{6''}{10''} = \dfrac{9''}{h}$

cross-multiplying,

(3) $6''h = 10'' \times 9''$

furthermore,

(4) $h = \dfrac{10'' \times 9''}{6''}$

solving,

(5) $h = \dfrac{90''}{6''}$

or,

(6) $h = 15$ inches

Answer: The original should be 15″ high.

*The proportional-rule method.* Proportional rules are also used to compute enlargements and reductions. Find the width of the original on the upper scale and adjust the rule so that this original width is directly above the desired width on the lower scale. The height of the reduction, or enlargement, is then read on the lower scale below the height of the original on the upper scale.

*The slide rule method.* The C and D scales of the ordinary slide rule may be used for computing reductions and enlargements. Find the original width on the C scale and set it above the desired width on the D scale. The desired height will be indicated on the D scale below the original height on the C scale.

## Specifying Reductions or Enlargements

The original copy should be marked on the tissue overlay or in the margins, to indicate the desired degree of enlargement or reduction. Specify this for *either* the width *or* the height (not both) in inches, picas, percentage, a fraction or a decimal. For example:

(1) A map 8 x 12 inches is to be reduced to 6 inches wide. The notation may read:

    a. Reduce to 6″ wide
    b. Reduce to 36 picas wide
    c. 75% enlargement (actually means 75% of the original width)
    d. ¾ enlargement
    e. Enlarge to .75

(2) A line drawing 20 picas wide is to be enlarged to 40 picas wide. The notation may read:

    a. Enlarge 200%
    b. Enlarge to 40 picas wide

NOTE: In forming the fraction for enlargement or reduction, write it as follows:

$$\frac{\text{Desired size}}{\text{Original size}}$$

which means to the cameraman:

$$\frac{\text{I (The image he sees on the ground glass)}}{\text{O (The object he places on the copyboard)}}$$

In measuring widths and heights of artwork for proofs, *do not include the blank margins* outside of the type or object, unless you intentionally wish to do so. Fig. 204 shows a way to mark copy.

## Preparation of Line Copy

Good photographic results can be expected from work prepared on dull-finished white stock with dense, black ink. Avoid high-gloss paper as it may cause unwelcome reflections in the camera.

### Line Drawings

Original drawings should be made about 1½ times the desired size. When they are reduced, the minor imperfections will also be reduced.

Anticipate a proportional reduction in the width of the lines of the drawings. If too thin, they may be lost completely or broken when reduced.

### Reversed Printing

If it is desired to show type in reverse, i.e., a solid black background with the letters "white," the line negative of the type matter is made in the usual manner; from this negative, a *film positive* is made in the darkroom by contact printing. On the film positive,

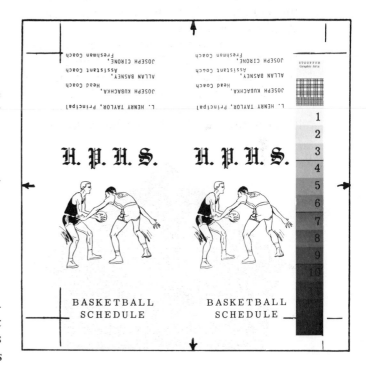

Fig. 204. Pasted-Up Copy Is Ready for the Camera Copyboard. The lines along the edges indicate the overall height and width of the copy (including the gray scale or, if the copy is small, a pertinent part of the gray scale). The arrows indicate the centers to be aligned with the centerlines on the camera copyboard.

the type characters or image appears black, and the background is transparent.

This film positive can be stripped into the "flat" to produce on the offset plate a solid area, with the letters not printing but instead, showing the color of the paper. This can be an eye-catching feature on a printed page. Specify it on the copy as a "reverse print."

### Ruled Forms

Ruled lines which are to appear in forms may be produced in a variety of ways. Brass or metal rule may be set with the metal type in hand composition, or the rules may be cast in machine composition along with the metal type on the same slugs or character bodies. However, when a great many lines are needed, and especially when there are cross-rules, composition costs can be cut considerably by setting the type without the rules, and then drawing the lines with pen and ink on the proofs, or scribing the lines through the emulsion of the negatives after photographing the proofs.

(1) *Ruling proofs with pen and ink.* The type is set in the usual manner, omitting the rules; or, proofs of the type headings may be pasted in place on the copy sheet for the camera. The ruled lines are then drawn on the sheet with a ruling pen and black India ink.

Fig. 205. Reverse Prints

(See page 351, for correct use of ruling pen.) If carefully done, with matched weights of lines, this method produces good, quick results.

(2) *Scribed lines.* The desired type matter may be set up without the rules. Proofs are taken and then cemented in place on the camera copy sheet which is laid out exactly as it will appear in the finished form. After photographing the copy, the negative is given to the stripper who scribes (scratches) the desired lines through the emulsion of the negative, using a scriber.

### Preparation of Halftone Copy

Because of the gradation of tone in original photographs or paintings and airbrush work, such illustrations can only be reproduced as "halftones," and are designated as "halftone copy." In photographing halftone copy, a halftone "screen" is placed in front of the film in the camera and the resulting negative is an image composed of dots of varying sizes.

Sometimes an illustration which has already been printed as a halftone may be photographed as "line copy" for reprinting. This is so because a printed halftone is actually only a multitude of dots, or "checkerboard" squares. Examine one with a magnifying glass.

### Reductions and Enlargements

For reductions and enlargements of halftone copy, follow the directions given earlier in this chapter. A halftone proof or a halftone negative which is already screened may not be reduced or enlarged without destroying the gradation of screening employed in the original photography.

### Crop Marks

In many cases, by eliminating irrelevant portions of a photograph, the remaining portion of the illustration can be emphasized or improved. Select the portion of the illustration which will best serve the intended purpose, and mark it as shown in Fig. 208. Place "crop" marks on all four sides of the illustration *on the tissue overlay.* Do not mark across the face of the illustration.

## Halftone Screen Rulings

On the tissue overlay of the photo or illustration to be reproduced as a halftone, indicate for the cameraman which *screen ruling* is to be used. Halftone screens are available in various screen rulings (Fig. 209); those used for photo-lithography are generally 120, 133, or 150 lines per inch. For special purposes, screens as coarse as 65-line, or as fine as 300-line, may be used. See Fig. 210, page 104.

The closer the lines on the halftone screen, the smaller will be the halftone dots which comprise the halftone reproduction, and on the proper paper, the finer the picture printed.

Fig. 208. Cropping Improves Some Pictures

Fig. 206. Landscape Halftone (Photo by Robert A. McCoy)

Fig. 207. Enlarged Section of Screened Negative for Fig. 206.

120 Line          133 Line          150 Line

Fig. 209. Reproduction Effect of Screen Rulings
(Photo by Robert A. McCoy)

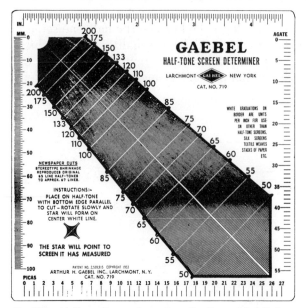

Fig. 210. Halftone Screen Determiner, For Determining Ruling Count of a Halftone Print (Courtesy Arthur H. Gaebel, Inc.)

Fig. 211. Combinations of Type and Photograph (Photo by Robert A. McCoy)

## Combinations

A printed halftone picture on which lettering and line work appear is known as a "combination" print. This combination may take several forms:

(1) normal (black) lettering, or type matter, superimposed on the halftone picture (surprinting)

(2) open lettering, or type matter, shown as white letters on the halftone picture (reverse print)

(3) a black rectangle, or open area, in a halftone picture, for later imprinting of type matter or for inserting type matter

(4) lines and arrowheads indicating nomenclature (names of parts) on a picture of a machine, etc.

This lettering, lines, and line drawing additions cannot be placed on the original photograph, or else they will reproduce as halftone dots. Also, the photograph possibly would be rendered unfit for future use.

For the combination print, it is necessary to make a transparent acetate or cellophane overlay, registered to the original photo. This overlay should best bear the desired lettering and line additions and be in correct position.

In making such an overlay, it is extremely advantageous to first reduce or enlarge the photo to the exact size to be reproduced. To this photograph, tape the overlay and register it in exact position.

## Screen Tints

A screen tint can be introduced by placing a portion of a commercial screen tint sheet (Fig. 212) between the negative and the offset plate during exposure of the plate — or by "double-burning" the plate (making one exposure on the plate through the screen tint, and a second exposure through the negative for the job).

The darkness of the printed tint can be varied by using a choice of a wide number of screen tint values. Fig. 212 illustrates values of commercial screen tint sheets. The screens with the coarser dots (such as 65 or 85 line) are used mostly in newspapers printed by letterpress. Commercial offset printing typically uses 133-line screens, though 110 or 120 line may be used on rough papers or for easier press runs. The 150-line screen should be used only on smooth, coated paper and requires more skillful reproduction.

The percentage values of gray (white is 0% and black is 100%) shown across the top of each shade in Fig. 212 are only approximate, depending on ink coverage, the reflection ability of the paper, and usual production tolerances. Typical values are given in the table (at the right) which is a part of Fig. 212. The transmission percentage of the actual film (center column) is low enough to allow for some dot spread in normal reproduction. This ink spread is minimized in smooth enamel-coated paper, but is more on standard (offset) papers. The white and black letters on each tint area show legibility of type on various tones.

To obtain a screened (or tinted) effect in line work such as in Fig. 200, a portion of a commercial screen tint sheet is simply taped beneath that part of the flat containing the portion of the negative to be screened. One

exposure during platemaking will suffice. In the exposure, the emulsion side of the screen tint is toward the plate.

In Fig. 213, the screened (tinted) bands were introduced into the job by making two exposures on the plate. For the first exposure, a flat containing the two tint bands was ex-

| (½A thru M) – Percentages and Densities | | | |
|---|---|---|---|
| | BY TRANSMISSION | | BY REFLECTION FROM REPRODUCTION |
| | | | Enamel Paper | Offset Paper |
| Tone Value | Densitometer Reading | Transmission Percentage | Density in % of Solid | Density in % of Solid |
| ½A | 1.52 | 3.02% | 3.88% | 5.22% |
| A | 1.22 | 6.03% | 6.20% | 8.70% |
| B | 1.00 | 10.00% | 9.30% | 13.91% |
| C | 0.77 | 16.98% | 14.73% | 19.13% |
| D | 0.61 | 24.55% | 18.60% | 25.22% |
| E | 0.51 | 30.90% | 26.26% | 33.04% |
| F | 0.41 | 38.90% | 28.68% | 42.61% |
| G | 0.39 | 40.74% | 32.56% | 46.09% |
| H | 0.25 | 56.23% | 45.74% | 64.35% |
| J | 0.19 | 64.57% | 55.04% | 74.78% |
| K | 0.13 | 74.13% | 66.67% | 85.22% |
| L | 0.09 | 81.28% | 81.40% | 93.91% |
| M | 0.05 | 89.13% | 91.47% | 97.39% |
| Solid | 0.00 | 100.00% | 100.00% | 100.00% |

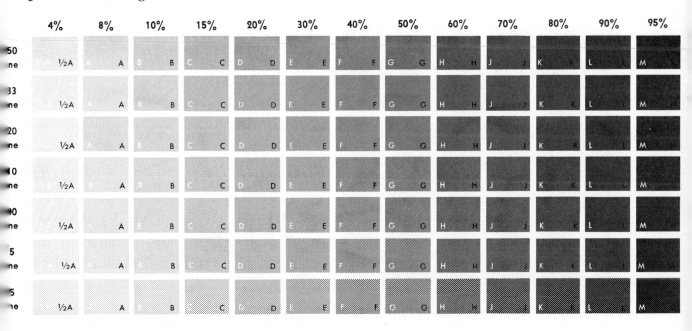

Fig. 212. Commercial Screen Tints Available in Sheets (Developed Film) of a Single Value (Courtesy ByChrome Company, Inc.) Note on the table (above) how the actual percentage varies from a transmission reading made directly from the film screen to a reflection reading from the printed sheet, both on smooth enamel paper and on a rougher offset paper.

posed to the plate. Then, for the second exposure, the flat containing the negative of the type matter (with a screen under most of the form) was exposed to the plate.

Although printed from one plate, in one pass through the press, the printed image in Fig. 213 has two tones. (If each exposure were made on a separate plate, the job could then be run in two colors. The possibilities are endless.)

For a highlighted effect as in Fig. 214, the line negative was first burned into the plate. The second exposure on the plate was made through a screen tint sheet over which was positioned an acetate overlay sheet carrying a mask to block out the arms and face of the pressman in the illustration (or the screen itself could be opaqued in these areas).

In Fig. 215, two methods of subduing a halftone are illustrated. The procedures are explained in the illustration caption.

Fig. 216 shows some of the many patterns of adhesive-type shading sheets. These are printed on clear plastic and have an adhesive coating for sticking directly to artwork. A knife is used to outline the area needed, so the rest of the sheet can be removed.

Additional information on screen tints is given in Chapter 10, Color Reproduction, beginning on page 155.

## Questions

1. What is "line copy"?
2. What is "halftone copy"?
3. What factor decides whether an illustration is to be reproduced as halftone copy?
4. What is the effect if a type proof is photographed as halftone copy?
5. What factors should be remembered when preparing line drawings for reproduction?
6. Use the graphic (diagonal line) method to determine the resulting width if a 6″ x 10″ illustration is increased in height to 12 inches.
7. How is camera copy protected from injury and dirt when it is not actually being photographed?
8. What is a proportional rule? How is it used?
9. A 5″ x 7″ photograph carries the notation: "75% enlargement." What will be the resulting dimensions?
10. What effect would reduction in size have in the reproduction of proofs of type faces which have very fine lines?
11. What is a film positive?
12. Describe the printed-on-paper effect of a film positive.
13. Describe two methods of producing ruled lines on a negative without setting them in type.
14. Describe how crop marks are used.

STOCK REQUEST

No. of Sheets_____ SIZE:_____

KIND_____

WT. _____ COLOR_____

CUT_____OUT, TO PRESS SIZE _____

NEEDED: DAY_____HOUR_____

SPECIAL STOCK: FROM _____

PO#_____ DAY NEEDED_____

SPECIAL INK REQUEST

Fig. 213. Screen Tint Used to Lighten Type Form, and to Add Gray Bands Behind Headings (Courtesy ByChrome Company, Inc.)

Fig. 214. Screen Tint Added to a Line Drawing (Courtesy By-Chrome Company, Inc.)

USE A NORMAL HALFTONE...     FOR BACKGROUND OF CHARTS...     OR FOR BOOKLET COVERS

NORMAL HALFTONE     SAME HALFTONE NEGATIVE SUBDUED WITH 150-D SCREEN TINT     SAME HALFTONE NEGATIVE SUBDUED WITH 150-F SCREEN TINT

Fig. 215. Subduing a Halftone with a Screen Tint (Courtesy ByChrome Company, Inc.) When a photograph is to be used for a background, a simple method of lightening it is to lay a screen tint under the halftone negative (at a screen angle 30° from that of the halftone). Note the two values shown to reduce the intensity different amounts.

15. What halftone screen rulings are generally available?
16. Describe the printed effect of a "combination" negative.
17. What is the letter of a screen tint that would be a middle gray?
18. Would it be better to use black or white (reverse) lettering over a 15% gray tint?

## Problems and Projects

1. Prepare a bulletin board display of halftone copy examples.
2. Prepare a bulletin board display of line copy samples.
3. Compute the following, by formula, and then by the diagonal-line method:

   a. 6" x 10", reduced to 4" in width
   b. 10" x 12", enlarged 200%
   c. Four picas wide, and three inches high, enlarged to 400%
   d. 6" x 9", reduced to .75

Fig. 216. Various patterns of adhesive-type shading sheets

4. Make a bulletin board display of film positives and the negatives from which they were made.

5. Make up (prepare) the camera copy for a ruled form, with hand-set type headings. Rule the lines with a ruling pen.

6. Prepare camera copy for a ruled form. The headings are to be hand-set foundry type. The ruled lines are to be scribed later on the negative.

7. On a tissue overlay, show how you would specify the desired "cropping" of a photograph.

8. Make up a display of printed samples of "combinations."

## New Words

1. advantageous
2. combination
3. computed
4. emphasized
5. emulsion
6. enlarged
7. enlargements
8. gradations
9. halftone
10. horizontal
11. imperfections
12. irrelevant
13. magnifying
14. nomenclature
15. percentage
16. platemaking
17. portraits
18. processes
19. proportional
20. reflections
21. registered
22. renderings
23. reproduced
24. reproduction
25. specifying
26. surprinting
27. transparent
28. variations

# Line Photography

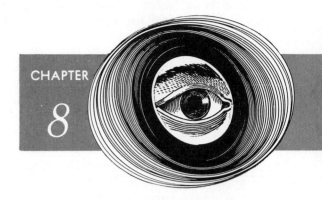

CHAPTER

*8*

Line photography is the copying on film (using the process camera) of original camera copy which is composed entirely of dots, lines and areas of a single color or tone — no con-

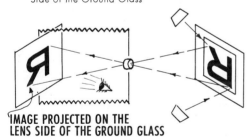

OBJECT (COPY) ON COPYBOARD, POSITIONED UPSIDE DOWN

BELLOWS

LENS

IMAGE AS SEEN ON OPERATOR'S SIDE OF GROUND GLASS

CAMERA     ARC LIGHT

Fig. 225. An Upside-Down Object on the Copyboard Appears as a Right-Reading Positive Image on the Operator's Side of the Ground Glass

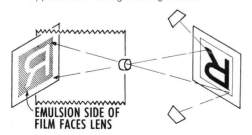

IMAGE PROJECTED ON THE LENS SIDE OF THE GROUND GLASS

Fig. 226. On the Lens Side of the Ground Glass, the Image Appears as a Wrong-Reading Positive.

EMULSION SIDE OF FILM FACES LENS

Fig. 227. Exposure of Film in the Camera Will Produce, on the Emulsion of the Film, a Latent Image of the Object

tinuous tones (gradations of tone). Good examples of line copy are proofs of type matter, pen-and-ink drawings or cartoons, etc. (See again Fig. 198, as contrasted with Fig. 199 which shows copy with gradations of tone.) The film negatives so produced are called *line negatives*.

Usually, line copy is prepared with black ink on white paper. For this reason, line photography is sometimes called simple "black-and-white photography" or "single-color photography". (Later in this chapter, instructions are given for using filters when photographing line copy which is other than black and white.)

## Theory of Photography

The copy usually is positioned upside-down on the camera copyboard. When the camera lights are turned on, light rays are reflected from the white areas of the copy. These reflected rays pass through the camera lens and are projected onto the ground glass of the camera back. From the operator's side of the ground glass, the image of the copy appears as right-side up and "readable". (See Fig. 225.)

If we could look from inside the camera, at the lens side of the ground glass, the image as projected would appear right-side up, but reversed, reading from right-to-left (Fig. 226).

NOTE: At this time, the following demonstration is suggested. Set the camera for "same size", and place the copy right-side up on the copyboard. With the image projected on the ground glass, note that the image is upside-down and unreadable.

**109**

Now position the copy upside-down on the copyboard and note that the projected image on the ground glass is right-side up and reading correctly.

Now, swing the ground glass out of position. Hold a piece of thin, white paper in the plane of the ground glass so the image can be seen through the paper. Then tilt the paper so it is possible to peer over the top or side of the paper and see the image on the lens side of the paper (reversed). Also, move the paper from and toward the lens so the image can be seen *in focus* and *out of focus.*

When an exposure is made (a picture taken) to make a line negative, the film is placed in the camera back with the emulsion (sensitized or coated) side facing the camera lens. During the exposure, the light rays reflected from the white areas of the copy pass through the lens, striking the film emulsion. This causes a chemical change in the silver particles of the film emulsion, creating a "latent image"*. See Fig. 227.

When this exposed film is developed, the result is a black-and-white film line negative — *or,* more correctly, a black-and-*transparent* film line negative (Fig. 228A). Those areas of the film which were struck by (exposed to) reflected light rays from the white areas of the copy are intensified in the developing process and show as dense, black, opaque areas on the negative — the "emulsion" areas; those areas of the film which received no reflected light from the black areas of the copy are washed away during the film developing and appear as clear, transparent areas on the negative — the "image" areas. This simple description of how the image is formed on the film will suffice for our purposes.

When a well-made line negative is placed over a sensitized offset plate in the platemaker and the exposure light is turned on, the opaque areas of the negative prevent light from passing through where no image is desired; however, the clear, transparent image areas of the negative permit light to pass through to create exposed areas on the plate coating, which will develop as a strong, firm plate image for satisfactory offset printing.

Usually, negatives used for offset plate-making should be "right-reading" (reading normally from left-to-right) when viewed from the base side (emulsion side down on a lighted stripping table).

The emulsion side of a negative is the duller of the two sides. For simple identification of the emulsion side, place the negative on a lighted stripping table and make a small scratch on it with a needle or knife, *outside* the image area. If the light shines through, you have scratched the emulsion side; if not, you have scratched the base side.

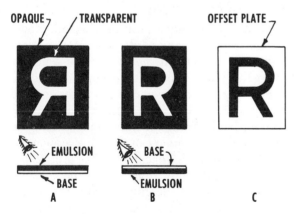

Fig. 228A.  a. After Developing, the Film Appears as a "Wrong-Reading" Negative when Viewed from the Emulsion Side
  b. With the Emulsion Side Down, the Film Appears as a "Right-Reading" Negative
  c. A Right-Reading Negative, when Exposed Over an Offset Plate, will Develop into a Right-Reading Positive Image on the Offset Plate.

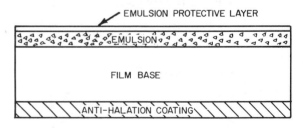

Fig. 228B.  Schematic Cross Section of a Graphic Arts Film

*Latent image — an invisible image which will become visible during the developing of the film negative.

## The Film

Most graphic arts film for line work is a relatively thin sheet of flexible-base plastic, about .003″ to .008″ thick. The plastic material usually is acetate, which is economical and suitable for most uses. For precision work, when maximum stability of the image size is needed, other plastics may be used, such as polyester (Estar) or polystyrene. This base material is coated on one surface with a light-sensitive emulsion of minute particles of silver salts suspended in gelatin. See Fig. 228B. This side is called the *emulsion side*.

The opposite surface (called the *base side*) is coated with an *anti-halation* material which (1) absorbs the light rays which penetrate the film base during the exposure; (otherwise, these might reflect back to the emulsion, spreading the image;) and (2) tends to offset, or minimize, the curling, distortion or dimensional changes caused by the gelatin emulsion when it absorbs moisture.

NOTE: For film which is to be exposed with the base side towards the lens for image-reversal procedures, it is recommended that *thin-base film* be used. This type has a *thin* and *clear* anti-halation coating which causes no appreciable loss of image detail.

For most of the line photography procedures discussed in this book, a film such as Kodalith Ortho Type 3 Film (both .007″ regular base and .0032″ thin base) is suggested. It will produce sharp line negatives of extreme contrast and will allow for considerable latitude (or variation) in exposure and processing.

For work where dimensional stability must be absolutely maintained (such as maps, color reproductions, etc.), glass plates, instead of flexible plastic-base film, have been used in the past, but polyester-base films are used now.

Additional information on films will be found in Chapter 9.

## Process Cameras

Process cameras used for offset photography are designed and equipped to render true images (at reductions, same size, and enlargements) of a flat surface, from corner to corner, over the entire copyboard.

Since the most modest of these cameras costs from several thousands of dollars and upwards, and since these cameras *must be marvels of precision*, the utmost care is essential in the operation and handling of the camera and its component parts.

### Horizontal Cameras

There are two basic ways of building process cameras — horizontally and vertically. Most large process cameras are *horizontal* ones, as shown in Figs. 229 and 230. The sliding copyboard is near one end on horizontal rails,

Fig. 229. 31″ Darkroom Camera (Courtesy Consolidated International Equipment and Graphic Supply Co.)

Fig. 230. Robertson 480 (24″ x 31″) Darkroom Camera (Courtesy Robertson Photo-Mechanix, Inc.)

Fig. 231. The 8″ x 10″ Copying or Gallery Camera (Courtesy Consolidated International Equipment and Graphic Supply Co.)

Fig. 232. Robertson 432 (19″ x 24″) Vertical Camera (Courtesy Robertson Photo-Mechanix, Inc.)

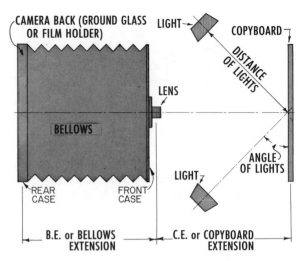

Fig. 233. Basic Nomenclature of the Camera

the film holder is at the other end, and the lens can be adjusted between the two ends on the rails. The horizontal process camera is much like a very large view camera used to make portraits. Horizontal cameras are made in various sizes designated by the largest sheet of film which can be accommodated — ranging from about 16″ x 20″ to 48″ x 48″ or even larger. However, some small horizontal cameras are essentially specialized view cameras in the 8″ x 10″ to 12″ x 18″ size range, Fig. 231.

### Vertical Cameras

*Vertical* process cameras (as in Fig. 232) are popular in the intermediate size ranges — 12″ x 18″ to 18″ x 24″. This type stands the traditional horizontal camera on end, that is,

the rails are vertical, the copyboard is low near the floor, and the film holder is mounted firmly at the top so the operator can look down at the ground glass image. The advantage of vertical cameras is that they take very little floor area (10 sq. ft. *vs.* 70 sq. ft. for similar capacity) and are convenient to use, as walking and waste motions are minimized. Vertical cameras cannot be built for large sizes of film without becoming too high, although special short-focus, wide-field lenses have made the height more convenient for larger vertical cameras.

### Darkroom and Gallery Installations

Process cameras also can be installed and used in two ways — as darkroom cameras and as gallery cameras. *Darkroom cameras* are installed in a light-tight room, or (the preferred way) have the back built into the wall of such a room, with the lens, lights and copyboard outside the room, so that film can be positioned and removed in the dark. *Gallery cameras* are installed completely in a lighted room and require a light-tight holder to be loaded in a darkroom, then taken to the camera.

The *built-in, horizontal, darkroom camera* (as shown in the darkroom plans in Chapter 11, page 189) has the advantage of separating the brightly lighted copyboard from the back of the camera. This makes focusing on the

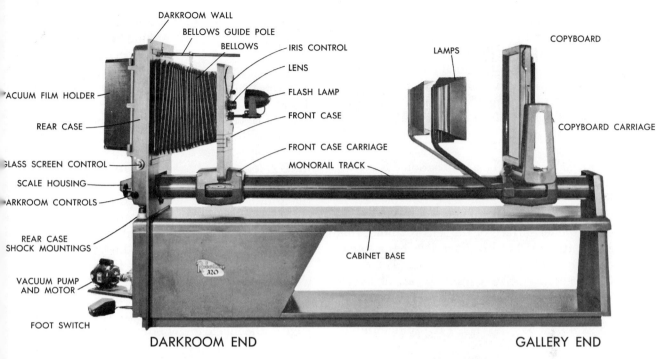

DARKROOM WALL
BELLOWS GUIDE POLE
BELLOWS
IRIS CONTROL
LENS
FLASH LAMP
FRONT CASE
FRONT CASE CARRIAGE
MONORAIL TRACK
LAMPS
COPYBOARD
COPYBOARD CARRIAGE
VACUUM FILM HOLDER
REAR CASE
GLASS SCREEN CONTROL
SCALE HOUSING
DARKROOM CONTROLS
REAR CASE
SHOCK MOUNTINGS
VACUUM PUMP
AND MOTOR
FOOT SWITCH
CABINET BASE
DARKROOM END
GALLERY END

Fig. 234. Nomenclature of the Robertson 320 (16" x 20") Horizontal Process Camera (Courtesy Robertson Photo-Mechanix Inc.)

ground glass easier and reduces the danger of fogging film in the darkroom, especially when more than one person is working in the darkroom. In operation, the cameraman mounts the copy and adjusts the lights before entering the darkroom. The rear case with the film holder and the controls for focusing and exposing are located in the darkroom, so that most of the rest of the work can be done from this position. Film processing can proceed in the same room as the camera back, even when the camera lights are on. Such horizontal cameras sometimes are built to be suspended from *overhead* rails (rather than having the rails built into the base), so that the operator can more easily move around the camera to adjust lights and load the copyboard.

## Basic Parts of the Camera

The basic parts of a process camera are the *lens* (front case), *bellows, camera back* (rear case), *copyboard*, and *lights* (Fig. 233). There are many more additional parts and features on any specific camera. See Fig. 234.

Fig. 235A. Goerz ARTAR Lens, 16" FL
(Courtesy C. P. Goertz, — American Optical Co.)

You should locate and become familiar with the comparable units on the camera you use.

### The Lens (Front Case)

The process lens is the most delicate, critical and expensive of all the camera parts (Fig. 235A).

*Lens Construction.* The lens is composed of several separate optical glass elements assembled into a barrel (Fig. 235B). The entire assembly generally is threaded into a lens board, mounted on the front case of the camera. The front of the lens is provided with a slip-fit protective lens cap, which should be kept on the lens at all times when the lens is not in actual use.

*Focal Length.* The abbreviation *FL* is used to indicate the focal length of a lens. Focal length, for a particular lens, is expressed in inches and, generally, is engraved or stamped on the inner surface of the lens-retaining ring as FL 10½″, or 14″ FL. Each lens has a *single, definite focal length*, and, in general, cameras for larger film sizes require lenses of longer focal lengths: that is, a 16″ x 20″ size might have a 14″ FL; 30″ x 30″, a 24″ FL; and 48″ x 48″, a 35″ FL. The FL also determines

the length of the rails needed for focusing — the above three lenses require rails about 10′, 16′, 20′ long, respectively. Special lenses are made for vertical cameras so that a 8½″ FL lens can be used for 14″ x 17″ film and with a 4′ rail.

As a rule, a lens of longer FL has less distortion of the image shape in a given area, and costs more: if the 8½″ lens costs about $200, the 35″ lens would be more than $1,000. Minimum distortion is especially important in ruled-form or map work, particularly when negatives are to be pieced together so that the left side of one image must fit the right side of another. Distortion would be very noticeable, for example, if an 8½″ x 11″ ruled form were copied at that size using a 7½″ FL lens which was designed to copy only a 5″ x 7″ area. In this case, straight lines around the edge of the image might bow outward as much as ⅛″ to ¼″.

Focal length may be defined as the distance from the nodal point within the lens (where the light rays converge) to that point behind the lens where the image can first be seen in focus, when the camera subject is at infinity (1000 feet or more away). See Fig. 236.

A more practical expression of focal length, as we use it in reproduction photography, is: FL equals one-quarter of the distance from the camera copyboard to the camera ground glass, when the focused image on the ground glass *is the same size* as the object on the copyboard. At this setting for same size or 100% (as is shown in Fig. 247), the bellows extension equals the copyboard extension, and each is twice the FL.

To determine the focal length of an unmarked lens, place a piece of copy on the copyboard, and adjust the camera so that the image is in focus and is the same size as the copy. Measure the distance from the copy to the image on the ground glass, and divide this by four.

*Diaphragm.* The diaphragm (or iris) is an arrangement of metal blades inside the lens barrel. When the knurled lens collar is rotated, the diaphragm blades can be seen to open or close, forming a circular "mask" or an *aperture*

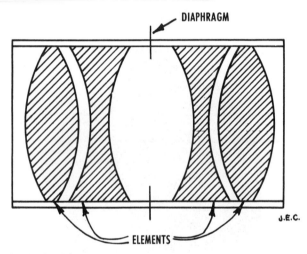

Fig. 235B.  Schematic Cross Section of a Typical Process Lens

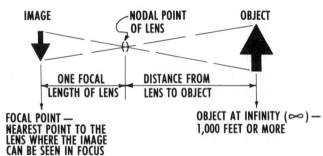

Fig. 236.  Focal Length

*opening* of the desired size, to admit light through the lens.

Stamped on the knurled collar is a series of *f-stop numbers*: *f*/11, *f*/16, *f*/22, *f*/32, *f*/45, etc. Each number is called an *f-stop*, and it expresses the diameter of the diaphragm opening as a fraction of the focal length of the lens. For example: a 16″ FL lens which is set at *f*/32 has an opening ("aperture") of ½″ diameter ($f = $ FL/d $= 16/\frac{1}{2} = 32,\ or$ d $=$ FL/$f = 16/32 = \frac{1}{2}$). See Fig. 237. Note that the larger *f*-numbers represent the smaller openings. The "speed" of the lens depends on the *area* of the aperture opening and not the diameter. The *f*-numbers have been selected so that each successively larger number cuts the aperture area in half — *f*/22 is half as fast as *f*/16, and *f*/45 is twice as fast as *f*/64.

To set the lens for a particular *f*-stop, rotate the knurled collar until the desired *f*-stop index line matches the lens barrel index line. The *f*-numbers, when set this way, are exactly valid only when photographing objects at a distance.

Corrections must be made for the close-up work on a process camera, as the image is nearly as large as the original (or even larger). Such corrections can be made by using the *manual diaphragm control* (iris control) on the lens. When set at the reduction or enlargement desired, this device will automatically adjust the lens to the proper *f*-number to admit the correct amount of light with the exposure time remaining constant. See Fig. 238. The *f*-numbers appear at the right of the bands, and each band contains the percentage scale for reduction or enlargement. In use, the *f*-number is selected, and the long pointer (connected to the diaphragm collar on the lens) is set to the percentage mark on the scale for that *f*-number. This system varies the *f*-stop with the amount of enlargement or reduction so that exposure time can remain relatively constant.

*Shutter.* For accurately controlling the length of exposure, some cameras are equipped with an electric solenoid shutter which is fitted behind the lens. An electric timer, adjustable for the number of seconds of exposure, oper-

ates the shutter. It can be set to hold the shutter open when focusing the camera, and to make exposures at set lengths of time. See Figs. 239A and B.

When the camera has no such shutter, exposure is made simply by removing the lens cap for the exposure time. If the lens also has

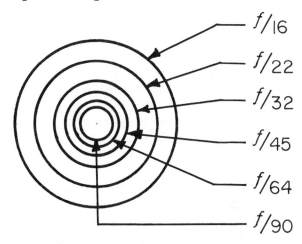

Fig. 237. Relative Sizes of Aperture Openings (f-numbers) of a Typical Process Lens

Fig. 238. The Diaphragm (Iris) Control (Courtesy Robertson Photo-Mechanix, Inc.)

no percentage scales for diaphragm control, an allowance must be made in exposure time for the amount of reduction or enlargement.

*Filter Slot.* This is the slot in the lens barrel through which square gelatin filters may be inserted when color work is being done; it also permits the insertion of "Waterhouse Stops" (diaphragms of paper or metal with small, specially shaped openings).

If the filter slot is not being used, the slot should be covered or taped, to prevent dust and stray light from entering.

*Lens Care.* As previously mentioned, of all the camera parts, the lens is the most delicate, critical and expensive. To minimize image errors (aberrations) several types of glass are used in lenses. Some are so soft that they are easily scratched.

Whenever you are not using the lens *for making an exposure,* cap it. If you remove the lens, cap both ends. This keeps dust from the surface of the lens.

Should dust settle on the lens glass, fan it off with a card held in the hand. While there is a danger of a lens brush scratching the glass, it can be used occasionally if one is very careful. Never touch the lens glass with your fingers as perspiration may etch the surface. If necessary, use special lens tissue dampened lightly with lens cleaner to remove any smudges remaining after a light brushing. Do not use

Fig. 239A.   Electric Solenoid Shutter Mounted Inside the Front Case (Courtesy Robertson Photo-Mechanix, Inc.)

Fig. 239B.   Electric Timer and Control Panel (Courtesy Robertson Photo-Mechanix, Inc.)

Fig. 240.   Manually-Operated Flashing Lamp Mounted on the Front Case (Shown Swung Over to Project Light Through the Lens) (Courtesy Robertson Photo-Mechanix, Inc.)

Fig. 241A.   Placing Copy in Copyboard

regular tissue or a handkerchief as these may be abrasive. Never dismantle a lens — leave this to a qualified lens mechanic.

When inserting (or removing) the lens assembly, hold one hand underneath the lens, and turn the lens into the mount with the other.

*Flashing Lamp.* A flashing lamp may be mounted on the front case of the camera for flashing halftones through a glass screen (Fig. 240). When a contact screen is used, a yellow safelight at the back serves this purpose.

### Copyboard (Gallery End)

The copyboard is a flat board usually equipped with a hinged glass cover, Figs. 241A and B. In use, the copyboard of a horizontal camera is turned to the horizontal, opened, and the copy positioned. The glass cover is closed and locked, and the copyboard is turned vertically to face the lens. A vacuum copyboard insures the copy being held tightly in a flat plane. An additional feature of some copyboards is shown in Fig. 242.

Here too, fingermarks, dirt and dust are objectionable, since they will be photographed just as the copy is. Handle the copyboard by the frame, keeping the fingers off the glass. If the glass is dusty, brush it with the camel's hair brush. If still dirty, clean it with a glass cleaner or, preferably, with a soft, clean cloth dampened with household ammonia. Clean both sides of the glass. It may be best to cover the glass when the camera is not in use.

*Lights.* There are several types of lights for the copyboard. *Incandescent bulbs* (photofloods) are weak in blue-white light so require long exposures. Also, except for the quartz-iodine type, they darken with use, further reducing efficiency. *Carbon arcs* give good light, but the open flame and dust may be objectional. *Pulsed xenon* (zee-on or zee-non) is an electronic flash which fires many times a second, giving good, clean lighting.

Some light arms are attached to, and move with, the copyboard. This is considered better than when the lights do not move with the copyboard (as on some vertical cameras), as distance to lights remains constant — though corrections can be made for this. When the distance between copy and lights increases, the illumination drops off rapidly: if distance doubles, lighting drops to one-fourth; if it triples, lighting drops to one-ninth.

Light reflectors must be kept dust-free. Do not touch lamp bulbs, especially the tubular, quartz-iodine type. Fingerprints may darken the bulb. When needed, all lamps should be

Fig. 241B. Foam Padding Behind the Glass Permits Holding an Object as Thick as an Open Book Flat in the Copyboard Plane (Courtesy Robertson Photo-Mechanix, Inc.)

Fig. 242. Transparency Opening in Camera Copyboard Permits Light to be Transmitted from Behind Transparent Copy (Courtesy Robertson Photo-Mechanix, Inc.)

replaced at the same time, to maintain equal illumination. Quartz bulbs should be handled with a cloth.

### Camera Back (Rear Case)

The camera back contains the following components, either as built-in devices or as separate accessories set in place as needed:

*The Ground Glass.* This device is used for focusing and adjusting the image prior to exposing the film.

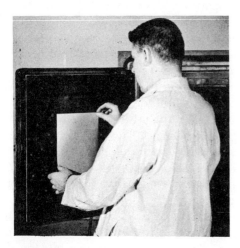

Fig. 243A. Loading the Film on the Vacuum Film Holder (Courtesy Robertson Photo-Mechanix, Inc.)

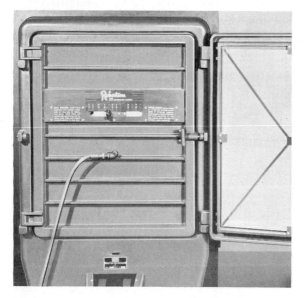

Fig. 243B. Vacuum Film Holder in Operating Position with Ground Glass Swung Out of Position (Courtesy Robertson Photo-Mechanix, Inc.)

*The Film Holder.* This component may be a coating of sticky, "stay-flat" solution on a flat surface, or it may be a vacuum film holder (vacuum back) which holds the film flat to its surface by means of suction generated by a vacuum pump. A vacuum film holder is a necessity for good work with contact halftone screens. See Figs. 243A and B.

On the simplest of cameras, contact screens may be used with a pressure frame, similar to a contact-printing frame. This consists of a board with a foam-rubber pad and a hinged glass cover. Exposure is made through the glass.

Gallery cameras which are used outside the darkroom, of necessity, must have a film holder which can be removed from the camera and taken into the darkroom for loading the unexposed film and for removing the exposed film. A thin, flat, metal slide passes through a slot in the film holder frame to cover the film entirely and protect it from the light. This cover is removed only during exposure of the film, and is replaced immediately after the exposure is made.

*Glass Halftone-Screen Device.* This may be a built-in device which lowers the glass halftone screen into position, allows it to be set for proper distance, and elevates it into a storage compartment when not in use. *Or,* it may consist only of screen bars in which the screen is mounted when needed and which can be adjusted toward or away from the film holder. Since the advent of the popular contact halftone screen (and its simpler procedures), glass halftone screens are found on fewer cameras.

*Bellows.* The bellows is that expanding box-like structure extending from the camera back to the front case (or lens board). It insures that only the light picked up by the lens is directed to the film in the camera. When periodically cleaning the camera, use a vacuum to remove any dust from inside the bellows. Do not handle the bellows; this might wear holes in the corners of the folds.

*Controls.* Most process cameras are equipped with two steel tapes or screws which have markings that indicate to the cameraman the proper position of the lens and of the copyboard for any reduction or magnification within the range of the camera (Fig. 244).

In addition to the automatic electric timer (mentioned above) for timing the exposures, the operator may have switches for controlling the vacuum pump for the vacuum film holder, and possibly one for the vacuum copyboard. See Fig. 245. A master switch should be provided for turning off all power to the camera when it is so desired.

## Setting the Camera for "Same Size"

The process camera is so designed that two distances can be varied: (1) bellows extension— the distance from the film holder (or ground glass) to the center of the lens — and (2) copyboard extension — the distance from the lens to the copyboard (perhaps actually measured as total distance from film to copy, minus the bellows extension). Variations in these distances produce an image (on the ground glass or film) which may be an enlargement, a reduction or the same size as the copy on the copyboard (Fig. 246).

To set the camera for 100% or for "same size" — that is, to set the camera so that the copy is reproduced as an image of the same size — adjust the copyboard extension and the bellows extension so that each is equivalent to two focal lengths (of the lens being used), as shown in Fig. 247. If focusing is done by predetermined markings on the camera, try using a tape measure to verify these measurements, so that you become more familiar with the focusing procedure.

Try this experiment: Set the camera to same size. Open the lens fully — smallest *f*-number. Place a piece of copy in the copyholder. Measure the height of the inverted and reversed image on the ground glass. Compare it with the height of the copy. Both should be equal. Check that the setting gives maximum sharpness by watching the image with a magnifying glass while shifting the copyboard slightly each way. If the images of the camera lights intrude on the image on the ground glass, move the offending light(s) outward to eliminate these "hot spots".

Unless you are told otherwise, position the camera lights at an angle of 45° to the centerline of the copyboard, and aim them at the

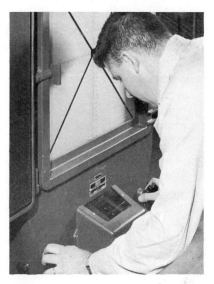

Fig. 244. Setting the Scales for Copyboard and Bellows Extensions (Courtesy Robertson Photo-Mechanix, Inc.)

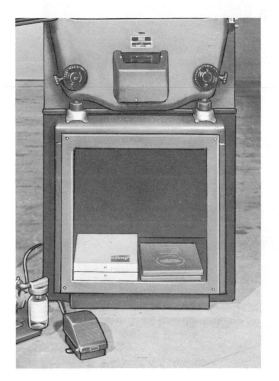

Fig. 245. Rear View (from Inside Darkroom) of Robertson "320" Process Camera (Courtesy Robertson Photo-Mechanix, Inc.)

centerline. (Refer again to Fig. 247.) Occasionally, a different pattern may give more even illumination. For example, for large pieces of copy, some cameramen leave the arms at 45°, but aim the lights at the far side of the copy, crisscrossing their pattern. A photoelectric exposure meter can be used to check evenness of illumination, athough this usually is not a problem when copy and negatives are small. It is best to check readings at the ground glass.

## Determining a Basic Exposure

Several factors, which may vary from shop to shop, must be controlled to produce a good negative: quality of copy, amount of lighting, exposure time, *f*-stop, focus, any enlargement or reduction, film type, developer, development time and processing temperature. Begin by varying only one factor, *exposure time*, and

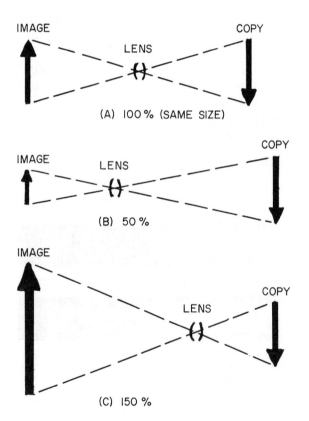

Fig. 246. On the Process Camera, Reductions and Enlargements Are Obtained by Changing the Bellows and Copyboard Extensions

hold all other factors constant and as ideal as possible. This will give a *basic exposure*, from which specific cases can be adapted.

To determine a basic exposure, use good *normal copy* (black type or lines with fine serifs, on bright white paper), with the camera set up for same size, as just described, and with the lens opening stopped down to the third-smallest *f*-number. For example, if the stops are *f*/11, /16, /22, /32 and /45, use *f*/22. This third stop should be close to the setting which gives the sharpest image and is often used.

Place the sheet of copy in the center of the copyboard, and place a sensitivity guide (gray scale) alongside the copy, as in Fig. 248.

With fresh film in the camera each time, make three exposures of the copy *including the sensitivity guide*, using a different length of exposure each time. Expose the first film for what you consider a normal exposure (say, 20 seconds); expose the second film for half that length (10 seconds); and expose the third for double the first (40 seconds). Use your normal film (for example, Kodalith Ortho, Type 3), and cut notches along the edge to identify each piece by its exposure time.

Develop the test films at the same time in fresh developer by the time-and-temperature method, as described in Chapter 11. Use the recommended developer and procedures — for example, Kodalith developer at 68°F., for

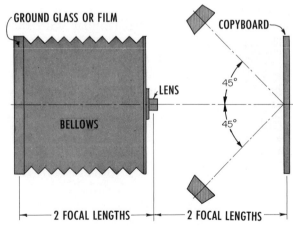

Fig. 247 Bellows Extension and Copyboard Extension for "Same-Size" Setting of Camera

2¾ minutes, with continuous agitation. After rinsing and fixing these films, examine them over a light table.

Determine from the test strips the exposure required to make Step 4 (of the sensitivity guide) just black, but leave Step 5 gray, or having only a few black specks. See Fig. 249.

If necessary, make further refinements in exposure time, until you get a good "Step 4" development. Record this time for future use. This is your standard basic exposure for normal copy at "same-size" reproduction.

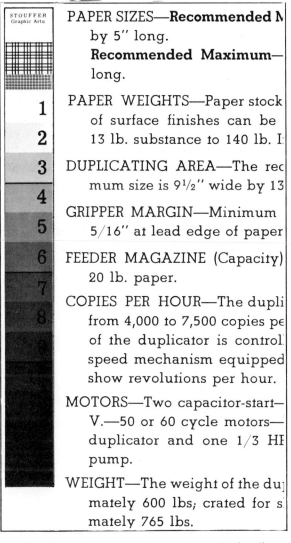

**PAPER SIZES—Recommended M** by 5" long.
**Recommended Maximum—** long.

**PAPER WEIGHTS—**Paper stock of surface finishes can be 13 lb. substance to 140 lb. I:

**DUPLICATING AREA—**The rec mum size is 9½" wide by 13

**GRIPPER MARGIN—**Minimum 5/16" at lead edge of paper

**FEEDER MAGAZINE (Capacity)** 20 lb. paper.

**COPIES PER HOUR—**The dupli from 4,000 to 7,500 copies pe of the duplicator is control: speed mechanism equipped show revolutions per hour.

**MOTORS—**Two capacitor-start— V.—50 or 60 cycle motors— duplicator and one 1/3 HF pump.

**WEIGHT—**The weight of the du] mately 600 lbs; crated for s mately 765 lbs.

Fig. 248. 12-Step Cameraman's Sensitivity Guide Shown Placed Next to Copy (Courtesy Stouffer Graphic Arts Equipment Co.)

## Determining the "Best f-number" of the Lens

Most lenses have a particular f-stop which will give the sharpest image. In determining the basic exposure, we assumed that the third stop was close to this best setting. You may wish to test this experimentally for your particular lens. All future exposures for line work could then be made using this same f-stop. This is referred to as the *constant-aperture system*.

To determine which aperture, or f-number, will give best results for your lens, set up the camera for "same-size" reproduction, as was done before. Place a page of fine (small) type matter in the copyboard. Make a series of exposures on different pieces of the film, using a different f-stop each time, beginning with the stop and the time determined for your basic exposure.

All exposures must be the equivalent of this basic exposure — each time the aperture size is doubled (next smaller f-number), the exposure time must be cut in half. When the aperture size is cut in half (next larger f-number), the exposure time must be doubled. For example, if the basic exposure has been found to be 20 seconds at f/22, then make your series of tests as follows:

f/11    5 seconds
f/16    10 seconds
f/22    20 seconds (basic exposure)
f/32    40 seconds
f/45    80 seconds

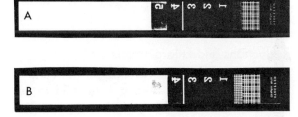

Fig. 249. Step-4 Development. (A) Step-4 development looks like this in the developer with overhead safelights, and appears about the same when cleared, dried, and placed on white paper and illuminated by overhead light. (B) **But** when viewed by transmitted light, Step 4 does not appear absolutely black. (Courtesy Stouffer Graphic Arts Equipment Co.)

In each of these combinations, the same amount of light is reaching the film, but note how much longer it takes to pass through the smallest opening ($f/45$). Notch each test sheet so it can be identified with its exposure.

Carefully develop this film by the "time-and-temperature" method, as was done for determining the basic exposure.

The sharpest image on the developed films indicates which of the $f$-stops is best for that particular lens.

If little difference is found in sharpness at various $f$-stops, then the most convenient combinations can be used. Times less than 10 or 15 seconds are difficult to duplicate exactly, and much longer than this becomes wasteful. If a range of $f$-stops produces a satisfactory image, then a *diaphragm control* (with its percentage settings) can be used to adjust the exposure for reduction and enlargement. This is called the *constant-time system*. Record your results for future use.

## Basic Camera Settings

Now that several basic camera settings have been determined, it will be well to post a chart next to the camera giving the *basic camera settings for same size*. These include:

(1) angle and distance of lights (if adjustable)
(2) best length of exposure for same size
(3) best $f$-stop
(4) bellows extension
(5) copyboard extension

## Reductions and Enlargements

Not all reproductions made on the camera are same size. Very often it is desired to enlarge or reduce an illustration or type matter to fit a given space or purpose. The camera is designed to reproduce any size image within its range, providing certain adjustments are made.

Most process cameras have markings for setting the desired reduction or enlargement. However, instructions are given here in setting the camera without the aid of these devices in order to better understand the process.

Setting the camera for either *enlargement* or *reduction* of the copy can be done by use of the following formulas, in the order given:

1.  Determine "M" (Magnification, for either a reduction or enlargement; 100% is same size.)

$$M = \frac{\text{Image (linear measurement)}}{\text{Object (linear measurement)}}$$

NOTE: Both linear measurements should be the same dimension (either the height or the width) and in the same units (picas or inches).

2.  Determine "CE" (Copyboard extension)

$$CE = FL + (FL \div M)$$

NOTE: FL is the symbol for focal length.

3.  Determine "BE" (Bellows extension)

$$BE = FL + (FL \times M)$$

NOTE: Check for focus on ground glass. The copyboard may be moved a bit to bring the image into perfect focus, if necessary.

4.  Find "F" (new "exposure-time factor")

$$F = \frac{(M + 1)^2}{4}$$

NOTE: F is the *factor* by which the basic exposure time for same size is multiplied to get an exposure time adjusted for the reduction or enlargement.

5.  Find new exposure time when distance of lights is changed.
    NOTE: Sometimes lights must be moved to the side to avoid "hot spots", or the lights do not move with the copyboard.

$$\frac{T_1}{(D_1)^2} = \frac{T_2}{(D_2)^2}$$

$T_1$ = Original time
$T_2$ = New time
$(D_1)^2$ = Original distance squared
$(D_2)^2$ = New distance squared

6.  Table 1 can often be used rather than steps 4 or 5 above.

## An Example in Setting the Camera

An actual problem in setting the camera for other than same size is worked out below. This example uses the constant-aperture system, and the exposure time is adjusted for the change in image size.

For this problem, certain information is assumed. Of course, in your situation, the information might be different. However, the problem would be worked out in the same manner.

### Basic Information

Focal length of lens is $10\frac{1}{2}''$
Best lens opening is $f/32$
Same size settings are:
     Lights at 45 degrees, $18''$ from center of copyboard
     Length of exposure is 2 minutes (120 seconds).

### The Problem

A photograph measuring $12''$ in height is to be reduced to $8''$ in height. Compute the necessary changes in the camera set-up and lighting.

### Table 1

#### Exposure-Time Factors For Various Degrees of Enlargement and Reduction

| Reproduction Size | Suggested Exposure-Time Factor | |
|---|---|---|
| | Lights Attached to Copyboard | Copyboard Moves, Lights Do Not |
| 200% | 2.40 | 2.00 |
| 175% | 2.00 | 1.70 |
| 150% | 1.60 | 1.40 |
| 125% | 1.30 | 1.20 |
| 100% | 1.00 | 1.00 |
| 90% | .92 | .92 |
| 80% | .85 | .84 |
| 70% | .75 | .75 |
| 60% | .68 | .67 |
| 50% | .60 | .60 |
| 40% | .52 | .55 |
| 30% | .44 | .50 |
| 20% | .38 | .50 |

(Courtesy Stouffer Graphic Arts Equipment Co.)

### The Solution

1. Find "M"

   (a) $M = \dfrac{\text{Image}}{\text{Object}}$

   (b) $M = \dfrac{8}{12}$ , or .67 (67%)

2. Find "CE"
   (a) $CE = FL + (FL \div M)$
   (b) $CE = 10.5 + (10.5 \div .67)$
   (c) $CE = 10.5 + 15.67$
   (d) $CE = 26.17''$

3. Find "BE"
   (a) $BE = FL + (FL \times M)$
   (b) $BE = 10.5 + (10.5 \times .67)$
   (c) $BE = 10.5 + 7.04$
   (d) $BE = 17.54''$

4. Find the exposure-time factor "F"

   (a) $F = \dfrac{(M+1)^2}{4}$

   (b) $F = \dfrac{(.67+1)^2}{4}$

   (c) $F = \dfrac{1.67^2}{4}$

   (d) $F = \dfrac{2.79}{4}$

   (e) $F = .697$, or .7
   (f) Basic exposure time is 120 seconds

$$\begin{array}{r} \times\ .7 \\ \hline 84.0 \text{ seconds} \end{array}$$

(exposure time adjusted for reduced image which concentrates light from copy)

5. If lights must be moved from their original distance of $18''$, to a new distance of $20''$ to avoid hot spots, what exposure time is necessary?

   (a) $\dfrac{T_1}{(D_1)^2} = \dfrac{T_2}{(D_2)^2}$
     substituting,

   (b) $\dfrac{84}{324} = \dfrac{T_2}{400}$

   (c) $324\,T_2 = 84 \times 400$

   (d) $T_2 = \dfrac{84 \times 400}{324}$

   (e) $T_2 = 103.7$, or 104 seconds

## Corrections Based on the Sensitivity Guide

It is a recommended practice to include a sensitivity guide (gray scale) along with the copy for every exposure. It is best placed in an open area near the center of the copy (and later blocked out), but may be included at the edge of solid copy. This serves as a general check on exposure, as well as a guide in developing. In addition, let us note here a possible special use for the sensitivity guide.

### Table 2

#### Critical Step on a 12-Step Scale For Various Types of Copy and Its Reduction or Enlargement

| Density of Copy | Reproduction Size | | |
|---|---|---|---|
| | 10-40% | 40-120% | 120-400% |
| EXTRA HEAVY COPY<br>  Black Bold type<br>  Etching Proofs<br>  Photo Proofs | 4<br>Black | 5<br>Black | 6<br>Black |
| NORMAL COPY<br>  Good black type proofs with<br>    fine serifs<br>  Pen and Ink Drawings<br>  Printed Forms | 3<br>Black | 4<br>Black | 5<br>Black |
| LIGHT COPY<br>  Gray Copy<br>  Ordinary Typewritten Sheets<br>  Printed Forms Light Lines<br>  Good Pencil Drawings | 2<br>Black | 3<br>Black | 4<br>Black |
| EXTRA LIGHT COPY<br>  Extra Fine Lines°<br>  Pencil Drawings<br>  Extra light gray copy. | 1-2<br>Black | 2<br>Black | 3<br>Black |

NOTE: Usually about two-thirds of all line copy can be processed as Step-4 copy. Other steps are for unusual situations. For proper contrast, normal film should develop in 2 to 3 minutes, and never more than 4 minutes. Step 4 requires a basic standard exposure, but exposure for other steps should be varied as indicated in Fig. 250.

°Difficult fine-line copy and extreme reductions can usually be improved using fine-line developer, or by still development (not agitated) in regular developer. (Courtesy Stouffer Graphic Arts Equipment Co.)

*Adjusting Development Time.* In determining the basic exposure, we used normal copy, same size, developed to a black Step 4 on the sensitivity guide, during the normal development time. It is possible to correct for both the density of the copy and for any enlargement or reduction simply by varying the *development time* enough to darken the negative to some other specific step on the gray scale. See Table 2. First, determine the column best describing the copy density; then locate the row giving the reproduction size. This gives the step to which the film should be developed. For example, normal copy at 100% size is still developed to Step 4, but typewritten copy reduced at 35% of original size is developed only to Step 2, while bold type being enlarged double size (200%) can be developed all the way to a Step 6. Without exposure correction, this last example would take an excessive development time.

*Adjusted Exposure Time Based on This.* It is recommended that *basic exposure time* be decreased for development to less than Step 4 and increased for development to more than Step 4. Fig. 250 shows negatives developed to various steps; at the left, are exposure-time factors for each step; and at the right, is an example of adjusted exposures if the basic exposure is for 20 seconds. For example, if Table 1 recommends a Step 3 development, multiply the basic exposure time by .71 (20 x .71 = 14.2 or 14 seconds). This adjusted exposure time will maintain a development time which is close to that recommended for normal copy at 100%, even though the negative is being developed to a different step from the normal Step. 4.

## Procedure for Shooting Line Copy

The following general procedures apply to almost any camera when making line negatives.

1. Clean the copyboard glass.
2. Place the copy in the copyboard.
3. Set the lens for the best *f*-stop. Remove the lens cap.

### DEVELOPMENT EXAMPLES

| A. EXPOSURE<br>Time Factors | | B. ADJUSTED<br>EXPOSURES<br>(Basic time = 20 sec.) |
|---|---|---|
| Step 1    35% | | 7 Seconds |
| 2    50% | | 10 |
| 3    71% | | 14 |
| 4   100% | | 20 |
| 5   141% | | 28 |
| 6   200% | | 40 |
| 7   280% | | 56 |
| 8   400% | | 80 |

Fig. 250. Exposure-Time Factors for Various Steps (with Development examples.) (A) Exposure factors (B) An example of the adjusted times. (Courtesy Stouffer Graphic Arts Equipment Co.)

4. Set the bellows extension and copyboard extension for desired magnification.
5. Check image for focus, size and lighting.
6. Estimate size of film needed, and cut to size.
7. Place film in camera.
8. Determine the exposure time, and expose the film.
9. Shut off lights, cap the lens, remove film.
10. Process the exposed film.

Exact procedures will vary, depending upon the type of process camera, and how the camera is equipped.

#### Procedure with Typical Darkroom Camera

The following procedure applies to most darkroom cameras equipped with the usual devices.

1. Clean the copyboard glass, inside and out.
2. Position the copy (inverted) in the center of the copyboard. Include a sensitivity guide (gray scale) at the edge of the copy or, preferably, in a gutter between columns of type. Place the copyboard in the exposure position. Set light carrier to 45° angle; aim at centerline.

3. Set the lens to the best *f*-number, or set the diaphragm control for the desired magnification on the proper scale. Remove the lens cap.
4. In the darkroom, set the control tapes for bellows and copyboard extensions according to magnification desired.
5. Turn off the overhead room lights, and turn on the safelights. (For Kodalith Ortho Type 3 Film, a Kodak Safelight Filter, Wratten Series 1A (light red) is recommended.)
6. Turn on the camera lights, and check for focus and size of image. To change the size of the image, move the copyboard; to sharpen the focus, change the bellows extension (or readjust CE). Check the focus with a magnifier, Fig. 251.

   If there are hot spots, move the lights until their image does not intrude on the image of the copy.
7. Determine the amount of film you will need.
8. Shut off the camera lights, and swing the ground glass out of position.

9. Remove a sheet of film from the light-tight storage, handling it by the edges, and cut from it the size piece you need. Return the extra film and *close the container*.

10. Turn on the vacuum back (or open the film holder). Holding the film by the edges, carefully place the film in the center with the emulsion side of the film facing you (and, ultimately, the lens). The film may be smoothed flat with the back edge of the palm of your hand — but avoid scratching the emulsion or making fingerprints on it.

    NOTE: The emulsion side is the lighter of the two sides. If the film sheets are notched by the manufacturer, the emulsion side will be facing you if the sheet is held by the notch on the top edge at the right-hand corner.

Fig. 251. Magnifiers: (a) Linen Tester; (b) Tripod Magnifier; (c) Swivel Desk-Stand Magnifier; (d) Pen-Clip Pocket Microscope; (e) Swivel Magnifier

11. Close the vacuum back (or position the film holder).

12. Set the timer for length of exposure desired, and make the exposure. The camera lights must be on during this time.

13. With the camera lights off, open the back. Remove the film (by the edges) by shutting off the vacuum or by stripping it from the adhesive coating.

14. The film is now ready for processing (developing). (See Chapter 11.) Cap the lens if no other shots are to be made.

### Procedure with Gallery Camera

The procedure for making line negatives with the gallery camera is substantially the same as that for the darkroom camera. Of course, since the gallery camera is located outside the darkroom, its film holder must be taken into the darkroom for loading the film and for removing the exposed film. An opaque slide is placed over the film after it is loaded in the holder. The holder is positioned in the camera just before the exposure, and the slide is removed only for the time of the exposure and is replaced before removing from the camera. Most slides are inserted in a reversed position, to indicate the film has been exposed. Silver-side out means unexposed film; black-side or marked-side out means exposed film.

## Colored Line Copy and Paper

Camera line copy which is in a color other than the usual black or which is not printed on white paper may be photographed to appear as though it were black-and-white camera copy by using a selected combination of filter and film.

### Film and Filter Combinations

Table 3 suggests combinations of films and filters to use for photographing the listed colors of the original copy. For example, camera copy consisting of a black ink printed on a yellow sheet may be photographed as though it were black ink on white paper by using a No. 16 Kodak Wratten Filter and Ortho film. (Where more than one filter is recommended, the first listing is preferred.)

## Table 3
### Film and Filter Combinations For Copying or Dropping Various Colors

| TO PHOTOGRAPH AS BLACK (to hold a color) use the film and filter* suggested below: | | | Color of Copy Being Photographed | TO PHOTOGRAPH AS WHITE (to drop a color) use the film and filter* suggested below: | | |
|---|---|---|---|---|---|---|
| Blue-sensitive Film | Orthochromatic Film | Panchromatic Film | | Blue-sensitive Film | Orthochromatic Film | Panchromatic Film |
| Not recommended | Orange (16) Yellow (15, 12) Green (61, 58) Yellow (9, 8) | Green (61, 58) | Magenta (process red) | No filter needed** | Can try: ** Blue (47B) Magenta (30) Blue (47) | Red (25, 29)** Magenta (30) Blue (47B) |
| No filter needed | Blue (47B) Magenta (30) Blue (47) | Blue (47B, 47) | Red or Orange | Not recommended | Not recommended | Red (29, 25, 23A) |
| No filter needed | Blue (47B) Magenta (30) Blue (47) | Blue (47B, 47) | Yellow | Not recommended | Orange (16) Yellow (15, 12) Green (61, 58) Yellow (9, 8) | Red (29, 25, 23A) Orange (16) Yel (15, 12, 9, 8) Green (61, 58) |
| No filter needed | Blue (47B) Magenta (30) Blue (47) | Magenta (30) Red (25) Blue (47B, 47) | Green | Not recommended | Orange (16) Yellow (15, 12) Green (61, 58) Yellow (9, 8) | Green (58) |
| Not recommended | Not recommended | Red (25) | Cyan (process blue) | No filter needed | No filter needed | Blue (47, 47B) |
| Not recommended | Orange (16) Yellow (15, 12) Green (61, 58) Yellow (9, 8) | Green (58) Red (25) | Blue or Violet | No filter needed | Magenta (30) Blue (47B, 47) | Blue (47B, 47) |

*Numbers are for Wratten filters, also known as follows: 8-K2, 9-K3, 15-G, 25-A, 29-F, 47-C5, 58-B, 61-N. Try in order listed; variations in color of copy and experience may suggest other filters.
**To drop magenta, it is best to use pan film and a No. 25 filter.                    (Courtesy Eastman Kodak Company)

There is a multitude of differences in shades of colors, and we do not all perceive colors the same. Experience may indicate other combinations than those listed. If so, post a record of satisfactory results for future use, showing samples of the copy, the numbers of the filters, the kind of film used, and the length of exposure or filter factor.

### Filters

Filters are of two forms — gelatin film and gelatin cemented between sheets of optical glass. They usually are square, 2″ x 2″ or 3″ x 3″, depending on lens diameter. The filter is inserted into the filter (Waterhouse Stop) slot of the lens barrel, or it is inserted into a filter holder mounted on the front of the lens barrel. As a precaution, check the focus carefully when doing critical work with filters. Also, close the filter slot (or place a piece of tape over it) when you are through using the filters.

### Filter Factors

A filter will transmit light of certain colors while it absorbs light of other colors, necessitating a lengthening of the exposure time. The correct length of exposure for each film and filter combination is determined by experimentation and manufacturer's suggested filter factors.

A factor of 2, for example, indicates that the standard exposure for that film and set-up should be multiplied by 2 (because of the filter interference).

### Questions

1. What is meant by "line photography"?
2. What is a "latent" image? What causes it on the film?

3. What happens in the development of the film?

4. Compare the appearance of the image on the ground glass with the appearance of the copy on the copyboard.

5. How does a vertical camera differ from a horizontal one?

6. How does the gallery camera differ from the darkroom camera?

7. What are the basic parts of the camera?

8. What precautions are observed in handling the lens?

9. If you had the choice of a camera with an 8½″ FL lens or one with a 16″ FL lens for a critical, large ruled form, which would you use and why?

10. What does "FL" mean? How is it defined?

11. Describe the copyboard. Tell how to care for it.

12. How is the film held in place on the camera?

13. What function is served by the "bellows"?

14. What may happen if the bellows develops a "leak"?

15. What kind and color of safelight should be used in the darkroom when handling undeveloped Kodalith Ortho Type 3 film?

16. On the ground glass, how do you make slight changes in the size of the image?

17. On the ground glass, how do you adjust for critical focusing?

18. What does the expression "same size" mean in photography?

19. Describe two methods for determining the emulsion side of a piece of unexposed film in the darkroom.

20. Why must a new exposure time be used if the distance of the camera lights is changed?

21. Name two basic systems for correcting for enlargement or reduction.

## Problems and Projects

1. Make a drawing showing the camera set-up for same size.

2. Determine the best length of exposure for same-size reproductions.

3. Determine the best *f*-number for the lens in your camera (as explained on page 121).

4. Make a chart showing the basic camera set-up for same-size reproductions. Include: BE, CE, angle and distance of lights, *f*-number to use and length of exposure.

5. Check your camera chart by setting up the camera according to your figures.

6. Using the instructions on page 122, find M, CE, BE, and F for the following:
   a. Copy 8 inches wide to be reduced to 6 inches wide.
   b. Copy 12 inches high to be reduced to 6 inches high.
   c. Copy 10 inches high to be enlarged to 11 inches high.

   Prove each problem by setting up the camera according to your calculations.

7. Write out an outline of the steps in shooting line copy, using the camera you will be using.

## New Words

| | | | |
|---|---|---|---|
| 1. | accessories | 24. | inserting |
| 2. | ammonia | 25. | intensified |
| 3. | aperture | 26. | inverted |
| 4. | components | 27. | latent |
| 5. | copyboard | 28. | linear |
| 6. | critical | 29. | magnification |
| 7. | definite | 30. | nodal |
| 8. | developed | 31. | normal copy |
| 9. | devices | 32. | objectionable |
| 10. | diaphragm | 33. | opaque |
| 11. | diaphragm control | 34. | projected |
| 12. | emulsion | 35. | rail |
| 13. | exposure | 36. | reflected |
| 14. | extension | 37. | reversed |
| 15. | filter | 38. | sensitivity guide |
| 16. | filter factor | 39. | sensitized |
| 17. | focal length | 40. | shutter |
| 18. | focused | 41. | solenoid |
| 19. | gallery | 42. | solution |
| 20. | gelatin | 43. | surfaces |
| 21. | gray scale | 44. | unreadable |
| 22. | image | 45. | vacuum |
| 23. | infinity | 46. | variation |

# Halftone

# Photography

Camera copy which contains *gradation of tone* (continuous tones) typically is reproduced by the halftone process, *i.e.*, by printing a broken pattern in which dots, though in an equally-spaced pattern, vary in size in different areas to give the illusion of lighter and darker tones.[1]

## Gradation of Tone

Gradation of tone is found in pencil drawings, original photographs (snapshots, portraits, landscapes, equipment, processes, etc.), oil paintings, watercolor renderings, lithographs, crayon art, etc. (See Fig. 199.) In each of these original pieces of camera copy, the tones vary — the elements of the illustration *are not all* either solid black or solid white. Rather, there is a gradual variation of tones ranging from the lightest parts of the illustration to the darkest. Examine a snapshot and you will see this *gradation of tone* (or *continuous tone*).

If we were to make a film negative on litho film from a continuous-tone original, using the same procedure as for line photography, the resulting film negative would have some clear and almost-clear areas, some dense and almost-dense areas, and, in the middle-tone areas, some spotty semi-opaque areas.

Now, if this negative were to be placed over a sensitized offset plate, and the plate then exposed and developed, those areas of the plate image which were produced by the semi-opaque negative areas would be washed away in the plate-developing process because of the underexposure. In other words, not enough light would pass through the semi-

opaque areas of the negative to harden or cause the necessary change in the plate coating. The result would be a disappointing loss in image detail on the plate, and, of course, this would be unacceptable for printing.

NOTE: If done intentionally, shooting "contrasty" halftone copy in the same manner as line copy (without a screen) may result in a printed illustration which resembles a black-and-white-ink-brush or line drawing, and which may be pleasing for some purposes. Try one. See Fig. 254. *Posterizing* is a similar process often printed in several blending colors — highlights, middle tones, and shadows are recorded on separate line-type negatives for printing in different colors.

### Optical Illusion

Most photographs which are used as illustrations in newspapers and textbooks are

[1]Though not now commonly used in any of the major printing methods, there are several reproductive processes which do reproduce shading as continuous tones rather than as a halftone dot pattern. The common *photographic print* (such as a snapshot or enlargement) is economically practical for copying when only limited quantities must be reproduced. The *collotype process* is an old established method of printing, but is limited largely to specialized work such as artprints. Collotypes are printed from a gelatin-type surface which absorbs varying amounts of moisture (and thus develops a varying resistance to being inked), so that continuous tones are transferred to the printed sheet. A new experimental printing plate for *screenless photo-offset* lithography uses a somewhat related system. In each of these three continuous-tone processes, the print can be enlarged five to ten times before the random grain pattern which produces the tones becomes readily apparent.

printed by the halftone process. Examine one (Fig. 255A) under a magnifier, and you will see that a printed halftone illustration is actually an *optical illusion.* There is no gradation of tone. Rather, the "picture" is composed of thousands of dots and checkerboard squares of varying sizes, as shown in Fig. 255B. Held

away from the magnifier, though, the printed halftone illustration *looks* like a picture. In fact, if the dot pattern is very fine, the printed halftone may closely reproduce most of the details of the original photograph. Note that in the fine screen of Fig. 255C, the stripes are clearer, and the line gauge and the type case label have become nearly legible. This is because there are 18,000 more dots than there were in Fig. 255A. The screen in Fig. 255C is also rather fine for the paper and printing process and each dot has spread slightly. This results in a slight grayish look and the reduced contrast which is characteristic of finer screens.

Fig. 254.   Produced by Photographing Continuous-Tone Copy without a Halftone Screen.

Fig. 255B.   Enlarged Portion of Fig. 255A.

Fig. 255A.   A 65-line Halftone Print.

Fig. 255C.   A 300-Line Halftone Print.

## Reflection of Light

Actually, our eyes see *reflected light*. Looking at a printed halftone, we see light reflected from the paper — not the black ink which merely serves to absorb light and control the reflection.

Areas of a printed halftone which are white (with extremely tiny staggered black dots) look to us as nearly white areas. If the black dots are larger, they cover more of the white paper, causing it to reflect less light, and so the appearance is gray. When the black dots are so large that they cover most of an area (leaving only tiny pinpoints of white paper) very little, or no, light is reflected, and our eyes see the darker portions of the illustration.

A dull-white paper reflects less light than a glossy-white paper. Yellow paper reflects less light than white paper, etc. The color and finish of the paper on which the halftone illustration is printed, then, may improve upon, or detract from, the final printed effect of a halftone illustration.

## Theory of Halftone Reproduction

The ink fountain of the offset press carries ink of a single tone of one color — for example, *black*. On the printed sheets of paper, then, the press can print only solid black dots, lines and areas, *or* it can leave an area of the paper blank.

To make a satisfactory offset printing plate which will reproduce the effect of a printed continuous-tone illustration, first the original continuous-tone illustration (camera copy) must be photographed in such a way as to produce a *film negative* composed of dense, opaque dots and squares and clear, transparent areas — no semi-opaque areas. Such a negative is called a "halftone negative".

The halftone negative is produced from continuous-tone camera copy (such as original photographs) by placing a halftone screen over the film in the camera before making the exposure.

When the exposure is made, light reflected from the copy (on the copyboard) passes through the camera lens and then through the tiny openings of the halftone screen, *before* it strikes the film emulsion where it causes a *latent image*[2] to be formed. When the film is developed and processed, the image is seen to be composed of *dots* — one dot for each opening of the halftone screen through which the light passed. Each screen opening acts as a tiny individual lens or film gray scale to produce its characteristic dot pattern on the film emulsion.

## Halftone Dots

The size of any individual black dot on the film emulsion is determined by the intensity of the light rays from a corresponding area of the copy on the copyboard, being focused through a single screen opening.

Since the original continuous-tone copy usually has a rather wide range of tones, the varying amounts of light (or intensities of light) which are reflected from the copy areas and pass through the screen openings, produce a range of dot sizes on the film. See Fig. 256.

The highlight (lightest) areas of the copy reflect the greatest amount of light, producing, on the negative, the largest black dots, which appear as black opaque areas or nearly so. These dots are so large and overlapping that they leave only tiny pinpoints of clear area on the film. This *darkest* area on the *negative* is called the *highlight area*.

The middle-tone (mid-tone) areas of the copy reflect a moderate amount of light, and so produce a checkerboard effect on the negative — alternating black and clear squares, whose exact size depends upon the shading of the copy mid-tone areas. These areas are called the *mid-tone areas* of the negative. The checkerboard pattern of the 50% tone is similar on either the negative or its print.

The shadow (darkest) areas of the copy reflect the least amount of light and thus produce, on the negative, transparent areas with tiny pinpoint black dots or, sometimes, no dots at all. The *lightest* areas on the *negative* are called the *shadow areas*.

[2]A latent image is present, but not visible until the film is developed.

Note that all the areas produced on the negative must be definitely *transparent* or

Fig. 256. Approximate Values of Halftone Dots (Enlarged): (A) Negative; (B) Print. In each of the above, the percentage figure indicates what percentage of the area is taken up by the black dots; 10% means that the black dots take up 10% of the total area; 90% means that the black dots take up 90% of the area, etc.

Note that a 10% highlight area on a print is produced from a corresponding area of the negative having a 90% dot. Actually, the black dots in the 90% area of the negative are so large that they overlap somewhat, leaving only a tiny white space (**or** dot) remaining.

definitely *black opaque*. The same high-contrast film as used for line photography is used for halftones, and there can be no semi-opaque or "brown" dots. When the halftone negative is used in exposing a plate, the transparent areas transmit light of equal intensity (though differing in size) to the sensitized coating on the offset plate. In the subsequent developing of the plate, then, all transparent areas will produce a hard, firm image area to print faithfully on the press.

### Possible Confusion

A comparison of the two sides of Fig. 256 should clear up any misunderstanding the beginner may have in referring to *shadow* and *highlight* areas of the halftone negative.

Remember that a negative is just the reverse of the printed illustration. Black on the negative becomes white when the work is printed, and clear areas become black.

In looking at a *halftone negative*, then, remember that the percentage size of the dots refers to the percentage of *black area on the film*.

On a *halftone print*, the percentage size of the dot refers to the *percentage of area covered by the ink*. For instance, a 30% dot means that the black dots cover 30% of the area on the print where they occur.

In Fig. 256, also note that a 10% shadow dot on the halftone negative will produce a 90% shadow dot on the halftone print; an 80% highlight dot on the negative will produce a 20% highlight dot on the print.

In summary, in black-and-white work: (1) halftone dots are always *black;* (2) on the negative, the size of the black dot is determined by the intensity of light from the reflected copy; and (3) the percentage size of the dot (whether on the film or printed paper) refers to the percentage of the area which is *black*.

### Screening Methods

Continuous-tone copy is broken into a halftone pattern by one of three techniques: (1) by passing the image through a glass halftone screen, (2) by passing the image through a flexible plastic contact screen, or (3) by making the exposure directly on a film which has a screen pattern built into its light sensitivity.

### Prescreened Film

This method involves the use of Kodalith Autoscreen Ortho film. This prescreened film allows halftones to be made in simple reproduction cameras which do not have either a glass screen or a vacuum back which would allow the use of a contact screen.

Also, this prescreened film can be exposed at the original scene in an ordinary press-type camera. However, with this latter technique, there are some important limitations: (1) a time exposure of about 10 or 15 seconds must be allowed, (2) the negative usually must be the same size, and (3) the original exposure must be correct. Such a technique works nicely for such uses as photographing houses for an economical listing published for real estate dealers. The resulting negative either can be stripped directly into the line negative for the type, or it can be printed photographically so the halftone can be pasted on with the type, and one line negative made of the composite. Either way, several steps are eliminated.

As this prescreened film is nearly double the cost of the usual litho films, its usage is somewhat limited to those places where its advantages are needed. In most commercial printing, either a glass screen or a contact screen is used. The latter type is quickly becoming the more popular for average work.

### Glass Screens

The glass screen (Levy screen) is the traditional halftone screen. It is made of two sheets of glass, each ruled in one direction with cut-in, parallel lines. The lines are filled with an opaque (light-stopping) material, and the two sheets of glass are then cemented face-to-face, with the lines on one at right angles to those of the other, Fig. 257A. In use, this screen is just enough ahead of the film that the screen casts a slightly fuzzy shadow. Dim reflections from the copy penetrate only the center of each shaded opening in the screen and, thus, make a small dot. Bright reflections penetrate more shadow, making a larger dot.

The spacing of screen rulings varies with reproduction requirements. Newspapers being printed by letterpress at high speed on rough paper use 65- or 85-line screens. Offset newspapers may use 110- or 120-line screens. For offset printing, 133-line is most common, with 120-line used for utility printing and 150-line used occasionally for top-quality work on gloss coated (slick) paper. Coarser rulings are easier to use but reproduce fewer details.

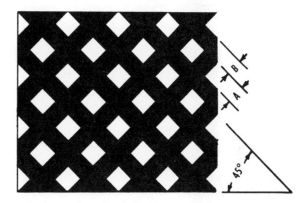

Fig. 257A. Enlarged Portion of a Glass Halftone Screen, 1 to 1 Ratio. Lines "B" and openings "A" are the same width. The number of diagonal lines per inch (counted at 45°) represents the ruling or lines per inch.

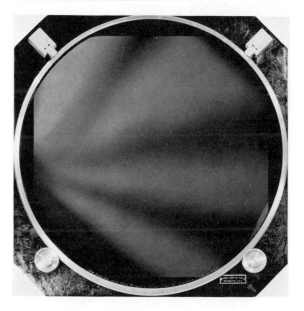

Fig. 257B. Circular Halftone Screen in Graduated Rotary Holder (Courtesy of Max Levy & Co.)

Circular screens, Fig. 257B, can be rotated to any angle. These are used in making the multiple halftone negatives needed for colored pictures. Process-color printing (for full natural colors) generally requires four separate printing impressions, each from a separate plate which prints a different color — usually yellow, magenta (process red), cyan (process blue), and black.

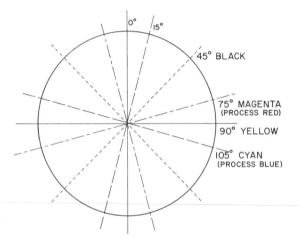

Fig. 258. Usual Angles for Printing Each of the Four Process-Color Plates.

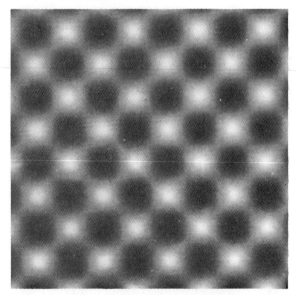

Fig. 259A. Contact Screen (Enlarged). Note that the vignetted dots form a 45° pattern. The number of dots in one inch, counted along a 45° line, represents the ruling, or lines per inch. (Courtesy Eastman Kodak Co.)

A halftone negative must be made for each color plate. When this is done, the screen angle is changed for each color negative so that, in printing, the dots of one color will not cover up the dots of another color. The usual screen angles are 90° for yellow, 75° for magenta (process red), 105° for cyan (process blue), and 45° for black. See Fig. 258. This explains the need for several angles, and more details of the process will be given in Chapter 10.

For halftones of a single color (black-and-white or any one color), the usual 45° angle is used as was shown in Fig. 257A. The pattern of the rows of dots is least noticeable at this angle. Rows are most visible at 90° (as vertical and horizontal lines), so this 90° position is reserved for the lightest color (yellow).

### Contact Screens

Contact screens for halftone photography are made of a flexible film support with a vignetted-dot pattern in the film emulsion. See Fig. 259A. These screens are used in direct contact with the film on the camera vacuum film holder. The emulsion side of the screen is positioned against the emulsion (dull) side of the film, and the contact screen is on the side toward the lens, Fig. 259B. They are available in screen rulings from about 65 lines per inch to 200 or more lines per inch.

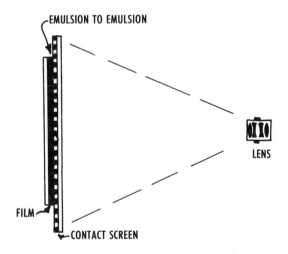

Fig. 259B. Camera Set-Up For Halftone Photography. Contact screen and film are placed in direct contact, emulsion to emulsion.

Some contact screens can be used for color-separation work, performing the same function as the glass screens. For this work, the camera copy or a single screen is rotated to the proper angle for each color, or separate screens with preangled patterns may be used for each separation.

*Theory.* Each vignetted dot (square) of the contact screen, as shown in Fig. 259A, varies in density from a tiny, almost transparent opening in its center to a surrounding almost-opaque area at its edge. Thus, in effect, each dot acts much as a film gray scale. A weak light will penetrate only the tiny center portion; a stronger light will pass through an increasing area; and an intense light will pass through a large portion.

*Types of Contact Screens.* A number of different types of contact screens are available, including: (1) *magenta contact screen for negatives,* which is recommended for making the usual halftone film negatives; (2) *magenta contact screen for positives,* which is recommended for making halftone film positives from continuous-tone negatives; and, (3) the *gray contact screen* for making black-and-white halftone negatives, but, more specifically, for *direct* color-separation negatives on panchromatic litho film from color copy.

The coloring of the magenta screen allows additional control of the range of tones of the halftone, and probably is most commonly used. Instruction here is primarily limited to the magenta screen.

*Care of Contact Screen.* Contact screens should be protected from scratches, dirt, and liquid stains. They should be handled only by the edges and kept in their original folders and cartons when not in use. They should never be handled with wet or damp hands, and never laid down on tables or counter tops.

The contact screen should be smoothed in place on the film holder, by covering it with a clean sheet of paper and rolling it flat with a soft rubber roller. If necessary, the screen can be dusted with a photo chamois — never with a camel's hair brush.

Liquid stains may be removed according to instructions packaged with the screen.

Screens may be taped into a cut-out area of a sheet of thin bristol board to facilitate handling. Each side of the screen can be identified for the beginner with a tape label: "Emulsion side — This side toward film" and "Base side — This side toward lens".

Small screens can be used by beginners. It is necessary only that the screen be about an inch larger in width and height than the film. Test the size with your particular vacuum-back settings to check that enough vacuum is developed to hold the screen tightly in place.

## Understanding Densitometry

Thus far we have seen how various tones can be reproduced by means of a halftone dot pattern and how the dots can be formed by various screening techniques. For tones to be reproduced *correctly,* however, it is necessary to understand more about tone variation and how it can be controlled. A brief explanation here introduces the basic concepts needed to produce better halftones, as well as those needed for understanding the information in your film and photographic manuals.

### Basic Terms

*Densitometry* is the measuring of the optical density (the degree of "blackness" or "light-stopping ability") of a particular tone area of a film negative or positive, of a photographic print, painting, or other tone copy, or of the printed reproduction. Density comes from the amount of developed silver or dye in the photographic process and from the amount of light-absorbing pigment in art processes and printing processes. In photography, densitometry is the practical application of *sensitometry* — the measuring of the sensitivity of a light-sensitive emulsion (on film or paper) to determine the characteristics of that emulsion.

The factors which can be measured in densitometry are opacity, density, transmittance, and reflectance. These will be defined first.

*Opacity* is the ability of a material (developed silver deposit, ink, dye, paper, etc.) to prevent light from passing through it. Opacity values are computed as follows:

$$\text{Opacity} = \frac{\text{Total amount of light that hits an area}}{\text{Amount of light that gets through that area}}$$

*or, again,*

$$\text{Opacity} = \frac{\text{Incident light}}{\text{Transmitted light}}$$

Opacity is expressed in decimal numbers from 1.00 (no opacity) to a practical point of 100.00 (which might seem quite opaque in normal light), to 1000.00 (at which only a very bright light might penetrate enough to measure).

*Density* means much the same as *opacity*, except it is measured on a different scale. This is the factor measured by a densitometer. Each reading obtained on the densitometer scale is actually an opacity reading, except that the density reading is expressed as a logarithm (to the base 10)[3] of that opacity. This gives smaller numbers and simpler calculations.

Fig. 260A illustrates density. Suppose that a sheet of film is opaque enough to pass only 1/10th of the incident light falling on it —

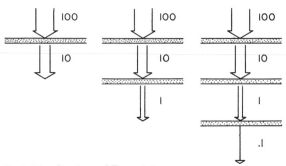

Fig. 260A.   Density and Transmission

[3]Abbreviated $log_{10}$. The log is the number of times the base numeral (10 in this case) must be multiplied by itself to give a certain number. Thus, the $log_{10}$ of 100 is 2 (10 x 10, or twice), and the log of 1000 is 3 (10 x 10 x 10). The in-between decimal steps can be computed mathematically. The scales on a slide rule are logarithmic. Log scales are such that succeeding steps are double the value of the preceding one (*i.e.*, ½, 1, 2, 4, 8, 16, etc.). Many factors for light, vision, and photography vary in such a geometric progression rather than a simple arithmetic progression (where each step has the same value — such as, 1, 2, 3, 4, or 5, 10, 15, 20).

reducing 100 units of light to 10. A second layer of this film doubles the density, but further reduces the 10 units of light reaching that layer to 1 unit. Three layers triples the density, but further reduces the light to .1 units. Thus, we see density is additive, but the effect is multiplied:

| Layers | Density | Light Passed | Opacity |
|--------|---------|--------------|---------|
| 0 | 0 | 100 | 1 |
| 1 | 1 | 10 | 10 |
| 2 | 2 | 1 | 100 |
| 3 | 3 | .1 | 1,000 |
| 4 | 4 | .01 | 10,000 |

Theoretically, the density numbers could continue indefinitely. However, for practical purposes, they run from 0.00 to a little less than 2.00 for light reflected from a print, and to nearly 3.00 for light transmitted through a negative or positive. At these upper points, there is so little light left that it is not very visible or even measurable.

*Transmittance* (or, transmission) is a percentage indicating how much of the light striking the surface (incident light) is transmitted (passed) through an area of the film negative or film positive (at 90°). If 1/20th of the incident light is transmitted, the transmittance is expressed as 5%. On a halftone negative, this would occur with 95% dots.

*Reflectance* is a percentage indicating how much of the exposure light (incident light) which strikes the surface is reflected from a tone area of, for example, a photographic print. See Fig. 260B. If only 1/10th of the

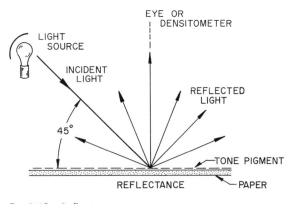

Fig. 260B.   Reflection

incident light is reflected, the reflectance is expressed as 10%, and the tone may be called a 90% (dark) gray. A black-and-white half-tone having a perfect checkerboard pattern (equal black and white squares) gives a 50% gray and, so, has a reflectance of 50%. However, its density (being measured on a different scale) is only about .30.

*Key points* (approximated slightly for clarity) show the basic relationships of density to transmitted and reflected light (and thus tones), and opacity.

| Density | Percent of Light (Gray Scale) | | (Halftone Dot Related to Col. 2) | Opacity |
|---|---|---|---|---|
| 0.00 | 100 | (clear or white) | 0 % | 1.00 |
| .05 | 90 | (light) | 10 % | 1.12 |
| .12 | 75 | (medium light) | 25 % | 1.32 |
| .30 | 50 | (middle tone) | 50 % | 2. |
| .60 | 25 | (medium dark) | 75 % | 4. |
| 1.00 | 10 | (very dark) | 90 % | 10. |
| 2.00 | 1 | (black and dense) | 99 % | 100. |
| 3.00 | .1 | (very dense) | 99.9% | 1000. |

The eye sees equal changes in *density* as equal steps in *tone*, and most gray scales are on this basis. The litho cameraman, stripper, and pressman usually think in terms of dot size, shown in column 3 (difference between column 2 and 100%). This is accurately measured on the density scale (column 1). It must be pointed out that there is no direct relationship between density and halftone dot percentage. Dot size also depends on film sensitivity and exposure. Note that a very small difference in density at the bright end of the scale makes a large percentage change in amount of light, but at the dark end of the scale, a much larger change in density is necessary to make a similar change in light.

Table 4 gives a more complete listing of tone factors. The interrelationships and conversion from one unit to another can be read directly from the table.

*Column "A" may be used for either reflection density or transmission density. For example — a reflection density of 0.15 (in column "A") indicates a reflectance of 70.79 percent (in column "B"); also a transmission density of 0.15 indicates a transmittance of 70.79 percent.
A density of 0.05 (in column "A") is read as an opacity of 1.12 (in column "C").

## Table 4
### Equivalent Density Factors

| Density (A)* | Transmittance or Reflectance (Percent) (B) | Opacity (C) |
|---|---|---|
| 0.00 | 100.00 | 1.00 |
| 0.05 | 89.13 | 1.12 |
| 0.10 | 79.43 | 1.26 |
| 0.15 | 70.79 | 1.41 |
| 0.20 | 63.10 | 1.59 |
| 0.25 | 56.23 | 1.78 |
| 0.30 | 50.12 | 2.00 |
| 0.35 | 44.67 | 2.24 |
| 0.40 | 39.81 | 2.51 |
| .45 | 35.48 | 2.82 |
| .50 | 31.62 | 3.16 |
| .55 | 28.18 | 3.55 |
| .60 | 25.12 | 3.98 |
| .65 | 23.39 | 4.47 |
| .70 | 19.95 | 5.01 |
| .75 | 17.78 | 5.62 |
| .80 | 15.85 | 6.31 |
| .85 | 14.13 | 7.08 |
| .90 | 12.59 | 7.94 |
| .95 | 11.22 | 8.91 |
| 1.00 | 10.00 | 10.00 |
| 1.05 | 8.913 | 11.22 |
| 1.10 | 7.943 | 12.59 |
| 1.15 | 7.079 | 14.13 |
| 1.20 | 6.310 | 15.85 |
| 1.25 | 5.623 | 17.78 |
| 1.30 | 5.012 | 19.95 |
| 1.35 | 4.467 | 22.39 |
| 1.40 | 3.981 | 25.12 |
| 1.45 | 3.548 | 28.18 |
| 1.50 | 3.162 | 31.62 |
| 1.55 | 2.818 | 35.48 |
| 1.60 | 2.512 | 39.81 |
| 1.65 | 2.239 | 44.67 |
| 1.70 | 1.995 | 50.12 |
| 1.75 | 1.778 | 56.23 |
| 1.80 | 1.585 | 63.10 |
| 1.85 | 1.413 | 70.80 |
| 1.90 | 1.259 | 79.43 |
| 1.95 | 1.122 | 89.13 |
| 2.00 | 1.000 | 100.00 |
| 2.05 | 0.8913 | 112.2 |
| 2.10 | 0.7943 | 125.9 |
| 2.15 | 0.7079 | 141.3 |
| 2.20 | 0.6310 | 158.5 |
| 2.25 | 0.5623 | 177.8 |
| 2.30 | 0.5012 | 199.5 |
| 2.35 | 0.4467 | 223.9 |
| 2.40 | 0.3981 | 251.2 |
| 2.45 | 0.3548 | 281.8 |
| 2.50 | 0.3162 | 316.2 |
| 2.55 | 0.2818 | 354.8 |
| 2.60 | 0.2512 | 398.1 |
| 2.65 | 0.2239 | 446.7 |
| 2.70 | 0.1995 | 501.2 |
| 2.75 | 0.1778 | 562.3 |
| 2.80 | 0.1585 | 631.0 |
| 2.85 | 0.1413 | 708.0 |
| 2.90 | 0.1259 | 794.3 |
| 2.95 | 0.1122 | 891.3 |
| 3.00 | 0.1000 | 1000.0 |
| 3.05 | | 1122.0 |

*Transmission density* and *reflection density* are readings taken by transmittance or reflectance which are adjusted for variation in the light source. They eliminate light intensity as a variable so that all tone values are expressed as relative to a set zero point.

*Transmission density* readings are used with negatives and positive transparencies.

*Reflection density* is a density reading of reflectance from a print or from artwork which is illuminated by a light at 45°, and measuring the light which is reflected 90° to the surface, Fig. 260B. The actual amount of reflectance varies with brightness of the illumination. It also is affected by the overall color and surface of the paper, as well as the tone in a specific area. Bright white and a glossy-coated finish on the paper are capable of more reflection. When the blank paper or an extreme highlight is used as the zero point on the density scale, all other tone values are expressed in relation to that point. Sometimes a block of white magnesia chalk is used for a standard zero reference point.

*Density Range.* Subtracting the minimum density from the maximum density of a negative or print gives us the *density range* of that item. Thus, density range is an indication of the amount of "contrast" in the negative or print. The term *density range* sometimes is used when referring to color materials and the term *density scale* when referring to black-and-white materials. Actually, they have the same meaning.

### Compressing the Density Range

A major problem in reproducing halftones is that the density range of the original photograph is usually more than that which can be printed by any process. Also, no print (even photographic ones) can produce the range of tones on a negative or transparency which is visible by transmitted light. With printed reproductions, whites are not quite as bright and blacks tend to be grayer, even under ideal conditions. Furthermore, if the printing ink is too light, there will be no blacks; if it is too heavy, the dots spread, the screen pattern clogs in shadow areas, detail is lost, and tones become darker throughout the scale.

Good original photos may have a density range of 1.70 to 1.80. A typical halftone is limited to a specific density range of less than 1.40 — perhaps as low as 1.10. If only a single exposure is used (as for line copy), detail at one of the two ends of the scale would be lost — or some from each end. Supplementary exposures can compress the excess density into the range which can be reproduced with specific papers, inks, processes, presses, etc. Both the main and the supplementary exposures vary with tonal range of the copy. Without the use of densitometric controls, each exposure requires a number of trial exposures to determine the right combination (or to develop enough judgment to make even approximate guesses).

### Classes of Copy

*Ideal photographic copy* normally should have a full range of tones which blend together smoothly. The photo should not appear *flat* and grayish, nor overly *contrasty* — with strong shadows and expanses of pure white. Several special types require extra care to reproduce the original effect. *Low-key photos* (such as a night street scene in the rain) have mostly blacks with only a few or weak highlights. *High-key photos* (light-colored objects in bright, flat lighting and white background)

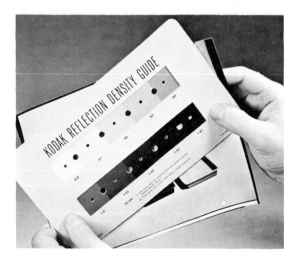

Fig. 261A. Calibrated Gray Scale Used as a Simple Densitometer (Courtesy Eastman Kodak Co.)

have many highlights and only a few or weak shadows. To maintain these special ranges of tone, the white border or a black patch should be used to determine what the full range would be normally.

*Drop-out halftones* are purposely slightly overexposed (or otherwise processed) to completely eliminate highlight dots — for example, to drop any tone around an outlined machine.

## Densitometers

A densitometer is a device for measuring optical density. The most inexpensive tool for this purpose is a *calibrated gray scale* with the density of each step labeled. This should be a 10- or 12-step scale with about .15 or .20 density change between steps. Accuracy can be improved by punching small holes in the middle of each step and between steps to limit the area of the copy being measured. (See Fig. 261A.) This is a big improvement over guessing at tone values. Accuracy is limited to about .10 units, and an individual's visual judgment is still quite a factor.

*Visual types* of densitometers (Fig. 261B) refine the gray scale technique. These use a system of lenses to superimpose a small circular area of tone from the copy directly into a calibrated continuous gray scale (the steps blend together). Readings can be made in .01 units, but visual judgment is still somewhat a factor, as individual readings may vary a few points, and colors are a problem. Cost of this type usually is under $100.

*Photoelectric types* of densitometers (Fig. 261C) are more accurate and reliable because they eliminate personal variation, are usable with filters for color, are read much more quickly, and have many additional applications. However, the cost is perhaps four to eight times as much as visual types, so they are used only when these advantages are needed.

*Transmission, Reflection, and Combination Units.* Either the visual or photoelectric types can be designed to measure transmission density, reflection density, or both. Transmission readings are used for negatives and positives,

so the units must have a light under the copy stage, and reflection readings require a top-lighted stage. Combination units require both lighting systems so are more expensive. See Fig. 261C. Most units are purchased for use at a particular work station, so this would mean using a reflection unit for copy and a separate transmission unit for negatives.

*Uses of Densitometers.* Our primary interest here is using the densitometer to measure the density range of tone copy and, perhaps, to check the halftone negative made from that copy. Advanced manuals or the instruction book for your densitometer will give details for many additional uses. Some of these uses are:

(1) to check camera lighting for level and evenness, (2) to determine camera exposures for changing conditions, (3) to determine ex-

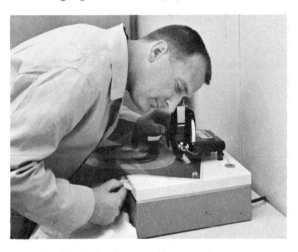

Fig. 261B.  Visual Densitometer (Courtesy Eastman Kodak Co.)

Fig. 261C.  Photoelectric Densitometer — Combination Unit for Both Transmission and Reflection Readings (Courtesy Welch Scientific Co.)

posure factors for colored filters used on the camera, (4) to check evenness of image at camera back, (5) to determine exposure times for continuous-tone photo prints, (6) to determine percentage grayness or percent dot, (7) to check ink level on press sheets, (8) to calculate exposures for color correction masks and separation negatives in process color work (see next chapter), (9) to check on amount and purity of process color inks, (10) to check trapping of one color over another in multicolor work, and (11) to determine paper opacity and brightness. Thus, it can be seen that the densitometer is a basic tool in quality-control work for graphic processes.

### Film Sensitivity

To obtain a full range of tones, both the exposure and development of film (or any photographic emulsion) must be controlled and correct. A knowledge of three important factors related to sensitivity will give a better grasp of the process. The first of these is the *contrast* of the film, as shown by the characteristic curve. The second factor is the *color sensitivity* of the film, as indicated by the terms blue-sensitive, orthochromatic, and panchromatic. The third factor is *film speed*, as indicated by the exposure index.

*Characteristic Curve.* A characteristic curve (Fig. 262A) illustrates graphically the *contrast characteristics* of a photographic emulsion under controlled conditions of exposure and processing.

In constructing a characteristic curve, a series of points is plotted on a graph. Each

individual point represents the density obtained by a series of exposures on a particular film or paper by means of a specific development technique. Each exposure is double the previous one, but the spacing on the graph paper is the same between each step. So the graph scale for *exposure* actually is *logarithmic* (rather than arithmetic, where the spacing would also double each time). This bottom scale often is labeled "Log Exposure," or "Log E." A line is then drawn through the plotted points, resulting in the *characteristic curve* — also called the *H & D curve*[4], *Density — Log E curve, D—Log₁₀E curve, or sensitometric curve* — for that particular film or paper. Such a curve also can be made by copying a step tablet (paper gray scale) and plotting the original density of each step (vertical scale) against the density of that step on the copy (horizontal scale).

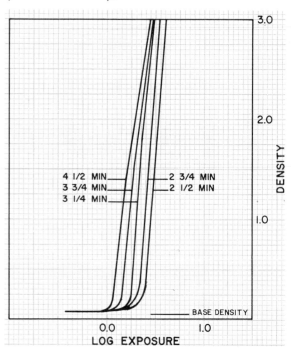

Fig. 262B. Curves for Kodalith Ortho, Type 3 Film. This is an improved extra high-contrast film. (Exposed to arc light, developed in Kodalith Super Developer with continuous agitation at 68° F. for the five times shown.) Zero point on exposure scale is recommended exposure.

[4]Named after Hurter and Driffield who originally proposed this curve in 1890.

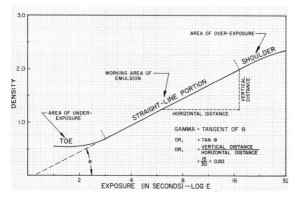

Fig. 262A. Characteristic Curve and Its Parts

Notice, in Fig. 262A, the three portions of the curve: the *toe portion*, the *straight-line portion*, and the *shoulder portion*. In the curved sections, there is a changing relationship between density and exposure; however, in the straight-line portion, there is a constant relationship — a corresponding increase in density for each increase in exposure time.

The *steepness* (or *slope*) which the straight-line portion of the curve forms with the horizontal edge of the graph is referred to by the Greek letter *gamma* ($\gamma$). Gamma indicates the *contrast* obtainable with that emulsion *(due to development)*.

The characteristic curve (sensitometric curve) for a typical litho (very high-contrast) film is shown in Fig. 262B. Litho film is a type intended for reproducing line and halftone copy (for making printing plates by almost any printing process). It has a rather steep straight-line portion, and so is said to have a *high gamma*. A relatively small exposure change results in a great increase in density. This sharp jump in density gives a clean break between image and non-image areas in reproductions. While not the recommended use, this same film can be used for medium-contrast continuous-tone copying through changing the development by diluting the developer to half

strength and increasing the time to 10 to 15 minutes.

Continuous-tone film, such as that used for snapshots, has a low sloping straight-line portion on its characteristic curve so it is termed a *low gamma* (or *medium contrast*) film. See Fig. 262C. The low slope of the straight-line portion of the curve indicates only a moderate increase in density for a wide range of exposures and, so, would reproduce faithfully a wide range of smooth gradation of tone from continuous-tone copy.

Gamma may be computed as indicated in Fig. 262A. A quick calculation can be made by dividing the number of vertical spaces by the number of horizontal spaces, as shown also in the same illustration.

*Color Sensitivity.* The color sensitivity of films is shown in the form of *wedge spectrograms* in film data books (Fig. 263). The height of the white patch in the spectrogram indicates the sensitivity of the emulsion to the various colors (provided the same kind of exposure light is used). Only the three main or primary colors of light (red, green, blue) are labeled. Yellow is located where red and green

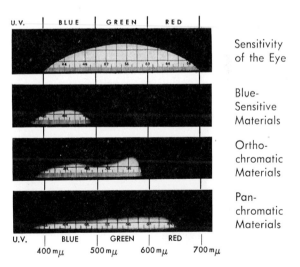

Fig. 263. Color-Sensitivity Classes for Photographic Emulsions. Blue-sensitive materials have only the near-ultraviolet and blue sensitivity inherent in every silver-halide emulsion. Orthochromatic materials have this sensitivity plus high green sensitivity. Panchromatic materials have a wide sensitivity which approximates that of the human eye.

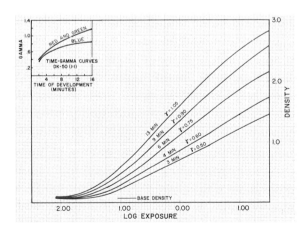

Fig. 262C. Curves for Super-XX Pan Film. This is a medium-contrast film for continuous tone use. Note gamma of each curve. (Exposed to arc light through a process lens and Wratten filter No. 25, developed in DK-50 (1:1) with continuous agitation at 68° F. for the five times shown.)

merge; violet is the left part of the blue band (next to the ultra-violet, U.V., light which is invisible to the eye). There is a more detailed discussion of the nature of color in the next chapter.

*Blue-sensitive films* (sometimes called "color blind" films) are sensitive only to blue light, and are blind to the other two-thirds of the spectrum — the greens, yellows, and reds. This is very convenient in the darkroom, because a relatively-bright (yellow or red) safelight can be used for general illumination and the film will not be fogged. Such film commonly is used for making a contact copy of an existing negative. Most photographic papers for contact printing and enlarging have a similar sensitivity. If blue-sensitive film is used to photograph an original scene or colored copy, only the tones containing blue will appear in their natural shades of gray. Green foliage or red lips, for example, will appear unnaturally dark.

*Orthochromatic films* (sometimes called "red-blind" films) are sensitive to blues, greens, and yellows, and are blind only to red light. Thus a red safelight can be used in the darkroom, which gives enough light for most camera and developing work. So ortho films

Fig. 264.   Halftone Negative (L) and Print (R) Showing Effect of Adding a Flash Exposure. The upper-left half of the negative received no flash; the lower-right half received normal flash exposure. Note how the shadow dots in the darkest portion of the lower-right half of the print (produced from the shadow dots in the corresponding part of the negative) bring out added detail.

are the standard film for copying black-and-white copy — the increased sensitivity allows the use of a magenta contact screen, exposures to yellow light to compress the density range of halftones, as well as some color variation in copy and in special copy preparation techniques. (Red transparent overlays photograph as black.)

*Panchromatic films* are sensitive to all colors and reproduce tones in shades of gray which appear in a natural relationship to each other. However, the film must be handled and developed in total darkness, which is not convenient unless the process is completely automated (as in modern development of snapshots). In printing work, pan film is used to reproduce colored copy in tones of a single color, especially when it is necessary to distinguish between reds and blacks. It also is used with colored filters (especially reddish ones) to emphasize or drop out certain colors on the copy. Its largest printing use is in color-separation work for process color reproduction in full, natural color. Special pan films are available for this purpose.

*Film Speed.* Films vary considerably in the amount of light they need. "Fast films" require very little light — a small diaphragm opening, a short exposure. "Slow films" require longer exposures and larger diaphragm openings to admit more light. Each film has an A.S.A. exposure index number which makes exposure calculations more exact. A film with an exposure index of 10 will require twice as long an exposure as one with an index of 20. There are separate indexes for white light (daylight and arcs) and for tungsten bulbs (which give reddish light). Very fast films tend to be more grainy, but this is no problem in reproduction work because the films generally are quite slow.

*Typical Examples.* It should be noted that contrast, color sensitivity, and film speed are independent of each other. For example, high-contrast (litho) films are available in each of three types of color sensitivity, and the same is true of medium-contrast (commercial) films. Some specific examples are:

| Film | Contrast | Color Sensitivity | Film Speed Arc | Film Speed Tung-sten |
|---|---|---|---|---|
| Kodalith Ortho, Type 3 | very high | orthochromatic | 10 | 6 |
| Kodak Commercial Ortho | medium | orthochromatic | 80 | 25 |
| Kodalith Pan | very high | panchromatic | 40 | 32 |
| Kodak Super-XX Pan | medium | panchromatic | 125 | 80 |
| DuPont Cronar Blue Sensitive Contact Film | high | blue sensitive | contact speed | |
| Dupont Direct Positive | very high | (special sensitivity for direct duplicates, see instructions) | | |
| Kodak Autopositive | high | | | |

## Making a Single-Color Halftone Negative

NOTE: The use of only the magenta contact screen is included in this book, though the gray screen can be used in almost the same manner. The glass screen is much more expensive, and its use is more complex, but its use follows the same general procedure.

Highly skilled operators employ a number of methods in making halftone negatives. It is suggested that the beginner master the method presented here — the "two-part" method (a white-light detail exposure and a flash exposure), in which the film is given, first, a *detail (main) exposure* with white light and, then, a *flash exposure* from a yellow flashing lamp. See Figs. 264, 265, and 268. (This second exposure is called the *flash* exposure. It serves to add some dot pattern in shadow areas, as well as to improve detail thereby lightening the dark end of the scale. This essentially compresses the density range to that which can be printed.)

Exposure times will be determined by using a Kodak Graphic Arts Exposure Computer[5]. These will be based on density readings of the copy, made with a densitometer or the Kodak Reflection Density Guide (which is essentially the simplest form of such a tool). Hereafter, these will be called simply the "Exposure Computer" and the "Density Guide".

[5]The exposure procedures and illustrations are from the Kodak publication, "How to Use the Kodak Graphic Arts Exposure Computer."

### Basic Procedure

For your copy, select an original glossy photograph with good contrast, about 4″ x 5″ to 8″ x 10″. (Positioning the copy upside-down on the copyboard will cause the image on the ground glass to appear right-side up.) For whatever size film is being used, select and use a contact screen which will extend sufficiently (generally, an inch or more) beyond the film on all sides, to insure good vacuum.

Blow the dust off the camera lens (with your breath), and clean the copyboard glass free of smudges, fingerprints and dust. Prevent overhead room lights and window light from striking the camera and copyboard (to eliminate unwanted reflection).

The following are the general steps in making a halftone negative:
1. Make density readings of highlight and shadow areas of copy; determine main and flash exposures.
2. Place the copy in the copyboard.
3. Set the lens opening, lights, and bellows and copyboard extensions for the magnification desired.
4. Focus and adjust for best image.
5. Place a sheet of unexposed film (such as Kodalith Ortho Type 3) on the vacuum

Fig. 265. Camera Lens Board Assembly with Lens Mounting on 3-way Turret Lens and Automatic Flashing Lamp, Controlled from Within the Darkroom (Courtesy Consolidated International Equipment and Graphic Supply Co.)

back of the camera, emulsion side of the film toward the operator and, ultimately, toward the lens. (The emulsion side of the film is the lighter side. This is easily determined in the darkroom with only the safelight on.)

6. Clean the contact screen with a photo chamois, and place the screen over the film with the emulsion (dull )side in contact with the film.

NOTE: To insure close contact between the film and the contact screen, it is recommended that a camera with a vacuum film holder be used.

7. Remove the lens cap and make the exposure. (This exposure of the film through the lens is called the *detail (main) exposure.*)

8. Open the camera back and expose the film set-up (screen still in place) to a flashing lamp.

9. Process the film.

### Use of the Exposure Computer

A *magenta contact screen (negative)* — which has highlight contrast improvement built in — or a *gray contact screen* is recommended for making halftone negatives. However, the magenta contact screen (positive) may better suit particular situations. This magenta screen is quite similar to screens previously designated by the manufacturer (Kodak): "For Photolithography."

There are several satisfactory ways of controlling contrast with contact screens. (1) The *shadow flash exposure* technique is the simplest. (2) The *highlighting* (or *bump exposure*) method can be used to increase highlight contrast, or even drop out highlight dots[6]. (3) *Still development* will lower contrast while improving definition. (4) The magenta screens can be used with *filters* (yellow for lower contrast and magenta for higher contrast).

The main exposure, as well as the flash (with or without highlighting) can be determined

Fig. 266. Kodak Graphic Arts Exposure Computer, Shown with the Included Kodak Reflection Density Guide, and Instruction Manual. (Courtesy Eastman Kodak Co.)

[6]When increased highlight contrast is needed for making halftone negatives, an additional *highlight bump exposure* is made with the film in place on the vacuum back, but *without the screen;* this is usually 5% to 10% of the detail exposure. The screen is then placed in position, and the detail and flash exposures are made. This highlight bump exposure to the copy without the screen adds light selectively — a lot to the highlights, less to the middle tones, almost none to shadows.

Fig. 267. Making the Detail Test Exposure. Use the Kodak Reflection Density Guide as copy and make a detail test exposure through a contact screen, keeping covered a one-inch edge strip of the film. (Courtesy Eastman Kodak Co.)

by using the Exposure Computer and the Density Guide (Fig. 266).

### Calibrating the Computer

The Exposure Computer must be calibrated for the type of contact screen and for the particular conditions and equipment. This is done by making a two-part test negative, the parts furnishing the calibration for what may be called a "detail" exposure and another for the "flash" exposure. After calibration, the computer is set for the particular conditions of use and usually will need no further calibration unless the camera lens, lighting conditions, screen, or type of developer is changed. If your standardized conditions change, simply repeat the following procedure.

*(1) Make the detail exposure (test).*

Mount the Density Guide on the camera copyboard (Fig. 267). Using Kodalith Ortho Film, Type 3 (and with contact screen in place over the film), make a same-size (100 percent) halftone negative of the guide; use a lens opening of $f/16$ (or an aperture ratio number of 32). First, cover up a 1-inch-wide strip of the edge of the film by taping opaque paper over the film and screen. Then, on the uncovered portion, make a single ex-

posure with all-white light through the screen. This should be 20 seconds when using two 35-ampere arc lamps at 48″ from the copy. (If your lighting set-up is different, increase your exposure to about 4 times that which you normally use for same-size line work with arc or pulsed xenon lights, and 6 to 8 times with incandescent bulbs.)

*(2) Make the flash exposure (test).*

a. Set up a lamp suitable for flashing in the camera darkroom, as shown in Fig. 268. This lamp, positioned 6 to 8 feet from the camera back, has a safelight filter, Wratten Series 00, and a 7½-watt frosted lamp in a darkroom lamp. A Wratten Series OA safelight filter can be substituted, but since it transmits less light than the Series 00, it should be used with a 60-watt frosted lamp at a distance of 4 feet and with about twice the exposure needed with the Series 00 filter.

b. *Uncover the covered area* and cover the exposed area on the test negative. With the contact screen still in place, and using several different exposure times shown in the left column of the flash exposure table on the computer (Table 5), make a series of separate flash exposures — such as 16, 24, 30, 40, 60 seconds.

### Table 5
#### Determining The Shadow Flash Exposure

| Basic Flash Exposure in Seconds* | Flash Exposure Times in Seconds for Excess Density Range | | | | | | | | |
|---|---|---|---|---|---|---|---|---|---|
| | 0 | 0.1 | 0.2 | 0.3 | 0.4 | 0.5 | 0.6 | 0.8 | 1.0 |
| 16 | 0 | 3½ | 6 | 8 | 9½ | 11 | 12 | 13½ | 14½ |
| 18 | 0 | 4 | 7 | 9 | 11 | 12 | 13½ | 15 | 16 |
| 20 | 0 | 4 | 7½ | 10 | 12 | 13½ | 15 | 17 | 18 |
| 22 | 0 | 4½ | 8½ | 11 | 13 | 15 | 16½ | 18½ | 20 |
| 24 | 0 | 5 | 9 | 12 | 14½ | 16 | 18 | 20 | 22 |
| 26 | 0 | 5½ | 10 | 13 | 15½ | 17½ | 19½ | 22 | 23½ |
| 28 | 0 | 6 | 10½ | 14 | 17 | 19 | 21 | 23½ | 25 |
| 30 | 0 | 6½ | 11 | 15 | 18 | 20½ | 22½ | 25 | 27 |
| 35 | 0 | 7 | 13 | 18 | 21 | 24 | 26 | 29 | 32 |
| 40 | 0 | 8 | 15 | 20 | 24 | 27 | 30 | 34 | 36 |
| 45 | 0 | 10 | 17 | 23 | 27 | 31 | 34 | 38 | 41 |
| 50 | 0 | 11 | 19 | 25 | 30 | 34 | 38 | 42 | 45 |
| 55 | 0 | 12 | 20 | 27 | 33 | 37 | 41 | 46 | 50 |
| 60 | 0 | 13 | 22 | 30 | 36 | 41 | 45 | 50 | 55 |
| 70 | 0 | 15 | 26 | 35 | 42 | 48 | 53 | 59 | 63 |
| 80 | 0 | 17 | 30 | 40 | 48 | 54 | 60 | 67 | 72 |

*Flashing-lamp arrangements which give basic flash exposures of less than 16 seconds are not recommended unless accurate timing devices are used, in which case this table can be expanded easily. For example, the times for a 14-seconds basic flash would be ½ those in the 28-second row; the times for 10 seconds, basic flash, ½ those in the 20-second row, etc. (Courtesy Eastman Kodak Co.)

*(3) Process the test negative.*

· a. Develop the resulting halftone negative for 2¾ minutes in Kodalith developer at 68° F. with continuous agitation. *Keep all processing absolutely consistent in making test negatives.*

b. Examine the negative of the gray scale. Its highlights should be at least as closed up as normal highlight dots (as in the second step of Fig. 269). If they are not, another negative should be made with more exposure. Shadow dots will be missing in areas of the negative representing the darkest steps of the gray scale (as in next to last step of Fig. 269). Locate the step which gives good highlight and the step which gives good shadow dots. Note the *density* of the corresponding steps on the Density Guide. For example, in Fig. 269, the second step was chosen as a good highlight dot, and halfway between the seventh and eighth steps, as a good shadow dot. Thus, in this case, a good highlight dot is produced from a step in the gray scale having a density of 0.21, and a good shadow dot is produced in the step which has a density of 1.31 in the original. Subtracting one from the other, we arrive at a *basic density range* of 1.10. This means that a single white-light exposure will make a good negative from copy having a density range of 1.10. In practice, it

may be found that the correct size of dots will fall between two steps of the density guide. If this happens, estimate what the density steps would be. A densitometer will give more exact readings.

*(4) Set the computer.*

a. Rotate the dials on the computer so that the 100-percent (same-size) magnification is opposite the aperture number $f/16$, as illustrated in Fig. 270.

b. Hold the bottom dial of the computer and rotate the top red "density" dial so that the density value of the step of the Density Guide which produced a satisfactory highlight dot (in this case, a density of 0.21 on the original) is opposite the exposure time of 20 seconds used in making the test negative. The dials are now set for computing detail exposure times for making halftone negatives of new copy at various sizes and apertures. A small piece of cellulose tape will hold the two dials together until recalibration is necessary (if your exposure conditions change).

When a magenta contact screen (negative) is used, highlighting exposures usually are not needed. However, if more highlighting is wanted or if the magenta contact screen for positives is being used for making negatives, highlighting exposures without the screen can be used and then should be included in the test exposure. For example, the technique could consist of a flash exposure through the screen with a flash lamp, a detail exposure

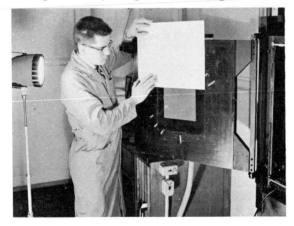

Fig. 268. Making the Flash Exposure on the Test Negative. Cover the detail exposure area and make a series of separate flash exposures on the previously-covered edge of film. Expose the yellow light through the Magenta Contact Screen. (Courtesy Eastman Kodak Co.)

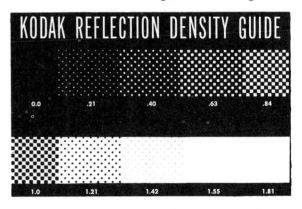

Fig. 269. Test Negative, Shown Diagramatically. The test negative should have highlights that are nearly closed up as in step .21 and with shadow dot missing as in 1.55. (Courtesy Eastman Kodak Co.)

through the screen, and a 10-percent high-lighting exposure without the screen (*i.e.,* 10 percent of the detail exposure). The detail exposure is used in the computation.

    c. Examine the series of shadow flash exposures on the negative and choose the time which produced a normal shadow dot. If necessary, make another flash test to refine the exposure — as 20, 22, 24, 28 seconds. The smallest printable dot should not necessarily be chosen, but rather whatever size dot is required (about 10%) in the shadow area of the negative. This is the *basic flash exposure.*

    NOTE: Steps 1 through 4, above, need be taken only once for a particular set-up of camera, film, lights, screen, and developer. Changes in magnification and lens aperture for different originals are computed by rotating the inner plastic dial, as explained in the following.

    *(5) Using the computer.*

    The following steps are those necessary when using the Exposure Computer for halftone negatives in a process camera.

    a. *Obtain the* **density range** *of the copy.* By using a densitometer or the Density Guide, determine both the *maximum (shadow)*

*density* and the *minimum (highlight) density* of the copy to be reproduced. Then subtract the minimum from the maximum density to obtain the *density range* of the copy.

    If the copy has no real highlights, make as good an estimate as possible. For example, if you want a dark original to be printed as a similarly dark reproduction, you may read the white margin of the copy as the *minimum (highlight) density* or you may assume it to be zero. However, if you desire a full range of tones in the reproduction, read the lightest density of the copy as a *minimum (highlight) density*, disregarding any minute areas in which no detail or gradation need be retained, such as the catchlights of eyes in portraits.

    b. *Determine the* **detail exposure** *by use of the computer dial.* Rotate the dials of the computer so that the magnification or reduction is opposite the lens aperture to be used for the detail exposure. Read off the exposure time in seconds opposite the highlight density of the original (on the red density scale).

    c. *Determine the* **flash exposure** *as follows:* First, calculate the *excess density range* by subtracting the basic density range (determined in step 3b, above) from the den-

Fig. 270. Set the Computer. Rotate the top red "density" dial so that the density of the step which produced a satisfactory highlight dot is opposite the exposure time which produced it. (Courtesy Eastman Kodak Co.)

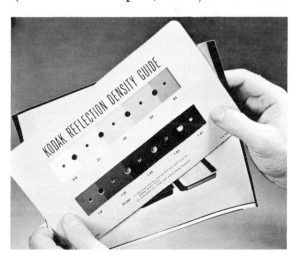

Fig. 271. Determining the Density Range of the Copy. Measure the highlight and shadow densities of the original which is to be reproduced, disregarding unimportant areas. The difference between them is the density range. (Courtesy Eastman Kodak Co.)

sity range of the copy. Then, locate the *flash exposure* in Table 5 (on the computer). Use the basic flash exposure (step 4c) and the excess density range. The flash exposure time in seconds is found where the proper line and column intersect. If this time tends to make the contrast on the negative too high or too low, use the flash exposure given in the next lower or higher line of the table.

### Examples of Use

Assume that the test exposure showed that the highlight density of 0.21 in the original copy produced a normal highlight dot with an exposure of 20 seconds, at a lens aperture of $f/16$ and 100-percent magnification. The dials should then be set so that $f/16$ on the inner black section falls opposite 100 percent, and the 0.21 density of the red section falls opposite the 20-second exposure time on the card. Refer again to Fig. 270. Also assume that a shadow dot was produced by a density of 1.31 on the original copy. Therefore, the basic density range is 1.31 minus 0.21, or 1.10. The basic shadow flash exposure is assumed, in this example, to be 20 seconds.

*Case 1.* The copy has a highlight density of 0.15 and a shadow density of 1.25. The reproduction is to be at 100-percent magnification, at an $f/16$ lens aperture.

| | |
|---|---|
| Detail Exposure ............... | 17.5 seconds |
| Shadow Density | 1.25 |
| Highlight Density | ( − ) 0.15 |
| Density Range of Copy | 1.10 |
| Basic Density Range | ( − ) 1.10 |
| Excess Density Range | 0.00 |
| Flash Exposure .................. | 0 seconds |

*Case 2.* The copy has a highlight density of 0.00 and a shadow density of 1.65. The reproduction is to be at 100-percent magnification, at an $f/16$ lens aperture.

| | |
|---|---|
| Detail Exposure ............... | 12.5 seconds |
| Shadow Density | 1.65 |
| Highlight Density | ( − ) 0.00 |
| Density Range of Copy | 1.65 |
| Basic Density Range | ( − ) 1.10 |
| Excess Density Range | 0.55 |
| Basic Flash Exposure | 20 seconds |
| Flash Exposure .................. | 14 seconds |

*Case 3.* Conditions are the same as in *Case 2*, except that reproduction is to be at 50 percent. Turn both dials to bring the lens aperture of $f/16$ to the magnification of 50 percent. Detail Exposure Time = 7 seconds.

*Case 4.* The copy has a shadow density of 1.50 and a highlight density of 0.10, with the exposure made at a lens aperture of $f/22$ and a 150-percent magnification.

| | |
|---|---|
| Shadow Density | 1.50 |
| Highlight Density | ( − ) 0.10 |
| Copy Density Range | 1.40 |
| Basic Density Range | ( − ) 1.10 |
| Excess Density Range | 0.30 |
| Basic Flash Exposure | 20 seconds |
| Flash Exposure .................. | 10 seconds |

Turn both dials to bring the lens aperture of $f/22$ to a magnification of 150 percent, and the new Detail Exposure Time (read opposite the highlight density of 0.10) is 48 seconds.

*Case 5. Highlighting.* The test exposures of 80 seconds for the detail exposure and 8 seconds for the highlight bump exposure were made at a lens aperture of $f/16$ and a magnification of 100 percent, and produced a highlight dot from a density of 0.10 in the original. The dials are *reset* so that $f/16$ on the inner black section falls opposite 100 percent and 0.10 on the red section falls opposite the 80-second exposure time.

A shadow dot was obtained where the original density was 1.10, so that the basic density range was 1.10 minus 0.10, or 1.00. The basic flash exposure, again, was 20 seconds. The copy has a shadow density of 1.65 and a highlight density of 0.00. The reproduction is to be a 100-percent magnification at an $f/16$ lens aperture, as in *Case 2*.

| | |
|---|---|
| Detail Exposure ............... | 64 seconds |
| Highlight Exposure .............. | 6.5 seconds |
| Shadow Density | 1.65 |
| Highlight Density | ( − ) 0.00 |
| Density Range of Copy | 1.65 |
| Basic Density Rrange | ( − ) 1.00 |
| Excess Density Range | 0.65 |
| Basic Flash Exposure | 20 seconds |
| Flash Exposure ............... | 15.5 seconds |

*Case 6. Exposure for Kodalith Autoscreen Ortho Film.* For Kodalith Autoscreen Ortho Film, calibrate the computer as described for halftone negatives (in the preceding description entitled "Calibrating the Computer for Use") except, of course, do not use a screen; also, make the flash exposures with the OA filter in the flashing lamp. Make the two test exposures described, on a single sheet of Autoscreen film. From the resulting halftone negative, select the step of the reflection density guide which produced the desired highlight dot size. With this information, set the computer exactly as described previously under the heading "Set the Computer".

### Evaluating the Negative

Ideally, a halftone negative should produce a plate which will print a reproduction as nearly like the original photo as possible. On the press, as the plate picks up ink, and the soft blanket exerts pressure, the printed highlight dots tend to get larger and the printed shadow dots tend to fill in or "plug up" a bit. This dot spread also occurs in making duplicate negatives or positives and in platemaking, so it is important to keep track of dot spread. Several such control devices will be mentioned in Chapter 11 with Darkroom Procedures.

The generally satisfactory halftone negative should have shadow areas (lightest areas) of dots ranging in size from tiny 10% black pinpoints to dots about 25% to 30%. These shadow areas reproduce on the printed sheets as black areas with tiny white pinpoints or, sometimes, as solid black areas.

The highlight areas on the negative (darkest areas) should have about a 90% dot, so as to reproduce about a 10% dot on the printed sheet. (Sometimes a smaller printed dot is preferable.)

The mid-tones should range smoothly from about a 35% dot to a 70% dot, having the characteristic checkerboard pattern in the center of the range.

In judging your negative, remember that the dots should be *black* — not brown. Also, the black dots on the negative are influenced by the amount of reflected light which strikes the film.

If the detail exposure is too long, the dark areas tend to close up solid, making the pinpoint transparent dots disappear. So, for *larger* transparent dots in the highlight area of the negative, *shorten* the detail exposure; for a denser negative highlight area with *smaller* transparent dots, *increase* the detail exposure.

To *add*, or *increase* the size of, black dots in the clear shadow areas of the negative, *increase* the flash exposure; for *smaller* shadow dots, decrease the flash exposure.

*Remember* the detail exposure controls the size of the highlight dots; the flash exposure controls the size of the shadow dots.

Under standard developing conditions, and with fresh developer, the image should begin to appear in about 30 to 40 seconds. Sooner than that indicates overexposure; longer than that indicates underexposure. Exposure should be such that the negative can remain in the developer for close to the recommended 2¾ minutes. However, if the dot size is inspected with a glass the last few seconds, some correction can be made in developing time. A longer time gives smaller highlight dots and may allow brownish shadow dots to turn black so they will print.

## Making a Negative from a Halftone Print

When an original glossy print of a photograph is not available for use as camera copy, sometimes it is necessary to reproduce an already-printed halftone picture.

### "Shooting" as Line Copy

Because a *halftone print* (a printed halftone picture) is composed of solid dots and areas which differ in size but not in tone, it may actually be treated as camera line copy — *i.e.*, a halftone negative may be made from it *without the use of a screen* in the camera. The screen pattern will be picked up from the copy (dot for dot), provided that this ruling is not extremely fine or indistinct. (Fig. 199 on page 98 was produced from a number of pasted-up halftone prints. The entire paste-up was shot as line copy.)

Halftone prints often are pasted up on a mechanical along with other line copy, such as type matter. The page of copy then is shot as line copy on one piece of film.

Enlarging or reducing a halftone print naturally will result in a correspondingly coarser or finer screen pattern or ruling. For example, if a newspaper halftone print which has a 65-line screen ruling is reduced 50% the resulting print will have a ruling of about 130 lines to the inch. Rulings reduced much finer than 150 lines per inch become difficult to print without plugging.

A change in the screen ruling may or may not be objectionable, depending upon the original screen ruling and the intended use of the resulting printed piece. One way to avoid objectionable change in fineness or coarseness of screen pattern is to photograph the halftone print at "same size" and then crop the negative to the size needed for the illustration.

### Rescreening

Sometimes it is necessary to reproduce a printed halftone illustration which has an in-

Fig. 272.    Moire — Objectionable halftone dot pattern caused by faulty rescreening of an already-screened halftone illustration. (This illustration actually is the accidental result of using a contact screen over an Autoscreen film.)

distinct screen pattern, a screen pattern which is too fine, or where a large reduction in size is necessary. In such cases, the halftone print is photographed through a screen (or *rescreened*).

Occasionally, the dot pattern of the screen used in the camera may not match exactly the dot pattern on the print. This mismatching may result in a disturbing pattern on the negative, which is very evident and unacceptable. This is called "moire" — pronounced "maw-RAY" See Fig. 272. Moire may be avoided by the following methods:

(1) A screen which has a ruling either 50 lines finer or 50 lines coarser than the screening on the original (at its new size) may be used. (2) When a screen is used, the copy or screen should be angled so the result is 30° more than the original angle. This angle must be accurate to minimize the pattern. If the original angle was 45°, the new print angle should be 75°. (3) The printed halftone may be enlarged, airbrushed, and then shot as an original photograph. (4) The original may be reduced greatly (to less than 40%), causing the original screen to drop out. (5) A clean piece of glass or clear film may be held before the lens and tilted back and forth during exposure.

## Making Halftones with Prescreened Film

Through the use of Kodalith Autoscreen Ortho Film, highly satisfactory halftone negatives may be made without the use of a halftone glass or contact screen[7].

Autoscreen film is very similar to other litho films, except that it has a 133-line-screen dot pattern built right into the emulsion. Thus, when the film is exposed and developed, it produces a halftone negative automatically.

### Theory

Unlike most films, Autoscreen film is not equally sensitive to light throughout its emulsion surface. Instead, the emulsion is composed of thousands of light-sensitive areas, each acutely sensitive at the center but gradu-

[7]Courtesy Eastman Kodak Company

ally decreasing in sensitivity around it. The same result is achieved on Autoscreen film as on other films exposed through a glass or contact screen. A weak exposure from the dark areas of the original produces an image only in the most sensitive portions of the emulsion, which are at the centers of the dots. A stronger exposure from the middle tones exposes less sensitive areas also, thus producing larger dots. With a maximum exposure from the highlights, an image is formed in all but small areas.

### Some Advantages

Because no separate screen obstructs light from the film's emulsion, because the film has great sensitivity, and because the exposed Autoscreen negatives are processed by still development, Autoscreen film can record finer detail than other halftone processes. Another advantage is that type matter and original photographs can be shot at the same time on the same sheet of film, without producing an objectionable screen pattern in the type matter. A third advantage is that Autoscreen film can be loaded into a *conventional view camera* to directly yield halftone negatives by photographing original subjects (or copy) at the scene, using a time exposure of several seconds.

### Exposure

Detailed instructions for exposing and processing Autoscreen film are packaged with the film.

Two exposures are made: (1) a detail white-light exposure, based upon the highlight density of the subject (or copy), and (2) a flash exposure, to control contrast.

The flash exposure is made using a safelight filter Series OA and a 60-watt bulb at 6 feet. An exposure of about 20 seconds to such a light usually is required.

Fig. 273 illustrates the highlight and shadow dots on a typical Autoscreen negative, as seen under an 8x magnifier. Highlight dots are about 95 percent, and the shadow dots are about 10 percent. Variations in dot sizes may be better for specific conditions.

Although detail and flash exposures may be determined experimentally, it is strongly recommended that both exposure times be determined in the same manner as described previously for the white-light plus flash technique (method used in making halftones with the contact screen using the Graphic Arts Exposure Computer, *i.e.*, make test negative for detail and flash exposures; calibrate the computer; then determine exposure times). Of course, no screen will be used. Remember to expose for the highlights and flash for the shadows.

### Processing

The exposed Autoscreen film can be developed either by the *inspection* method or the *time-and-temperature* method. (For complete information on these methods, see Chapter 11 on film developing.) For best results, the still-development technique described below should be employed.

Develop in fresh Kodalith developer for *each* negative, using 1 part A, 1 part B, and 1 part water, at 68° F. Use a Wratten Series 1A (light red) safelight filter in a suitable safelight holder with a 15-watt bulb, at no less than 4 feet. Do not turn on the safelight until the film has been in the developer for 1½ minutes.

Fig. 273. Highlight and Shadow Dots, as Seen on a Typical Autoscreen Negative, Under an 8x Magnifier. (**Left**) Highlight dots are about 95%. (**Right**) Shadow dots are about 10%. (Courtesy Eastman Kodak Co.)

Whichever method of developing is used, remember that the dot quality of the negative may be impaired if the film is exposed to the safelight for a *total time longer than 3 minutes*.

*Inspection Method.* Use a white enamel tray for reflecting the light of the safelight from the bottom of the tray. (Do not turn on the safelight until the film has been in the developer for 1½ minutes.)

Agitate the developer vigorously for a few seconds. Immerse the film, and again agitate the developer for 2 minutes. Then allow the film to lie perfectly still in the bottom of the tray for about one minute. Inspect at frequent intervals. *Total* developing time should be about three minutes for normal developing.

*Time-and-Temperature Method.* Develop for 3 minutes at 68° F. (plus or minus ½° F.), employing constant agitation.

*Further Processing.* After developing, rinse the negative in the stop bath for 10 seconds, agitating continuously. Then fix, wth *continuous agitation*, for 2 to 4 minutes, or for twice the time that it takes for the film to clear. Finally, wash about 10 minutes in running water (65° to 70° F.).

To minimize drying marks, treat the negatives in Photo-Flo solution after washing, or wipe surfaces carefully with a photo chamois, a soft viscose sponge, or a rubber squeegee or other soft squeegee (such as a windshield wiper blade). Then hang the negatives to dry in a dust-free place.

### Originals Containing Type Matter

Type matter can be exposed together with pictures, without the usual loss of legibility caused by the screening of fine lines. The detail exposure should be sufficient to close up the highlight dots in the white background of the type, and the flash exposure should be such as to give normal dots in the shadows of the picture area (Fig. 273). If special prints are to be made for combination with type matter, the highlights of the pictures should be slightly darker than the white paste-up paper or the paper on which the type is printed. The results obtained from picture-type combinations with this film are far better than those obtained with a crossline screen and even better than those obtained with a magenta contact screen. It is commonly used for reproducing (on a single negative) photographs which have parts labeled with lettering and labels.

### Duotones

A duotone is a halftone printed in two colors. Although it usually is made from a black-and-white photograph, it involves some of the techniques of color printing and so will be illustrated in the next chapter. The principal negative, usually printed in black or a very deep color, is exposed and processed for nearly normal contrast, but it favors detail in the shadow end of the scale and has only sketchy highlights. The second negative, usually printed in a lighter color, must have the screen angled 30° to the first. It favors detail at the high end of the scale, so usually is lighter. Some duotones are printed black on black, so as to use a double layer of ink to increase the density range of the printed copy.

### Questions

1. Which of the following pieces of artwork must be reproduced by the halftone process if it is to be printed by offset?
   a. Charcoal drawing
   b. Snapshot of a person
   c. Proof of hand-set type
   d. Portrait in oils
   e. Pen-and-ink map
   f. Typewritten page

2. What single factor determines whether a piece of original copy is to be shot as halftone or line copy?

3. Why would an ordinary snapshot negative be unsatisfactory for the making of an offset plate image?

4. Describe a halftone screen.

5. During the making of a halftone negative, where is the halftone screen placed?

6. Of what two kinds of material are halftone screens made?

7. Which tonal areas of the copy will reflect the most light?

8. Which tonal areas of the copy will produce tiny, opaque dots on the halftone negative?

9. What is the usual screen angle for shooting black-and-white halftones?

10. List the steps in the basic procedure for making a halftone negative.

11. What advantage is there in making a trial negative before attempting to engage in halftone photography?

12. Describe the physical set-up for making a detail exposure.

13. Describe the physical set-up for making a flash exposure.

14. How would printed type matter appear if it were reproduced by the screened halftone method?

15. What advantages are there in using Autoscreen film for making a halftone negative?

16. How is the developer solution for Autoscreen film prepared?

17. What is meant by the "still-development" technique?

18. Describe the precautions to be observed in using the safelight when developing Autoscreen film.

19. Why are density readings made of tone copy before making a halftone negative from it?

## Problems and Projects

1. Examine, through a magnifying glass, a halftone print or negative which was made with a coarse screen. Make a sketch of the shape of the dots in the highlight area, the mid-tone area, and the shadow area.

2. Make a satisfactory test negative, using an average piece of halftone copy assigned by the instructor. Prepare a wall chart showing the camera set-up and exposure conditions which proved satisfactory for the main exposure:

    a. Rating of arc lights
    b. Length of exposure
    c. Bellows extension
    d. Copyboard extension
    e. Angle of lights
    f. Distance of lights
    g. Screen ruling
    h. Lens aperture (*f*-number)

    Also, make a diagram of the physical set-up for the flash exposure. Show:

    a. Distance of flash lamp
    b. Length of flash exposure

3. Prepare a detailed list or order of operations for making a halftone negative. Mount this on the wall near the camera.

4. Produce satisfactory halftone negatives, using a detail and a flash exposure. Keep a record of all computations and exposures made.

5. Prepare a display of printed halftone samples or clippings from newspapers, magazines and advertising pieces. Label each with the screen ruling and other pertinent information. Include examples of screened type and process color work.

6. Prepare a list of tools, equipment, supplies and materials needed for halftone photography. Using the shop catalogs, prepare a purchase requisition. Include prices, specifications, and quantities.

7. Make a satisfactory halftone negative from (a) a coarse-screened already-printed halftone picture; (b) from a fine-screened already-printed halftone picture.

## New Words

1. bump exposure
2. calibrate
3. characteristic curve
4. checkerboard
5. circular screen
6. color blind film
7. consistent
8. contact screen
9. continuous-tone
10. cyan
11. densitometer

12. density
13. developing
14. exposure
15. film speed
16. flash exposure
17. flexible
18. gamma

19. gradation of tone
20. halftone
21. highlight
22. illusion
23. incident light
24. latent image
25. litho film

26. magenta
27. moire
28. opacity
29. opaque
30. orthochromatic
31. panchromatic
32. prescreened

33. processing
34. reflectance
35. reflection density
36. sensitometry
37. transmission density
38. transmittance

# Color

# Reproduction

**CHAPTER**

*10*

Printing in colors (other than black and white) adds snap, eye appeal, and realism to the reproduction. Two main classes of color printing are flat color and process color printing.

In *flat color printing*, part of the type, part of the ornamentation or illustration, or a background tint is done in color. (It is easy to use too much color.)

*Process color printing* reproduces an illustration in the full, original hues. It does this by overprinting halftones for each of the subtractive primary colors — yellow, magenta and cyan — as well as one for black to give better tone control. Process color requires more advanced skills than flat color. Often both flat color and process color are used on the same page — as when a headline or a tint area is produced by a combination of the same colors of ink used to reproduce a colored photograph.

The purpose of this chapter is to develop an understanding of: (1) light, color, and pigments, (2) films to record colors of light, and

[1]Named after Anders Jonas Angstrom (1814-1874), Swedish scientist. A millimeter is one-thousandth of a meter (or .04 inches). A micron is one-thousandth of a millimeter, and a millimicron is one-thousandth of a micron (so 1 m$\mu$ = 1 millionth of a millimeter, 1 billionth of a meter, or 25 millionths of an inch). One millimicron equals ten Angstrom units. As all electromagnetic radiation travels at the same speed (186,300 miles/sec. or 3 x 10$^{10}$ cm./sec.), the *frequency* of the vibration is sometimes used rather than the wavelength (especially for radio waves). Thus green light of 500 m$\mu$ has 20,000 waves in every centimeter of path for a frequency of 6 x 10$^{14}$ cycles per second.

(Eye symbol courtesy of Printing Production Magazine — separations by Seidel-Farris-Clark, Inc., Toledo; from a transparency by Interchemical Corporation.)

(3) process color printing. Following this are some basic procedures for doing some color printing — both flat and process.

## Color

Color is a visual sensation which occurs when light rays of varying wavelengths reach the eye. Without light, there is no color. To understand how light creates the sensation of color, let us examine some aspects of light.

### Light

Natural light is a form of electromagnetic radiation produced by the sun's heat and transmitted to earth by rays which travel in a waveform (Fig. 274A), similar to the ripples caused by tossing a stone into a pond. A bundle of rays might be called a "beam". Wavelengths (the vibrations) are measured from the crest of one wave to the crest of the next. Radio waves, also a part of the electromagnetic spectrum, are long enough to be measured in meters (1 meter = 39.4 inches) — so we speak of the 40-meter short-wave band. Light waves are much, much smaller and therefore are measured either in millimicrons (m$\mu$) or in Angstrom[1] units (A° or A.U.).

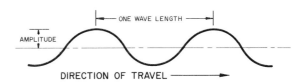

Fig. 274A. A Ray of Light Travels in a Wave Motion

**155**

These rays are identical in all respects, except that they differ in wavelength, Fig. 274B. Only a very narrow band of these rays is visible in the form of light. These are the rays whose wavelengths measure between 400 and 700 millimicrons (4000 and 7000 Angstrom units) in length, Fig. 274C.

*Suggested Demonstration:* With the aid of a prism, a beam of natural (white) light can be spread out into a visible spectrum (Fig. 274D). The colors of the spectrum gradually blend into each other — violet, blue, green, yellow, orange and red.

From the above, then, it is evident that projected light is a combination of all the spectrum colors.

Usually these basic colors are shown with the various hues around a closed circle (or polygon). This arrangement shows the *purples* (mixtures of colors from the two ends of the spectrum) which are not spectrum colors themselves. See Fig. 275A for such an arrangement which has long been used for colored lights and filters. Literature of the Graphic Arts Technical Foundation (hereafter called GATF) gives details for graphs arranged in a circle, a triangle, or a hexagon for specific testing purposes.[2]

## Color Dimensions

The spectrum and color wheels show only one dimension of color — that of changing hue. To identify or specify all possible variations of colors, three dimensions are required. These are: *hue, value* (lightness or darkness), and *chroma* (saturation or strength). See Fig. 275B.

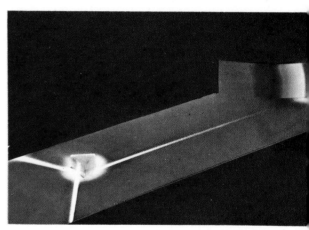

Fig. 274D.  Prism Spreading White Light (Courtesy GATF)

When light, traveling in air, enters a more dense medium such as glass or water, it is **refracted** or bent to a new line of travel. The **refractive index** indicates the amount of bending — more dense media have higher indexes. This explains why a pole stuck into water appears bent. Glass lenses refract light to focus an image at a point. However, prisms and simple lenses refract the shorter wavelengths more than the longer wavelengths, so the prism above can spread out a narrow beam of light into a visible spectrum. Camera lenses tend to focus different colors at different points, unless color performance is corrected by the incorporation of several types of glass into a lens having several elements.

Some of the light hitting a lens or prism is **reflected** without entering the surface — note the beam extending toward the bottom of the picture above. Coatings on the surface of a lens minimize the light lost by reflection.

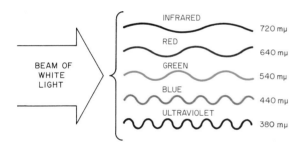

Fig. 274B.  White Light Has Rays of Many Wavelengths

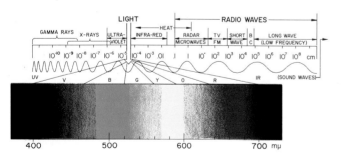

Fig. 274C.  Electromagnetic Spectrum with Visible Portion Enlarged

[2]See Graphic Arts Technical Foundation, *The Lithographers Manual,* 1966 edition, plates following p. 7:6, also p. 7:11; or *LTF Research Progress,* No. 53, Sept. 1961 (General Memo No. 5). Address: 4615 Forbes Ave., Pittsburgh, Pa. 15213.

*Hue* is the name of the color, as it is identified on the color circle as red, blue, etc.

*Value* (brightness) is the "tone", the lightness or darkness of a hue, such as a light red, a dark red, etc. The value of a color is changed by adding white or black.

*Chroma* (saturation) is the intensity or degree of grayness of a color. We can change the chroma of a color, without changing its value, by adding a gray of the same value as that of the color.

A visual comparison system by which the hue, value, and chroma can be designated by numbers is the "Munsell Book of Colors"[4], sometimes called the Munsell Color System (Fig. 275C).

In the Munsell system, a hue and its value and chroma are designated by the scheme: H V/C. See the small diagram in Fig. 275B. Fig. 275C shows a three-dimensional model of the Munsell Color System.

These illustrations show how the specification numbers for *Hue, Value/Chroma* for a

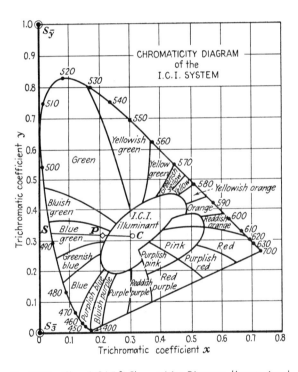

Fig. 275A. Closed C.I.E.[3] Chromaticity Diagram (International Commission on Illumination) (Courtesy GATF)

[3]The letters C.I.E. are based on the French form which is standard in international usage.

[4]Munsell Color Co., Inc., 2441 North Calvert St., Baltimore, Md. 21218. Two books are made: one with matte-finish chips and one with glossy color chips. Each book is expensive because each chip color (of lacquer) is carefully mixed separately, and color variation is held to very close tolerances.

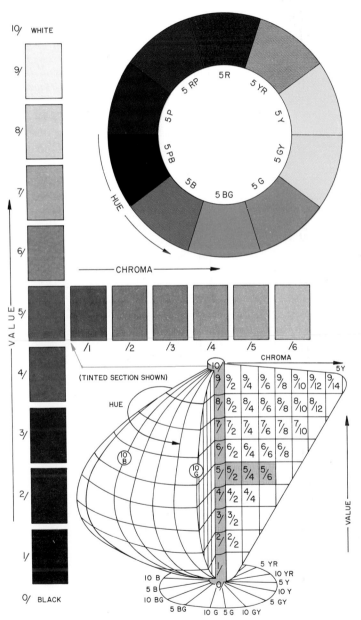

Fig. 275B. The Three Dimensions of Color (Courtesy Munsell Color Company)

certain color sample can be obtained by comparing a sample of the color with the hue circle and actual color samples in the book. First, the hue is identified from the hue circle. Then, the patch which matches the sample can be located on the page of the book showing samples of all variations in value and chroma for that hue. The number of that patch can then be specified for a color match by anyone also having the "Book of Colors". Sample books of ink companies are also used for this purpose.

## Color Temperature (Radiation Temperature)

The temperature of a light source affects the spectral quality of the light it gives off. This is because an object cannot reflect colors which are not present in the light. As the temperature of the light source increases, the color of the light first becomes reddish, then bright red,

then yellow. Increasing the temperature further produces full, white light. See the lines for various temperatures in Fig. 276. A similar situation exists with sunlight. During the day, the sky scatters the blue end of the spectrum more than the red, coloring it blue; this produces a blue-white light. When the angle of the sun is low, as at sunset, light passes through the maximum amount of atmosphere. At this time, all blue is absorbed, leaving the sun yellow, then orange, and finally a deep red. Table 6 shows the color temperature of some common light sources.

Color temperature is expressed in degrees Kelvin[5] ($^{\circ}$K). This is the centigrade temperature plus 273 degrees.

If there is a loss in voltage to camera or printing lights, the normally-emitted white light may become undesirably reddish, with a resulting adverse effect on length of exposures and colors transmitted. As a protection, camera or printing light systems should include a constant-voltage device.

When matching colors, a standardized light source should be used. Usually, standardized daylight-fluorescent bulbs are used wherever colors are being checked or matched.

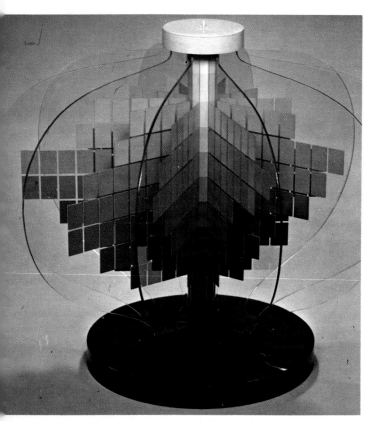

Fig. 275C.   Munsell Color Tree Showing the Three Dimensions: Hue (the 10 panels), Value (note the center gray scale), and Chroma (intense color at outer edge) (Courtesy GATF)

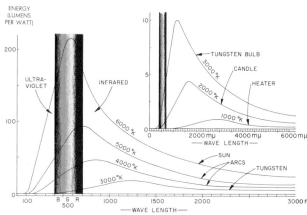

Fig. 276.   Wavelengths Emitted by Sources at Various Temperatures. The same 3000°K line is shown in both scales. Temperatures are approximate for typical sources listed. Note that most artificial light has more red light than blue light, but that sunlight is nearly balanced.

[5]William Thomson Kelvin ("Lord Kelvin") 1824-1907, British mathematician and physicist.

### Table 6
### Color Temperatures (°K) of Common Light Sources

| | |
|---|---|
| Sun | 6000 |
| North Skylight | 12000° |
| Daylight (typical) | 5900° |
| Noon Sunlight | 5400° |
| Carbon Arcs: High Intensity | 5500 |
| White Flame | 5000 |
| Ordinary | 4000 |
| Flash: Electronic, or blue-tinted | 6000 |
| Clear | 3800 |
| Photofloods: 500-W, 34 lumens/watt | 3400 |
| 500-W, 27 lumens/watt | 3200 |
| Utility Bulbs: 100-W, 17 lumens/watt | 2900 |
| 40-W, 12 lumens/watt | 2650 |
| Fluorescent Lamps: From Daylight | 5500° |
| To Soft White | 3000° |
| Standard Candlelight | 1930 |

°Relative numbers only — not an actual temperature. Some artificial lights emit only selected colors rather than a continuous spectrum — mercury-vapor lights are mostly a spectral yellow; some fluorescents have strong blues.

One of the most dramatic examples of the effects of light source occurs in the darkroom. Under the red illumination of the safelights, red, yellow and white all appear the same color, and, of course, greens appear to be black.

The human eye automatically adjusts to the more common of the color effects caused by varying light sources. However, films do not make these adjustments, and the eye will not compensate for an off-color rendering in a color print. Therefore, films and color prints must be carefully corrected to white-light conditions. Indoor color film is especially sensitive to blue (less to reds) so as to appear natural under the warm colors of artificial lighting.

## How We See Color

Color is non-existent as a substance in itself. The sun, or a lighted lamp, "appears" to be a certain color because of the variety of wavelengths of light rays which it transmits to the eyes (or to a *spectrophotometer* — a device for measuring the brightness of the various portions of the spectrum).

A "white" lamp, when it is turned on, appears white because it is transmitting or radi-ating wavelengths of white light (which actually includes all basic colors of the spectrum). See the 6000°K line for sunlight in Fig. 276.

NOTE: The term "apparent color" is sometimes used. For example, if an object appears red to the eye, we say "the apparent color is red".

This same white light, when transmitted, for instance, through a red glass, causes the glass to appear red. The pigment in the red glass transmits to the eye only those wavelengths of light in the red range of the spectrum. It absorbs wavelengths of all other colors. In this respect, the pigment serves the same purpose as a radio tuner does in the radio spectrum. The molecules of each pigment are resonant at specific wavelengths, and this causes the absorption.

Red printed areas on white paper have the apparent color of red because the ink and paper together reflect only those wavelengths of light in the red range of the spectrum; they absorb all other wavelengths. The unprinted portions of the white paper have the apparent color of white because the white paper reflects to the eye all wavelengths of white light.[6]

NOTE: It can be seen from the above that the color and finish of the paper being printed upon can have an important effect on the apparent color of the ink image.

These facts, then, are evident: (1) Except for an original source of illumination, color is apparent in an object only when that object *transmits* (allows light to pass through) or *reflects* light to the eyes, and (2) the *reflected* or *transmitted* apparent color (that which we see)

[6]Some special cases of apparent colors are not the result of absorption of a part of white light. Coloring such as the rainbow, a spectrum from a prism, halos, multi-colored oil slicks on water, colors on soap bubbles, Newton's rings (multi-colored circular waves around a pressure point, sometimes found in vacuum contact-printing frames), and iridescent colors (as on peacock feathers) are the result of the *diffraction* of light. These may be caused by two reflecting surfaces which are very close together alternately cancelling, then reinforcing, reflected light. *Diffraction gratings,* which have closely spaced lines (500 or more to the inch), also can cause an iridescence.

depends upon the wavelengths of the rays of light which reach the eyes because of the *transmittance* of a viewed transparent object or the *reflectance* of a viewed opaque object. See Fig. 277A.

## Color Mixing

All color mixing can be described by two processes: *additive* color mixing and *subtractive* color mixing.

### Additive Color Mixture

In an additive color mixture, light rays of certain colors are added to other light rays to produce (add up to) a new color. The additive primary colors are blue light, red light, and green light. (A *primary color* is a basic one which cannot be made by mixing other colors.)

If three projectors are set up, as in Fig. 277B, one with a blue filter, one with a red filter, and one with a green filter, three circles of projected light are produced on the screen — blue, red and green.

At the center, where the three projected circles of light overlap, the effect is white. (Blue, red and green light, mixed in the proper proportions, produces white light.)

Where the blue circle of light overlaps the red circle of light, the resulting projected color of light is *magenta;* red light and green light overlapping results in *yellow* light; and green and blue light results in *cyan* light.

This summation is then evident:

Blue light  + red light    = magenta light
Red light   + green light  = yellow light
Green light + blue light   = cyan light
Blue light + red light + green light
                            = white light
Lack of any light          = black

Magenta, yellow and cyan each is a complementary color of one of the primary colors of light: green, blue and red, respectively. *Complementary colors* are opposites on the color wheel.

| *Primary* | *Corresponding Complementary* |
|-----------|-------------------------------|
| Green     | Magenta (blue + red)          |
| Blue      | Yellow (red + green)          |
| Red       | Cyan (green + blue)           |

When each complementary color of light is mixed with its corresponding primary color of light, the mixture will be neutralized — *i.e.,* it will form white.

Green + Magenta (blue+red) = White light
Blue  + Yellow (red+green) = White light
Red   + Cyan (green+blue)  = White light

Fig. 277A. Why We See Color. Why is the tomato or glass of clear juice red? The pigment in both absorbs green and blue light but not the red. Opaque objects reflect the unabsorbed light. Transparent objects transmit the unabsorbed light straight on through. In either case, we see only light which is not absorbed. (Courtesy Eastman Kodak Company)

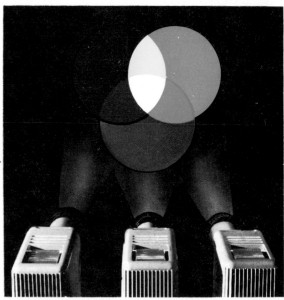

Fig. 277B. Additive Mixtures of Colored Light (Courtesy Eastman Kodak Company and GATF)

The color formed by adding the individual beams of light is brighter than each of the components.

NOTE: Additive light principles, discussed above, should be thoroughly understood, since the terms and principles are the foundation for process color separation, as well as for such processes as color photography, color television, and stage lighting.

### Subtractive Color Mixture

In a subtractive color mixture, white light interacts with a colorant — in an ink, a dye, a pigment, or a filter, for example — which *subtracts* (absorbs or filters out) some of the colors from the white light and allows the unabsorbed colors to be seen by the eye. Each color formed by subtraction is not as bright as the original.

The principal subtractive primary colors of pigments are magenta, yellow and cyan.[7]

(These are the names which identify the three colors of the transparent inks used in process color printing.)

Fig. 278A illustrates the subtractive method of mixing colored pigments. Three patches of transparent process color inks (magenta, yellow and cyan) have been printed on white paper so that they overlap. Where a pair of the primary colors of pigments overlap, a complementary color is produced:

Magenta ink + yellow ink    = red
Yellow ink    + cyan ink      = green
Cyan ink      + magenta ink = blue
Magenta ink + yellow ink + cyan ink = black

Green, blue and red, respectively, are the subtractive complementary colors of yellow, cyan and magenta transparent process inks.

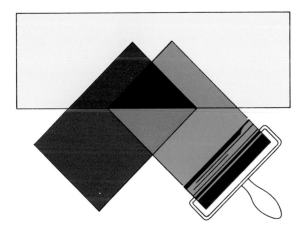

Fig. 278A. Transparent Inks Subtract from the Reflectance of the Paper. Paper reflects most of the light waves, so it appears white. Black ink reflects almost no light.

[7]Older books and non-technical sources may list the primary colors as red, yellow and blue. While not quite correct, they can be used as the basis for mixing paints and inks. Red and blue colors of printing ink, not requiring careful color control, are much less costly than the specific process colors of magenta and cyan. These non-technical sources also list the complementary colors as purple, green and orange, which pairs up incorrect opposites. This explains why the combination of all three primaries (an olive-drab color) was so far from producing the theoretical black.

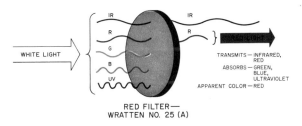

Fig. 278B. Filters Subtract Part of the Light (Courtesy Eastman Kodak Company)

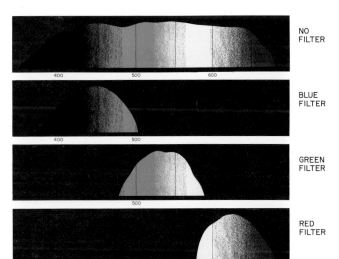

Fig. 278C. Separation Filters Make Panchromatic Films Sensitive to Various Sections of the Spectrum

## Filter Action

A filter will transmit light of its own color and will absorb light rays of most other colors. For example, in Fig. 278B, when white light (containing all colors) strikes the red filter, only those rays of the red wavelengths pass through; all rays of other wavelengths are absorbed (or blocked).

NOTE: Since filters thus absorb some of the incident light, exposures through filters should be increased over normal "no-filter" exposures. Relative increases in exposures (filter factors) when using filters may be determined experimentally or obtained from filter data books.

In color separation photography, three filters usually are used — a blue, a green and a red — each for a separate exposure. This results in three separation negatives for printing the three colors of process inks — yellow, magenta and cyan. See Fig. 278C.

The blue filter transmits blue light and absorbs green and red light (yellow light). The resulting negative then is most opaque in blue areas and least dense (nearly clear) in green and red areas. The printing plate made from this, in turn, carries yellow ink in areas to be colored green or red (or yellow, which is their spectral combination). If screened, the halftone dots produce tones of yellow. So the blue filter produces the yellow printer, and the filter may be called "minus-yellow."

In a similar manner, the green filter transmits green light and absorbs blue and red light (magenta light) — and may be called "minus-magenta." The red filter transmits red light and

absorbs green and blue light (cyan light) — and may be called "minus-cyan."

Stated another way: A filter will absorb its complementary color of light.

Fig. 278C shows the portions of the spectrum range which the red, green and blue filters each transmit.

NOTE: In selecting filters for use in color separation photography, the reader is cautioned to follow the recommendations of the film manufacturer for the particular process being employed.

## How Inks Reproduce Color

A film of transparent or opaque printing ink appears colored because its particles of pigment absorb light selectively. Let us assume for this discussion that a red ink is composed of a finely-ground, red-glass pigment suspended in a vehicle (such as linseed oil).

### Transparent Inks

Refer to Fig. 279A. If the refractive index[8] of the vehicle in our experimental ink is the

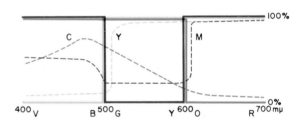

Fig. 279B. Reflection Curves for Process Colors. The theoretical curves are shown as solid lines, and these should be at 100% reflection for two squares, then drop straight down to 0% reflection for the complementary color. The actual curves for typical inks now available are shown as dotted lines. Note the actual curve for yellow is nearly perfect — reflecting R, O, Y, and G, but little B or V. Magenta is fair — good for R and O, but it appears to be degraded elsewhere as if it contained some cyan and yellow pigments. The cyan curve is poorest. Although it has no reflection in the reds, it lacks strength in its own two squares, as if it contained some magenta and yellow pigments. This is the reason that separation negatives for process colors must be carefully corrected by removing some color in specific combinations.

[8]For a brief explanation of refractive index, see Fig. 274D.

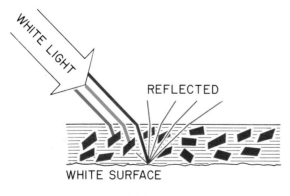

Fig. 279A. Transparent Red Ink

same as that of the pigment, a beam of incident light will pass freely through the vehicle and reach the red-pigment particles. These particles will absorb from the white light all colors other than red, and they will transmit the red rays through to the surface of the white paper. The red rays will reflect back from the paper surface, giving the apparent color of red.

However, if the surface below is such that it *will not* reflect the light rays, the resulting apparent color will not be red, but black.

If, in another instance, a transparent yellow ink is superimposed on a transparent blue ink, the subtractive effect produces an apparent *green* color. By overprinting with selected combinations of cyan, magenta and yellow process inks, most colors can be reproduced. See the reflection curves for these transparent process colors in Fig. 279B.

### Opaque Inks

Refer to Fig. 279C. If the particles of our red-glass pigment have a higher index of refraction than that of the vehicle in the ink, reflection of the incident light rays will occur at every boundary between the pigment and the vehicle, and all the red light rays will be reflected without striking the paper. Rays of light other than the reds will be absorbed.

With opaque inks, the color of the light that is reflected from the *printed image surface* depends very little on the color of the paper or on other colors printed under it. Opaque inks

are required for true colors on colored paper or overprints. The apparent color of opaque inks is more constant (than that of transparent inks) when the amount of ink varies during a press run.

### Combining Ink Colors

Either transparent or opaque inks may be mixed prior to printing, so as to produce new colors according to the subtractive color theory. Mixing a second color to the first color can only *subtract* from the reflected light, producing another color.

Varying the size of the halftone dots with which any hue of ink is printed will vary the value, or tone, of that color. Note in Fig. 279D that if the cyan halftone dots cover 100% of the area, the effect is full-color value; a 50% dot size will lessen the value in that area, etc. By

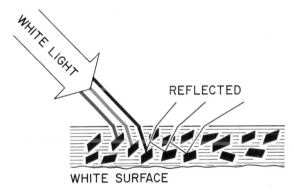

Fig. 279C.  Opaque Red Ink

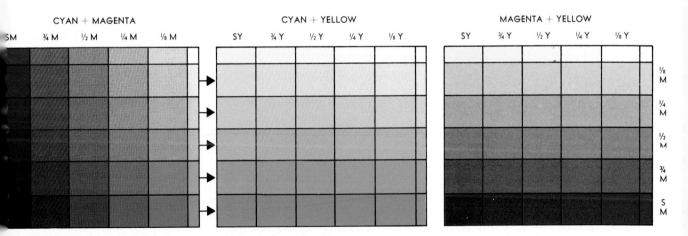

Fig. 279D.  Two-Color Combinations of Process Ink Hues

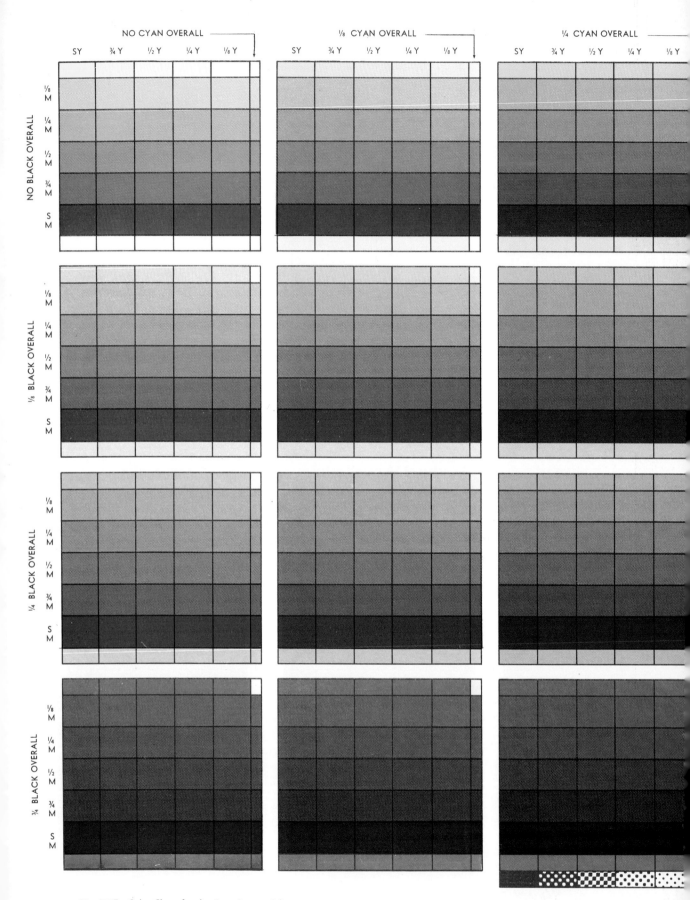

Fig. 279E. Color Chart for the Four Process Inks

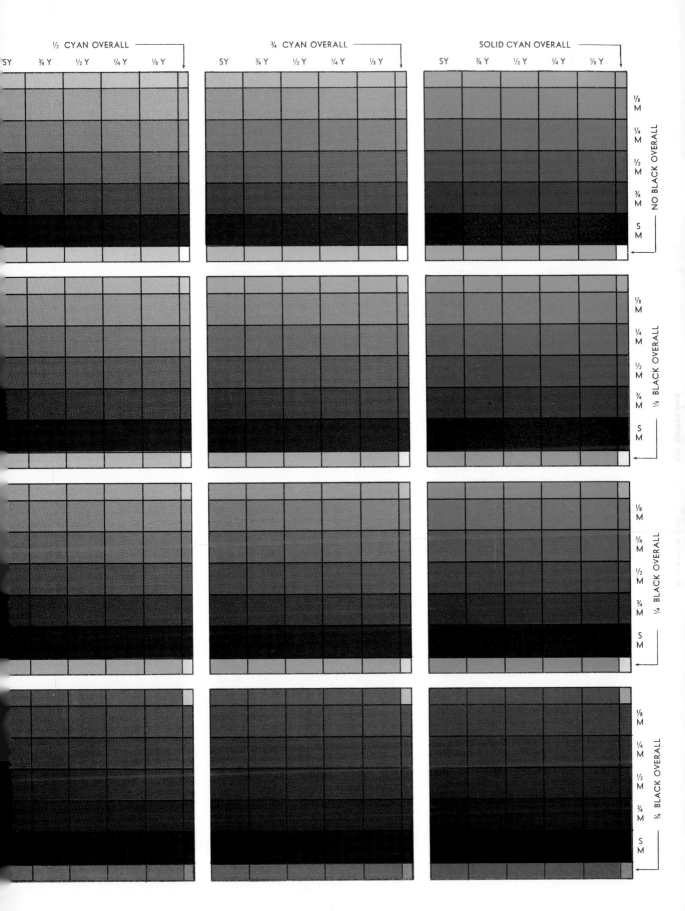

½ CYAN OVERALL    ¾ CYAN OVERALL    SOLID CYAN OVERALL

Fig. 279E. Color Chart for the Four Process Inks (Continued)

varying the proportions of each color when overprinting, new hues can be produced. Fig. 279D shows the range of hues available in two-color overprints of the primary colors of process inks, using various tones of each color. A tone of cyan produced by an approximate 25%-dot area is labeled "¼C"; a solid tone of magenta is labeled "SM", etc. Such a chart is very useful when producing artwork or selecting screen tints for color printing. For example, on the basis of this chart, the color "blue" in the illustrations for this chapter were produced by overprinting a solid cyan and a 25% magenta. The two-color overprints are most valuable for determining the best combinations to produce the key colors of R, O, Y, G, B, and V.

However, to better demonstrate the complete range of colors available in four-color process printing, all the possible overlaps must be shown, as in Fig. 279E. The two-color overprints of magenta and yellow are shown at the top-left corner. This identical block is repeated in all 24 locations, except that increasing amounts of cyan are overprinted in each column to the right, and increasing amounts of black are overprinted in each row down the page. Such an abbreviated chart can give only key combinations; many intermediate mixtures are possible. It should be noted that (as in single-color halftones) inks cannot produce as complete a range of tones as can color transparencies.

To be of most value, such a chart should be produced in your own plant, using your specific

⁹See Graphic Arts Technical Foundation, *The GATF Color Chart,* a 34-page pamphlet. The GATF chart, on which the Fig. 279E layout is based, has more combinations (1,760) shown in its 44 color blocks. Film positives can be purchased from them for running the chart on a single 22″ x 29″ sheet. Those working on smaller sizes of presses may wish to run the blocks shown in the top row on a single sheet, and then overprint with black ink on a separate page for each percentage, thus reducing the page size. If room allows, it would be desirable to also include ¹⁄₁₆ tones of magenta and cyan, as well as ¹⁄₁₆ and ½ overprints of blank. The basic magenta block in Fig. 279D contains four small strips of commercial screen tints (at 75°) contact printed 24 times and registered to the black. Yellow is produced similarly. The cyan flat has larger tints over windows cut to register with the black.

conditions, presses, inks, papers, etc. Producing such a chart is a good introduction to color printing problems.⁹

### White and Black

The "colors" white and black are not really visible colors. White is the full reflection of visible rays of light of all wavelengths (all colors of light combined). Grays are the partial reflection of waves which can neutralize each other. Black is the total absorption by an object of all wavelengths of light — *i.e.,* the *absence* of color sensation.

## Films to Record Colors of Light

The manner in which a film will record transmitted light rays of various wavelengths (different colors) depends on the composition and construction of its emulsion. *Monochromatic films* produce images of black and white; *color films* produce images in full color.

### Monochromatic Films

These are the familiar *blue-sensitive, orthochromatic* and *panchromatic* films which, when exposed to transmitted light, produce an image of black-and-white densities on the processed negative. Such films were first described on page 142, and specific examples are listed on page 203. These "single-color" negatives are used for making an offset plate to print in a single color or for making a photoprint in a single color (normally black on white).

The emulsion of the monochromatic film consists principally of light-sensitive silver salts. Upon exposure to transmitted light, the silver salts create a latent image which, upon processing, is rendered as a density (of blackened silver) on the negative.

In photographing copy which is a black image on white paper, the light which is reflected from the paper on the copyboard results in the *black density* on the negative; the black areas of the copy — the image — reflect no light, so the processed negative has no densities in the areas corresponding to the black areas of the copyboard image. (This is the clear area of the negative.) Tones are reversed again when the negative is printed photographically on paper or on a printing plate.

NOTE: A black-and-white contrast negative may be produced on monochromatic film from copy which is other than black and white, by the use of filters in the camera lens. (See chart on page 127.)

Because the three main types of monochromatic emulsions have applications in color film, it would be good to review briefly their characteristics.

*Blue-sensitive film* (sometimes called "color-blind" film) is sensitive only to the ultra-violet and blue portion of the color spectrum. Fig. 263 on page 141 shows this sensitivity. Greens, yellows or reds are recorded no more than blacks are. Blue-sensitive films and papers have their main application in contact printing or enlarging from negatives. Here there is no need for color sensitivity in the image, and there is less danger of accidentally fogging the emulsion in the darkroom.

*Orthochromatic film* historically followed the first blue-sensitive films and was sensitive to so much more of the spectrum that it was optimistically called "true color" ("ortho" means true or correct). However, it is still blind to the red third of the spectrum. Ortho films have their primary use when some color sensitivity is desired, but when red can be recorded as black or when a red safelight is desired.

*Panchromatic film* has a wide sensitivity to colors, which approximates that of the eye. It is the film which is used for a black-and-white recording of an original scene in tones of gray which appear most natural, and for color separation work in process color printing. Processing must be carried on in total darkness for most of the developing cycle.

Each of the three types of film is available with emulsions of various contrast ranges and film-speed ranges (though the three types tend to be progressively faster in the order listed, due to the more complete use of all elements of white light). We will also see that three emulsions, each similar to one of these three types, can be combined to produce a film capable of recording a scene in full, original colors.

## Color Photography

Color photography employs film and photoprint papers whose emulsions of silver salts and dye-forming compounds are capable of rendering images in full color when exposed to full-color original copy or subjects and then processed.

The end products of color photography are familiar as (1) *color negatives,* from which (2) *color photoprints* may be contact printed or projection printed; and as (3) *reversal color film* (direct positives or color transparencies) which must be viewed by transmitted light.

The "secret" of how a *single film* or a *photo-paper* can reproduce an image in the full range of spectrum colors is based on the additive and subtractive theories of color mixing. This "secret" can be understood best by beginning with the structure of a color film.

*Structure of a Color Film.* This first, simplified description applies to color-reversal film (such as color film for motion pictures or slide transparencies), which, when processed, has the same colors as the original scene or copy. Negative color film has a similar structure, except that the colors produced in the color negative are the subtractive complementary colors of the original.

Color film is built up of three light-sensitive layers of emulsion (each about 0.001″ thick). See Fig. 280A. The top layer is sensitive to only blue light; the middle layer, to blue and green light; and the lowest layer, to blue and red light. *However,* a yellow filter layer is interposed beneath the blue-sensitive layer so that blue light cannot reach the two lowest layers. This, in effect, makes the emulsion layers sensitive to, respectively, *blue* in the first layer; *green* in the second layer; and *red* in the bottom layer.

Each of the single-color-receptive emulsion layers consists of an emulsion containing a solution of silver salts (like that of monochromatic film) *plus* another compound known as a "dye coupler." Upon exposure, a latent image is formed in each emulsion layer by the color of light which penetrated through to register in that layer. During reversal processing, the unexposed areas of the emulsion are exposed

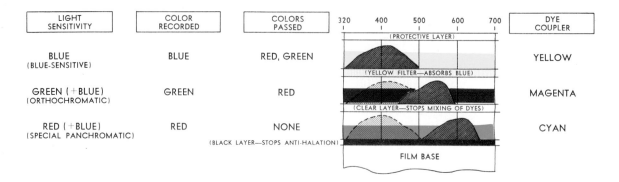

| LIGHT SENSITIVITY | COLOR RECORDED | COLORS PASSED | | DYE COUPLER |
|---|---|---|---|---|
| BLUE (BLUE-SENSITIVE) | BLUE | RED, GREEN | | YELLOW |
| GREEN (+BLUE) (ORTHOCHROMATIC) | GREEN | RED | | MAGENTA |
| RED (+BLUE) (SPECIAL PANCHROMATIC) | RED | NONE | | CYAN |

Fig. 280A. Cross Section of a Color Film. The cross-hatched areas show the color sensitivity of each of the three emulsion layers. The dark areas show the colors actually registered. The light areas indicate the blue-sensitive portions of lower layers which remain unexposed because of the yellow filter above them.

(fogged) and developed to black metallic silver in a color developer. The developer is simultaneously oxidized and combines with the dye coupler to form a dye color — each layer forming its own single dye color — in this case, either yellow, magenta or cyan. Further processing removes the black silver, leaving only the grainless dye colors in the emulsion layers to form a positive image.

*Picture Formed by Negative Materials.* If colored photoprints are desired, the original scene usually is recorded on a negative color film (such as Kodacolor). This, in turn, must be contact printed or enlarged onto a similar negative-working color-sensitive photopaper (for viewing by reflected light) or on color copy film (for projection or viewing by transmission).

(1) *The original subject* to be photographed in full color is shown as the colored squares at the top of Fig. 280B. These represent all basic colors of light being reflected, although many variations of these in tone and in combinations, are possible. In order, from left to right, the squares represent these colors of light: white (mixture of blue, green and red), blue, cyan (mixture of blue and green), green, yellow (mixture of green and red), red, magenta (mixture of blue and red), and black (absence of reflected light).

(2) *The latent image* is formed on the film during exposure (cross-hatched areas of Line 2 in Fig. 280B).

The blue light waves (from the white, blue, cyan and magenta areas of the original) record an image in the silver of the top blue-sensitive layer of the emulsion. (Although the two lower emulsions are also sensitive to blue light, the yellow filter layer prevents blue light from reaching them.)

The green light waves (from the white, cyan, green and yellow areas) pass through the blue-sensitive layer, through the yellow filter, and finally register on the green-sensitive layer.

The red light waves (from the white, yellow, red and magenta areas) pass through the yellow filter and the green-sensitive layers and register on the red-sensitive layer.

In registering on their respective layers of emulsion, these transmitted light rays create a latent image in the silver emulsion of each layer.

NOTE: White light registered as part of each color. Black did not register, because it reflected no light.

*Color development* also is shown in Line 2. During development of the latent image, a black metallic silver image is formed in each of the emulsion layers. The action of the developer on the exposed silver salts reduces it to metallic silver. The developer reacts with the dye coupler to form the dye — either yellow, magenta or cyan — one color in each layer, depending on the composition of the coupler. This dye remains in the layer where the dye coupler was deposited originally during manufacture of the film.

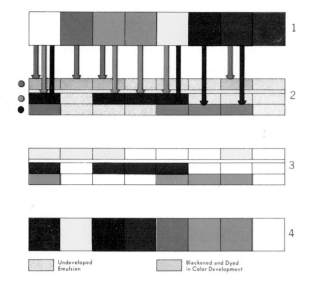

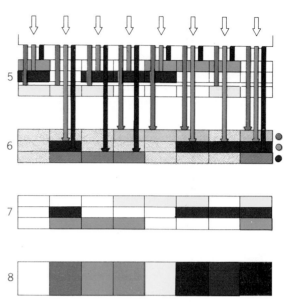

Fig. 280B. Forming a Color Negative. The arrows show the action of light rays from the subject. Circles show color sensitivity of each layer.
(1) Original colors of subject.
(2) Exposure and development blacken the silver emulsion and activate the dye.
(3) Metallic silver is eliminated, leaving the dye.
(4) Negative image as viewed.

Fig. 280C. Printing a Color Negative Gives a Positive Image
(5) Color negative (from previous Fig., but inverted) in a contact printer or enlarger. Color layers act as filters.
(6) Exposure and development of emulsions.
(7) Cleared image gives the positive.
(8) Positive on paper reflects natural colors.

(3) *Final processing and fixing* removes the opaque-silver negative image from each layer, leaving only the three colors of dye — yellow, magenta and cyan (Line 3 in Fig. 280B). Color negatives also may have a thin, orange-colored mask.

(4) *The color negative* shows a full range of tones and colors (when held up to the light and viewed), but tones are reversed (as in any negative), and the colors are the complements of the original colors (Line 4 of Fig. 280B). Because a color-correcting mask is built into the negative, it usually has an orange-colored cast.

(5) *In enlarging or contact printing,* the color negative acts as a selective color filter when light is passed through it. Each small area of the negative passes its components but absorbs its complementary color (Line 5, Fig. 280C).

(6) *The copy emulsion* (film or paper) produces the latent image by exposure to the color negative. This copy emulsion has the same three color-sensitive layers — blue, green and red — as the original negative film. It does not, however, need the yellow filter under the blue-sensitive layer, and the lower two emulsions can be made insensitive to the controlled blue light transmitted from the negative (Line 6, Fig. 280C). Color development of the copy film or paper essentially is the same as for the negative. Note, however, that the locations of the latent image and the dye couplers are exact opposites from those of the original negative.

(7) *Final processing* of the copy emulsion removes the opaque silver and leaves the grainless dye layers to form the positive image (Line 7, Fig. 280C).

(8) *The color positive,* when viewed, now should have the full range of tones and colors in positive form, much like the original subject (Line 8, Fig. 280C). Actually, the color balance may be incorrect because of a number of possible problems (such as: aged emulsion, manufacturing differences, composition of orig-

inal lighting or printing light, under- or over-exposure, development variation, or a color cast in the lens of the camera or enlarger). If not excessive, this color balance can be corrected in subsequent prints by the addition of color-correction filters over the light source. These filters are tinted lightly to remove part of the white light, so that some colors can be minimized and others accented.

*Reversal Color Film (for Transparencies).* A positive image in full color is produced directly on this color film, for use as transparencies or motion pictures to be viewed by projected light. See Fig. 280D.

The latent image is produced in the different layers in the same way as for the color negative film. However, the reversal film is first developed in a black-and-white developer which produces silver images in each of the three

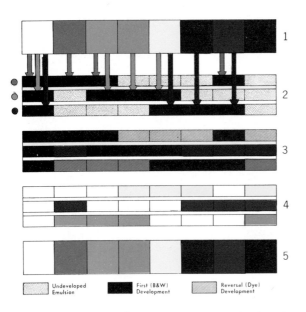

Fig. 280D. Forming a Transparency on Reversal Film. The arrows show the action of light rays from the subject. Circles show the color sensitivity of each layer.
 (1) Original color of subject.
 (2) After exposure and first development, the silver emulsion is blackened.
 (3) During color development, the unexposed areas are darkened and, simultaneously, a dye image forms.
 (4) The black grains of silver and the antihalation layer are eliminated.
 (5) Image as viewed.

emulsion layers (Line 2, Fig. 280D). The first development is stopped by a stop bath, and the film is re-exposed (fogged) to artificial light to obtain reversed tones. Then it is treated in a color developer.

In the color developer (Line 3, Fig. 280D), all portions of the emulsions which were not developed by the first development are now blackened due to the fogging exposure. At the same time, the cyan, magenta and yellow dye images are formed. These will form a positive image of the original in the original colors.

As a last step, the film is bleached and fixed, removing the yellow filter dye and the black dye in the anti-halation layer (Line 4, Fig. 280D). The original colors can now be seen by projected light (Line 5, Fig. 280D). No color correction is possible in reversal color film after it has been exposed. As with any color film, color-correction (CC) filters can be used on the camera lens to correct for light source. If prints are desired, usually an intermediate negative is made.

## Process Color Reproduction

We have already seen how flat screen tints printed in the four colors of process inks can produce a broad range of colors — in various hues, tones and chromas (Figs. 279D and 279E). Such a chart is especially valuable in determining the percentage of each of the component colors for any desired hue. For example, locate in Fig. 279D some common colors, and determine how they were made (such as those containing cyan):

| | |
|---|---|
| yellow-green = $\frac{1}{8}$C + Y | blue = C + $\frac{1}{4}$M |
| green = $\frac{1}{8}$C + $\frac{3}{4}$Y | purple-blue = C + M |
| blue-green = C + $\frac{1}{4}$Y | purple = $\frac{1}{2}$C + M |

Note that the two-color overprints illustrated in these three blocks cover the entire spectrum of bright colors. The three- and four-color overprints on the next two pages merely add the less intense shades.

We shall now see how a colored photograph or painting can be separated into its three component primary colors, so that the tones of each single primary are recorded as a halftone negative on monochromatic film. After this negative is made, the rest of the printing process is much like reproducing black-and-white halftones, except that colored inks are used and a much higher degree of quality control is required throughout.

The three colors of process inks are yellow, magenta and cyan. Carefully controlled tones of each are printed from separate plates in perfect register to produce the composite reproduction of the original color copy. While these three primaries theoretically should reproduce the full range of colors (as color film does with the same primaries), usually a fourth plate, printed in black ink, also is used. The black serves to: (1) increase the density range, (2) improve shadow detail, and (3) make control of the other three colors less critical as to ink balance.

It is impossible here to give a complete description of the many procedures for process color reproduction. It is hoped, however, that this introduction will give the reader enough of an insight into the process so that he will better understand its principles, be induced to study it further, and perhaps even undertake some elementary process color reproduction.

Materials and methods in the field of process color reproduction constantly are being researched and improved. The reader is advised to seek detailed and up-to-date information from the published materials of such organizations as the Graphic Arts Technical Foundation, Eastman Kodak Co., the Gevaert Co. of America, or the Photo Products Div. of DuPont.

## Copy for Color Reproduction

Camera copy for process color reproduction may be *reflection copy* (on an opaque base) or *transparent copy* (which must be viewed and copied with transmitted light). Transparent copy has a much wider range of density and color values, so color separation techniques are somewhat different. Since printing inks have neither the density range nor the color purity of photographic materials, some adjustments must be made.

*Reflection copy* includes such items as watercolor paintings, oil paintings, casein paintings, pastel drawings, colored crayon drawings, carbro prints, dye-transfer prints, color photoprints, or hand-colored photographs, in almost any size.

*Transparent copy* includes such items as slides or transparencies on reversal (positive) color film (Kodachrome, Ektachrome, Anscochrome, etc.) or on negative color film (Kodacolor, Ektacolor, etc.), from 35mm to 8″ x 10″ (or even larger) in size.

## Types of Process Color Separations

There are two basic procedures for making color separations. These are the *direct* and *indirect* methods. (Since the direct method is the simpler of the two methods, we will use it for our basic explanation, even though indirect methods generally are used in the trade when separations are made on the process camera. The direct method typically is used for transparencies separated on an enlarger rather than a camera. On the camera, the exposure times may become so long as to be prohibitive.)

*The direct method* of process color separation is shown in full color in Fig. 281A.

*Making the Separation Negatives.* The original color copy is set up on the copyboard. Four separate exposures are then made, each on a separate piece of film (usually a panchromatic litho film), with a different filter in the camera lens for each exposure and with the screen rotated to a different angle for each exposure. The colors of the original color copy which are recorded on the separation negatives appear on the negatives as black-and-white densities.

The *first exposure* records the *cyan* in the original copy. It is made with a red filter (the complement of cyan) in the lens and with the screen at an angle of 105° over the film. This negative will be the cyan record negative, also known as the cyan printer negative. It will be used to expose the offset plate for printing the cyan ink on the press. Cyan (blue-green) is used to produce blues, greens, and purples. This action is summarized in Fig. 281B.

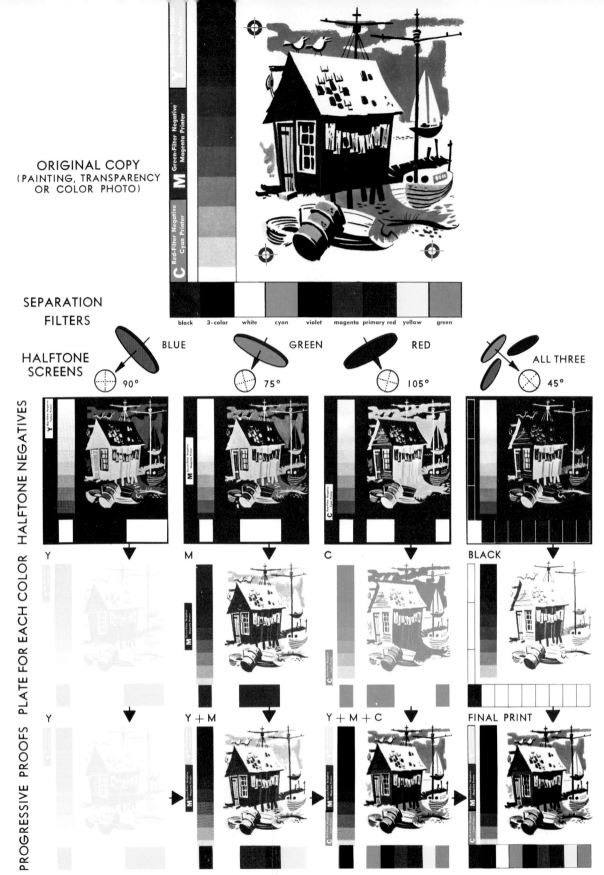

ORIGINAL COPY
(PAINTING, TRANSPARENCY
OR COLOR PHOTO)

SEPARATION
FILTERS

black   3-color   white   cyan   violet   magenta   primary red   yellow   green

HALFTONE
SCREENS

BLUE   90°          GREEN   75°          RED   105°          ALL THREE   45°

HALFTONE NEGATIVES

Y          M          C          BLACK

PLATE FOR EACH COLOR

Y          Y + M          Y + M + C          FINAL PRINT

PROGRESSIVE PROOFS

Fig. 281A.   Direct Method of Process Color Separation and Reproduction   (Courtesy Eastman Kodak Co.)

The *second exposure,* for the *magenta* printer negative, is made with a green filter and the screen at 75°.

The *third exposure,* for the *yellow* printer negative, is made with a blue filter and the screen at an angle of 90°.

The *fourth exposure,* for the *black* printer negative, may be made as three partial exposures on the one piece of film. The first partial exposure uses the *red* filter; the second, the *green* filter; and the third, the *blue* filter. The screen is rotated to, and remains at, 45° for these three partial exposures. Some techniques use a single exposure through a yellow or orange (85B) filter.

Fig. 278C, on page 161, shows the densities made on panchromatic film for each of the separation negatives produced through a different filter for each one.

*Color Correction.* Color correction provides a means of printing *less* ink of certain colors in appropriate areas of the reproduction printing, in order to compensate for the color-absorbing deficiencies of process inks. For example, since magenta inks act as if they were contaminated with traces of yellow ink, some of the yellow should be removed below magenta areas wherever this combination is to overprint. Similarly, both yellow and magenta must be reduced under cyan, and all three must be removed under black.

Achieving a set of color-corrected separation negatives (or positives) may be accomplished by photographic masking, electronic scanning, hand retouching of the halftone negatives or positives (localized dot etching), etc. Fig. 281C shows the correction achieved by photographic masking.

The simplified correction techniques made possible by *photographic masking* have been one of the keys to the increased use of process color. In photo masking, a special color film is prepared, which in one method is the same size as the copy. When placed over the copy for certain exposures, it automatically removes the necessary amounts of color intensity wherever needed. In camera-back masking, the mask is prepared to be placed in contact with the unexposed film, and the light rays reflected from

the copy must pass through this selective filter. Photographic masking, while removing most of the tedious hand work of localized dot etching, still requires careful judgment of the cameraman.

*Electronic scanners* use computers to determine where the impulse from the colored image should be weakened for color correcting. This procedure completely automates the separation and correction. See Fig. 281D. A single-color electronic scanner is shown in the chapter on platemaking, page 245.

If separations are being made for non-critical work or for experimental or demonstration projects, color correction may be omitted to simplify the procedure. This has been known as "short-run" process color or "pleasing" color. This is adequate for some types of copy and some classes of work.

*Making the Plates.* Plates are made from the separation negatives — one for each color to be printed.

*Running the Plates.* The plates are run on the press, in the progressive order shown — yellow, magenta, cyan and black. Each plate transfers the correct amount of one of the colors to the paper. Four separate runs are made on a single-color press, and the ink is allowed to dry between each run. On a two-color press, the magenta is laid down directly over the wet yellow ink in one run, and then the black is

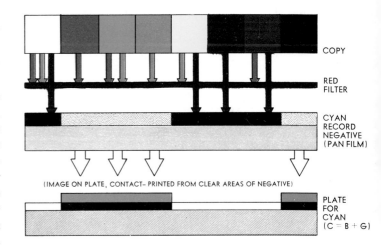

Fig. 281B.  Action of the Red Filter in Process Color Separation

laid over the wet cyan in a second run. It is necessary for the top ink to be thinner than the one laid down first; otherwise, the top ink will not *trap* properly — *i.e.*, the second layer fails to adhere and it removes some of the first layer. Four-color presses apply all four inks (wet) in one run, and each color must be progressively

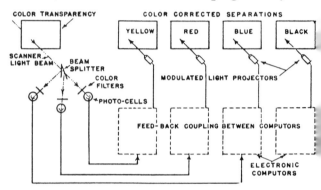

Fig. 281D. Diagram of an Electronic Color Scanner (Courtesy GATF)

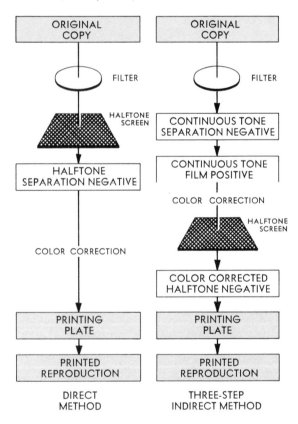

Fig. 281C. Uncorrected Reproduction of a Color Photograph (above) and the Same Copy Color Corrected Using Only Photographic Masking Methods (Courtesy DuPont Photo Products Department and GATF)

Fig. 281E. Two of Many Possible Methods of Producing Color Separations. In each method, the procedures are repeated for each of the four colors.

thinner. The color balance may vary some with the order in which the colors are run and how well they trap.

The *indirect method* of color separation is diagrammed in the flow chart of Fig. 281E. It involves more steps than the direct method, but it is often preferred (especially when colors are corrected by hand), and it offers the convenience of color correcting on the continuous-tone film positives, plus the advantage of using the same set of color-corrected positives for enlargements or reductions prior to screening.

Note, in this method, that the separation negatives are exposed *without the screen* in the camera, resulting in continuous-tone separation negatives from which continuous-tone film positives are made.

Color correction is done before these continuous-tone film positives are contact printed *through the halftone screen*. The final result is color-corrected halftone negatives for each of the printing plates.

Sometimes the continuous-tone positives (step 2) or even the separations (step 1) are made on paper rather than film, so that the separations can be handled more like original one-color artwork or halftones. If separations are made directly on paper, a panchromatic-type paper is required — such as Kodak Resisto (contact speed) or Resisto Rapid (enlarging speed) panchromatic papers. The latter paper is especially convenient in school laboratories for making positive continuous-tone separations from a Kodacolor negative in an enlarger. The resulting black-and-white print can be made into halftone negatives in exactly the same manner as any monotone copy — except that the screen angles must be changed for each and extra care is required for register and tone range.

## HOW-TO PROCEDURES FOR COLOR PRINTING

### Procedures for Flat Color

The easiest method of introducing color into a piece of printing is simply to print the entire form with a colored ink. While black ink normally is preferred for maximum legibility of text and line matter or for the maximum density range for halftones, such dark colors as browns, greens or blues might also be used. Another simple method of adding color is to print on colored stock — this is especially appropriate for pamphlet covers and posters.

In addition, of course, it is possible to combine a single color of ink with a colored stock to obtain at least two colors, with little more work or expense than would be required for black on white. There is also the possibility of obtaining a range of tones of a third color. For example, if an *opaque* blue (unaffected by the paper color) were printed on yellow stock, screened tone areas would blend the two colors producing shades of green — a 10% blue dot plus a 90% yellow paper giving a yellow-green, or a 90% dot giving a blue-green. Again, the two-color chart of overprints shown in Fig.

279D can be used for *ideas*, even if somewhat different colors and results are involved.

Methods of introducing more than one color into a job vary from the simpler methods of line separation to the more-complex methods

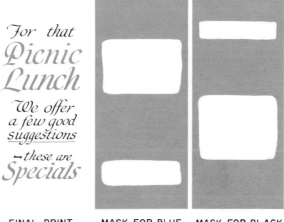

FINAL PRINT    MASK FOR BLUE    MASK FOR BLACK

Fig. 282A. Template Masks for Separating a Simple Job into Two Colors

of process color separation of full-color originals, as color photographs, transparencies, etc.

### Masked Separations

The masking separation may be used where lines or blocks of type matter (or illustrations) are to appear in different colors. See Fig. 282A.

From the single, stripped-up flat, a separate plate is prepared for each color. Each plate is exposed through a mask, so that only a portion of the flat is printed each time. Other masks are prepared for exposing plates for each of the other colors.

The masks may be prepared from flat-size sheets of goldenrod paper registered to the flat. The goldenrod sheet simply is placed in register over the flat on the lighted stripping table. Then the "windows" for the first color are cut out. The flat is labeled with the color it is intended for. This is repeated, making a template mask for each of the other colors.

A separate plate is then exposed for each color to be printed by superimposing the appropriate template mask over the flat when exposing each plate in the platemaker.

### Duplicate Negatives for Stripping

When the details being separated for color are too complex for convenient masking, it is better to make a duplicate negative for each color. Then the unneeded parts of each negative are opaqued. For example, look back at Fig. 274B. It has lines in black, red, green and blue and is only one of many figures on that plate. From one inked drawing (which included all details), a negative and three duplicates were made. On the negative for yellow, all was opaqued except the red and the green lines. On the negative for cyan, only the green and blue lines remained. On the negative for black, only the three colored lines were opaqued, leaving the rest open. On the negative for magenta, all was opaqued except the red and the blue lines; then a piece of 25% tint screen was placed under the opening for the blue line, because blue is formed by cyan plus 25% magenta.

When colors must fit perfectly, this method is preferred, because the images are identical. If separate inked lines (in the example above) were attempted for the yellow and the magenta (to overprint as a single red line), they probably would not register as well.

### Hand-Cut Ruby Film

In this method, considerable accuracy can be achieved in adding colors. It is commonly used for applying flat color to areas or objects or around an outline. See Fig. 282B.

The masking material is a separable two-ply acetate film — usually a ruby-red film adhered to a clear-film base.

The original artwork is "keyed" (identified) for colors and equipped with register marks.

The acetate mask is taped in register over the artwork. The areas of the mask to be

Fig. 282B.  Using Hand-Cut Ruby Film for Color Tint (Courtesy Separon Company)

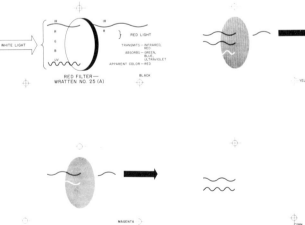

Fig. 282C.  Separations Drawn on Separate Overlays (See Fig. 278B for the color print of this.)

"opened" for the color are then outlined with a sharp knife, cutting through only the red layer of the two-ply mask (not cutting through the base layer). The red color is opaque to the blue light needed for exposing a plate, but it is clear enough to see through. The red layer is then peeled from the film, leaving a "window" effect in the red film. Register marks are copied on the film. Ruby film can also be cut to fit the master negative after it has been made.

This film is then stripped into a sheet of goldenrod to be used as the flat for exposing a plate to print that color. A separate acetate mask is prepared (including register marks) and stripped up for each of the other colors to be printed.

### Overlays

Line color work, such as multicolored maps, can be drawn on overlays using a separate sheet or flap for each color to be reproduced. (Each sheet is registered over the others and carries register marks.) Transfer type, lettering and film tint areas may be added where desired. Fig. 282C shows a drawing and three overlays for the color. It can be seen in color in Fig. 278B.

Overlays can be made on clear acetate sheets or even on tracing paper. Acetate requires lacquer-like ink which will adhere to the glossy surface. Also, some inks tend to chip off, but this can be minimized by a clear spray (fixative) applied over the ink work. India inks can be used on tracing paper. Artwork is in black on white, no matter what the final printing color is to be.

Each color sheet may then be photographed separately as line copy (reducing as necessary). Clear acetates may be contact printed to produce the separate film negatives (or positives) for each color. Also, if the image is black enough, the drawings themselves may be used for exposing positive-working offset plates.

### Key-Line Art

Adjacent colors which appear to meet actually should overlap slightly. This allows some variation in register without showing an unsightly gap between colors. Since such an overlap is difficult to draw accurately on overlays, key-

line drawings are prepared. An example is shown in Fig. 283A.

One drawing in black India ink incorporates all the colors. A fine line (the width of the desired overlap) is drawn where two colors meet, but the areas to be printed in color are not inked close to this margin. Usually the edge of the solid inking is left jagged to show it is unfinished.

Two identical negatives of the artwork go to the stripper, along with a drawing indicating the final appearance of the design. The stripper then opaques up to one side of the line and scrapes away unwanted emulsion on the other side. For example, study the yellow dot superimposed in the letter "F" of our example. On the negative, the key line is clear, with a ragged, narrow, black area surrounding it. The negative for yellow requires a clear round dot at this point, so the "F" is opaqued out up to the key line. Then a sharp knife is used to remove the emulsion on the ragged black ring inside the circular key line. On the cyan negative, the dot is opaqued and the ragged outline outside the key line is removed. On the yellow negative, it is necessary to opaque only ¼″ or so around the four yellow spots — the rest can be masked on the top side with tape or paper.

Fig. 283A. Key-Line Art (above) and Its Division into Two Colors by the Stripper

## Tint Screens

When a flat shade of a color (including black) is required over an area, it usually is provided by placing a piece of screened photographic film over that area of the flat. Tint screens for a number of gray tones (usually designated by capital letters) are available commercially. While such screens could be made on the job by exposing flat halftone negatives from a clean piece of gray paper at various exposures, these are not accurate enough for most purposes. Also, while the commercial screens can be contact duplicated, even this is not as accurate as using the original commercial screen. (See page 105 for tints available.)

An easy method of incorporating the screen is to cut an opening in the goldenrod paper of the flat and then to tape the screen tint below the opening. If the tint is to register to another negative, the flat is registered with that negative below the goldenrod for the tint, and the image showing through the top goldenrod is used as a guide for cutting the opening.

If process colors are being used, any shade shown on the color chart (Fig. 279E) can be laid smoothly onto an area by applying the necessary combination of tint screens. The color chart itself is a good example of what can be done with commercial tint screens. If a screen overprints another, the screen angles must be positioned carefully. See page 181.

## Filter Separation of Line Copy

Line artwork in colors can be photographed one color at a time to produce separate negatives for each color. The appropriate filter and film combination to use is indicated in Table 3 on page 127. The negative for each color then can be stripped up for exposing its appropriate color plate.

For example, if copy is in red and blue, a red filter (25) and pan film will copy the blue, but they will drop the red; a blue filter (47B) and pan film will copy the red but will drop the blue. Black cannot be filtered out, but it sometimes can be removed by opaquing or masking.[10]

## Duotones

Duotones are illustrations printed in two colors, commonly a principal (dark) color (at a screen angle of 45°) and a second (lighter) color (at a screen angle 30° from the first — either 15° or 75°). See Fig. 283B.

Usually black is used as the principal color, and some other color is used as the lighter color. *Or* the principal color may be a primary color and the other a complement or another primary color, such as: purple and yellow, blue and yellow, or red and green. Two such colors are capable of reproducing a considerable range of the spectrum.

Original copy for producing the duotone negatives is usually a black-and-white photo-

Fig. 283B. A Duotone Made from a Black-and-White Photograph

[10]For a more complex system of separating line copy containing a number of key colors see: GATF, Research Progress No. 63, "Color Separating Line Copy," December, 1963. The technique described allows map work (for example) to be drawn in six basic colors on one sheet for later separation as solid line copy.

graph; no filters are required. Duotones also are made from colored originals (such as color transparencies), by using filters in making the screened separation negatives.

In producing the negatives from black-and-white copy, the negative for the principal color should be made so that it is of normal contrast, but lacking somewhat in highlights. The negative for the lighter color may have a little more contrast and carry the highlights quite well. In this way, the second color of the duotone gives "sparkle" to the colored reproduction. Note the natural look of the silverware in Fig. 283B.

### "Fake" Color

"Fake" color is an unfortunate term, since each method of color separation has its own legitimate use in producing effective and sometimes simply-produced separations. Perhaps "hand-drawn process separations" would be a more descriptive name, but "fake" is more common.

In this chapter, the spectrum illustrations are "faked," rather than being recorded on color film, separated photographically, and then color corrected. The artist simply made a shaded white-to-black drawing for each of the four process colors. These are illustrated in Fig. 283C.

In this instance, it was felt that the colors could be reproduced accurate enough and much more directly by using this method. The colors had to be positioned carefully and had to be pure and relatively true — a major task if done photographically. The specifications for the artwork are shown at the bottom of Fig. 283C.

The procedure used is simple enough that many inexperienced workers can duplicate it:

1. Make a drawing in color, or study existing color prints.
2. Find each key color on the color charts (Figs. 279D or 279E), and identify the components required — such as ¼M + ½C.
3. Experiment with making different tones of gray. Retouching grays, various grades of drawing pencils, or an airbrush or pencil shading on pebble-tone paper (Ross Board) might be used. For the spectrum, a "coral"-finish type of offset book paper (which has an embossed pebble-tone sur-

face) was used together with a black marking crayon. Drawings were made four times larger than final size, and *line* negatives were made at 25% original size (no screen-angle problems).

4. Make a long, gradated tint running from pure white to a solid dense black. Calibrate this at key points — ⅟₁₆ (6%), ⅛ (12%), ¼ (25%), ½ (50%), ¾ (75%), solid (100%). Use a densitometer or a calibrated gray scale. A working density for each of the above key points is approximately: .05, .10, .15, .30, .60, and 1.60 (adjusted somewhat to allow for loss in copying). Make a copy negative to test how accurately the densities can be reproduced. Readjust as necessary.
5. Make an outline drawing showing the areas to be colored. Mark the component tones required at each key point.
6. Make a tone drawing (in grays and black) for each component color. If possible, use a reflection densitometer to check the accuracy of the tones. Correct as necessary.
7. Make copy negatives and a Color-Key proof to check results. Retouch shaded tones and reshoot if this is necessary.

At one time, "fake" color was rather common, especially in elementary textbooks printed in two colors. Today, such artwork is more apt to be done in full process color from colored artwork or a color photograph.

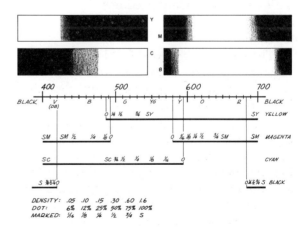

Fig. 283C. Tone Drawings for "Fake" Color in Fig. 274C.

## Procedures for Process Color

Process color separation methods and materials constantly are being researched and improved. For complete details of equipment, materials and procedures for process color separation, including color-correction methods, the reader is referred to the following publications, among others:

Eastman Kodak Company:
*Basic Color for the Graphic Arts* (Q-7)
*Color Correction with Kodak Tri-Mask Film* (Q-6A)
*Direct-Screen Color-Separation Method* (Q-114)
*Camera-Back Silver Masking* (Q-109)
*Three-Color Separation Prints from Color Negatives with Resisto Rapid Pan Paper* (E-47)
*Angle Indicator for Kodak Contact Screens* (Q-31)
Graphic Arts Technical Foundation:
*Color Separation Photography*
The Gevaert Company of America, Inc.:
*Masking with Multimask Film*

At present, commercial-quality color-corrected process color separations may be beyond the scope of the average school's available time and equipment. However, the following discussion is presented with the hope that schools will acquire at least the minimum equipment and will do *some* process color separation, even though it might be experimental in nature. It even may be necessary to omit color-correction procedures.

### Equipment

The basic items needed for elementary color separation procedures are described here. Other desirable items are mentioned and described in the publications listed above.

(1) *Camera.* The process camera should be equipped with a color-corrected lens (apochromatic, for example); a vacuum back for holding the contact screen tightly against the film; a transparency opening in the copyboard (for transparent copy); a white-light source, such as white-flame carbon arcs or high-intensity tungsten lights (3200°K).

For reflection copy, the lights generally are set at 45° to the center of the copyboard; even intensity of light over the entire copyboard can be checked with a photo-electric photometer (with a neutral gray test card in the copyboard). To get even illumination over large copy, it might be necessary to aim the lights at the far side of the copyboard.

For transmission copy, the camera should have lights which can be swung around (or placed) behind the copyboard, so that light can be directed *through* the copy in the transparency opening on the copyboard. The copyboard should be covered with a dull-black material, and the entire camera should be shielded to keep reflected and room light at a minimum.

With transmission copy, a condenser-type *enlarger* is more efficient than a process camera since shorter exposures are possible. An enlarger operates much like a process camera which has transparency illumination, except that the bellows cover the space between the lens and the copy (rather than between the lens and film), and the effective lighting is much brighter and is completely enclosed. See the large color illustration opposite page 1 for such an enlarger designed for color separation. Most "enlargers" can reduce the size of a transparency as well as make it larger.

(2) *Contact Halftone Screens.* For the *direct method* of color separation, the Kodak gray contact screen is preferred because of its neutral color. For the *indirect method* of color separation, where halftone positives are to be made from the continuous-tone separation negatives, the Kodak magenta contact screens or the Kodak pre-angled magenta contact screens are used.

(3) *Contact Screen Angling.* To achieve the four rotation angles, either the copy is rotated on the copyboard, or, more accurately, the contact screen angle is changed for each exposure. Screen angles for common uses are shown in Fig. 284A.

a. *"Circular Screen"*. One method of achieving the angled positions of the screen on the vacuum back of the camera is to cut a single screen (as shown in Fig. 284B), so that it is "circular" in shape, with four chords (straight sections) along its perimeter. A straightedge is then taped (with double-faced tape) to the vacuum back. Each of the chord sections of the screen is then butted, in turn, against the straightedge to achieve the four rotation angles.

Prior to using the screen, the screen alignment for each chord should be checked carefully with the Kodak angle indicator (as described in its accompanying instruction booklet). The necessary corrections, if any, should then be recut.

Instead of using the "butting" method of positioning the screen on the vacuum back, more precise positioning is achieved by punching a pair of register pin holes along each of the four chord sections. The vacuum back is then fitted with a pair of register pins to accommodate these punched holes during each rotated position of the screen.

In preparing the "punched" screen, the screen angles must be precisely determined by use of the Kodak angle indicator.

b. *Angling a Small Screen.* For beginners and for small work, a smaller screen can be mounted in a cut-out "window" in the center of a sheet of acetate of the same outside dimensions as the template, and taped in place. The large sheet of acetate can be cut to the outline of the template and then checked for accuracy as for the large "circular" screen.

c. *Set of Four Screens.* A set of four separate screens — one designed for each rotation angle — may be prepared using the angle indicator and a register punch. (Instructions are in the "Angle Indicator" booklet).

d. *Notch Coding the Screen Angles.* To enable the worker to identify the screen angles in the dark, each screen or screen chord can be notched with a code — one notch for 90°, two notches for 75°, etc.

e. *Testing the Angled Screen.* After preparing the angled screen (or screens), it is best to perform the following test. Set up the camera for same-size reproduction, with a white card in the copyboard and a piece of orthochromatic litho film on the vacuum back. Make four suc-

**TWO-COLOR SCREEN ANGLES**

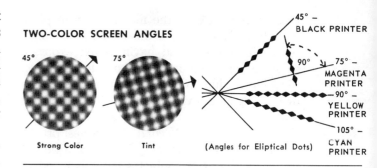

Strong Color    Tint    (Angles for Eliptical Dots)

**THREE-COLOR SCREEN ANGLES**

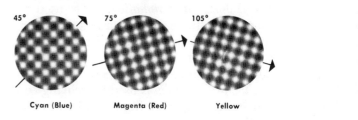

Cyan (Blue)    Magenta (Red)    Yellow

**FOUR-COLOR SCREEN ANGLES**

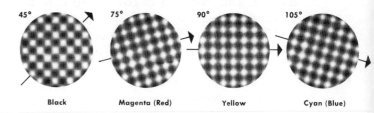

Black    Magenta (Red)    Yellow    Cyan (Blue)

Fig. 284A. Screen Angles for Various Purposes (Courtesy Eastman Kodak Company)

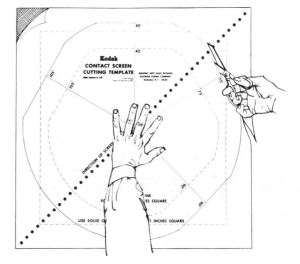

Fig. 284B. Cutting a "Circular" Screen (Courtesy Eastman Kodak Company)

cessive exposures on the film (screen in place over the film), using a different screen angle for each exposure and having each exposure sufficient to make a 10% dot on the negative. Develop the film as for a halftone. If inspection of the negative reveals no objectionable moiré pattern, the screen is ready for use.

f. *Size Screen Needed.* The largest practical-size screen of each angle which can be cut from stock sizes of contact screens is listed in Table 7.

(4) *Films. Panchromatic film* is used for making the halftone separation negatives from the original color copy (in the direct method), and for making continuous-tone separation negatives from original color copy (indirect).

*Orthochromatic film* is used for making contact halftone negatives from continuous-tone separation negatives.

*Masking film* (Multimask or Tri-mask) is used, in some methods of color correction, for making a correction mask.

(5) *Safelights.* For each type of film, consult the manufacturer's instructions (enclosed with

the package) for the safelight and darkroom-handling of that particular film. Panchromatic and masking film generally require total darkness for all, or a major portion, of the handling and processing procedures.

*When handling film in total darkness,* identify the emulsion side of the film as that side facing you when the film notches are at the top edge of the upper right-hand corner. If sheets are cut, place them emulsion-side up in the box or drawer. Use strips of taped-on cardboard on the film-cutting board and the camera vacuum back as an aid in cutting and positioning film.

(6) *Guides.* Guides are mounted on the copyboard along with the copy to help in evaluating the separation and color correction; to identify the separation negatives; and to act as a quality-control check in the final printing.

*Reflection copy guides* include color blocks, gray scale, register marks and color-control patches. These are shown mounted in Fig. 281A on page 172. These guides are available as a set, in 7″ or 14″ size, as the Kodak color separation guides. The 7″ size is used for copy which is to be enlarged; the 14″ size is used for copy which is to be reduced.

*The transparent copy guide* is for back-lighted copy. The Kodak Tri-Mask guide is shown in Fig. 284C. It includes color blocks and a modified gray scale. A photographic step tablet (11- or 21-step film gray scale) and register marks (on film or tape) should also be included on the copyboard.

*The color blocks* (one each for the cyan, magenta and yellow printer negatives) indicate (after processing the negatives) which negative is to be used for making each of the printer plates or positives.

*The color-control patches* (usually nine blocks) indicate on the film a monochromatic record of the color densities in the form of film images. In one convenient strip on the negative, these patches show the effects of the color separation and of the color correction (if performed at this step). If the patches show up correctly, the corresponding colors in the copy are showing up correctly (as black-and-white densities).

### Table 7
### Screen Sizes Needed for
### Making Angled Screens

| Size of Uncut Screen in Inches | 45° Angle in Inches | 75°, 90°, and 105° Angles in Inches |
|---|---|---|
| 9 x 11 | 9 x 11 | 5 x 6 |
| 12 x 15 | 12 x 15 | 6 x 8 |
| 15 x 18 | 15 x 18 | 9 x 11 |
| 17 x 21 | 17 x 21 | 9 x 11 |
| 25 x 25 | 25 x 25 | 15 x 18 |
| 31 x 31 | 31 x 31 | 19 x 23 |

(Courtesy Eastman Kodak Company)

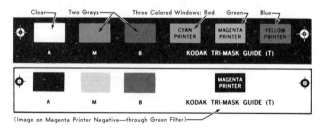

Fig. 284C. Tri-Mask Guide (T) (Courtesy Eastman Kodak Company)

Note, in Fig. 281A, the reproduction of each of the color-control patches on each of the separation negatives.

The color-control patches on the cyan printer negative show the "wanted" colors — cyan, violet and primary green — as equal to the black area in density; as further evidence of correctness, each of the three wanted colors shows up equal to the three-color area in density. These correspond to the image areas of the separation negative which will permit exposure of the offset plate to print the cyan ink.

On the same cyan printer negative, the "unwanted" colors in the original copy — yellow, magenta and primary red — have a density equal to the white patch area. Since cyan requires none of these colors in the press printing, these dense areas of the separation negative prevent an image in the exposure of the offset plate, thus printing no ink in those areas (of that color).

*The gray scale* is used to measure and compare density, density range, etc. of the separation negatives. It is especially useful in color correction procedures.

*Register guides* on paper are intended for use with reflection copy. Register guides for transparent copy may be purchased ready-prepared on film or transparent tape. However, they also may be produced in the shop as film positives by line-photographing the guides which are printed on paper. Then the negative is contact printed onto ortho film which has been intentionally slightly fogged by exposing the film for a few seconds to a yellow flashing lamp. (The fogging produces a slightly-grayish background on the film positives which helps insure that the register marks will not be overexposed when included later with the copy on the copyboard.)

Although not recommended, register marks sometimes may be scribed on the dark edges of transparent copy — *outside the working area of the copy* — if this will not damage the original copy for further use.

For quality control of ink and identification during the press run, film images of color blocks, color patches, register marks, etc. are stripped into the flat so as to print in the waste margin of the printing sheet. The color being printed or overprinted can be checked visually, or with a densitometer, against the master sheet and by comparison with the original color patches

(7) *Filters.* For the color separation procedures discussed later in this section, the following Kodak Wratten filters are recommended in this order of use (but others are possible):

> 23A (or 25) (red) for the cyan printer
> 58 (green) for the magenta printer
> 47 (or 47B) (blue) for the yellow printer

(8) *Densitometer.* For serious work, acquisition of a densitometer should be considered for measuring densities.

### Focusing the Camera

Camera focus should be checked and carefully adjusted at the magnification setting prior to exposing the film. For a camera equipped with calibration tapes, one check should be sufficient; tape settings then may be used without additional focus checks.

### Determining Exposures

The following procedures are suggested for arriving at the $f$-number (aperture), the detail (main) exposure time, and the flash (shadow flash) exposure time for each of the separation negatives, when using the direct method of producing color-separation negatives through filters.

(1) *f-Number of Lens.* Usually an $f/22$ or an $f/32$ setting is the best lens setting to use for the separation exposures. The $f$-number which produces satisfactory halftone negatives usually is satisfactory for process color separation.

(2) *Detail (Main) Exposure.* This procedure traditionally is based on the correct exposure for exposing the cyan printer negative through the No. 25 (red) filter. Once this red-filter exposure time is determined, exposures through each of the other filters can be calculated by multiplying the red-filter exposure time by the filter ratio for each of the other filters as indicated on the film data sheet. If the newer No. 23A (red) filter is being used, its exposure time must first be increased by ¼ to determine the equivalent time of the No. 25 filter. An ap-

proximate test exposure can be determined from the film instructions or by means of an exposure meter as follows:

With the lights set up as for an exposure, set a light meter according to the manufacturer's directions, using the film exposure index (speed number) given on the film data sheet. (For Kodalith Pan film, this is ASA 8 for white-flame arc lamps and ASA 10 for tungsten bulbs.)

Select the exposure time which corresponds, on the meter scales, with the *f*-number you have decided to use.

*Corrected Exposure Calculation:* The exposure time determined by use of the light meter must be corrected to allow for (1) reproduction (magnification or reduction) size, (2) interference of the halftone screen, and (3) absorption of the filter (filter ratio).

Use this formula to establish the corrected exposure time for the red-filter separation negative:

$$E_{1mr} \times F_m \times 10 = \text{Exposure time when making the red-filter exposure}$$

*where:*

$E_{1mr}$ = Exposure time obtained from the light-meter reading.

$F_m$ = Factor of magnification. For 100% magnification, use the factor "4." For magnifications other than 100%, determine the factor by using the Kodak Copying Dataguide.

10 = A constant, to be included when using the Kodak gray contact screen. The screen offers an obstacle to the reflected light. In effect, using the "10" in the above formula, automatically multiplies the exposure by 10.

The corrected exposure time calculated above is for the cyan printer negative, using the red filter in the exposure.

*Exposures for other filters* are arrived at by multiplying the corrected red-filter exposure time by the filter ratio of the filter to be used. The filter ratios are given in Table 8 or on the film data sheet enclosed with the box of film.

### Table 8
#### Separation Filter Ratios

These ratios are based on an exposure of approximately 2 minutes through the filter No. 25

| Light Source | Kodak Wratten Filter-Numbers | | | | | |
|---|---|---|---|---|---|---|
| | 23A | 25 (A) | 58 (B) | 47 (C5) | 47B | 8 (K2) |
| | Red | Red | Green | Blue | Blue | Yel. |
| Wh.-Fl. Arc | 0.8 | 1.0 | 3.0 | 2.5 | 3.0 | 0.50 |
| Tungsten* | 0.8 | 1.0 | 6.0 | 10.0 | 20.0 | 0.60 |

*Photoflood or other high-efficiency tungsten.

*For Example:* If the correct exposure to white-flame arc through the Wratten Filter No. 25 (filter ratio 1.0) has been determined to be 90 seconds, the exposure through the No. 47B (filter ratio 3.0) would be 270 seconds (90 x 3.0) or 4½ minutes.

*Example of Exposure:* Under average shop conditions, in making a 1:1 line reproduction, using Kodalith Pan Film with two 35-ampere arc lamps about 48 inches from the copyboard, expose for about 10 seconds at f/32 through the Wratten Filter No. 25. With a Gray Contact Screen, the exposure will be 8 to 10 times longer.

(Courtesy Eastman Kodak Company)

(3) *Flash (Shadow Flash) Exposure.* Position the continuous-tone color copy in the copyboard. Insert the specified red filter in the lens barrel. Observing the safelight precautions listed on the film data sheet, place a sheet of panchromatic film on the vacuum back. Place the screen over the film. Cover a 1"-wide strip of the film with black paper, and make a separation exposure of normal *f*-number and normal main-exposure length on this film. Open the camera back, and remove the strip of black paper. Make a series of test exposures with the flashing lamp, alone, on this strip. This is done to determine what length of flash lamp exposure will produce a density of 0.3 on this test strip of the negative, when the negative is developed to produce the desired highlight and middletone contrasts on the image portion. Flashing procedure and setup is the same as that described on pages 143-145, except a Series 2 (red) filter usually is used with pan film.

### Making a Set of Separation Negatives

The following is an outline of the steps in making a set of separation negatives by the *direct method:*

1. Check the copy and work order for instructions.
2. Install the proper safelights in the darkroom for the kind of film to be used.
3. Set the camera for reproduction size.
4. Set the lens at the desired *f*-number.
5. Install a resolution guide in the copyboard (for focusing).
6. Set camera lights at proper position and angle.
7. Check the camera focus.
8. Mount the copy and guides on the copyboard.

    NOTE: In mounting a transparency on the copyboard, place it between two pieces of glass to hold it flat. All copy should be secured with pieces of tape at the top edge in case the vacuum accidentally is shut off before all exposures are made.

9. Set the camera exposure timer for length of main (detail) exposure.
10. Determine the size of film needed. (Kodalith Pan film, Estar base, is suggested.)
11. Under proper safelight conditions, cut the film needed and place it in the box or drawer.
12. *For cyan printer negative:* Place the red filter, 23A (or No. 25, also called the A separation filter), in the filter slot of the lens barrel.
13. Place film on the vacuum back.
14. Place the gray contact screen at 105° over the film.
15. Make the main (detail) exposure.
16. Make the flash exposure.

Using a new piece of film, repeat the procedure for the magenta printer negative, rotating the screen to 75° and using a No. 58 (or B) filter. For the yellow printer negative, rotate the screen to 90° and use a new piece of film and a No. 47B filter — or a No. 47 (the C5).

For the black printer negative, expose on one sheet of film, with the screen at 45°, successively and individually through the red, green and blue filters; each exposure time should be roughly proportionate to the filter ratios. For example, in using the red filter, expose for 25% to 30% of the time as when exposing for the cyan printer negative; likewise, a 25% to 30% exposure through the green filter should be used, and a 35% to 45% exposure through the blue filter.

### Color Correction

Normally, some form of color correction is included either during the separation exposures or after the separation negatives are made.

When copy is a transparency masked with Tri-Mask film, often additional correction is not needed.

Note, in Fig. 281C, that the uncorrected reproduction lacks the purity of the colors that the corrected reproduction has — especially in the blues and greens. Color correction would have brought them up to strength.

### Processing the Negatives

Process the negatives by the time-and-temperature method (again, observe safelight and processing instructions on film data sheet).

### Evaluating the Negatives

Examine the negatives over a viewing table for obvious faults such as scratches, streaks, etc.

Check to see that the shadow and middle-tone areas do not lack dots and that the highlight areas are not plugged up. Remember, as for halftones, that the flash exposure controls the shadow dots (in the clearer areas) and that the detail exposure controls the highlight area dots (in the darker areas). Changes in exposures (detail, flash or both) may be necessary.

The gray scale images should show a complete range of tone, from 5% to 10% dots at the highlight end of the scale, to 90% to 95% dots at the shadow end.

The color patches (reproductions on negatives) should be examined to see how well the colors have been separated — which colors registered and which dropped out.

Check register by superimposing each of the negatives, in turn, over the cyan printer negative. Examine closely to see that the register marks coincide exactly.

## A Demonstration Project

The following demonstration project in process color separation may be conducted with a minimum of equipment, yet it will show the basic principles of color separation. For more complete instructions, see the Kodak booklet, *Three-color Separation Prints from Color Negatives with Resisto Rapid Pan Paper* (E-47).

1. Place a color (Kodacolor) negative in an enlarger.
2. Make three (or four) exposures on Resisto Rapid Pan paper, using the appropriate filter for each exposure.
3. Using the continuous-tone positive separation prints (made in 2, above) as camera copy, make a halftone separation negative of each on ortho film. Remember to use the proper screen angle for each halftone separation negative.
4. Make proofs of the halftone separation negatives on 3M Negative Color-Key material to demonstrate combining the colors, as they would be when printed. (Instructions for using Color-Key materials are given below.)

## Color Separation Proofs

After the color separation negatives (or positives) have been made (and before the job is actually printed on the press), a complete, full-color progressive proof of the job should be available to show color breaks, registration, fit, color values, copy details, proper stripping, and condition of tints and tones. It also serves as a progressive proof for the pressman during the press printing. Such a proof can be made conveniently with 3M "Color Key" proofing material, as described below. (Technifax Diazachrome film is a similar type of material, which also can be used for color proofing. It often is used in drafting rooms and for audiovisual transparencies. Diazochromes develop in ammonia.) While these quick techniques are adequate for most work, a short press run under actual conditions may be necessary for proofing critical jobs.

### 3M Color Key Proofing Material

3M Color Key proofing material (available as positive or negative) is a light-sensitive polyester-base film supplied in any one of a number of colors. The process colors — yellow,

cyan, magenta and black — are used for making a proof of each color separation negative.

Each individual proof made from the separation negative is actually a color transparency. The four transparencies may be taped in register on a sheet of bright-white paper, in the proper printing sequence. When illuminated by overhead (reflected) light, the assembled proofs render a true, full-color proof of the job as it actually will appear when printed.

### Proofing the Separation Negatives

The following procedure is recommended for making a set of 3M Negative Color Key proofs from a set of color separation negatives.

*Equipment and Chemicals.* Most standard exposure equipment employing ultraviolet light may be used — *e.g.*, black-light tubes, carbon arcs or photoflood lamps. Carbon arcs are preferred since they are faster and provide sharper, more even light.

Lighting in the immediate developing area is not critical. Yellow lights are desirable, but normal incandescent or fluorescent lights are satisfactory.

A 10- or 21-step, platemaker's continuous-tone sensitivity guide, with a density of approximately .97 at Step 7 is useful for checking proper exposure.

Negative Color-Key Developer is the only developer recommended for Negative Color-Key material.

A non-woven cotton wipe (4¾″ x 7½″) wrapped around a wooden applicator is recommended for applying and spreading the developer solution.

A sheet of glass should be placed on a horizontal support in the developing sink, handy to running cold water. A rubber squeegee is recommended for squeegeeing water from the back side of the Color Key material.

*Handling.* For ease in handling, the Color Key material can be removed from its tube and placed in a film or Color Key dispensing box.

The coated side of the negative Color-Key film is facing the worker if the sheet is held vertically with its two notches in the upper right-hand corner. (Scratching a leftover piece of Color Key film will identify coated side.)

*Exposure of Negative Color Key.* Place the Color Key, coated-side down, on black paper (to prevent halation). Place the photographic film, emulsion-side down, on the Color Key. Expose in a standard exposure frame to ultra-violet light. The proper exposure for an operation can be determined by stepping a typical negative across the Color Key at different exposures, using a sensitivity guide with each exposure. The exposure that produces the best dot reproduction is the one to use. This is usually a solid 3 or 4 on negative Color Key. This should be repeated for each color, although usually the same exposure can be used on all colors.

*Developing.* Place the exposed Color Key, coated-side up, on a horizontal sheet of glass. Pour a liberal amount of developer on the center of the sheet, and spread over the entire sheet with a wipe wrapped around a wooden applicator. Use enough developer to cover the entire sheet; then rub lightly with the wipe, removing the coating from the non-image areas. Keep the applicator flat against the sheet. Clean out halftones and tints by turning the wipe over and applying more developer to the sheet. When development is complete, flush with cold water. Turn the sheet over, flush with water and then squeegee the *back side.*

If shadow areas are not cleaned out or if a yellow cast appears in the image or non-image areas, apply more developer and redevelop the sheet. Blot or wipe dry.

The Color Key now is ready for immediate viewing, in the manner described earlier.

## Questions

1. Name and describe the two main classes of color printing.
2. What is color?
3. What is the range, in millimicrons, of natural visible light?
4. What are the spectrum colors?
5. Name and describe the three dimensions of color.
6. What effect does a drop in camera-lighting voltage have on the color of light it transmits?
7. What is an "apparent" color?
8. Why does a red glass appear red?
9. Of what colors of projected light are the following colors composed? (a) magenta, (b) cyan, (c) yellow, (d) black, (e) white.
10. Of what colors of transparent process printing inks are the following printed colors composed? (a) green, (b) black, (c) red, (d) blue?
11. What color of light is transmitted through a green filter? Why is this so?
12. If a transparent blue ink were printed on other than white paper, what changes would you expect in the apparent color?
13. What advantages are gained by using opaque (rather than transparent) inks?
14. What is meant by the expression: "changing the dot sizes in an area of printed color will change the value or tone of that color"?
15. Why does a panchromatic film lend itself well to making a separation negative directly from a continuous-tone color photograph?
16. Why would an orthochromatic film not be a good choice for making the above separation negative?
17. What safelights may be used for the three types of monochromatic films?
18. What two kinds of image-producing materials are there in each layer of a color film?
19. What is the function of the "dye coupler" in each layer of color film?
20. What function is served by the yellow filter layer in the color film emulsion?
21. Why does red light penetrate through to the lowest layer of the emulsion of a color film?
22. What happens in the final processing and fixing of an exposed color film?
23. What four colors of ink are used in process color reproduction?
24. Name the two kinds of copy for process color reproduction, and give examples of each.
25. Briefly describe the *direct method* of making process color separations.
26. Explain the purpose of color correction.

27. Are there any presses which will print more than one color on the paper in one pass through the press? If so, describe them.
28. Briefly describe the *indirect method* of making process color separations.
29. Describe how two colors may be printed on a job by the masking-separation method.
30. What other methods besides masking can be used to produce separate flat colors?
31. What are key-line drawings?
32. Why is the term "fake color" misleading?
33. How does a duotone differ from four-color process reproduction?
34. On notebook paper, make a table, as shown, filling in information not given:

### Indirect Method of Color Separation

| Printer Negative | Screen Angle | Filter No. & Color | Ink Color on the Press |
|---|---|---|---|
| Cyan | 105° | | |
| | | Green, No. 58(B) | |
| | | | Yellow |
| Black | | | |

## Problems and Projects

1. Produce your own color chart, using your own inks, press, etc.
2. Mount samples of ink colors to make a color tree.
3. Make a list of the equipment, supplies and aids needed to produce process-color separation negatives by the direct method.
4. Using latest catalogs, prepare a requisition for ordering the items in 3, above.
5. Determine detail (main) and flash exposures for exposing direct-method process-color separation negatives using the equipment and facilities in your shop.
6. Make a set of four process-color separation negatives (direct method) from reflection copy.
7. Make proofs with Color Key of the separation negatives in 6, above.
8. Arrange for a local craftsman to come in and demonstrate one or more methods of color separation.
9. Arrange for a field trip to a plant which specializes in process-color separation and process-color printing.
10. Contact firms who print process-color separation work and arrange for a loan or gift of (1) a set of process-color separation negatives, or (2) a set of progressive proofs of process-color printing.
11. Plan a job involving a method of color separation other than that of process color.
12. Produce the job in 11, above.
13. Bring your shop files up-to-date with advertising literature and catalogs on equipment and supplies for process-color separation work.
14. Prepare angle markings on a gray contact screen and on the camera back.

## New Words

| | | | |
|---|---|---|---|
| 1. | additive | 31. | overprinting |
| 2. | Angstrom | 32. | oxidation |
| 3. | black | 33. | perfecting |
| 4. | chroma | 34. | photo-electric |
| 5. | Color Key | 35. | pigment |
| 6. | color negative | 36. | pleasing color |
| 7. | color positive | 37. | pre-angled |
| 8. | complementary | 38. | primary color |
| 9. | composite | 39. | prism |
| 10. | cyan | 40. | process color |
| 11. | duotone | 41. | projected |
| 12. | dye | 42. | radiation |
| 13. | electromagnetic | 43. | receptive |
| 14. | flat color | 44. | reproduction |
| 15. | fluorescence | 45. | reversal color film |
| 16. | hue | 46. | scanner |
| 17. | incandescent | 47. | sensitivity |
| 18. | incident | 48. | separation |
| 19. | infrared | 49. | spectrogram |
| 20. | interposed | 50. | spectrophotometer |
| 21. | Kelvin | 51. | spectrum |
| 22. | laser | 52. | subtractive |
| 23. | magenta | 53. | superimposed |
| 24. | masking film | 54. | tandem |
| 25. | millimicron | 55. | transmitted |
| 26. | monochromatic | 56. | transparency |
| 27. | multi-colored | 57. | transparent |
| 28. | negative color film | 58. | ultraviolet |
| 29. | neutral | 59. | voltage |
| 30. | opaque ink | 60. | wavelength |

## Film Developing

## and Darkroom Procedures

A darkroom must be provided for handling and developing film, and for making contact prints, combinations and positives.

## Layout of the Darkroom

Fig. 285 illustrates a comfortable darkroom. A temperature-controlled sink holds the four processing trays: developer, short-stop, fixer and running water. A safelight is provided above the developing tray for inspection of the negatives as the developing progresses.

For certain films (such as the orthochromatic film used for the general run of work) a red safelight is used. However, always check the manufacturer's directions for the proper safelight to be used with each type of film.

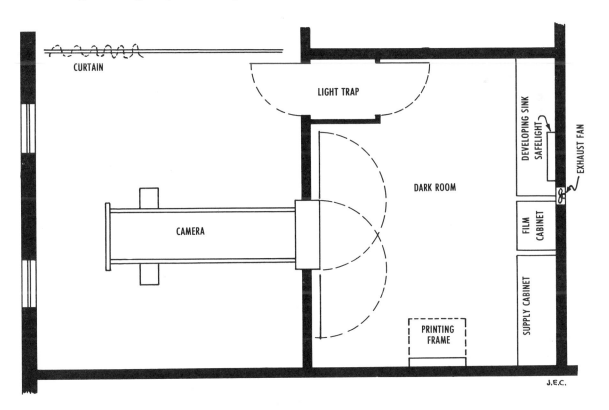

Fig. 285. Comfortable Darkroom

On the wall or worktable is an exposure frame for making contact prints and combinations. Above the contact frame is the contact-frame exposure light.

A ventilating fan is a necessity for removing fumes and odors. If no fan is available, do not mix or weigh dry chemicals in the darkroom. Leave the doors open for ventilation when the room is not in use.

Shelves should be provided above and below the sink and worktables for graduates, trays, and other accessories. Bottled chemicals should be stored on the *lowest* shelves for safety.

A film-drying rack may be attached to the underside of the shelves over the sink.

A work-top, shallow-drawer cabinet should be provided for the storage and handling of film and other camera accessories.

| DEVELOPER | SHORTSTOP | FIXER | RUNNING WATER |

Fig. 286.  Order of Trays in Darkroom

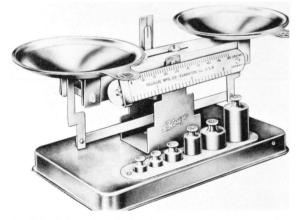

Fig. 287. Pelouze R-47 Scales. Operating Hints: 1. First set the beam sliding poise at zero. Place pan "L" at left, and pan "R" at right with the handles facing the operator. 2. Balance the scale, if necessary, by turning the counterpoise unit either right or left, until the indicator line is directly in line with the index line. 3. Place the desired weights in the right-hand pan. 4. Add the material to be weighed to the left-hand pan until balance is obtained, when indicator line and index line coincide.

Entrance to the darkroom is by way of a light baffle.

If a darkroom camera is used, an opening in the wall of the darkroom is provided to admit the back of the camera and its controls. Space between the camera back and the opening is sealed light-tight. In this manner the film need not leave the darkroom, and may be inspected and focused at greater advantage in the darkness of the darkroom.

If necessary, and if there is room, the darkroom camera may be placed and used within the darkroom, but it is best to protect the developing area from the bright lights.

## Order of Trays

Four trays are generally used in the developing process. They contain developer, shortstop, fixer and running water, Fig. 286. The trays are placed in that order in the sink, and always maintained in the same order to eliminate confusion in the dark. While commonly in order from left to right, the actual order may vary with the sink arrangement.

## Theory of Negatives

Reflected light during exposure of the film in the camera produces a *latent* image on the film. This is a chemical change in the composition of the film emulsion which cannot be seen until the film is in the developer.

The complete "developing" (processing) of exposed film is accomplished by placing the film through the four successive tray baths — developer, shortstop, fixer, water.

The action of the four baths is as follows:

The *developing* bath (chemically a base) causes the latent image to become visible as the developer solution frees the exposed silver particles in the film emulsion, causing these particles to form a dense, black or *opaque* background. At the same time, the particles of silver which were not struck by the light form a transparent image area on the film.

The *shortstop* bath is a mild acid which quickly neutralizes the action of the developer solution when developing has been completed.

The *fixing* bath is an acid which removes all unexposed particles of silver and the antihalation backing from the film.

The *running-water* bath washes away all traces of the chemicals used and prevents later darkening of the clear areas of the film.

## Preparation of Tray Solutions

Purchase the developer and fixing chemicals recommended by the manufacturer of the particular film to be used. Follow his instructions in mixing the chemicals and in developing the film. See Figs. 287 and 288. In general, the procedure is as follows:

### Developer

The developer is usually sold in concentrated powder form in two separate containers: one containing *Part A*, and the other containing *Part B*. Prepare each part separately according to the instructions on the package. Store them in two jugs marked "A" and "B." When you are ready to develop film, pour equal amounts of A and B into the developer tray and stir the solution. Such developers are discarded after use.

### Shortstop

The shortstop solution (stop bath) is prepared by pouring 8 ounces (liquid) of 28% acetic acid into a gallon of water. Store this in a jug labeled "Shortstop Solution". Discard after use.

NOTE: To make approximately 28% acetic acid from glacial (concentrated) acetic acid, add 3 parts of glacial acetic acid to 8 parts of water.

Glacial acetic acid liquid or vapors may cause severe irritation or burns if allowed to come into contact with eyes, skin, or clothing. In case of accidental contact, immediately flush the affected parts with running water for 15 minutes and seek a physician's aid.

Store glacial acetic acid in an area maintained above 62° F., and where there is no danger of accidental spilling.

### Fixer

The fixer is generally purchased in powder form, and mixed according to the package directions. Store this in a jug marked "Fixer."

Fixer is also known as "hypo." Wipe up spills thoroughly as they will look like white paint when dry. Fixer (if still clearing film in about 2 minutes) is usually returned to its jug after use.

### Water

The tray containing the water should be provided with some means for continuously changing the water. A tray siphon may be used, or a temperature-controlled faucet set at 68° F. may be allowed to continuously run water into the tray.

### Filling the Trays

Select trays of a size a little larger than the film to be processed, and place them in order in the developing sink.

Into each tray, pour enough of the appropriate solution to suit conditions — about ¾" deep will do to start.

For the first tray, equal parts of *developer* "A" and "B" solutions should be mixed; the second tray contains the *shortstop* solution; the third tray contains the *fixer* solution; and the last tray is at least half full of water at 68° F.

Now, place the sink overflow pipe in position, and turn water into the sink to achieve and maintain the tray temperature desired.

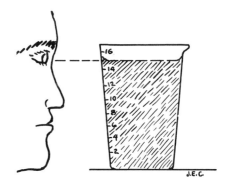

Fig. 288. Measuring Liquids. For accurate measuring, hold the vessel level and at eye level.

## Developing Procedure for Negatives

The exposed film is processed in the dark-room with the overhead white (or yellow) lights *turned off*, and illumination provided only by the recommended safelight (at least until the film is in the wash bath). For example, the recommended safelight for processing Kodak Ortho Type 3 Film is a Kodak Safelight Filter, Wratten Series 1A (light red), in a suitable safelight lamp, with a 15-watt bulb, at not less than 4 feet.

### Removing the Film

After exposure of the film with the *gallery camera*, replace the film-covering metal slide in the film holder. Remove the film holder

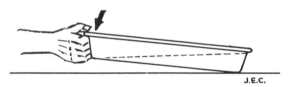

Fig. 289.  Agitating Developer in Tray

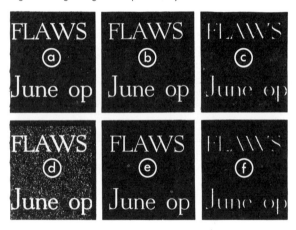

Fig. 290A.  Judging the Line Negative after Processing. (a) Under exposure — elements tend to thicken; (b) Normal exposure; (c) Overexposure — fine lines and serifs are lost; (d) Underdeveloped — background not sufficiently opaque; (e) Normal development; (f) Overdeveloped — fine lines and serifs are lost.

NOTE: These illustrations are grossly exaggerated. Because of the wide latitude of exposure tolerance of a good line film, Fig. "a" shows only a little thickening of the lines, despite an exposure only one-sixth of normal; Fig. "c" was exposed four times the normal exposure to achieve the above results.

from the camera, and take it into the dark-room. Be sure that only the safelights are on. Remove the film holder metal slide cover, and carefully peel off the film. (Handle the film only by its edges.)

If the film exposure has been made on a *darkroom camera*, the overhead lights already are *off* and the safelights are *on* — so, open the camera back and remove the film, again handling it only by the edges.

### Developing the Film

Holding the film by an edge, with the free hand lift the near edge of the developing tray about an inch or so. Then immerse the film, emulsion side up, in the developer and lower the tray, causing the developer to flow completely over the film. Agitate the developer solution during the developing procedure by alternately raising and lowering the near edge of the tray, Fig. 289.

As the developing progresses, at frequent intervals, check the increasing density of the negative by lifting it out of the developer, letting it drip for a moment, immersing it quickly in water, and holding it up to the safelight for inspection. If the negative needs more developing, return it to the developing solution.

A well-developed negative, when viewed before the safelight, will have a dense, black background, and a clear, transparent image

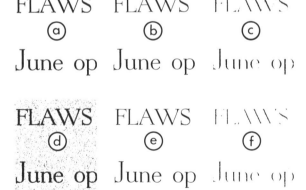

Fig. 290B.  Print Made from the Stripped-Up Negatives in Fig. 290A. Compare each print from its corresponding negative.

area. See Figs. 290A and 290B for examples of over- and under-exposure, as well as over- and under-development.

Note: For additional information on the developing step, see "Three Methods of Developing Film", below.)

## Shortstop Rinse

When the negative is satisfactorily developed, lift it out of the developer, allow it to drip a bit, and then immerse it in the shortstop bath for about 10 seconds, with continuous agitation.

## Fixing Bath

From the shortstop bath, place the film in the fixing bath for 2 to 4 minutes, agitating frequently.

Inspect the negative to see that all the "milky" coating is removed from the emulsion side of the film, and that the clear portions of the negative are perfectly transparent. Overhead lights may be turned on briefly after a few minutes of fixing (provided no one else in the darkroom is processing film or photographic contact paper). The general rule for fixing film is to leave the film in the fixer for twice the length of time it takes it to clear. Paper prints are usually fixed for 30 minutes.

## Washing the Film

Wash the fixed negative in running water for 10 minutes (after the last negative was added to the wash tray). Do not hurry this step, as poor washing may not remove all unwanted chemicals and may result in a later discoloration of the film.

Paper negatives (and photo print papers) absorb more of the chemicals during processing, and so must be washed much longer — usually 30 to 60 minutes.

## Drying

After washing, treat the negative in a Photo-Flo solution. Then squeegee or sponge off the excess water, and hang the negative by a corner in a dust-free place to dry.

Paper prints can be dried between sheets of white blotting paper for a dull finish. For a glossy finish, the wet prints are placed face down on chromium ferrotype plates and rolled to remove bubbles. They pop loose when dry. A print dryer with a heated ferrotype surface speeds the process.

## Summary

For review, the steps in the complete procedure for processing exposed film are as follows:
(1) Prepare the tray solutions
(2) Provide proper safelight illumination
(3) Remove exposed film from the camera
(4) Process the film (typical times given)

|  | | Litho Film | Azo Paper |
|---|---|---|---|
| (a) | Develop | 2¾ min. | 2 min. |
| (b) | Rinse in shortstop | 10 sec. | 20 sec. |
| (c) | Fix | 4 min. | 30 min.* |
| (d) | Wash in water | 10 min. | 60 min.* |
| (e) | Dry | | |

This procedure is typical, but there are many variations — for example, fast fixers reduce fixing time considerably. Follow the instructions which come with your chemicals.

## Three Methods of Developing Film

Three methods of developing exposed film are: (1) by inspection, (2) by time-and-temperature, and (3) by aid of a gray scale (or sensitivity guide).

### Inspection Method

In the inspection method, the operator develops the film until he decides, by visual inspection, the the film is sufficiently developed; then he develops a bit more, for good measure. Consistency of quality in successive negatives depends to a good extent upon the operator's "eye".

### Time-and-Temperature Method

In the time-and-temperature method, the operator develops the film both for the length

*Time may be cut in half, if maximum permanence in bright light is not needed or if Kodalith paper is used.

of time and in solutions of temperatures as specified by the manufacturer. In addition, other specifications of the manufacturer must be followed for the particular film being processed, such as, exposure, processing solutions, and methods of agitation during processing.

This is the method of developing described by the manufacturer in his instruction sheets. However, because of the number of variables possible in different situations (including partial exhaustion of developer solutions), some operators may have difficulty in achieving consistently uniform negatives. Consequently, many operators may start out using only the time-and-temperature method, but later combine this with the inspection method.

### Gray-Scale or Sensitivity-Guide Method

The gray-scale or sensitivity-guide method of developing exposed film gives good control of development and corrects for minor variation in exposure, temperature, used developer, etc. It requires that a sensitivity guide be placed alongside, and photographed with, the copy. In developing the film, the operator observes the progressive development of the

Fig. 291. Set-up for Contact Printing. The adjustable point-source light is installed above the vacuum frame of a flip-top plate printer. (Courtesy nuArc Co.)

[1]Courtesy Stouffer Graphic Arts Equipment Co., manufacturers of the 12-step Cameraman's Sensitivity Guide.

steps of the guide (on the film being developed in the tray). Step 1 develops up most quickly — it first appears light gray, then speckled black, then solid black. Then, in about 15 seconds, Step 2 turns black — then Step 3, etc. When the desired step turns black, the film is transferred to the shortstop bath, and the remainder of the processing is completed in the usual manner.[1]

For this method, it is recommended that test negatives be developed in new Kodalith (or similar) developer at 68° F. for the manufacturer's recommended time (2¾ minutes). The exposure then should be adjusted to give a critical Step 4 with this development.

Fig. 249 in Chapter 8 shows how the sensitivity-guide image looks on a negative which has been developed to Step 4. The caption notes the difference in appearance when viewed in the tray and when inspected by transmitted light.

NOTE: When the guide has been placed along the edge of the copy, use caution to prevent excessive tray agitation, as this may super-develop, or intensify, the edge and give a false reading.

### Darkroom Printing Operations

Some of the common darkroom printing operations which can be performed safely by the beginner, and with a minimum of equipment and supplies, are described below. Most of these have to do with making *contact prints*. These can be made either from film *positives* or film *negatives*. They can be made on *film* or on photographic *paper*. The purpose of contacting usually is (1) to reverse the *tones* from positive to negative, (2) to *flop the image* from left to right, or (3) to make *duplicate copies* of the original film. Further special techniques include: (1) darkening or lightening the image, (2) screening continuous-tone negatives, (3) combining the images from several sources (as in overprinting type on a halftone), and (4) any of a number of special effects possible, by adding or combining solids, tones and colors.

## Introduction to Contacting

Whenever possible in the following operations, the emulsion side of the completed film negatives and positives should be on the bottom (away from the operator), when viewing the image as it will appear on the printed sheet. This is for two reasons: (1) so that the film emulsion will be tight against the sensitized coating of the offset plate during the plate exposure, preventing image spread, and (2) so that the film emulsion will be on the bottom of the flat, where it will not be cut into when the stripper cuts the "windows" into the goldenrod masking sheet.

*Contacting Equipment.* A *vacuum printing frame* is desirable for all-around contact printing work. A plate printer can be equipped with a point-source light for this purpose. See Fig. 291. Otherwise, a simple glass-topped printing frame can be equipped with a foam-rubber pad, about ½ inch thick. See Fig. 292.

The *light source*, if broad and placed close to the printing frame, allows light rays to reach the image from many angles and causes the duplicated image to be bolder than it was on the original being printed. On the other hand, a light projected from an absolute pin point minimizes the image spread, but it will duplicate any dust or speck on the cover glass and so requires more opaquing.

Usually, the light source should be spaced 3 to 5 feet (or, at least, the diagonal distance of the printing frame) from the cover glass. The opening over the light should be reduced to ½ inch or 1 inch in diameter. Most commercial lights are on a low-voltage circuit, controlled by a rheostat to vary the brightness. The light can be dimmed for use with faster emulsions, keeping the exposure time in a convenient range. A timer control gives more accurate exposures. Exposure frames often have a bright light source for exposing plates or blueline proofs. This should not be used for normal contact work.

*Test Exposure.* The first exposure made with a specific light setting or with a different photographic material must be determined experimentally. Use a section of the negative or positive being duplicated which will produce some fine lines, some solid areas, and some fine white areas surrounded by solids. A special test negative could also be used. Make the test exposures on a small strip of the material to be used for the contact print. Expose in the printing frame, as given in the specific procedures which follow; however, use a series of exposure times.

Hold a piece of opaque paper on the glass of the printing frame so that only about one-fifth of the test strip is exposed. Turn on the light for 5 seconds. Then uncover two-fifths of the test strip, and expose for another 5 seconds. Continue until five such exposures have been made. The test strip will have been exposed in five steps for 25, 20, 15, 10, and 5 seconds.

Develop the test strip according to the directions which came with the material (and in the same manner to be used on the final

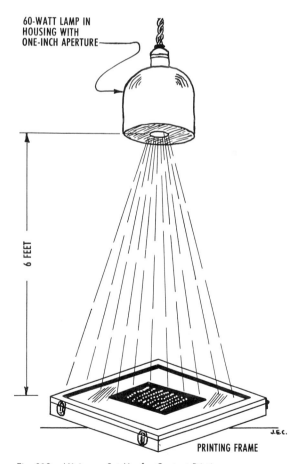

60-WATT LAMP IN HOUSING WITH ONE-INCH APERTURE

6 FEET

PRINTING FRAME

Fig. 292.  Minimum Set-Up for Contact Printing

print). After the strip has been in the fixer a minute of two, rinse in water, and inspect in bright light. The correct exposure should be a step or two longer than the one giving a noticeably gray-looking solid, but less than the step showing any spread in fine black or white lines.

A negative gray scale could also be used as a test negative by making exposures in very narrow strips across its width. The correct exposure should just produce a solid Step 3 (three steps from the clear end of the negative).

It may be necessary to make additional test strips to refine the exposure time. Usually the light intensity should be adjusted so that the exposure time is in the range of 10 to 20 seconds. If the light is too dim (or too distant), the time will be excessively long. If the light is too bright, the exposure time may be so short that it cannot be timed accurately.

*Image Gain Control.* In printing operations, there is a general tendency for the image to broaden (to gain or spread) each time it is transferred to another surface. There may be a number of such transfers: from copy to negative, to positive, to duplicate positive, to plate,

to blanket, and finally to paper — seven successive transfers in this example. If image spread were not under careful control, on the seventh transfer, the lines would be much broader and tones much darker. Several devices are available to signal such image spread.

Fig. 293 shows the GATF[2] Dot Gain Scale which can be used for a control in contact printing, in platemaking, and during press runs. The scale has a gray background with a coarse, 65-line screen. The scale works on the principle that fine screen tints are more sensitive to dot gain than a coarse screen. The numbers on the scale are in a very fine, 200-line screen which is a successively lighter gray toward the higher numerals. On the original scale, the figure "2" is the same tone as the background, so is invisible when viewed from 20-24 inches. As dot gain gets progressively worse, this invisible number moves up the scale to the "9". A gain of a step or two should be expected, but several high numbers should be lighter than the background.

The slur gauge at the right is sensitive only to directional gain (horizontal or vertical) rather than a general gain in all directions. *Slur* is commonly caused on the press by bad gears or by a poor adjustment between rotating cylinders or rollers. Slur across the gauge causes the word "Slur" to appear in dark letters; slur down the length of the gauge causes the word to appear in light letters.

It is recommended that a dot gain scale be used (especially by beginners) to test for the amount of image gain being encountered. It is especially important whenever tone values are critical. The image should be added where it can be masked out in stripping. An *original* scale should again be included in a trim margin of the flat for exposing the plate, in order to give a check on image gain during the press run.

## Contacting on Paper

A contact photo print (photographic print) may be made on photographic print paper from either a film negative or a film positive.

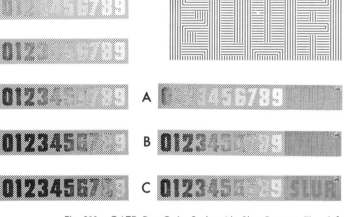

Fig. 293. GATF Dot Gain Scale with Slur Gauge. The left row shows indications of increasing amounts of dot or image gain. The right shows the addition of the Slur Gauge (enlarged at top). (A) shows a printed image closely approximating the original. (B) shows dot gain without slur. (C) shows dot gain caused by slur. If crowded for space in a trim margin, only half need be used, reducing width to 1/8".

[2]Graphic Arts Technical Foundation, 4615 Forbes Avenue, Pittsburgh, Pa. 15213.

On the film negative, the image is transparent and the background is opaque; on the resulting positive photo print, the image appears black and the background white (the white paper). The reverse is true when a film positive is used.

Contact papers (such as Azo or Velox), or enlarging papers (such as Medalist or Koda-bromide) which are faster, can be used. These should be in a glossy (F) finish, a high-contrast (No. 4 or 5) grade, and a thin weight. Kodalith Ortho Paper can also be used, especially when a faster, higher-contrast paper is needed, but it is more expensive.

Contact prints are fastened to the paste-up (mechanical layout) along with the line copy. The entire paste-up is photographed as line copy on one sheet of film, to facilitate striping the flat.

*To make a positive print* from a film negative, place a sheet of photo paper, emulsion side up, on the bed of the contact printing frame. Place the film negative, emulsion side down, over the paper. Make the exposure and process the photo paper as specified by the instructions packaged with the paper. See Fig. 294 for the procedure. Fig. 295 shows a positive print made from a film negative.

A *reverse photo print* (called a "reverse") is made by contact printing on photo paper from a *film positive*. The procedure is the same as for the positive print, above, except that a film positive is used, instead of a film negative. The film positive will look much like Fig. 295 (except that white areas are clear film) and the reverse print will look like Fig. 296.

*Halftone Contact Prints.* Since a halftone negative contains just halftone dots (no continuous tones), it may be treated essentially as a line negative, when reproduction is by contact printing. The procedure follows that for other contact photo prints, except that a vacuum bed is essential for tight contact, and the dot structure of the print must be accurate.

Since the original halftone negative is now contact-printed, and the print is then photographed as line copy to produce the negative for printing the plate, these extra, interme-

diary reproduction steps will change dot sizes somewhat. This should be anticipated and allowed for in making the original halftone negative. The smallest shadow dot may have to be about 20%, and the highlight dots about 80%, to produce a 10% to 90% range on the final print. The use of the dot gain scale is recommended.

### Contacting on Film

*Film Positive from a Film Negative.* To make a film positive from a film negative, proceed as shown in Fig. 297. Place a sheet of film such as Kodalith Ortho Thin-Base or a blue-sensitive contact film (emulsion side up) on the bed of the printing frame. Cover this with the film negative (also emulsion side up). Make the exposure to a point-source light and process the film.

Fig. 294. Making a Photographic Contact Positive Print

# Idle Fox

Fig. 295. Positive Photo Print. Exposed and developed paper on which the image is black on a white background.

Fig. 296. Reverse Photo Print. A print or photographic paper where the image is white on a black background. (A "reverse" has the opposite, or reverse, tones of a "positive print".)

Fig. 297. Making a Contact Film Positive from a Film Negative

Here, the emulsion of the negative is not in the usual direct contact with that of the film below since the base of the negative separates them. This is necessary so that the emulsion will be down in platemaking.

NOTE: Some prefer to have both emulsions *down* (not up), but if regular .005″ or .007″ film is used for the positive, the image may spread excessively as it passes through the base of the undeveloped film. This can be minimized by using thin-base or special contact film (.003″-.004″ thick). The backing of these films is thin and clear enough to readily pass light rays, but even so, the exposure time may be somewhat longer.

*Film Negative from a Film Positive.* The same procedure described above (for film positive from film negative) may be used, except that a *film positive* is placed over the unexposed film on the bed of the contact printer. See Fig. 298.

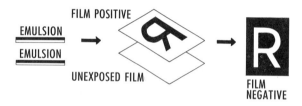

Fig. 298. Making a Contact Film Negative from a Film Positive

Fig. 299. Diagonal Reverse-Positive Combination

## Contacting on Duplicating Film

It is often necessary to duplicate film negatives (or positives) — in other words, to make a negative from a negative (or a positive from a positive). For example, this would be necessary when a job is to be run 4-up on the press sheet, and three additional negatives (exactly like the original) are needed. Normal film always reverses tones, requiring that an intermediate film positive be made, so that three extra negatives can be exposed from the intermediate. This means two additional generations of duplicates with possible loss of some fine detail each time.

The film for this use is a *direct-duplicating film* — such as Kodak Autopositive or DuPont Direct Positive film. These two films have the unique ability to be exposed and then to be unexposed (the exposure removed) at will. Exposure to white light produces a latent image which can be removed by exposure to yellow light. The process can be repeated several times. During manufacture, the film is carefully fogged in white light. If developed without further exposure (just as it comes from the box), the film would be solid black (normal film would be clear). However, if the film is exposed through a negative to yellow light, the light will remove the latent image in the same places that the original negative is clear. When developed in the usual litho developer, the result is an exact duplicate of the original.

It is suggested that the instructions packaged with the film be studied carefully prior to using this film. Basically, the exposure for contact printing is much like that for regular film (Fig. 297), except that a piece of yellow sheeting is placed on the glass of the printing frame. This filter gives the yellow light necessary to remove the emulsion. Exposure then is made to a bright white light, such as an arc light or photoflood bulbs. A platemaking exposure frame is often used. The film can be handled briefly in subdued white light without a safelight.

Direct-duplicating films can also be used to flop the image from left to right — also called *lateral reversal* of the image. The duplicating film is exposed emulsion side up. This essentially puts the emulsion on the opposite side of the base to allow an emulsion-to-emulsion contact in later operations (after the image has been flopped over).

*Negative-positive combinations* can be produced on the same piece of direct-positive film. See Fig. 299 for an example. Remember that white light builds emulsion and yellow light removes it. An opaque mask can be made to restrict the first yellow light exposure to part of the film — say the upper right beyond the diagonal of Fig. 299. Then a yellow-light exposure is made through the negative to the lower left, and a white-light exposure (no yellow sheeting) through the negative to the upper right. This produces the combination film needed to expose the plates to produce the print shown. Care is necessary to position the two masks and the original negative on three separate flaps so each can be placed over the film in accurate register. See Fig. 300.

Such combination uses of direct-positive film usually should not be attempted until basic skills are developed. The above negative-positive combination requires successive test exposures for the original yellow-light exposure and then for the white-light re-exposure.

A somewhat *easier method* of making the above combination can also be given. It uses regular film and paper, but requires three generations of exposures, rather than just two.

Prepare a film negative of the entire design, and make a positive photo print of it. Tape the print to a backing sheet. Tape the negative, in register, over the print. Then cut through both with a sharp knife where desired. Tape half of each — the negative and the print — to a sheet of bright-white card stock. Shoot this on the camera for a split reverse.

*Reflex Copying.* With this method, a same-size film positive of line copy drawn or printed on paper can be made without a camera. The copy is placed face up in the exposure frame. It then is covered with a piece of direct-duplicating film (one of the two named above) with the emulsion down next to the copy. The frame is closed, covered with yellow sheeting, and exposed to bright white light. The light

passes through the film (all over), but is reflected back again only from the white paper and not from the black image. This differential is enough to make the exposure produce a film positive. With this technique, even a shop without a camera can do photographic copying. The film directions should be studied before beginning work.

*Faster Direct-Duplicating Films.* Films such as *DuPont Contact Reversal Film* are much faster than the original Autopositive or Direct Positive films. Since they are exposed to white light, they are replacing the yellow-working films for many uses. Exposure is to a point-source light; positives give positives, negatives yield negatives, and combinations require an intermediate step. Exposure removal and reflex copying are not possible.

### Contacting Spreads and Chokes

Sometimes, rather than carefully holding the same width of lines on the image, it is desirable to cause them to widen or to become thinner. These are called *spreads* and *chokes* (or weighting and thinning, or fats and skinnies). It may be necessary to make type look a little bolder or to produce special effects in large type. A common need for a spread is when color is added to a type reverse. The original negative (which was used to make the positive for the reverse) could be used for the color, but it would fit only when in *perfect* register — and some variation is expected during the press run. So it is desirable to have the color image overlap slightly.

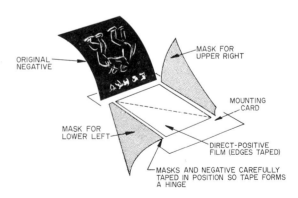

Fig. 300. Exposure Set-Up for Combination Negative-Positive Print on Autopositive Film

A *spread* is contacted on film from a negative. The set-up is nearly the same as for usual contacting, except the light must strike at an angle of about 20° to 45° — the greater the angle, the more the spread. For exposure, a small printing frame can be placed on a lazy Susan and spun to cause the spread in all directions. See Fig. 301. With large vacuum frames, it may be easier to swing the exposure light in a circle over the edges of the frame. Moving the light in a square pattern may produce sharper corners.

There never should be an emulsion-to-emulsion contact between the negative and the film. For small spreads, the base of the unexposed film (as in Fig. 297) may be sufficient spacing. For larger spreads, a clear piece of acetate (.004″ to .006″ thick) between the negative and the film allows a greater undercutting of the image on the negative. Experiment for the right effect. Either regular or direct-duplicating film can be used, depending on the results desired.

A *choke* is contacted in the same manner, except that a positive is used.

*Outline letters* can be produced from solid type by making a spread and a choke, and then making a regular contact print through the two in register. Another method is to make a normal positive from the negative and to use this in the following order to make a spread (from bottom layer upward): (1) unexposed film, (2) film positive, (3) clear acetate spacer, and (4) original negative. *In-*

*line letters* (thin centers) are made in the same way, except the order of the positive and the negative is interchanged.

### Off-Camera Screening

*Halftone Film Negative from Continuous-Tone Film Positive.* A same-size halftone film negative can be made from a continuous-tone film positive by using the set-up shown in Fig. 302. Kodalith Ortho Thin-Base Film, Type 3, is placed, emulsion side up, on the vacuum frame bed. Over this is placed the magenta contact screen (negative), with emulsion side down. The unscreened (continuous-tone) film positive is placed over the screen, emulsion side up. Detail and flash exposures may be determined experimentally.

Autoscreen film can be used in place of the Litho film, in which case, the contact screen is omitted.

*Halftone Film Positive from Continuous-Tone Negative.* This operation follows essentially the same procedure as in Fig. 302, except, of course, the continuous-tone *negative* and the magenta contact screen *(positive)* are used.

*Halftone Projected Prints from Continuous-Tone Negatives.* This is an extremely useful operation. For example, snapshot negatives can be reproduced as halftone prints in the size and area needed for pasting up on the mechanical layout, to be photographed along with the line copy on one sheet of film. Needed are a photo enlarger and projection-speed photo print paper.

If your enlarger does not have a vacuum board, arrange your set-up so you can use your vacuum-printing frame for the easel. For 120- and 133-line screen patterns, use the magenta contact screen (negative); for coarser screen rulings, use the gray contact screen. Dot gain will be more of a factor in a ruling as fine as 133-line. For main and flash exposures with either type of screen, use the white light and yellow flash as for the magenta contact screen when used in the camera.

Place the continuous-tone negative in the negative carrier of the enlarger, emulsion side down, and focus the enlarger. Place a sheet

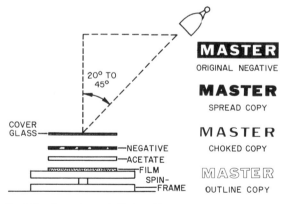

Fig. 301. Spreads and Chokes. The set-up is shown at the left, and examples are shown at the right.

of the projection-speed paper on the vacuum-frame bed, emulsion side up. Place the half-tone screen over this, emulsion side down, overlapping about an inch all around for good vacuum draw. Determine the detail and flash exposures experimentally, using different sections of the same sheet of film. With fresh film, make the detail and flash exposures.

### Special Techniques

*Open or Blank Areas.* An open or blank area may be produced on film negatives, film positives and prints in the contact-printing procedure by placing a piece of red or black opaque paper of the required size and shape over the appropriate area of the negative (or positive) in the printing frame. Stripping tape can also be used.

*Silhouetted Halftone Prints.* By opaquing the unwanted background on a halftone negative, the resulting halftone print will appear with a white background, as in Fig. 303.

*Lettering on Halftone Illustrations.* A simple way to have lettering appear on a halftone illustration is to place transfer-type letters (or to hand letter) directly onto the face of the original photo. The lettering can also be done on a *thin* piece of clear acetate fastened as a flap over the photo (an overlay). If copied in one shot on the camera, Autoscreen film can be used to prevent a screen pattern from showing on the letters.

A more exacting method requires that the lettering be on the overlay. Then two separate negatives are made to be surprinted (over-printed) later. A halftone negative is made only of the photograph (with the overlay folded back). Then, at the same focus (and without changing the location of the copy), the overlay is flopped into place, a clean white sheet is inserted between the overlay and the photo, and a line negative is made of the lettering. If any of the lettering is to appear in reverse (as white letters against a dark section of the halftone), it will be necessary to contact a film positive from the line negative of the lettering, and the halftone should be on thin-base film.

These then may be combined in the dark-room by surprinting on film, so that a single negative is used in stripping and platemaking. This probably is desirable when the image must be repeated a number of times on the plate. Another method is to strip two separate flats and do the surprinting on the plate. This probably is desirable for a single (one-up) image on the plate.

Refer to Fig. 211 on page 104, as an example. This has four sections of type to be combined with the photograph — two lines are reversed, one is overprinted, and a pair are in a blocked-out area. The line positive must have all but the two reversed lines scraped off (or removed chemically). Then this is placed *over* the thin-base halftone for one exposure. The clear positive must be larger than the halftone, because the film edge would cause a line to print. Tape placed on the top surface of the halftone negative forms the open

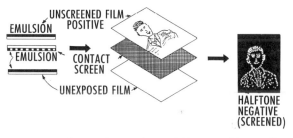

Fig. 302. Making a Contact Screened Negative from an Unscreened Film Positive

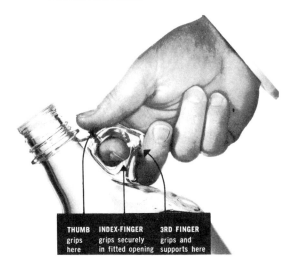

Fig. 303. Silhouetted Halftone Print

area for the block-out. Then, the two unwanted lines on the line negative (which will be reversed and are on the positive) are opaqued. This negative is printed in register in a second exposure — either onto duplicating film or onto the plate.

*Registering Multiple Exposures.* In the surprinting, explained above, the image for each exposure must be carefully located, so as to be in perfect register. There are several ways to do this. The *flap* method, shown in Fig. 300, is accurate and easily done. The use of simple *register marks* is explained as a stripping procedure in Chapter 12 and is illustrated in Fig. 331.

*Register pins,* however, are the most accurate and now the most common. (See Fig. 304.) They are used in darkroom printing operations, in stripping, in positioning flats for platemaking, and even, occasionally, as an aid in positioning plates on the press. The register pin is turned carefully to ¼″ diameter, is about 1/16″ high, and is spot welded to a thin metal backing which can be taped in position. Similar plastic buttons (without the backing) are also

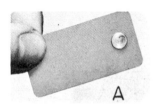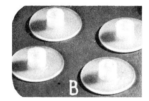

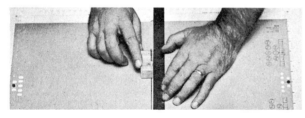

Fig. 304. Register Pins (A) and Buttons (B). The view below shows two pins being used with prepared step-masking sheets. (Courtesy Raden C Auto-Step Co.)

Fig. 305. Screened Type

available. Two ¼″ holes are punched in all sheets to be registered. The sheets can be aligned and then punched at the same time. Sometimes masking sheets are punched, and the film images are taped into openings in register on the sheets. Pins are placed in the two holes of a punched sheet, and the pin backs then can be taped in position to a backing sheet which is placed in the exposure frame. For stripping work, the pins are taped directly to the glass of the light table. More complete directions come with the pins.

*Screened Type Effects.* Screened type effects, such as those produced in Fig. 305 with Phototypositor screens, are easily made by interposing a patterned screen between the film negative (or film positive) and the print in the contact frame.

For screened type, use a film negative of the type matter; for screened background, use a film positive.

## Proofing Methods

It is recommended that a test exposure be made of complex forms before the plates are made for the press run. This is particularly true with the work of beginners or when an okay must be obtained before the press run. A plate printer, or a vacuum frame and arc light, can be used for each of the following. Exposures will be about 2 minutes to 4 minutes.

### Silverprint (Brownline or Vandyke) Proofs

Silverprint proofs are the easiest to use for proofing single-color flats. The brownprint paper is cut from a roll, exposed through the negative flat, developed in a water bath, fixed in the regular photographic fixer, washed, and dried. A less permanent print can be processed somewhat faster by setting the color in stop bath rather than in fixer bath (because the final wash time can be shortened). Brownprints have a brown image on white paper.

### Blueline Proofs

Blueline proofs are much like silverprints, except that the image is blue — standard blueprinting paper is used. After exposure, the proof is developed in water until cleared, and fixed with a hydrogen-peroxide solution (4 oz. to a gal. of water). A potassium-ferricyanide solution (1 oz. to 10 oz. of water) is a more traditional, but possibly toxic, fixing solution.

Blueprint paper can show some gradation in tones of blue, so it often is used to proof two-color jobs. For example, the key flat (for black ink) can be exposed for two minutes to produce a deep blue; the flat for the color can be exposed for 30 seconds to produce a light blue on the same sheet. Three colors can be proofed in a similar manner (but may be a bit difficult to interpret) — perhaps at exposures of 3 minutes, 45 seconds, and 25 seconds. For pamphlets and book signatures, two-sided blueprint paper is available; but because of possible show-through, exposures must be reduced some — two-tone exposures might be made at 1½ minutes and at 25 seconds. A clearer proof is produced by exposing each side of the signature on separate sheets and rubber-cementing them together back to back, before folding and trimming.

### Colored Diazo Transparencies

The 3M Color Key is popular for showing proofs in actual color. A colored diazo print is produced on a clear sheet, so each color can be viewed in register with others when superimposed. About 10 standard colors are available, either for negatives or for positives. Processing is simple. See page 186 for directions and further information.

Technifax Diazochrome film is a similar type of material which can also be used for color proofing. It is often used in drafting rooms and for audio-visual transparencies. Diazochromes develop in ammonia. Although economical, it is not made especially for proofing.

### Coating Solutions for Proofing

Several solutions are available for coating sheets of paper or matte-finished plastic for making color proofs. The coating is wiped on (some require a whirler), dried, exposed to the flat, and the one-color image is developed. At this point, a coating for a second color can

be applied over the first and developed in a similar manner. As many colors as desired can be applied to the sheet. Usually about eight standard colors are available (including process colors), but these can be intermixed to produce any color desired. These are sometimes called "Watercotes"[3] — the brand name of one such coating material — but litho suppliers may have other brands.

### Supplies

A few of the films, photographic papers, and solutions commonly used in the regular run-of-work are briefly described below. The user is advised to consult latest catalog listings for complete offerings, and to follow the packaged instructions for exposure times and processing procedures.

### Films

See also descriptions in Chapters 8 and 9, page 111 (the Film), page 127 (Colored Line Copy), and pages 140-43 (Film sensitivity).

*Kodalith Ortho Film, Type 3.* This is an extremely high-contrast, orthochromatic film (on .0053″ acetate base), designed primarily for making line and halftone negatives and positives. With *Kodalith Ortho Thin-Base Film, Type 3*, the negatives can be printed with the image toward the light source for lateral image reversal, since the .0032″ anti-halation base is thin and clear. Exposure index is 10 and 6.[4]

This film should be handled under Kodak Safelight Filter, Wratten Series 1A (light red), in a safelight lamp, with a 15-watt bulb at no less than 4 feet.

*Kodalith Royal Ortho Film.* This is a very fast, extreme high-contrast, orthochromatic film, designed primarily for making halftone negatives and positives from continuous-tone images in a camera *or an enlarger* where Type 3 Kodalith is too slow. Exposure index is 32 and 20.

[3]Manufactured by Direct Reproduction Corp., 835 Union St., Brooklyn, New York.

[4]First index number is for white light (arc or daylight); second is for artificial (tungsten) bulbs.

This film should be handled under a Kodak Safelight Filter, Wratten Series 1A (light red), in a suitable safelight lamp, with a 15-watt bulb, at no less than 4 feet. If greater safety is needed, a Wratten Series 1 (red) filter should be used.

*Kodalith Pan Film.* This is an extreme high-contrast, fast panchromatic film for making line and direct color-separation negatives and positives. The .004″ polyester (Estar) base provides dimensional stability. Exposure index is 40 and 32.

The recommended safelight is a Kodak Safelight Filter, Wratten Series 3 (dark green), in a safelight lamp, with a 15-watt bulb at no less than 4 feet from the film.

*Kodalith Contact Film.* This is a high-contrast, blue-sensitive film, designed primarily for making contact negatives or positives from positives or negatives, respectively, with less spread than with usual litho films.

It may be handled under a safelight filter, Wratten Series OA (greenish yellow), in a safelight lamp, with a 15-watt bulb, at no less than 4 feet from the film. This safelight is brighter than the usual red (1A) darkroom illumination, which also can be used.

*Kodalith Autoscreen Ortho Film.* This is a high-contrast, orthochromatic film, in which a halftone dot pattern has been incorporated. When exposed to a continuous-tone image, a dot pattern is produced automatically, just as if a halftone screen had been used in the camera. Its chief use is in making halftone negatives from photographic prints or combinations with type. It also can be time-exposed directly in a view camera. Exposure index is 5 and 3 (4 in daylight).

This film should be handled and developed by the light of a Kodak Safelight Filter, Wratten Series 1A (light red), in a suitable safelight lamp, with a 15-watt bulb, at no less than 4 feet. Under these conditions, the film should not be exposed to the safelight longer than 3 minutes. (See also page 151.)

*Kodak Autopositive Film.* This a relatively-slow, high-contrast film which yields positive copies from positive originals by contact or reflex printing, with strong yellow light and normal developing. It is particularly suitable for making direct duplicates of line and half-tone negatives and positives. See page 198 for more details. NOTE: A newer Autopositive *Projection* film is much faster and is designed for normal uses, but lacks the re-reversal and re-flex copying capabilities.

For room-light tolerances and detailed use, refer to the instructions packaged with the film.

*DuPont Contact Reversal.* This is a newer type of direct-duplicating film, which is much faster than DuPont Direct Positive or Kodak Autopositive films. Exposure is to a point-source light. Positives are yielded from positives, but exposure removal or reflex copying is not possible.

*Kodak Commercial Film.* This blue-sensitive film is of moderately-high contrast. It is used for making continuous-tone negatives in copying continuous-tone subjects and for other work not requiring green or red sensitivity. Exposure index is 20 and 8.

The film should be handled under a Kodak Safelight Filter, Wratten Series 1 (red), in a suitable safelight lamp, with a 15-watt bulb, at no less than 4 feet from the film.

*Kodak Super-XX Pan Film.* This is a high-speed panchromatic film of moderate contrast and full-color sensitivity. It is used for continuous-tone negatives from colored copy and through filters.

It is suitable for color-separation negatives and making color correcting masks for color transparencies. Total darkness is required for processing. Exposure index is 125 and 80.

### Photographic Papers

Photographic (sensitized) papers are available in a variety of finishes and contrasts for many purposes. Four especially useful types are mentioned here.

*Kodak Azo Paper (grade F4)* and *Kodak Velox Paper (grade F4)* are white, glossy, smooth contact-printing papers for making positive contact halftone prints, positive contact line prints, or reverses for use as camera copy — especially for pasting up made-up pages including line and halftone prints along with proofs of type matter. Thin papers are best for paste-ups.

*Kodabromide Paper (grade F4)* is a white, glossy, smooth enlarging (projection) paper for making enlargements, especially for use as camera copy. Projection papers can be used for contacts, but are faster and so take less light or a shorter exposure than contact papers.

*Kodalith Ortho Paper.* This sensitized material is available in two types — standard and thin. It is intended for making paper negatives of great contrast. It can be used either in a camera, or for making contact prints in a printing frame. Exposure index is 8 and 5.

This paper should be handled and developed under a Kodak Safelight Filter, Wratten Series 1A (light red), in a suitable safelight lamp, at no less than 4 feet from the film.

## Solutions

While the specific solutions used in the darkroom depend on the films and papers required (and the brand used), several typical examples are given here as a guide.

*Kodalith Developer,* parts A and B, is a standard litho (extra high-contrast) developer, which is discarded after use. *Kodalith Super Developer* (at the same price) can be replenished with use to maintain strength, so is discarded less often. It commonly is used in automatic machines or where there is little danger of contaminating the solution. *Kodalith Fine-Line Developer* is for special use when maximum detail is needed — as in dot-for-dot copying.

*DK-50 Developer* is a typical continuous-tone film developer. It is replenished by DK-50R after each use and thus saved for re-use.

*Dektol* and D-72 are typical paper developers. A concentrated *stock solution* is diluted for use. Diluted Dektol can be saved for re-use until its action slows down. In beginning school laboratories, sometimes single batches of a general-purpose developer (such as Ansco Vividol) is mixed each time paper printing is done.

*Glacial Acetic Acid* is 99½% concentrated, so is dangerous and is often stored separately.

28% *Acetic Acid* (short stop stock solution) is diluted 3 parts into 8 parts water. *Short Stop* (Stop Bath) is 8 oz. of 28% acid in a gallon of water. The bath is replaced anytime it discolors and is never returned to the bottle. Short stop can be used to set the color of silverprint proofs.

*Kodak Fixer* is a good all-purpose, economical fixer for film or paper. It is saved for re-use as long as it will clear a scrap of Kodalith film in about 2 minutes. *Rapid Fixer* cuts fixing time in half but is nearly double the cost. Fixer is also used for a permanent image on silverprint proofs.

*Kodak Photo-Flo* is a wetting agent which minimizes drying marks. Film is immersed briefly in a tray of solution before hanging up to dry. The solution is returned to the bottle. Paper thus treated glosses better and is less apt to curl or stick to the dryer. *Pakasol* is a paper treatment recommended by a company making print dryers.

*Hydrogen Peroxide,* 4 oz. to a gallon of water, is used to set the color of blueprints or blueline proofs. Potassium ferricyanide (1 oz. to 10 oz. of water) can also be used. *3M Negative Color Key Developer* is used for acetate color proofs.

## Questions

1. List the usual items of equipment found in the darkroom.
2. What determines the color of the safelight to be used (if any) in the darkroom?
3. Why should bottled chemicals be stored on the lowest shelves of the cabinets in the darkroom?
4. Why is a ventilating fan needed in the darkroom?
5. If there is no ventilating fan, how is the darkroom ventilated?
6. What advantage is there in having the back of the darkroom camera inside the darkroom?
7. Name the order of trays in the darkroom.
8. Why are the trays always kept in the same order?

9. Tell how an image is produced on a negative.
10. Tell the function of the developer, the shortstop, the fixer, and the water bath in the developing of film.
11. Tell how the concentrated developer chemical is prepared for use.
12. Describe the use of the film referred to as prescreened or "Autoscreen" film.
13. Describe the procedure for making approximately 28% acetic acid from glacial acetic acid.
14. What precautions must be observed in handling glacial acetic acid? What are the first-aid procedures in case of accident?
15. Tell how you would combine 28% acetic acid and water to make one-half gallon of shortstop solution.
16. Describe the inspection method of developing film.
17. How do you develop film by the time-and-temperature method?
18. Describe a sensitivity guide (or gray scale).
19. Describe the gradual emergence of the image of the gray scale (or sensitivity guide) on the film in the developing tray.
20. What advantages are there in using a gray scale (or sensitivity guide) in processing film?
21. Outline the procedure in developing a negative.
22. Tell how to make a positive on film from a negative.
23. How is a contact print (photograph) made from a negative?
24. Tell how a combination negative is made.
25. How do you provide a blank space on a negative or print?
26. What kind of work is photographed on orthochromatic film?
27. What kind of a safelight is used with orthochromatic film?

## Problems and Projects

1. Make a scale drawing of a darkroom for an offset plant, plan a new darkroom for the shop, or make plans for remodeling the present one. Use catalogs in the shop library for your planning. Estimate the cost of the equipment you have selected.
2. Make a wall chart showing the order of trays in the darkroom. Ink the drawing and photograph it, to be used later to make an offset plate for printing.
3. Prepare a container of A and a container of B developer solution in the quantity specified by your instructor.
4. Prepare a container of fixer solution in the quantity specified by your instructor.
5. Using 28% acetic acid and water, prepare one-half gallon of shortstop.
6. Prepare the four trays for developing film. Use the quantities specified in these instructions, or those specified by your instructor.
7. Expose and develop a negative from the copy and problem specified by your instructor.
8. Make a film positive from the prepared negative in problem 7.
9. Make a contact print from the negative *and* the positive in problems 7 and 8. Provide a blank area on one.
10. Make a combination line and halftone negative from copy and problem specified by the instructor.
11. Make a halftone negative, using self-screening film.
12. Prepare a wall chart showing how the sensitivity guide is placed next to the copy on the copyboard, and how the sensitivity guide looks when it is developed to a specified step on film. Make your own negatives and prints for this display.

## New Words

1. accessories
2. acetic
3. agitate
4. alternately
5. anticipate
6. chemicals
7. combination
8. concentrated
9. consecutive
10. controlled
11. density
12. developer
13. discoloring
14. exhaustion
15. fixer
16. glacial
17. graduates
18. gray scale

19. halation
20. hypo
21. illumination
22. immerse
23. mechanical
24. mimeograph
25. negative
26. opaque
27. particles
28. penetrating
29. positive
30. safelight
31. sensitivity guide
32. shortstop
33. solution
34. specifications
35. squeegee
36. successive
37. unexposed
38. vapors
39. ventilation

# Laying Out and

# Stripping the Flat

After the negatives for a job have all been made, they are taped, in reverse, on a laid-out sheet of goldenrod paper the same size as the press plate, in the relative positions called for on the layout. The goldenrod paper is then turned over, and "windows" are cut out of the goldenrod, exposing the desired portions of the negatives. This paper, with its taped-on negatives, is called the "flat." Arranging and mounting the negatives on the flat is referred to as "stripping."

Fig. 310. Stripping up a Large Flat
(Courtesy Western Printing & Lithographing Co.)

The stripped-up flat is placed, readable side up, over a sensitized offset plate, and exposed to an arc (or other) light. The plate is then developed to bring out the image and to make the image ink-receptive on the press.

## Goldenrod Paper

The stock generally used for stripping, or making the flat, is an 80-pound double-coated goldenrod *paper*. This allows non-actinic light to penetrate so that the image can be seen through it, yet it will not allow actinic* light rays to affect the sensitized coating of the plate when exposure is made. Thus the goldenrod acts as a light mask, the same as the opaque portions of the negatives. Goldenrod *plastic* sheets are used for maximum stability.

## Equipment and Supplies

After the exposed plate has been developed, the image on the plate is an exact duplicate of the image on the flat.

On a finished offset plate (unlike a type form), it is impossible to add spacing between lines; neither can an illustration be moved in respect to other illustrations or type matter on the page. All images on the plate are fixed in their relative positions — these positions are determined by the positions of the negatives on the flat. Thus, the flat must be stripped with great accuracy and care.

The following minimum list of tools, equipment and supplies should be available and in good condition:

*A light ray which causes photochemical changes.

A frosted-glass stripping table, lighted from below

80-pound double-coated goldenrod stock, cut to press-plate size

    Dispenser with colored litho tape

    Dispenser with transparent tape

    Stripping knife, or single-edge razor blades

    Steel T square

    Steel straightedge (steel ruler) with bevelled edges

    Steel triangles, 30-60 and 45 degrees

    Set of scribing tools

    Paper-cutting shears (scissors)

    Black (India) drafting ink

    Draftsmen's ruling pen and 5″ dividers (a set of drafting tools is useful in the shop)

    Opaque solution

    Various sizes and shapes of artist's brushes

    Linen tester magnifying glass

    Steel square, to suit sizes of layouts

    Other tools may be added as the need arises.

## Layout Table

The precision layout table (or line-up table) is a glass-top table, lighted from below and equipped with moveable horizontal (across) and vertical (up-and-down) straightedges positioned at perfect right angles to each other. It is a tremendous time saver, and a great aid to accuracy in lining-up, registering, negative opaquing, retouching, negative and plate ruling, copy layout, masking and stripping, placing register marks, and as a precision check on work in progress.

Intricate ruled forms which require that lines be accurately spaced are easily accomplished by using the stops and automatic spacer on the vernier mechanism shown in Fig. 313.

Fig. 312. Precision Photo-Lith Layout Table (Courtesy Craftsman Line-up Table Corp.)

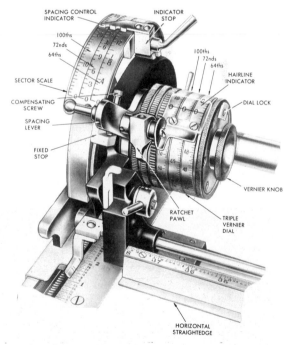

Fig. 313. Enlarged View of Craftsman Layout Table Showing Triple Vernier Spacing Mechanism (Courtesy Craftsman Line-up Table Corp.)

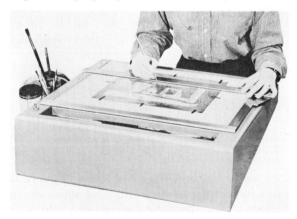

Fig. 311. The 17″ x 22″ Light Table for Layout, Stripping and Opaquing (Courtesy Robertson Photo-Mechanix, Inc.)

## Preparation for Stripping

Remove all traces of tape from the glass top of the stripping table with a razor blade. Wash the glass top with glass cleaner and dry thoroughly. Select the T square you will use, and be sure to use this same T square for all work on the same flat. (Another T square may vary slightly in squareness.)

In using the T square, work from only one edge of the table. Use triangles and the square to draw lines at angles to the T square blade. (Detailed instructions on the use of drafting instruments are given in the appendix of this book.)

## Laying Out the Flat

Place a sheet of goldenrod paper (cut to press-plate size) on the stripping table. One long edge of the sheet, which will be referred to as the gripper or feeding edge, should be

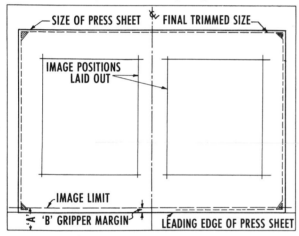

Fig. 314. Laying Out the Flat

Fig. 315. A Film Negative With Image in "Unreadable" or "Wrong-Reading" Form

parallel to the edge of the table nearest the stripper. This edge corresponds to the leading edge of the plate and of the paper as it is fed into the press. (On small presses, such as a 10 x 15, the lead edge is the short dimension, and can be placed at the left.)

Line up the lower edge of the paper with the upper edge of the T square, and fasten the paper to the glass top with pieces of tape, working from diagonal corners, and smoothing the paper before taping it. Mark the flat in a corner with the number or name of the job to identify it.

Lay out the flat according to Fig. 314. Distance 'A' represents that portion from the leading edge of the press plate to where the image will actually start to print; distance 'B' represents the portion of the press sheet which is gripped by the press grippers during printing, and thus cannot receive an impression.

NOTE: In all the following operations, remember that the gripper margin area, and the area beneath it, cannot carry an image. Therefore, when stripping in the negatives, avoid placing the image area of the negatives in or below the gripper margin.

Locate and draw a vertical centerline on the sheet. Label it "₵" at the top.

Measure and lay out the length and width of the sheet of paper to be run. Measure the width up from the line representing the leading edge of the press sheet. Measure and *mark* half the length on each side of the vertical center line. Draw the outline of the press-size sheet of paper a little heavier than other lines.

If the printed press sheets are to have a final trim after printing, rule in the trim lines on the layout.

At this point, it will be helpful for the beginner to shade in the corners of the rectangle for the final trimmed size of the press sheet.

Inside the finished sheet size area, indicate the exact size and position of each of the *images* (not the entire negatives) which are to be included on the flat. Draw all lines with a sharp pencil, and extend the lines about ⅜ inch beyond the corners of the rectangles, to assist in positioning the negatives on the flat. Be sure to use a scale with beveled edges. If the scale has a thick edge, hold it on edge to get accurate measurements.

If the images on some of the negatives do not have parallel or flush sides, it may be helpful to draw a centerline in each of those image rectangles on the flat to later match up the negatives.

## Stripping-In the Negatives

The stripper works in "reverse" — all negatives are placed on the flat with the emulsion side *up*. In this position, the negatives are "unreadable" — the image is reversed from right to left. See Fig. 315. The stripper soon learns to work with ease in reverse.

### Determining the Emulsion Side

If a negative is made correctly, the emulsion side is the unreadable, or back side. The stripper can easily determine the emulsion side of a negative — it is the duller of the two sides. Furthermore, if the emulsion side of a negative is scratched with the point of a knife or a razor blade, a transparent line or area is produced. (In scratching, a portion of the emulsion is removed, exposing the clear acetate base of the film.) See Fig. 317.

In stripping, the negatives are placed on the flat with the *emulsion side up* (in the *unreadable position*) so that when the flat is pressed against the coated plate (during the plate exposure), the emulsion side of the negative will be tight against the coating on the plate. If the negative were placed with the emulsion side *down* on the flat, when the flat were turned over and windows cut to expose the film, the emulsion would be scratched. This would require opaquing which could have been avoided. Also, during plate exposure, there would be a space the thickness of the goldenrod paper along the edge of the film, holding it away from the plate coating and allowing the light rays to creep underneath and spread (or blur) the edge of the image being formed on the plate. This creeping and spreading of the light rays is called "halation."

## Opaquing and Trimming

Lay the negatives on the lighted stripping table, emulsion side up, and inspect for scratches and pinholes. Coat these with opaque (if they are in the area of the negative to be exposed). Avoid making further scratches and marks. Handle the film by the edges.

Trim the negatives to within ¼ inch of the images. The trimming need not be perfectly square, but be sure to leave the ¼ inch for taping the negatives to the flat. Use either scissors, or a steel straightedge and single-edge razor blade or knife (cut on plastic sheeting to protect the glass).

## Scribing Reference Marks

Reference lines are scribed into the emulsion of the negatives to aid in placing the negatives in accurate position on the layout.

Place the negative, emulsion side up, on the lighted stripping table. Lay a steel straightedge across the negative so the far side of the straightedge lines up with the top of the first line of type on the negative. With the edge of a razor blade (or a sharp knife) scribe a

Fig. 316. A Film Negative with a "Readable" Image

Fig. 317. Correctly Made Negative will Show Transparent Lines when Scratched on the Back with Knife or Needle

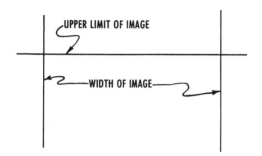

Fig. 318. Stripping a Negative — Lay Out Position on Flat which Image Will Occupy

Fig. 319. Stripping a Negative — Scribe Reference Lines Through Emulsion

Fig. 320. Stripping a Negative — Trim Negative to Within 1/4" of Image

Fig. 321. Stripping a Negative — Position Negative on Flat with Aid of Reference Lines

line through the emulsion to the left and right of the top of the first line of type. Scribe at the edge of the negative (on the left, and then on the right) to within about ⅛ inch of the image. *Do not scribe into the image.*

Next, lay the straightedge along the left side of the image, and scribe a line through the emulsion from the top edge of the negative to within ⅛ inch of the image. This line, and the two described above, will give three reference lines on the negative with which to line it up with the marked-out position on the flat. See Figs. 319 to 321.

**Taping the Negatives**

Place the negative (emulsion side up) over the area on the flat where it is to be fixed. The head of the type matter should be toward the marked-out head of the laid-out rectangle on the flat. Match the three reference lines of the negative with the corresponding reference lines of the marked-out rectangle on the flat. Fasten the negative at the corners with little squares of red, amber, or black tape. If needed, fasten the negatives along the edges with additional pieces of tape, but use no more than is absolutely necessary. In any event, never tape the negative any closer to the image than ⅛ inch. See Fig. 322.

Fig. 322. Stripping a Negative — Tape Negative in Place

Fig. 323. Stripping a Negative — Flat Turned Over and "Window" Cut Out Close to Image

### Cutting the "Windows"

Free the flat from the table top by cutting along the edges of the flat, through the tape at the corners of the flat. Turn the flat over and remove the goldenrod paper covering the images by cutting through the flat with a razor blade, or sharp knife, being sure to cut only through the paper and *not through the negatives*. Make the cuts ¹⁄₁₆ to ⅛ of an inch outside the image areas.

Scan the negative areas carefully for any pinholes or scratches which might allow light to come through. If any are found, opaque them on the emulsion side of the negatives.

If halftone negatives have been stripped into the flat, the opening in the flat is cut out and the halftone framed to the proper size with strips of tape on all four sides.

A halftone may also be painted with opaque to the desired outline after the outline has been ruled with opaque in a ruling pen.

### Scribing Lines on the Negatives

If the printed work is to include lines or borders which do not appear on the negatives, they may be provided by scribing (scratching) them through the emulsion of the negatives.

Film-scribing tools may be used for scribing lines on negatives. Each tool head has two cutting edges. A complete set will enable one to scribe single or parallel lines of various weights and combinations.

If scribing tools are not available, a lithographer's needle may be sharpened to a flat chisel-shaped end of the desired width.

It is distinctly time-saving to intentionally omit rules in type composition. Negatives of the type proofs are made with only the type characters printed. A more uniform and neater job can be obtained by scribing these rules or lines on the developed negatives.

### Reference Marks Cut Into the Flat

Certain marks are provided on the flat to aid the platemaker, pressman, and papercutter. (These marks are shown in Fig. 327.)

### Gripper Edge

The gripper edge of a flat is identified by a wedge-shaped piece cut out of the edge of the flat. One side of the wedge is cut along

Fig. 324. How to Splice Two Negatives

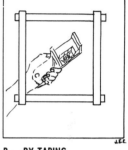

**A — BY OPAQUING**     **B — BY TAPING**

Fig. 325. Cropping Negatives

Fig. 326. Film Scribing Tools (Courtesy Roberts & Porter, Inc.)

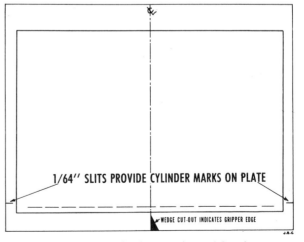

1/64″ SLITS PROVIDE CYLINDER MARKS ON PLATE

WEDGE CUT-OUT INDICATES GRIPPER EDGE

Fig. 327. Reference Marks, Gripper Edge and Cylinder

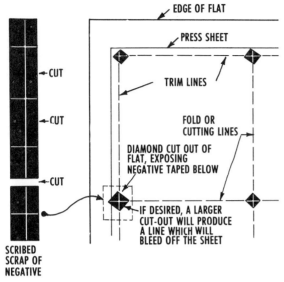

Fig. 328. Providing Trim, Fold and Cutting Lines on Flat

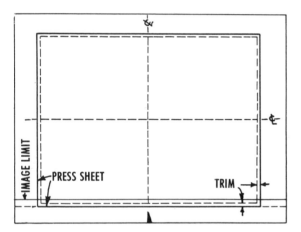

Fig. 329. Layout of Flat for Running a Job 4-Up, Allowing for Trim after Cutting

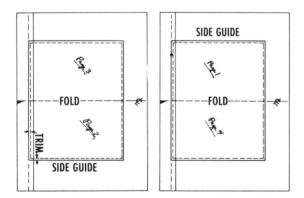

Fig. 330. Flat Layouts for 4-page Folder Printed from 2 Plates. Note that flats are laid out in reverse. When printed, page 1 will be a right-hand page, and will be backed up by page 2.

the centerline. The point of the wedge should not intrude far enough toward the image to print on the paper. The gripper mark *does* print on the plate, and tells the platemaker and pressman which edge of the flat is used in lining up the plate.

### Cylinder Marks

A cylinder reference mark should be cut through on each side of the flat outside of the printing area, and extending to the edge of the flat, removing a $\frac{1}{64}$-inch sliver of paper from the flat. If each flat is provided with cylinder marks in the same location, corresponding to the position of the marks on the plate cylinder, successive plates may be registered and run with a minimum of plate shifting.

### Trim, Fold, and Cut Marks

If trim, fold and cutting marks are desired on the printed sheets, a thin sliver of paper may be cut out of the flat so that a thin line will print on the paper. Or, a portion of the flat may be cut out and a piece of opaque negative can be taped in. Lines scribed on the negative emulsion will print on the paper. These lines indicate where to trim, fold or cut the finished printed sheets. See Fig. 328.

### Additional Layouts for Imposition

It is economical and time-saving to use a press sheet as large as can be accommodated on the press for the press run, and to print on that sheet as many images of the job as can be accommodated. Then, later, the job can be cut apart.

Fig. 329 shows a layout for a job to be run "four-up," and which will be cut into the four pieces after printing. Notice that, in this job, a trim has been allowed on all sides of the press sheet.

Fig. 330 shows the layout for printing a four-page folder (both sides of one sheet), using two plates. Notice that the work is done in "reverse" on the flats. When the flats are turned over for use in exposing the plates, the pages will be in normal order — page one will be a right-hand page, and will be "backed-up" by page two of the second plate.

## Step-and-Repeat Work

Fig. 331 shows how a job can be stripped up to expose one image a number of times on the same plate without duplicating the negatives for each unit area.

A register flat is laid out for the entire plate, to include the number of unit areas required. Register cross marks are provided, as shown, in the non-printing areas.

Another piece of goldenrod paper is placed over one of the unit areas on the flat, and the layout for that area is traced onto this piece of goldenrod — which is now called the "mask." The negatives for *one area* are now stripped into the mask, and the image window is cut out of the mask. Register windows are cut out of the mask as shown.

Portions of the flat, larger than the image areas of the mask, are cut out in each of the units on the flat.

In exposing the plate, the register flat is taped at diagonal corners to the plate. The mask is registered over the first of the units on the flat, and the remaining openings in the flat are covered with other pieces of goldenrod paper to prevent the exposure light

from striking them. The exposure for this area is then made. The process is repeated for each of the other areas on the flat. (See page 225 for additional information on step-and-repeat work.)

## Combinations

Combination printing, in which lettering is superimposed over a halftone picture, can be achieved with the lettering appearing in positive (black) over the picture, or as reverse printing (open letters) on the picture area.

### Positive Lettering

The photographer must furnish to the stripper a halftone negative of the desired illustration, plus a line negative of the desired lettering which is to appear over the illustration.

The stripper strips up two flats, in register. On the main flat, he strips up the halftone negative. On the second flat, he strips up the line negative, being careful to align this flat in the exact desired position.

The platemaker will expose the plate to the halftone flat and then remove that flat,

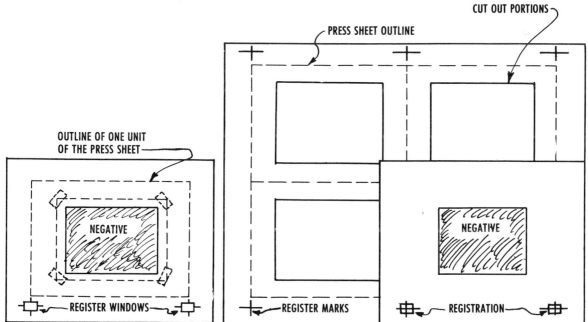

Fig. 331. Repeating Exposures of One Negative on a Plate. Mask with negative taped in exact position is placed over the register flat for use in printing the first of four exposures on the plate.

Then the line negative flat will be exposed in registered position over the plate. Upon development, the plate will carry a combination halftone and line illustration, with the lettering in black over the halftone picture.

It may take a little experimentation to arrive at a proper exposure time for the plate-making.

### Reverse Lettering

The photographer should furnish the stripper with a halftone negative of the desired illustration, plus a line positive of the desired lettering.

The stripper strips up the halftone negative in the desired location on the flat, and then crops it. The flat is then turned over and the window cut out of the flat for the halftone negative. The line positive is stripped in place over the halftone negative — in register with it.

In this position, the emulsions of both the halftone negative and the line positive are *down,* and the line positive is "readable".

The platemaker need make only one exposure with this combination flat to produce a combination image on the plate — the lettering on the halftone image will be open, or "white". The color of the paper will show through the halftone.

### Stripping for Two Colors

If separate parts of the sheet are to be printed in two or more colors, the stripper can proceed to strip up all the negatives for the job on one flat, called the main flat. For example, on this flat, or on the layout for the flat, indicate in circled notations, the lines of type or type matter or illustrations that are to be printed in black, and those that are to be printed in red. Mark register crosses in diagonal corners of this main flat and turn the flat over.

Over this main flat, place a second sheet of goldenrod. Trace register marks on this sheet, and cut out little register windows at the center of the register marks to expose the regis-

ter cross. Cut windows out of this flat to expose each part of the flat that is to be printed in black. Mark this flat the "black" flat.

Place a third sheet of goldenrod over the main flat, and cut out the parts that are to be printed in red. Mark this flat the "red" flat. Provide register marks as for the preceding flat.

The platemaker will tape the main flat to the plate, and then register the black flat to the main flat. After exposure and developing, the plate will bear the image for all the black printing.

For the red plate, the platemaker will remove the black flat and tape the red flat over the main flat. Exposure and development of the plate will result in a plate which will print all parts that are to appear in red.

This method could be enlarged to include as many colors as desired, if a separate flat is cut for each of the colors. See also pages 175-180 in the chapter on color reproduction.

### Questions

1. What is a "flat"? For what is it used?
2. What kind of paper is generally used for the flat?
3. What is meant by "stripping"?
4. What is actinic light?
5. At what point in the offset process does the last opportunity appear for introducing more or less space between elements in the printed job?
6. List the tools, equipment and supplies generally used in stripping a flat.
7. Why are steel T squares, triangles, and straightedges used in stripping a flat?
8. Why is it important to use a beveled-edge scale or rule for measuring and marking distances?
9. Of what use is a "linen tester"?
10. How do you clean the glass top of the stripping table?
11. Tell how to fasten the goldenrod paper squarely on the stripping table.
12. Why does the stripper work in "reverse"?
13. How do you determine the emulsion side of a negative?
14. Why are the negatives placed emulsion-side-up on the flat?

15. What is "opaque solution"? How is it used? Why?
16. Tell how to scribe the reference marks on the negatives.
17. Of what use are these reference marks?
18. Tell how to tape the negatives on the flat.
19. How are the negatives registered in position on the flat?
20. Describe how to cut the "windows" in the flat.
21. What reference marks are generally provided on the flat for the platemaker, pressman and papercutter?
22. How can economies be effected by running large sheets on the press?
23. What is meant by running a job "4-up"?

## Problems and Projects

1. Make out a requisition for a ream of goldenrod paper suitable for flats. Use current paper catalogs in the shop.
2. Make out a requisition, including prices, catalog numbers and correct terminology, for a list of equipment, tools and supplies for stripping flats.
3. Lay out and strip a flat, using your own negatives or those supplied by the instructor, for a single-negative job. Center the image on the sheet. Make this flat for the press specified by the instructor.
4. Plan a four-page folder, in cooperation with your instructor, for which you will make the layout, prepare the camera copy, make the negatives and strip the flat. Make a dummy layout first.
5. Prepare layouts and perform stripping for jobs as required by the instructor. Include a job which must be cut apart and trimmed for padding, or one of several sheets which must be printed on both sides and then folded, assembled, stapled and trimmed.

## New Words

1. accuracy
2. actinic
3. beveled
4. combination
5. diagonal
6. dispenser
7. duplicate
8. equipment
9. experimentation
10. exposing
11. goldenrod
12. identified
13. image
14. intricate
15. layout
16. magnifying
17. measurements
18. minimum
19. penetrate
20. precision
21. relative
22. scissors
23. scribing
24. sliver
25. straightedge
26. successive
27. superimposed
28. triangles
29. T square
30. unreadable
31. vernier

# Platemaking

An offset plate is a thin sheet of paper, plastic or metal from whose surface the inked printing image is transferred to the offset blanket during the operation of the press.

## Plate Characteristics

Plates differ in materials, styles of ends, coatings, areas, etc.

### Plate Surface Areas

The offset plate surface has two distinct and separate areas: (1) the "clear" area and (2) the "image" area. See Fig. 332.

The *clear area* of the plate bears no image. Because of its graining, or water-holding nature, this area will attract and hold a thin film of water (fountain solution, or dampening solution) on its surface, which repels any attempts by the ink rollers to deposit ink on it. (This area also is known as the "non-printing", "non-image", "ink-repellent", or "water-receptive" area.)

The *image area* of the plate is actually the printing image, which has a slightly "greasy" nature so that it repels the application of water, but *accepts* a film of applied ink. (This area is also known as the "printing", "image-bearing", "ink-receptive", or "water-repellent" area.)

### Surface Grain

The surface of an offset plate must be "grained" to make it water receptive, Fig. 333. Graining may be done either chemically or mechanically and results in minute pits or indentations on the plate surface which will readily retain small amounts of water or fountain solution.

In *chemical graining*, the metal plate is subjected to the controlled action of an etching acid or an anodizing solution.

In *mechanical graining*, the metal plate is placed in the trough of a plate-graining machine, where it is covered with an abrasive powder. Then a quantity of steel, glass or wood marbles is placed in the trough, which is made to oscillate rapidly. The action of the marbles rolling over the abrasive causes the roughening (or graining) of the plate.

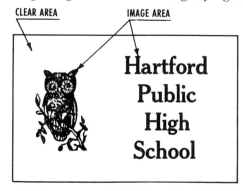

Fig. 332. An Offset Plate

Fig. 333. Grain of a Metal Offset Plate, Enlarged 50 Times
(Courtesy Graphic Arts Technical Foundation, Inc.)

Other forms of mechanical graining are produced by "brush graining" (in which rotary brushes revolve against an abrasive powder on the surface of the plate) and by "sand-blasting."

Paper and plastic plates, and some metal plates, are formed and treated during manufacture so that their surface retains an applied film of moisture. These are termed "grainless plates".

### Thickness and Form

Plates vary in thickness from about .005″ to .012″ for the smaller plates, to .020″ and above for the larger plates.

Most plates are sold cut to press size and, in smaller sizes, are available in four different styles of plate ends: (1) straight; (2) round-hole, or pin-bar punched; (3) slotted, or oval hole; and (4) serrated, or looped. See Fig. 334. The style of plate end needed depends upon the kind of plate clamps with which the press is equipped.

Plate material is used in roll form on some automated platemaking machines, which expose the plate, develop it, and deliver it in cut form, ready for the press.

### Usable Surfaces

Some photographic plates are sensitized so that they are usable on one side only, although many have two usable surfaces (even though only one surface may be guaranteed).

### Masters and Plates

In trade literature and catalogs, the term "master" is used interchangeably with the term "plate" to indicate an offset plate of metal or other material — though "master" usually refers only to plates for the "duplicator" or smaller sizes of offset presses.

### Material of Manufacture

Common offset plates are made of the following materials: paper (cellulose-base); plastic-impregnated or plastic-coated paper (sometimes called "plastic" plates or "paper" plates); acetate; zinc; aluminum; aluminum laminated on paper; plastic on steel; and copper on aluminum, chromium, or stainless steel. Other materials also are used. Zinc was once standard, but now aluminum is most common.

The term "multimetal" refers to those plates consisting of two or three layers of metal (bi-metal or tri-metal respectively).

## General Care of Offset Plates

Since the printed result depends upon the condition of the offset plate, the following instructions should be rigidly observed.

### Precautions with Unused Plates

Keep plates flat and wrapped in original containers in a cool, dry location. Handle sensitized plates in subdued light only; they should not be unduly exposed to room light or sunlight. Pick up plates by gripper ends, keeping fingers and moisture off the plate printing surface. Avoid scratching one plate with the corner of another.

### Care of Developed Plates

Directly following the developing of a plate (or the placing of an image on a plate), the plate is generally "gummed", *i.e.,* it is given a thin coating of gum arabic solution. This prevents deterioration of the clear area of the metal plate which might destroy the ability of this area to repel ink. Also, the gumming protects the clear areas from smudges of ink, grease or dirt which might cause these areas to "scum" or pick up ink when running on the press.

A gummed plate may be used immediately, or its use may be delayed a number of days, since the gum coating serves as a preservative.

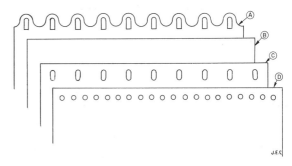

Fig. 334. Styles of Plate Ends: (A) serrated, or looped; (B) straight; (C) slotted, or oval hole; and (D) pin-bar punched, or round-hole punched.

If a developed albumin or deep-etch plate is to be stored for any length of time, it should be both gummed and "put under," *i.e.,* coated with asphaltum. The asphaltum is non-drying and so maintains the image ink-receptive. If not given this coating, the developing ink on the image area might dry and thus not accept ink when placed on the press. This procedure also is advised if the plate is to print any color other than black. The gum and asphaltum coatings each can be removed when the plate is on the press, leaving the clean image to accept the colored ink. Presensitized plates have a durable lacquer coating, and so, they do not usually require being put under. However, no harm is done, and almost any plate can be put under if desired.

Procedures for gumming, putting the plate under, and caring for the plate on the press are given below.

*Gumming a Plate.* With a clean sponge or small pad, wet the entire plate surface with gum solution. Then, using a pad of clean, dry cheesecloth or another pad, rub the gum briskly and evenly, up and down and across the plate, to a thin, hard finish, free of streaks. Fan the plate dry.

NOTE: The plate may now be mounted on the press. However, if an albumin or deep-etch plate is to be stored for any length of time, a coating of asphaltum should be applied over the gum.

*Putting the Plate Under (Asphaltum).* This process is used primarily on albumin and deep-etch plates, which have a soft developing ink. After gumming, remove the developing ink from the image with a little solvent (turpentine or press-cleaning solvent). Using a cheesecloth pad, apply a thin coating of asphaltum to the plate. Rub this thin and dry.

*Care on the Press.* Attach the plate on the plate cylinder of the press. When the press is ready to run, wash the gum (and asphaltum over the gum, if applied) from the plate with a clean sponge dipped in water.

If the press run is interrupted for more than a few seconds, a metal plate is likely to lose water, and it will oxidize. Gum the plate immediately.

NOTE: Before gumming a plate on the press, turn the press "off." To get at all parts of the plate, manually turn the press handwheel.

When ready to resume the press run, wash off the gum with sponge and water.

At the end of the press run, "run down" the plate by running off a few sheets, with ink and dampener rollers in "off" position, to remove much of the image ink. Then gum the plate, remove it from the press, and store it for re-run. For extended storage, wash out the remaining image ink with solvent and apply asphaltum.

### Care in Storage

Offset plates may be stored in shallow (approximately 1″ high) drawers, in envelopes, or face-to-face. A more common method is to store them vertically, on hangers, in plate file cabinets or on two rods.

### Gum Arabic

In the lithographic field, gum arabic solution (1) is the base of deep-etch coatings, (2) is mixed with plate etches and fountain solutions, and (3) is applied directly to many types of offset plates to prevent oxidation of the non-image areas, either when the press is stopped or when the plates are removed for storage. The solution also protects the plate from dirt, ink and grease smudges. It can be sponged easily from the plate surface with water.

### Where Obtained

Gum arabic (or gum acacia, as it is sometimes called) is a natural product, containing salts of Arabic acid. It is obtained from either of two species of trees — the *Acacia senegal* and the *Acacia scorpioides* — which grow in both the Sudan and Senegal, Africa.

The Acacia tree, which normally grows only 8 to 10 feet in height, forms a liquid gum beneath its bark during the dry season from November to June. At this time, workers cut slashes through the bark, and the gum copiously flows out and dries in the wound and on the surface in an attempt to heal itself.

The dried gum is picked off, and most of it is transported to Khartoum, the capital of

Sudan, where it is shipped to all parts of the world for processing.

The purest varieties of gum arabic are nearly white or colorless, and transparent, amber-like in color; some varieties, which may contain some tannin, may be considerably darker in color — yellowish to brownish red.

Gum arabic is available commercially in the form of flakes or sorts, or the user may purchase it as a prepared solution. Some plates require a special gum — both in platemaking and on the press. Even if purchased ready to use, it is interesting to know how it is prepared.

### How To Make a Gum Arabic Solution

A standard gum arabic solution may be prepared in the shop as follows.

Measure out the following quantities:

5 ounces (avoirdupois) of gum arabic crystals

12½ ounces (liquid) of water

Make a pad of several thicknesses of cheesecloth, about seven inches in diameter. Place the gum arabic in the center, fold the cloth around it, and tie the neck of this "sack" with string, Fig. 335.

Suspend the sack of gum arabic crystals in the graduate containing the water so that the crystals are fully submerged, but not touching the bottom. Place a stick across the top of the graduate and tie the string to it, to keep the sack at this level. Cover with a piece of paper and allow the gum to soak overnight.

The following day, remove the sack of gum arabic crystal residue (without squeezing) and wash it or discard it. Take a density reading of the solution, and, if necessary, add water to bring the reading to 14 degrees Baumé.[1] It is now ready for use.

NOTE: A gum arabic solution of 14° Baumé is recommended when gumming a plate on a table or bench. However, when gumming a plate on the press, a 7° or 8° Baumé reading is recommended.

If the gum solution is to be used only for gumming plates, its useful life may be extended many days by adding a few drops

[1]See Appendix 8 for use of Baumé hydrometer; sometimes abbreviated as: Bé.

of formaldehyde. For other uses, none should be added.

Freshly-mixed gum solution has a sweet smell. When it smells sour, it should be discarded. Keeping it in a cool place may help prolong its useful life. Some prefer to make this solution fresh for each day's use.

### Main Types of Offset Plates

Among the main types of offset plates commonly used are:

1. Surface plates
   a. Direct-image
   b. Presensitized
      (1) Contact-printed
            Positive-working
            Negative-working
      (2) Photo-direct (camera exposed)
   c. Whirler-coated (Albumin)
   d. Wipe-on
      (1) Diazo
      (2) Albumin
   e. Transfer
      (1) Gelatin-silver emulsion
      (2) Silver-diffusion
      (3) Thermographic (infrared)
   f. Electronic scanning (Facsimile)

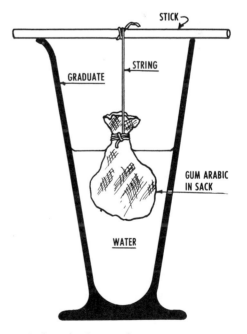

Fig. 335. Soaking the Gum Arabic

g. Electrostatic
   (1) Contact
   (2) Projection
2. Deep-etch
3. Relief plates
   (*Plus* multimetal plates, which can be either the deep-etch or the relief type.)

Fig. 336 illustrates the relative image and non-image heights of various types of plates. The three main types are described briefly below, and then a description of each specific type follows.

### Surface Plates

The image area of a surface plate is *on the surface* of the plate, *i.e.*, the image is said to be *level with* the clear portion of the plate (although the inked image actually may be minutely above the surface of the non-printing area). Surface plates are the most popularly used plates, especially with the smaller offset presses and duplicators.

Surface plates may be purchased as ready-cut, press-size plates or in continuous-roll form (as used on some automated platemaking ma-

chines). The base material may be paper, plastic-impregnated wood pulp, acetate, aluminum, zinc, or aluminum foil laminated to paper. They are available as "presensitized" plates, with a light-sensitive coating on their surface; or, they may be purchased without this coating. The latter includes direct-image plates, plates to be coated in the shop, and plates intended for use with electrostatic, facsimile, transfer, and other platemaking methods.

Instructions for the preparation of a number of types of surface plates are provided later in this chapter.

### Deep-Etch Plates

The printing (image) area of the deep-etch plate is chemically etched to a depth slightly below that of the non-printing area.

The etched image (which carries the ink) in this metal plate has a greater ink-carrying capacity and a longer press life than the surface plate described above. (See also page 250.)

### Relief Plates

Relief plates sometimes are referred to as "dry-offset", "letterset", "low relief", or "shallow-relief" plates, in addition to trade brands.

During processing, the non-printing areas of the plate are removed to a considerable depth below that of the printing areas. Consequently, when a relief plate is run on the press, it requires only inking; the dampening operation is unnecessary.

More detailed information on several kinds of relief plates is given beginning on page 252.

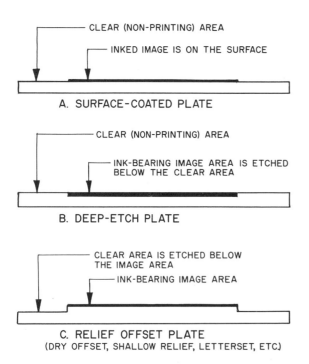

Fig. 336. Relative Image and Non-Image Heights on Some Types of Offset Plates

DEEP-ETCH TYPES (FROM POSITIVES)

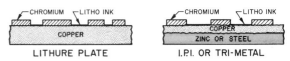

RELIEF TYPES (FROM NEGATIVES)

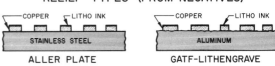

Fig. 337. Types of Multimetal Plates

## Multimetal Plates

Multimetal plates are multilevel plates; the image is either slightly raised or slightly etched below the surrounding surface so as to expose an additional metal. The metal on the raised surface should be one which will wear better than the usual plate metals. At the same time, the metals used should have a special affinity for either ink or water, but not both. For example, unpolished chromium is very hard and attracts water (but not ink). Copper is especially attractive to image inks.

Fig. 337 shows the composition of four typical, long-run, multimetal plates. In each, the top layer (or layers) is electroplated to the base metal and is very thin — about .0002" to .0003", or less than 1/10th the thickness of the paper this page is printed on. Unwanted surface metal can be etched away, exposing another metal beneath. Since the metals do not have the usual graining, they have a more faithful dot shape. They print by the planographic principle and depend on dampening solution in the non-image areas. Multimetal plates have been known to print 2½ million impressions. Other plates must be replaced more frequently — perhaps every hundred thousand copies when using good presensitized plates.

## Plate Exposure Devices

Most general-purpose plates are light-sensitive and require the use of some type of exposure unit. This applies to both presensitized and shop-coated surface plates, as well as to deep-etch plates, relief plates, and multimetal plates. Even duplicator departments specializing in a utility class of work (using direct-image plates, transfer plates, electronic scanning, or electrostatic plates) probably will use some light-sensitive plates for jobs requiring top quality halftones and, therefore, have some plate-exposure device. Fig. 338 gives the basic procedure for exposing a flat.

### Exposure Frames and Printers

Typically, the light-sensitive plate is placed beneath (in direct contact with) the stripped-up flat in an exposure frame. Positive contact is best insured by a vacuum pump which exhausts the air pressure under the plate; thus, atmospheric pressure holds the plate snugly against the flat and the cover glass. It may take several minutes for the full vacuum to build up, but this method gives the most even contact. Even then, it is possible that halftone screens may not make full contact where openings were cut into the flat or where an extra layer of tape or film causes poor contact in

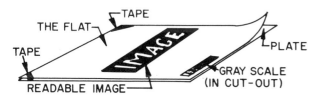

Fig. 338. Flat Positioned for Exposing a Light-Sensitive Plate by Contact Printing

1. Place the plate, sensitized side up, on the bed of the exposure frame or platemaker.
2. Register the flat over the plate with the image readable.
3. Tape corners of flat at gripper edge.
4. Place a gray scale in cut-out of flat, so it will print at trailing edge of plate.
5. Close glass lid and clamp shut.
6. Apply vacuum (if so equipped), check for even contact and clean glass.
7. Make exposure.

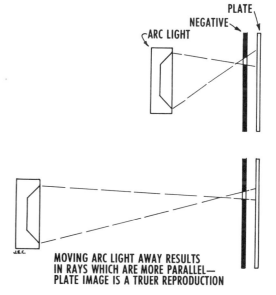

Fig. 339. Minimizing Undercut by Moving Arc Lights Away

Fig. 340. Duplicator-Size Vacuum-Frame Plate Printer (Courtesy Addressograph Multigraph Corp.)

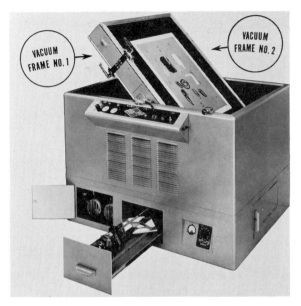

Fig. 341. Flip-Top Platemaker with Back-to-Back Vacuum Frames (Courtesy NuArc Company, Inc.) This allows one side to be loaded while the other is being exposed to the arc (below); also common with frame on one side only.

nearby areas. More simple contact frames may use a foam rubber pad or an air bag to make this necessary contact.

Common light sources are an arc light or a mercury-vapor light bulb (the common suntan lamp). A newer type is the pulsed-xenon light; this is essentially an electronic photoflash lamp which fires brilliantly many times a second. The bulb usually is coiled, so as to provide almost a point-source light which helps to control image spread. See Fig. 339. When the light source is a part of the unit, it usually is called a plate printer (or platemaker). See Figs. 340 and 341.

*For exposure,* the frame is faced to the light which is positioned straight toward the frame. The distance from the light to the frame should be equal to the diagonal measurement of the printing frame, and this distance may remain constant for all exposures.

Maintaining a constant distance between the arc light and the printing frame is a most convenient method of exposing the plate. However, should you decide at some future time to change this distance, then you must also change the length of the exposure. Determine the new length of exposure as follows:

$$\frac{\text{New Distance}^2}{\text{Old Distance}^2} \times \text{Old Exposure Time}$$

In using the above formula, *both distances* must be expressed *in inches,* or *both* must be expressed *in feet.*

Here is a sample problem: Suppose you are exposing plates for two minutes at 3 feet, and you decide to move the light to a new distance of 6 feet. What would the new length of exposure be?

By using the formula:

(a) New distance, squared = $6 \times 6 = 36$
(b) Old distance, squared = $3 \times 3 = \phantom{0}9$
(c) Old exposure time = 2 minutes
(d) Set up the problem:

$$\frac{36}{9} \times 2 = ?$$

$$\frac{\overset{4}{36}}{\underset{1}{9}} \times 2 = 8 \text{ minutes}$$
$$\text{(new exposure time)}$$

The length of exposure is determined experimentally in the shop, and a careful record

Fig. 342. Step Gray Scale (Screened for Reproduction)

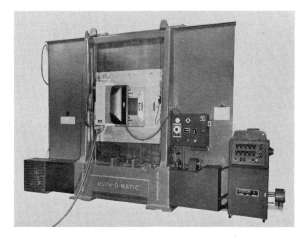

Fig. 343. Ruth-O-Matic Automatic Photo-Composing (Step-and-Repeat) Machine. A single master image can be programmed to repeat accurately in a number of vertical and horizontal positions. (Courtesy Rutherford Machinery Company, Division of Sun Chemical Corp.)

kept so that a plate may be successfully exposed with consistently good results.

*Exposure Control.* To provide a "measuring stick" so as to obtain consistent exposure and development of offset plates, it is advisable to use a *step gray scale* (Fig. 342) each time a plate is exposed.

The gray scale should be placed along the gripper edge of the plate, and a corresponding "window" should be cut out of the flat so that the gray scale is not obscured. Thus, the gray scale will receive the same amount of exposure as the rest of the image.

Since the gray scale is made up of progressive areas or stages of increasing density, the darker areas which do not receive sufficient exposure will wash away during development of the plate. Those areas not so dense will produce an image on the plate.

Generally, if the gray scale image develops to a solid Step 6, it indicates a sufficiently ex-

posed and satisfactorily developed plate. If steps on the gray scale above the seventh are retained in the development, it usually means that the image has spread enough to "plug up" any halftones on the plate. If the plate contains only coarse line work, it probably can go as far as the eighth step without any "filling in."

### Photo-Direct Platemakers

The photo-direct platemakers incorporate a camera which projects the reflected light directly from the original copy or pasteup to the fast emulsion on a plate (reducing or enlarging as needed). See Figs. 352 through 354 for examples.

### Step-and-Repeat Work

Very often one image is repeated a number of times on a single, light-sensitive plate so that its entire capacity may be utilized. Letterheads, labels, cards, tags, calendars, etc. are often printed many at a time in this fashion.

Instead of stripping up enough negatives for the entire plate, one (or a few) negatives are stripped up on a mask. This mask is then registered and exposed in a number of locations to cover the entire plate. (Of course, during each exposure of one section of the plate, all other areas are masked, usually with

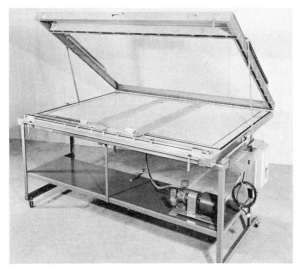

Fig. 344. Model XT Anderson Step-and-Repeat Machine (Courtesy Paul Anderson Manufacturing Co.)

Fig. 345. Example of Step-and-Repeat Work (Courtesy Paul Anderson Manufacturing Co.)

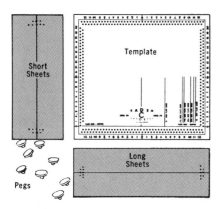

Fig. 346. Pin-Register System for Step-and-Repeat Work on a Regular Plate Printer (Courtesy Raden C Auto Step Co.)

goldenrod paper, to protect them from exposure.) This type of work is known as "step-and-repeat" work.

Fig. 66 on page 23 and Fig. 343 show step-and-repeat platemaking machines.

Fig. 344 shows an exposure-frame printer specially made for step-and-repeat work. In use, a stripped-up mask, containing one or more negatives, is attached to the chase, which is shown in the center of the bed. This chase is movable (back and forth or up and down) to any series of pre-set dimensions. For exposure, the frame is clamped, the vacuum is turned on, and then the frame is tilted vertically to face the arc light.

Fig. 345 shows a 77-on sheet produced by stepping a single negative 7 times on direct-duplicating film to produce a 7-on film negative. This 7-on negative was then stepped across the printer 11 times on the plate, producing a 77-on plate. All work could also be done on film for a single exposure on the plate.

Fig. 346 shows a template which has holes along its edge for pins or pegs which are used to step the image using a regular plate printer. For example, for the butterflies in Fig. 345, the 7-on film negative would be located in one of the "short sheets," and pegs would be placed in holes at the top and at the bottom of the template for 11 exposures across the plate. An 11-up film could also be used with a long sheet for 7 steps down the plate. Devices such as this can be shop-constructed, also.

## SURFACE PLATES

### Direct-Image Plates

Direct-image plates (or *masters*, as they are more apt to be called) have no sensitized coating on their surface when purchased. They are available as press-size plates or in roll form. Base materials usually are paper, plastic-impregnated paper, or acetate (or, in some cases, aluminum or aluminum foil laminated to paper).

Direct-image masters are commonly used to duplicate typewritten forms and for multiple copies in *systems work*. An example of systems work is where information for filling a supply order (as the customer's name and address, billing information, items ordered, prices, shipping information and costs) is typed onto a paper master which has been preprinted with the blank order form. In processing the order, perhaps 12 copies of the order will be needed throughout the various departments of the firm: for inventory records, a packing slip, an address label, shipping record, job envelope, etc. The master together with the specific information added by typing is sent to the offset duplicator to run 12 copies, perhaps some copies being printed on envelopes or special types of paper. The duplicator is running thousands of such orders, but only a few copies of each.

*Types Available.* The durability of direct-image masters varies with the length of the run needed and whether or not the master will be re-run. Short-run systems masters cost only a few cents apiece, and may produce up to 50 copies (if ink and water level are never excessive). Medium-run masters will cost a little more, but are designed for runs of perhaps 1000 copies. In the past, "long-run" direct-image masters were available (for runs of about 5000 copies), but these have been largely replaced by short-run, presensitized plates capable of running perhaps 20,000 copies.

### Imaging Methods

Since the direct-image plate is not sensitized, the image is placed on it by one or a combination of the following methods:

(1) *Hand Method.* The image may be typed directly onto the direct-image plate, using a typewriter equipped with a special fabric, carbon or plastic ribbon. Hand work also may be written, lettered, or drawn with pencil, pen or brush and ink, lithographic crayon, ball-point pen, ruling pen, or pantograph lettering device. In addition, typing can be done through carbon paper, or a rubber stamp can be used.

In each of the methods, the inks, pencils, etc. have a slightly greasy nature — they are termed "reproducing" materials and are available from lithography dealers.

(2) *Mechanical Method.* Letterpress forms (including type and relief plates) may be proofed directly onto direct-image plates, using a letterpress proof press or a letterpress printing press; or by preprinting all, or part, of a form or image by letterpress or offset press. (The latter is called "printing a master from a master".) A reproducing ink is used on the presses for this type of operation. (See litho catalogs.)

When only guide lines are to be imprinted or preprinted on a plate, to be used only as a guide for placing an image on the plate, a "non-reproducing" ink is used. (Guide lines also may be placed on the plate with a non-reproducing pencil.)

(3) *Photo Method.* Direct-image plates may be coated in the shop with albumin or diazo wipe-on solutions to make them light-sensitive, so they may be exposed through negatives or positives. If so coated, they then are handled as presensitized plates. (See later pages of this chapter.)

(4) *Other Methods.* Images may be placed on direct-image plates by electrostatic, transfer, facsimile, and other methods. Some of these methods are described in the following pages of this chapter.

*Caution!* Since direct-image plates are especially sensitive to grease, handle them no more than necessary — and only by the clamping edges, with *clean hands.* Keep unused plates boxed until ready for use.

### Preserving (After Use)

Sometimes direct-image plates are discarded after one press run. However, if it is desired to preserve them for re-run, follow the procedure for gumming a plate as was given on page 220.

### Typing a Direct-Image Plate

Keep space at top and bottom (leading and trailing ends) of plate to allow for plate mounting and gripper margin. Some plates are preprinted with lines indicating the allowable typing space. If not, draw these lines lightly with non-reproducing pencil.

Use a typewriter with sharp, clean keys, and a special water-resistant ribbon which will yield a dense, dark image. A one-time carbon or plastic ribbon is best, to avoid the "fabric pattern" of a cloth ribbon.

With manually operated typewriters, use firm, uniform strokes on the keys, but avoid punching through the surface of the plate. A sheet of acetate between the plate and typewriter platen will help prevent punching through. This is especially noticeable with periods, which characteristically reproduce as hollow "donuts". Electrically operated typewriters are advised for consistently uniform dense letters.

Make deletions with a special rubber eraser — first rubbed clean on paper. Erase just the greasy ink *lightly* — don't scrub through the top surface of the plate. Large image areas may be eradicated with a special deletion fluid available from dealers.

### Letterpress Impressions

Letterpress forms (type forms, relief plates, etc.) may be printed directly onto one or more direct-image plates on the proof press or other letterpress printing press. (This saves photographing proofs of these forms.)

Use greasy-base (linseed-base lithographic) ink, and make provision for correct register of impression on the press.

Before mounting the direct-image plate on the offset press, let the impression dry overnight, or dry it sufficiently with a drying lamp to cure the ink and prevent smearing.

### Preprinting

To preprint all, or a part, of a form (to be reproduced) on direct-image plates, use an offset press or relief press and preprinting ink. Additions to the plate image, if desired, can be made later by typewriter or other hand methods.

To preprint non-reproducing guide lines, use a *letterpress* and a non-reproducing water-soluble ink.

## Presensitized Plates

Presensitized plates, when purchased, are already surface-coated with a light-sensitive material. To prepare the plate for press use, it is necessary only to expose the plate, process it briefly to bring out the image, and then mount it on the press — requiring a total of 5 to 15 minutes. Before presensitized plates were first put on the market in 1950, the platemaker had to coat an albumin or deep-etch plate (and perhaps even prepare the coating) — requiring as much as an hour or two to prepare a single plate for the press. Along with the savings in time and money provided by presensitized plates, other advantages also are possible, including: more consistent quality, fewer problems on the press, elimination of the danger of chromic poisoning for platemakers and pressmen, to name only three. It is little wonder that most lithographers now use presensitized plates. See page 363, "How to Make an Albumin Plate-Coating Solution."

### Light-Sensitive Coatings

In looking for the best light-sensitive materials for coating offset plates, manufacturers had several possibilities, and, then, in their research departments, they developed others. While not all of the following light-sensitive materials are used for presensitized plates, it seems worthwhile to describe the main types at this point.

(1) *The Silver Halides.* These are chemicals such as silver bromide or silver chloride which darken to grains of metallic silver after being exposed and developed. They are used for photographic films and papers and (more recently) for projection-speed, presensitized offset plates which are exposed through a camera. Unlike most of the rest of the materials (which are sensitive primarily to ultraviolet light), the silver halides can be made sensitive to almost any or all colors and in a variety of emulsion speeds.

(2) *Bichromated Coatings.* These are chemicals such as ammonium bichromate, used to sensitize egg albumin in the traditional shop-coated offset plate, and also potassium or sodium bichromate used to sensitize gelatin coatings, carbon tissue, and pigment papers in collotype, gravure, and photo silk screen printing. Bichromate is also called dichromate. Since the coatings begin to set up without light

(in the same manner as when exposed), they usually are sensitized immediately before use.

(3) *Diazo Materials.* These are various chemicals containing two atoms of nitrogen (azote) which are released after exposure to bright light and are developed by compounds like ammonia. Besides presensitized plates, diazo coatings are used for making "white-prints" (which replaced blueprints for duplicating working drawings), films having a transparent colored image (such as 3M Color Key proofing film), and wipe-on coatings for offset plates.

(4) *Ferric (Iron) Compounds.* These are used in various types of blueprinting papers. Ferric ammonium citrate is combined with potassium ferricyanide in blueprints to form a deep blue ferrous ferricyanide where exposed to light and developed in water. Vandykes (brown prints or silver prints) substitute silver nitrate for the second chemical, and the print forms a dark-brown metallic silver image. A direct-positive blueprint paper is also possible, but uncommon. These materials have largely been replaced by the more versatile diazo materials, but blueprints are usually preferred when color fastness is important. They are also handy for proofing flats in platemaking.

(5) *Photopolymers.* These are synthetic plastics and lacquers and have been developed largely by industrial research. Plastics with simple atoms are known as *monomers;* when these link together in chains, thus solidifying or forming a new substance, they are called *polymers.* *Photo*polymers are those in which light (rather than heat or another chemical) causes the linking. Examples of photopolymers are Dycril plates and Kodak Photo Resist solution.

(6) *Photo-Electrostatic Coatings.* These are used in Xerography. Light neutralizes individual charges of static electricity in the coating, leaving the image charged so that it can attract a powdered ink. After the image is formed, it usually is transformed to paper and warmed to cause it to fuse to the paper.

(7) *Thermographic Coatings.* These are sensitive to the *heat variation* which accompanies exposure to visible light energy. The dark image absorbs heat which causes the duplicated image to form and be transferred, as in the 3M Thermofax process.

*Summary.* While all of these sensitized materials have their place in offset platemaking, the diazo materials are the most common coatings for presensitized plates. It should be noted that the term "presensitized plate" refers primarily to a specific type of commercially-made plate which replaces the traditional shop-coated offset plate, not to some of the *special* systems which use materials sensitized during manufacture. These will be studied later.

### Contact-Exposed Presensitized Plates

Presensitized plates made for direct-contact exposure usually are coated with a relatively slow-speed diazo sensitizer. Most of the general-purpose plates used today are of the presensitized, contact-exposed, diazo-coated type.

*Diazo Theory.* Ultra-violet light rays which pass through the transparent areas of the film cause the diazo molecules in the corresponding areas on the plate to release their nitrogen and become inactive. Under opaque areas, the diazo compound is not decomposed and so is capable of acting as a *dye parent.*

After exposure, the plate surface is swabbed with a desensitizing solution which serves as a *dye coupler.* Depending on the type of diazo material in the coating and the specific coupler used, diazo images can be made to change to almost any color or even be reversed from a positive image to a negative one. Thus, it is highly desirable that the manufacturer's instructions (and, usually, his chemicals) be used in the preparation of the plate. Also, it is important in platemaking that the non-image areas be soluble in the solution and so wash away, and that the image areas be insoluble.

Some plates could be put on the press at this point, and a number of copies could be run, but the image is apt to be short lived. Usually the image areas are rubbed-up with a coating which will make them more ink-receptive and will cause them to wear better. At the same time, the coating must not stick to the non-image areas. Usually it is an oil-in-water type of emulsion — gum arabic and a wetting agent in the water, mixed with a synthetic lacquer resin. Unlike the rub-up ink used on albumin plates, this lacquer ages well and so normally does not require being put under asphaltum for long-term storage.

It is important that presensitized coatings have a shelf life of about six months. Most diazo coatings meet this criterion well, but they may require an increased exposure if aged that long. This is the reason that most albumin coatings must be mixed fresh and coated shortly before exposure and developing. The bichromate sensitivity usually begins to deteriorate as soon as the two parts are mixed for coating.

A possible source of trouble is that most diazo compounds are capable of reacting with the aluminum plate. Therefore, it is important that aluminum plates be specially treated to prevent this reaction. Most presensitized plates are grainless (having been chemically treated to attract water and be inert to the diazo compounds), and so the smoother texture requires less water and less ink on the press than the typical grained (albumin) plate.

### Varieties of Presensitized Plates

*Negative- and Positive-Working Plates.* The terms "negative-working plate" and "positive-working plate" are used to designate two kinds of light sensitivity in plates, both of which yield a positive image upon final processing of the plate.

*Negative-Working Plate.* The negative-working plate is intended for exposure beneath a flat composed of film negatives, yielding a positive image on the plate when developed. (Of course, if the flat contains any film positives, their corresponding images on the plate would emerge as "reverses" — clear image and dense background.) The negative-working plate is probably the most common plate.

This type plate should be prepared in accordance with the directions of the manufacturer. General steps are as follows:

(1) Expose the plate behind a flat composed of negatives.

(2) Desensitize the plate.

(3) Develop (lacquer) the plate.

(4) Gum the plate.

The plate is now ready for the press, and it may be stored this way.

*Positive-Working Plate.* The positive-working plate is intended for exposure beneath a flat composed of film positives or transparencies, yielding a *positive* image on the plate when developed.

Whatever is transparent on the flat will appear as a clear area on the plate; conversely, whatever is opaque will appear printed. (Thus, should the flat contain any film negatives, their corresponding areas on the plate will appear with clear image and dense background.)

Prior to exposure, if the film positives are not to cover the entire plate, a plate-size sheet of acetate should be interposed between the positives and the printing-frame glass to keep the plate coating from touching the glass.

Usually, the positives (and transparencies) are stripped to a plate-size sheet of acetate with clear transparent tape. After exposure, the image is evident (not latent), and may contain some unwanted marks or small areas. (Edges and joints between film positives show as fine lines.) These are painted out with a "staging" solution. During development, both the coating on the non-image area and the staging solution are washed away. The resulting image then is intensified with lacquer, if needed, and the plate is gummed. Specific plate manufacturer's directions should be followed. The general steps are outlined below:

(1) Expose plate to film positives or transparencies.

(2) Stage out.

(3) Develop.

(4) Intensify with lacquer (if needed).

(5) Gum.

The positive-working plate has several advantages:

(1) Film positives can be obtained directly from photo-type-composing equipment, and the resulting positives stripped directly into the flat.

(2) Film positives are easier (than negatives) to superimpose in register when stripping several flats for surprinting and color runs.

(3) Standing type forms or letterpress plates can be proofed on acetate or other trans-

parent plastic material and stripped into the flat. Thus, camera work is eliminated. Before the acetate is printed, an impression is printed on the tympan of the press, so that ink will be on both sides of the acetate for more opacity.

(4) Unscreened film positives can be contact-printed to autoscreen film, resulting in positive-screened negatives.

(5) Hand art for posters can be painted or lettered on plate-size sheets of acetate, and these sheets exposed to the plates.

(6) Regular film negatives can be used for reverses simply by stripping them into the flat.

NOTE: Deep-etch plates are also prepared as positive-working plates. See page 250.

*Additive and Subtractive Lacquer Coatings.* Thus far, only the traditional *additive type of coating* has been mentioned. With this type, the sensitized coating is exposed; during development, the non-image areas are washed away; finally, the image is intensified by *adding* a lacquer to the printing area only. Carelessness may cause streaks or a weak lacquer coating, which may wear off during the press run and result in less than the maximum possible life.

On plates with the *subtractive type of coatings,* the lacquer coating is applied in the factory over the entire plate. This provides a degree of consistency not possible with shop-applied coatings, and results in longer runs. After exposure (in the same manner as additive plates), the *lacquer coating is removed* (subtracted) along with the unwanted diazo sensitized coating from the non-printing areas.

*Wipe-On Sensitized Coatings.* Although this section is concerned with *presensitized* plates, it should be pointed out that plates without any sensitized coating can be purchased. The diazo coating (as well as the added lacquer coating) then is applied in the shop. This type will be explained later in the chapter.

*Base Material, Run Length, Etc.* Manufacturers offer presensitized plates for short, medium, and long runs — meaning a possible expectation of perhaps 10,000 copies, 40,000 copies, and 80,000 copies respectively. In some cases, longer runs may be possible; conversely, press problems may cause much shorter runs.

To obtain the longer runs, heavier, more durable coatings and base materials are necessary. Some of these base materials include: paper, aluminum foil laminated to paper (one side), foil laminated to paper on both sides, and sheet aluminum. Larger press sizes require heavier gauges of sheet aluminum (from about .005″ for a 10″ x 16″ plate to about .020″ for some very large sizes). Short-run plates may be designed for either one-time use or for re-runs; they also may be coated on one or both sides.

*Precautions.* Store unexposed presensitized plates in a cool, dry area, away from light. Do not remove them from the original carton until ready for exposure. After removing a plate from the carton, refold the carton edges to protect against light.

Handle by plate-clamping edges only, in subdued light, keeping fingers off the surface.

Purchase only enough plates at one time as you can reasonably expect to use during the stated shelf life of the plates.

Finally, follow manufacturer's directions.

### Processing Presensitized Plates

Presensitized plates are being made by a number of manufacturers. The first successful presensitized plate was the 3M Type "R", introduced in 1950. This section will give the specific processing procedures, as typical examples, for several types of the popular 3M brand of plates.[2] The following table summarizes the main types of 3M plates available:

| 3M Type | | Sides | Run | Flat | Lacquering |
|---------|--|-------|-----|------|------------|
| E | (Foil) | One | Short | Negative | Additive |
| L | (Foil) | Two | Short | Negative | Additive |
| R | (Regular) | Two[3] | Medium | Negative | Additive |
| K | (Simple- | | Med.- | | |
| | Processing) | One | Long | Negative | Subtractive |
| S | (Subtrac- | | | | |
| | tive) | One | Long | Negative | Subtractive |
| SP | (Surface | | | | |
| | Positive) | One | Long | Positive | Subtractive |

[2]Illustrations and procedures are reproduced with the permission of Minnesota Mining and Mfg. Co.

[3]Type "R" plates are coated on both sides, but only one is often used. It is recommended that the beginner expose and develop both sides for the experience, and use whichever is best. Listing is in approximate order of cost — running from about one-half dollar to more than two dollars each in the size for a 14″ x 20″ press.

*Preliminary.* Keep fingers off plate surfaces and handle only under yellow light before exposing. Store unused plates in a cool, dry place and observe the expiration date. The face side of the plate is indicated by the trademark in the upper-right-hand corner.

*Exposing.* Expose the plates (preferably) in a vacuum frame, with an ultra-violet light, such as black-light fluorescent tubes, carbon arcs or quartz-iodine lamps. If yellow room light is not provided, shield the unexposed plate from unnecessary white room light.

Include a gray scale in a cut-out portion of the flat along the gripper edge of the plate, outside the printing area (Fig. 347). Expose to a solid Step 6, as shown in Fig. 348. This guarantees that the plate has been exposed properly for maximum press life. (For very short runs with "E" and "L" plates, the exposure may be shortened, and a solid Step 4 is satisfactory.)

If you expose through more than one layer of film, increase the exposure time. One extra layer, even though it seems transparent, usually requires about one step more exposure.

To check the exposure on a negative-working plate, expose the gray scale onto the plate. Then develop the plate in the usual manner.

For an "E", "L", or "R" plate, after washing off the excess developer, rub the gray scale image vigorously with the fingers while the plate is wet with water. Loosely-bonded developer will rub off quickly.

For the "S" plate, add a small amount of "S" developer to the gray scale image. Then, using the 3M developing pad, rub with brisk, circular motions, keeping the pad flat. This generally will remove two or three steps from the scale. Exposure time for an "S" plate is approximately 1½ times that for the "R" plate.

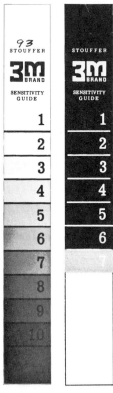

| TO INCREASE ORIGINAL GRAY SCALE READING BY: | 1 STEP | 2 STEPS | 3 STEPS |
|---|---|---|---|
| Multiply your original exposure time by: | 1.4 | 2 | 2.8 |

| TO DECREASE ORIGINAL GRAY SCALE READING BY: | 1 STEP | 2 STEPS | 3 STEPS |
|---|---|---|---|
| Divide your original exposure time by: | 1.4 | 2 | 2.8 |

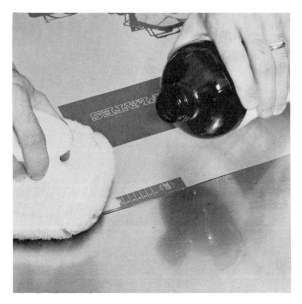

Fig. 347.  Gray Scale Image on Gripper Edge of Plate

Fig. 348.  (Top) 10-Step Gray Scale and Appearance of Solid Step-6 Exposure; (Below) Charts To Adjust Plate Exposure Time If Gray Scale Readings Indicate Under or Overexposure.

Underexposure *can* affect plate mileage. Cover an exposed but undeveloped plate with slipsheeting or masking paper to minimize image fade. However, if the image does fade, this will not affect the developing or running characteristics of the plate.

*"E" and small "L" Plates.* The "E" plate has aluminum foil laminated to one side of a strong paper backing, while the "L" plate has foil laminated to both sides of the paper. Both are recommended for short-run duplicating jobs, featuring speed and handling ease.

Depending upon the type of work and the desired length of press run, either plate can be processed by one of the three methods described in Figs. 349 A, B, and C.

*"R" Plates (Sizes up to 19¾ x 23).* The "R" plate is an all-aluminum plate, sensitized on both sides. It is recommended for medium runs (about 40,000 copies or more). Its processing is described in Figs. 350 A-F.

*"S" Plates.* The "S" plate is recommended for long runs up to 100,000 or more. It is included here as an example of the procedure for *subtracting* rather than adding lacquer (in rub-up). The "S" plate is processed as shown in Figs. 351 A-F.

Accidental water splashes may slow plate development, if not wiped off immediately. Also, a worn developing pad can have the same effect. Remember to use "S" developer, *not water*, to moisten the developing pad. Scratches appearing during platemaking are caused by a dry or dirty developing pad or dirty gumming cloths.

Only "S" gum should be used on an "S" plate — both in platemaking and in the pressroom. While 3M "S" gum can be used with other plates, other gum solutions, including standard gum arabic, must never be used on "S" plates.

*"K" Plates.* The "K" plate is a one-sided, presensitized, negative-working, aluminum, prelacquered surface plate for medium-long runs. After exposure, the subsequent processing of the plate removes the factory-applied lacquer

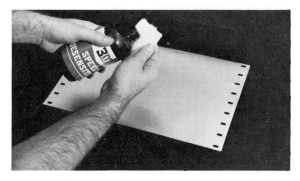

Fig. 349A. Processing 3M "E" and Small "L" Plates—Method 1. For the fastest operation, use speed desensitizer to desensitize the plate, either immediately before or after mounting on the press. Wipe the desensitizer on the entire plate, using a cotton wipe. No developer is needed. (For greater ease and efficiency, it is recommended that the plate be desensitized before mounting on the press.)

Fig. 349B. Processing 3M "E" and Small "L" Plates — Method 2. Apply one-step developer, using a soft, clean cellulose sponge (about 2" x 4" x 4"). This desensitizes the background, develops the image and gums the plate for storage. For very short runs, it is not necessary to develop to a deep-blue image.

Fig. 349C. Processing 3M "E" and Small "L" Plates — Method 3. Best for maximum run. First apply "R" process gum, to desensitize the plate. Then, use "R" developer to produce a visible image. The processing details are the same as for the "R" plates in Figs. 350A-F.

Fig. 350A. Processing 3M "R" Plates — Step 1. Wipe "R" process gum evenly over entire plate surface, using a clean, soft cellulose sponge. Remove excess gum so that only a thin film is left on the plate.

Fig. 350D. Processing 3M "R" Plates — Step 4. Flush off excess developer and inspect plate. Image should not be streaked or plugged, and should not be easily rubbed off with the fingers.

Fig. 350B. Processing 3M "R" Plates — Step 2. Before gum dries, apply pool of "R" developer (red lacquer). Image area determines amount — too much causes slow rub-up and a weak-pink image. Use a small "R" pad in a circular motion over **entire** surface.

Fig. 350E. Processing 3M "R" Plates — Step 5. Squeegee plate dry. Caution: if the gum dried before the lacquer was rubbed smooth, or if the sponge used for lacquering had been used earlier with gum arabic, the result will be an image which rubs off easily.

Fig. 350C. Processing 3M "R" Plates — Step 3. Continue rubbing until strong-red, uniform image appears. Try to maintain even pressure while rubbing. If developer starts to dry before image is a strong red, add small amount of water; do **not** add more gum.

Fig. 350F. Processing 3M "R" Plates — Step 6. Spread a small amount of "R" process gum with a small cellulose sponge. Polish the gum dry with a piece of soft, clean cheesecloth. Never use a fan to force the gum to dry.

Fig. 351A. Processing 3M "S" Plates — Step 1. Place plate on a cool surface, and moisten a developing pad with "S" developer. Use only the 3M pad, never moisten it with water, and replace it before it is badly worn.

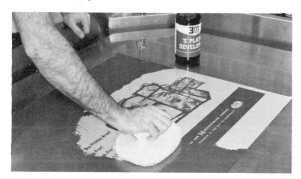

Fig. 351B. Processing 3M "S" Plates — Step 2. Pour the developer onto the center of the plate, and distribute it over the entire surface with the developing pad. Wait a few seconds; then rub off the blue coating, using firm, uniform pressure and circular motions. Keep the pad **flat.** Inspect the plate closely. If screens and halftones do not appear clean, add a little more developer and rub briskly. Squeegee off developer, and flush immediately with water — do not allow developer to dry.

Fig. 351C. Processing 3M "S" Plates — Step 3. Keep developing pad clean. When necessary, scrape it with a clean, stiff rubber squeegee. Loose coating that clings to the developing pad reduces its ability to clean out the non-image areas.

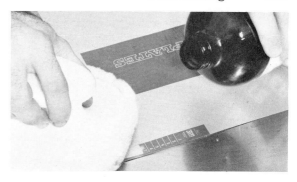

Fig. 351D. Processing 3M "S" Plates — Step 4. Add developer and develop the gray scale. Then add more developer and rub briskly with pad flat to remove more steps. If exposure is right, a solid Step 6 will result. Squeegee off developer; flush with water.

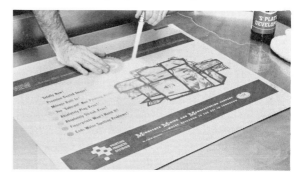

Fig. 351E. Processing 3M "S" Plates — Step 5. Rinse thoroughly with tap water; then squeegee. Flush excess developer with water from underneath the edges of the plate. Rub water over the plate with a clean wad of cheesecloth or disposable paper wipe. While rinsing, rub until developer has been completely removed with water. Tip plate to remove excess water; then lay plate down and check for uniform wetness. Rinse until the entire background (non-image area) of the plate accepts water.

Fig. 351F. Processing 3M "S" Plates — Step 6. Move plate to a dry area for gumming. **Use only "S" gum.** Pour a liberal amount on the plate and spread it over the entire surface with a clean sponge or wipe. Polish plate dry with a **clean cheesecloth.**

from the non-image areas. Development is very simple, and automatic machine processors are available for use with this plate.

To develop, pour a quantity of the "K" developer on the center of the plate, and distribute it evenly over the entire surface with the developing pad. Allow the developer to stand until the plate image is visible. Then, using the pad in a circular motion, remove the coating from the non-image area (Fig. 351G). Add more developer if halftones and tints are plugged.

Squeegee off the developer, and, before the remaining developer dries, flush the plate off with water while rubbing with clean cheesecloth or a suitable wipe.

Develop the gray scale by adding more developer to that portion and rubbing briskly with the pad.

To prevent slow developing, the temperature of the developing table surface should not be less than 60° F.

Rinse the plate with running water to flush the developer from underneath the plate. Then flush the surface, rubbing with the pad until the developer has been completely removed. Tip the plate to drain excess water, and check for uniform wetness. Rinse until the entire non-image area accepts water.

On a separate work surface, gum the plate with 3M "R" process gum, using a clean sponge or wipe. Polish the plate dry with clean cheesecloth. Avoid highly-bichromated fountain solutions on the press.

*Additions, Deletions and Repairs.* On "R" and "S" plates, broken lines can be repaired and minor additions (such as register marks) can be made by scratching the surface of the plate with a sharp needle or knife held at a slight angle and filling the scratch with printing ink.

Holes in solids can be repaired with plate tusche. The tusche should be applied to the plate with a cotton-tipped swab, rubbing for 30-35 seconds. The area will turn tan; it then should be neutralized immediately with tap water (not etch), and dried. Ink should be rubbed into the area before gumming the plate. On the press, ink should be rubbed into the area before dropping the dampeners.

Deletions can be made with a clean, soft rubber eraser moistened with water or fountain solution. For large areas, a special deletion stop-out solution should be used. (These deletion methods are effective for "L" and "E" plates also.)

A #2 pencil may be used to make small additions and repairs to the "L" and "E" plates. Draw on a dry plate with sufficient pressure to indent (but not tear) the aluminum surface. Fill the indentation with press ink.

Fig. 351G.  Processing 3M "K" Plates. "K" developer removes the factory-applied coating from the non-image areas.

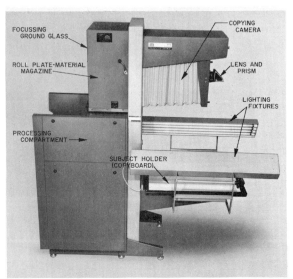

Fig. 352.  Itek Project-A-Lith Platemaster Unit for Automatically Making Offset Masters from Copy (Courtesy Itek Business Products)

### Photo-Direct (Projection-Speed) Plates

Photo-direct presensitized plates have a faster silver-halide coating and are used in an automatic or semi-automatic camera- or projector-type platemaker. (See Figs. 352 through 354.)

In the photo-direct process, the use of a negative intermediary is eliminated. Instead, the presensitized plates are loaded into the platemaker, the original copy material is placed in the copyboard, the platemaker is focused for size, etc., and the exposure is made. Light rays from the original copy material are reflected through a prism-lens arrangement to the plate (inside the processing compartment of the platemaker). The plate is then automatically processed and delivered ready for use.

Since the photo-direct platemaker (processor) is its own camera, projecting the image directly onto the concealed plate, no darkroom is required for this entire sequence of platemaking. It is designed primarily for simplified techniques in duplicating work, rather than for general use by commercial printers on more complex work.

### Albumin Plates

Not many years ago, whirler-coated albumin plates were standard in the photo-offset industry. Today, having been replaced largely by the diazo presensitized plate, albumin plates are a rarity — most inventories of heavy zinc plates have been sold for scrap metal, and the whirlers (used for applying an even coating by spinning the plate), if still around, are apt to be idle. The lithographers' homemade plate is disappearing in this generation, much as the darkroom-coated, collodion-and-glass, wet plates of the photographer disappeared with the advent of commercial film several generations back.

However, the albumin light-sensitive coating still is interesting to study and experiment with, and it remains one of the easiest light-sensitive coatings to prepare directly from the basic chemicals. Schools continue to use albumin plates for instructional purposes. Therefore, Appendix 8 at the back of this book gives information on how to make an albumin solution, as well as how to prepare, expose, develop and use albumin plates. Whirler-coated plates on zinc or aluminum, and simple, wipe-on sensitized paper plates both are explained in detail.

The main ingredients in an albumin coating solution are albumin, ammonium bichromate (or dichromate), and water. Most albumin is prepared from the whites of eggs, although a chemically-compounded albumin is also used.

Fig. 353. Model 705 Automated Photo-Direct Camera Processor, for Making Offset Masters Directly from Copy (Courtesy Addressograph Multigraph Corp.)

Fig. 354. Robertson "Electricon" Automatic Camera/Processor, for Making Offset Plates (Paper and Metal) Directly from Copy: (A) Tilting vacuum platen picks up and carries the plate during entire platemaking cycle; (B) Master control panel; (C) Ground glass and auxiliary focussing controls; (D) Plate loading station; (E) Copyboard; and (F) Front case. (Courtesy Robertson Photo-Mechanix, Inc.)

The albumin, when dissolved in water, actually remains suspended in minute particles in the solution. The addition of the ammonium bichromate (a deadly poison if taken internally) renders the coating solution light-sensitive.

In platemaking, an offset plate is coated with the solution and dried. It is placed under the negatives composing the flat and then is exposed to a strong light which penetrates the negative's transparent areas and hardens the exposed areas of the coating solution on the plate below. The plate surface is then rubbed-up with developing ink and placed in water. The unexposed areas of coating solution are washed away in the water, leaving the inked image on the plate.

Lithographic supply houses often can furnish ready-made platemaking solutions. Some platemakers still make their own. Albumin solutions can be used for simple wipe-on coatings.

Presensitized surface albumin plates also are available. These are already coated, ready for exposure.

## Wipe-On Plates

The wipe-on (surface-coated offset) diazo plate is coated in the shop, prior to exposure. Briefly, the procedure consists of spreading a diazo sensitizer on a fine-grained aluminum plate, the surface of which has been chemically treated (after graining) to prevent oxidation and also to serve as a base for the coating. No whirler is used in the wipe-on coating procedure. (Note also the wipe-on procedure explained for albumin plates in Appendix 8, on page 369.)

At present, brush-graining and sandblasting are two common methods of graining plates to be coated by the wipe-on process.

### Instructions for Wipe-On Plates

Keep unused plates wrapped. Needless exposure to sunlight or white fluorescent light may cause background toning in the subsequently exposed plate. It is also recommended that the plates be coated under either subdued or yellow light.[4]

1. *Coating.* The wipe-on sensitizer is supplied in unit form, consisting of separate containers of diazo powder and a base solution. This packaging prevents deterioration, thereby giving a longer shelf life. When the sensitizer is mixed, it is usable for a period of at least ten days, if kept in a light-protected area. Store both the sensitizer unit and any mixed solution in a cool place.

To make a ready-to-use sensitizer solution, simply pour the entire container of diazo powder into the bottle of base solution, and shake until completely dissolved.

Select a fine-grain, photographic-grade, cellulose sponge as an applicator. Prepare it by saturating with water, and then wringing as dry as possible. Pour a pool of the sensitizer solution on the center of the plate, and spread the solution over the entire plate surface with the sponge. Use straight strokes, first wiping horizontally across the plate until the entire plate area is covered, and then wiping vertically.

Turn over the sponge, and smooth the coating by repeating the above spreading method. Use only a light pressure, with a steady motion back and forth across the entire plate. At this point, the coating should be smooth and even. Eliminate any excess coating by repeating the horizontal and vertical strokes. Finally, fan the coating for at least one-half minute, to dry it completely.

A slightly streaked appearance will not affect the finished plate or printing, provided that the plate is covered completely with coating solution.

It is not necessary to rinse the sponge after coating each plate, but it is suggested that the sponge be rinsed at intervals.

2. *Exposure.* Expose wipe-on plates for approximately four minutes, with a single, 35-ampere arc lamp, at 36 to 40 inches distance. This may vary according to individual shop conditions and equipment. When the

[4]Instructions reproduced by permission of Litho Chemical and Supply Co., Inc., suppliers of "Wipe-O" brand plates and related chemicals.

plate is normally exposed and developed, a solid sixth step should be obtained, using a platemakers' sensitivity guide.

3. *Developing and Lacquering.* The plate is developed and the image lacquered in one operation. Wet a separate cellulose sponge and wring out the excess water. Shake the lacquer-developer thoroughly, and pour a sufficient pool in the center of the plate; spread this over the entire surface, using firm pressure. The background areas immediately will begin to develop, and the image will accept the lacquer ingredients of the solution. Use a circular motion to rub up the image, applying more lacquer-developer, if necessary.

While rubbing up the image, squeeze the sponge over the center of the plate, forming a pool of excess water and lacquer-developer. Starting with the sponge in this pool, again go over the entire image area. With this technique, the free water will remove any residue of the developer phase of the solution from the image and will permit full coverage of the image by the lacquer phase.

Usually, there is a color intensity of the image during the last rubbing-up operation. When it appears that the background is fully developed and the image is rubbed up solidly, flush the plate well with water to remove dissolved coating and excess developer.

When the plate is clean, squeegee and apply gum etch, rubbing down dry. The gum etch has a grease-receptive ingredient which assures quick roll-up. (Do not apply asphaltum to the plate, since it is not necessary and the asphaltum would tend to penetrate the gum film.) The plate is now ready for the press.

4. *On the Press.* Remove gum with water sponge, and start the press run in the usual manner.

Deletions can be made with a rubber hone or regular slipstone, followed with plate etch or fountain solution.

If the plate has been subjected to scratches which print, apply Plate Kleen for one-half minute. This solution will remove the ink and will build up a new protective and hydrophilic (water-attractive) surface. Follow the same procedure if background toning is present.

5. *Storage.* For storage, the plate should be gummed with diluted gum solution (8° Bé), and washed out with asphaltum.

*Additional notes:* After coating, if the lacquer film of the plate coating is not perfect, apply a second coating of the sensitizer without washing off the first coating. Merely pour on a second application and re-wipe as above. If the plate is wet with rinse water, squeegee off the excess water before applying the lacquer-developer a second time.

## Transfer Plates

Thus far, each type of offset plate described has had the printing image produced or exposed directly on the press plate. In transfer plates, the light-sensitive material forms the image on an intermediate surface. This surface is then placed against the press plate, so that the image-forming material can be transferred or printed onto the plate.

In general, the transfer methods have not yet been developed to the point where they can produce as sharp an image as those reproduced from the usual film intermediates — as from flats exposed on presensitized or deep-etch plates, for example. Transfer plates typically have been used to reproduce typed material with simple line drawings, although halftones can be reproduced if the screen is not too fine. The newer photo-direct presensitized plates are now aiming at this market.

There are several methods for forming the image and making the transfer. Two processes are very similar and, sometimes, are classed together. These are the gelatin-silver-emulsion process (Kodak Ektalith) and the silver-diffusion process (Agfa-Gaevert). The first is related to the Verifax system of office photocopying. A third technique is the thermographic process (3M Thermofax, also related to an office photocopying technique).

Electronically scanning the image — an outgrowth of a method for making mimeograph stencils — transfers the image directly from copy to plate by means of electronic impulses.

An additional process also is actually a transfer technique, but is different enough to be listed separately. This is the Xerographic electrostatic dry transfer process (pioneered by Haloid, now the Xerox Corporation). It also is an outgrowth of an office photocopying method. At present, Xerography can be used to produce directly a limited number of clean photocopies, or it can be used to prepare a lithographic plate so that longer runs can be made on an offset press. However, already in operation are experimental presses which use the electrostatic process to do fine-quality color printing at near-normal press speeds without the need of any intermediate film or plates.

### Gelatin-Silver-Emulsion Transfer Plates

The Kodak Ektalith method of offset plate-making is a gelatin and silver-halide emulsion transfer method.

When combined with a process camera, the Ektalith method is capable of producing plate images which are enlarged, reduced, or same-size from line copy or screened halftone prints (up to 120 lines per inch).

*Theory.* The theory of the Ektalith method is shown diagrammatically in Fig. 355.

(1) A sheet of Ektalith transfer paper is exposed, in a process camera, to the original copy material on the camera's copyboard. A latent image is thus formed in the orthochromatic, gelatin and silver-halide, projection-speed, emulsion of the transfer paper.

(2) The transfer paper is developed ("activated") in a colored processing solution. In this processing, the gelatin in the emulsion of the transfer paper becomes hardened in those areas where enough light reached it (*i.e.*, in those areas corresponding to the light parts of the original copy).

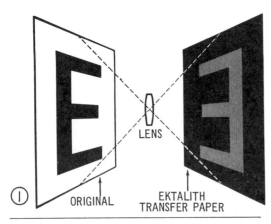

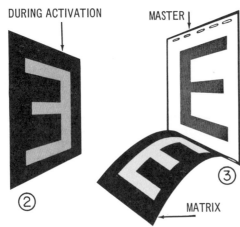

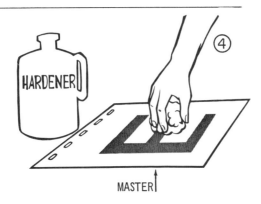

Fig. 355. The Ektalith Method (Courtesy Eastman Kodak Co.)

Fig. 356. Ektalith Loader-Processor, Model 2, for Room-Light Loading and Processing of Ektalith Transfer Paper and Negative Material (Courtesy Eastman Kodak Co.)

In those areas where little or no light was reflected from the original copy, the emulsion becomes softened and acquires a "tanning" (image density) due to the color of the activator solution. (This tanned portion will be the image portion.)

Upon completion of this activation, the transfer paper is known as a "matrix".

(3) The matrix is placed in contact with a direct-image master. By application of light roller pressure, some of the softened, unexposed emulsion in the image areas of the matrix is transferred to the master. (Actually, some of the emulsion remains on the matrix and may be used for additional transfers.) The hardened areas of the exposed emulsion remain on the matrix.

The matrix is then stripped away from the master.

(4) Application of a liquid hardener to the surface of the master completes the platemaking operation.

*Procedure.* It is recommended that the operator first study and understand the detailed instructions of the manufacturer for the specific equipment and supplies to be used. Fig. 356 shows the loader-processor to be used. Any process camera which will receive the paper holder can be used.

*(1) The Copy.* Position the copy in the process camera, and set it for size, focus, etc.

*(2) Load the Paper Holder.* At the loader-processor, put a sheet of transfer paper into the paper holder, Fig. 357.

*(3) Expose the Paper.* Place the loaded paper holder into a special adapter on the camera's rear case (Fig. 358). Remove the dark slide from the paper holder, and make the exposure. Then replace the dark slide, and remove the paper holder from the camera.

*(4) Activate the Paper.* Place the paper holder into the lower-left opening of the loader-processor (Fig. 359), and slide the transfer paper into the activator tray directly to the right. After a short activation period (about 20 seconds), remove the "matrix" from the

Fig. 358. Ektalith Transfer Paper (in Holder) Being Placed in Copying Camera for Exposure to Original Copy (Courtesy Eastman Kodak Co.)

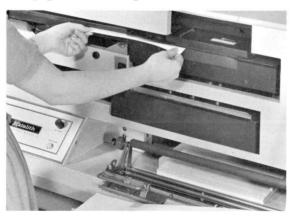

Fig. 357. Loading Ektalith Transfer Paper into Holder (Courtesy Eastman Kodak Co.)

Fig. 359. Inserting Exposed Ektalith Transfer Paper (Still in Holder) into Loader-Processor. This is done prior to sliding the transfer paper into the activator tray (directly to the right). (Courtesy Eastman Kodak Co.)

activator, and slide it downward into the vertical front compartment of the transfer unit (Fig. 360).

(5) *Imaging the Master.* Partially withdraw the master from the plate storage com-

Fig. 360. Ektalith Matrix Being Lowered into Front Compartment of Transfer Unit (Courtesy Eastman Kodak Co.)

Fig. 361. The Transfer Operation — Pulling Ektalith Matrix and Master Through Pressure Roller of Transfer Unit (Courtesy Eastman Kodak Co.)

Fig. 362. Stripping Ekalith Matrix from Master. The master is now imaged. (Courtesy Eastman Kodak Co.)

partment directly above the transfer unit, and position it to the plate stops.

NOTE: Kodak EV paper masters are recommended for this method of platemaking, although any direct-image plate that accepts and holds an image may be used.

Grip the master and the matrix with the fingers, and pull through under roller pressure (Fig. 361). Immediately strip the matrix from the master (Fig. 362), leaving the image now evident on the master.

Pass a water-dampened sponge lightly over the master to remove any activator solution. Remove any unwanted details with a moistened eraser.

After air-drying for a short time, apply hardening solution to the plate surface, using cotton and minimum pressure.

*Presensitized Masters.* Presensitized offset masters also may be produced by the Ektalith method. A Kodak Ektalith (paper) negative is exposed to the original copy, processed in the same manner as for the Ektalith transfer paper, and then washed and dried. The dry negative can be exposed to any presensitized metal or paper master.

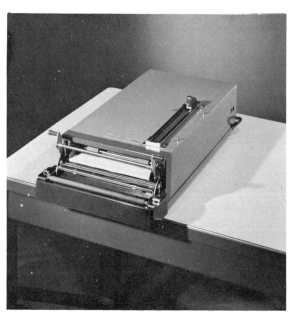

Fig. 363. Ektalith Copy Unit, Model 1, for Making Direct Paper or Transparent Copies from Ektalith Transfer Paper (Courtesy Eastman Kodak Co.)

*Direct Copies.* Ten or more paper or transparent copies can be made directly from Ektalith transfer paper by use of the Ektalith copy unit shown in Fig. 363.

### Silver-Diffusion Transfer Plates

Agfacopy plates are an example of the silver-diffusion transfer method of offset platemaking. Most of the materials are made in Belgium and are imported under several tradenames. In this process, the original copy (typed, drawn, type proofs, halftones, etc., with 120-line screens or coarser) is either contact-pointed or projection-printed onto a silver-sensitized negative paper. See Figs. 364 and 365. This produces a latent image on the negative paper. The exposed negative paper is then placed face toward the grained side of an aluminum plate, and together they are immersed into a developing bath (Fig. 366).

The developing bath converts the exposed silver salts on the negative emulsion into black metallic silver. As the plate and negative are withdrawn together from the bath (under roller pressure), this silver is transferred by diffusion to the surface of the offset plate, forming the image on the plate.

The negative paper is then stripped from the plate (Fig. 367), and the plate is given an application of fixer-lacquer to clear the plate and intensify the image (Fig. 368).

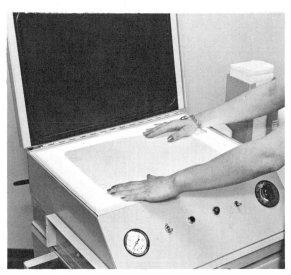

Fig. 365. Step 1. Using Agfacopy negative paper OCpG, align emulsion (glossy) side in contact with surface of original. Place into position on exposing glass of plate processor with negative toward light source. Close lid, turn on vacuum pump, set timer and expose. Fine details require shorter exposure time and colored backgrounds a slight increase. (Courtesy Agfa Inc.)

Fig. 366. Step 2. Tape exposed negative on plate (emulsion facing grain). Insert into dip tank with plate on the outside, allowing divider to separate plate and negative. Immerse in tank. Agitate for about 4 seconds; engage rollers and draw set out of tank with straight and even pull. (Courtesy Agfa Inc.)

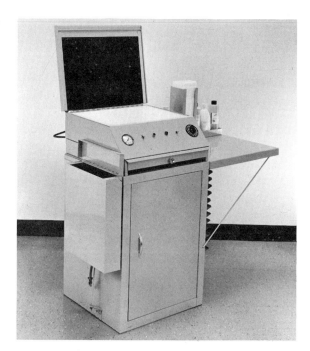

Fig. 364. Agfa A-64 Platemaker, for Silver-Diffusion Method of Platemaking (Courtesy Agfa Inc.)

Fig. 367. Step 3. Strip negative from plate, starting at end first to enter and last to leave tank. With roller-driven developers, separate from the end that first left the machine and pull apart at approximately the same speed at which the negative and plate passed through the rollers. (Courtesy Agfa Inc.)

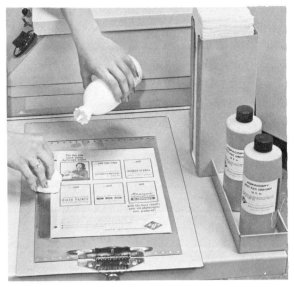

Fig. 368. Step 4. After separation, apply fixer-lacquer to surface of plate and distribute evenly with firm cotton pad. Then to clean surface of plate and preserve it until ready to run, apply Agfacopy plate conditioner, using fresh pad of cotton. Polish the conditioner dry, to avoid image deterioration. (Courtesy Agfa Inc.)

The plate then may be run on the press or preserved for future use.

### Thermographic (Infrared) Transfer Plates

The thermographic process of platemaking uses heat from infrared radiation reacting with plastic-coated film or paper to transfer an image to a direct-image plate. Fig. 369 shows such a copying machine.

For typed copy, the typing is done on a specially coated paper. This typed original is then placed over a direct-image plate, and the two are run together through the infrared copying machine. Here the image is developed and transferred to the plate surface (Fig. 370).

Plates may be made from original copy such as documents, newspaper clips, etc., by first exposing it to a "transfer" (plastic-coated) paper. Then this transfer paper, together with a direct-image plate, is passed through the infrared copying machine, producing the image on the plate.

### Electronic-Scanning Facsimile Plates

There are several brands of facsimile electronic-scanning platemakers which will produce same-size facsimile offset plates — line or half-tone — from original copy. See Fig. 371.

The original copy is wrapped around the right side of the drum, and a special offset master unit is wrapped on the left side. As the drum rotates, an electric eye, moving left to right, scans the original. Electrical impulses, varying according to the intensity of the image of the original, actuate a burner needle, which

Fig. 369. Thermo-Fax "Secretary" Infrared Copying Machine (Courtesy 3M Co.)

heats tiny spots on the surface of the offset master unit. The spots thus heated form the ink-attractive image on the paper offset plate. Darker areas cause a larger dot. The plate is then placed on the press and run in the conventional manner.

## Electrostatic Plates

### Xerography

Xerography is pronounced "zee-rog-ra-phy"; the name is a combination of the Greek words "xeros" (meaning "dry") and "graphein" (meaning "to write").

Xerography is a dry photo-electrostatic process of producing an image (same size, enlarged or reduced) from any original: typed, drawn, printed or photographed. See Fig. 372.

Xerography is commonly employed in the offset printing field for the making of paper offset plates (masters) and metal offset plates.

For the preparation of both types, a powder image first is electrostatically produced on a xerographic plate. This image is transferred (again electrostatically) to either a paper or metal offset plate and then is "fused" for permanency. The entire operation is "dry", employing no liquids or intermediary film negatives.

### Preparing the Xerographic Intermediate

The copy to be reproduced may be written, typed, drawn or printed. Either of two Xerox cameras may be used. Commonly, the Xerox Model 1 camera is used for reproducing "same-size" images (Fig. 373). The Xerox Camera No. 4, accommodating originals up to 17″ x 22″ in size, will reproduce at from 50% to 150% of the original size. See Fig. 374.

Fig. 371.   Gestefax Facsimile Electronic-Scanner (Courtesy Gestetner Corp.)

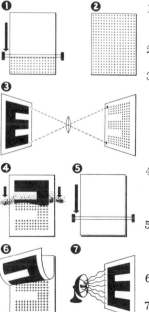

Fig. 370.   Processing a Direct-Image Plate by the Thermographic Transfer Process. (Left) The typed original and the master are passed through the (Thermo-Fax) copying machine. (Right) The imaged plate is mounted on the press. (Courtesy 3M Co.)

1. Surface of selenium-coated plate is electrically charged under wires.
2. Plus marks represent positively-charged plate.
3. Original document is projected through camera lens. Plus marks here represent latent image retaining positive charge. Charge is drained away in areas that are exposed.
4. Powder (negative-charge) is cascaded over plate and adheres to positive image. Latent image is visible.
5. Sheet of paper (or paper offset master) is placed over plate, and paper is given positive charge.
6. Positively-charged paper attracts image powder.
7. Print or offset master is fused by heat.

Fig. 372.   How Xerography Works (Courtesy Xerox Corp.)

*Exposing for a plate image.* Place the camera copy in the camera so it faces the lens, and adjust the camera for focus and size (if camera No. 4 is used).

Remove a xerographic plate (in its holder) from the plate dispenser section of the processor unit, and place it "face up" in the charging chamber of the processor. After charging, place the shield into the plateholder, to prevent light from striking the charged surface of the plate.

Then slide the plateholder into the camera plate chamber, with the shielded side toward the camera lens. Remove the shield, and make the camera exposure. Replace the shield and remove the plateholder from the camera.

*Developing the plate image.* Pull the developer tray (top tray) all the way out on its sliding supports. Place and attach the plateholder (shield side down) on the developer tray. Remove the shield.

Fig. 373.  Xerox Heat Fuser (Left); Xerox Processor D (Center); Xerox Model 1 Camera (Right) (Courtesy Xerox Corp.)

Fig. 374.  Xerox Camera No. 4 (Courtesy Xerox Corp.)

Turn (rotate) the tray upside down, causing the developing powder in the tray to accumulate at the bottom. Continue rotating the tray slowly until the powder can be heard "cascading" over the plate. Hesitate at this sound; then continue rotating to a little beyond the vertical. Repeat this in the opposite direction. Then repeat again, once in each direction. Finally, remove the developed plate from the tray.

The developed image on the xerographic plate is a visible, wrong-reading positive. See Fig. 375.

### Preparing a Paper Offset Plate (Master)

To prepare a paper offset plate by the xerographic method, first photograph and develop an image on a xerographic plate, as described above.

*Transferring.* Place an unsensitized, direct-image, paper offset plate over the image on the xerographic plate, and secure it to the plate with the holder guide, Fig. 376.

Turn on the "positive charge" of the processor unit, and slide the plateholder (with

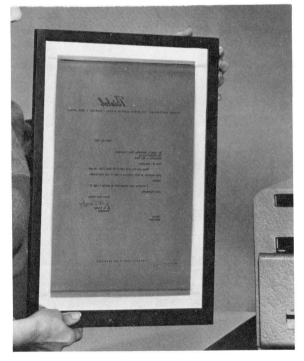

Fig. 375.  Developed Image on a Xerographic Plate — A Wrong-Reading (Flopped L to R) Positive (Courtesy Xerox Corp.)

the paper plate) all the way into the processor chamber. Then slowly pull the plateholder and plate out. Turn off the "charge."

Release and remove the paper offset plate from the plateholder. At this stage, the paper offset has a positive, visible, correct-reading image, Fig. 377.

*Fusing.* The powder image on the paper offset plate is made permanent by fusion with heat. (A vapor unit also may be used.)

Preheat the xerographic fuser unit for 30 minutes. Pull out the fuser tray, and lay the paper offset plate on it, "face up." Be sure that the wire paper lifter is underneath the offset plate. Push the tray all the way in, Fig. 378.

Allow the offset plate to fuse for 8 to 15 seconds; then remove.

*Run on press.* The completed paper offset plate may now be run on the offset press or offset duplicator in the usual manner.

### Preparing a Metal Offset Plate

To prepare a direct-image metal offset plate, first photograph and develop an image on a xerographic plate as described earlier.

*Charging.* Slide the xerographic plate (with its prepared image) into the charging compartment of the processor unit, and give it an electrical charge, Fig. 380. Then slide a light shield into the plateholder, to protect the

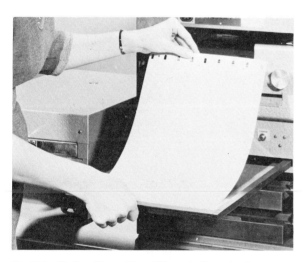

Fig. 376. Placing Paper Plate (Master) Over the Image on the Xerographic Plate (Courtesy Xerox Corp.)

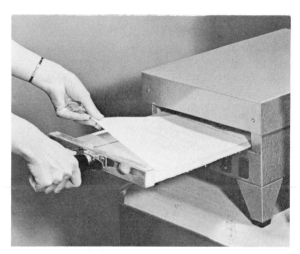

Fig. 378. Inserting Paper Offset Plate into Fuser (Courtesy Xerox Corp.)

Fig. 377. Charged Paper Offset Plate Has Positive, Visible, Correct-Reading Image (Courtesy Xerox Corp.)

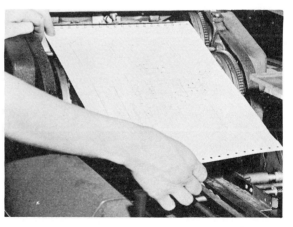

Fig. 379. Attaching Fused (and Finished) Paper Plate to Plate Cylinder of Press (Courtesy Xerox Corp.)

Fig. 380. Sliding Xerographic Plate into Charging Compartment of Processor Unit (Courtesy Xerox Corp.)

Fig. 382. Placing Unsensitized Metal Offset Plate "Face-Down" on Light Shield (Courtesy Xerox Corp.)

Fig. 381. Sliding Light Shield Over Image (Courtesy Xerox Corp.)

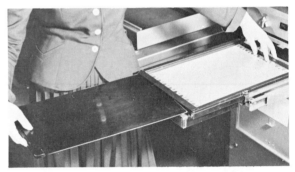

Fig. 383. Withdrawing Light Shield from Between Xerographic Plate and Offset Plate (Courtesy Xerox Corp.)

charged image, Fig. 381. Remove the plate and holder from the processor unit.

*Transferring.* Place the xerographic plate and holder on the withdrawn developer tray of the processor unit, with the light-shield side up. Place the unsensitized metal offset plate "face down" on the light shield, Fig. 382. Withdraw the shield slightly, making visible ½″ of the xerographic plate border. Then slide the metal plate forward to the edge of the frame, and hold it firmly (with the fingers) to the visible ½″ of the xerographic plate. Withdraw the light shield from between the xerographic plate and the offset plate, Fig. 383.

While still holding the offset plate firmly in position with the fingers, gently go over the entire back of this plate with a cotton swab, Fig. 384. Now carefully peel the offset plate from the xerographic plate, Fig. 385. The offset plate now carries the image.

*Fusing.* Place the metal offset plate in the fuser for ninety seconds.

### Halftone Images

Halftones may be reproduced on offset plates by the xerographic process. Original photographs, or copy containing gradations of tone, must first be screened, and prints placed on the paste-up. After this, they are treated the same as normal line copy.

After screening, the toned copy is photographed onto a xerographic plate. The exposed plate then is developed in the *tone tray* of the xerographic processor, using the same procedure as for the developer tray (described previously), but increasing the cascading rotation to eight "passes." See Fig. 386.

### Automatic Projection Plates

In this method of making electrostatic plates, no negative intermediary is handled;

Fig. 384. Swabbing Back of Offset Plate (Courtesy Xerox Corp.)

Fig. 385. Peeling Offset Plate (Now Carrying an Image) from Xerographic Plate (Courtesy Xerox Corp.)

Fig. 386. Xerox Tone Tray (Courtesy Xerox Corp.)

Fig. 387. Robertson "Electricon" Automatic Dry-Process Electrostatic Camera/Processor (Courtesy Robertson Photo-Mechanix, Inc.)

thus, the entire operation is carried out in room light. The camera/processor is much like the one for photo-direct plates (shown earlier as Fig. 354), except it is adapted to the xerographic process.

Fig. 387 shows a Robertson "Electricon" automatic, electrostatic camera/processor, which will make paper and metal offset plates directly from copy in 70 seconds.

First the metal or paper plates are loaded at the plate-loading station. Copy is locked in the glass-covered copyboard, and the camera is set (for enlargements up to 200% or reductions down to 40%). Lights and exposure are set, and the camera is focussed on the ground glass (if desired).

A press of a button begins the automatic sequence: a vacuum platen picks up a plate and carries it to exposure position; exposure is made; the plate is carried through the electrostatic image-transfer process and is delivered. The plate is then run through an automatic plate fuser and is ready for the press.

## Minor Surface Plate Corrections

Sometimes a developed surface plate reveals the need for repairing the image area or removing the unwanted spots, before the plate is sent to the press.

### Deletions

Immediately after developing a surface plate, and while it is still wet, inspect the entire plate to determine if there are any unwanted spots, lines, words or other portions of the image. These can be removed by alternately wetting with water and gently rubbing with a rubber eraser, scotch hone or snake slip. Too vigorous rubbing, or dry rubbing, may polish the rubbed area, robbing it of its grain and rendering that area non-receptive to water.

NOTE: Deletions on paper plates should be made with only a rubber eraser, wetting either the eraser or the plate.

Should the grain of a metal plate be destroyed by too vigorous rubbing, it may be restored by rubbing the area with a water-dampened cotton swab on which has been sprinkled a little pumice.

If available, an air eraser (one which sprays compressed air and pumice) is an excellent device for making deletions, while still preserving the grain structure of the plate surface.

Minor deletions may be made while the plate is on the press. Run down the image, stop the press and gum the plate. Sponge off the area to be worked on with water, and rub out the undesired work or defect with an eraser dipped in water or fountain solution, or with a hone while the area is maintained wet with water. Then gum the area again. Proceed to other areas on the plate, if necessary, and repeat.

### Additions or Corrections

Lines may be added or repaired, and other parts of a broken image restored to a gummed metal plate, either on or off the press, by scratching through the gum just deep enough into the metal surface to make it ink receptive. A lithographer's needle, sharpened or shaped on the end to suit the work, may be used. Finally, developing or printing ink should be rubbed into the scratches to complete the work.

## DEEP-ETCH PLATES

Deep-etch plates differ from surface offset plates in that the image area of the deep-etch plate is etched slightly below the surface of the plate. This gives the deep-etch plate greater ink-carrying capacity, and results in a more brilliant coverage. In addition, this plate has a much longer press life, and the halftone dots are longer lasting. Since the advent of subtractive presensitized plates, fewer deep-etch plates are being used, but they still are the best plate for very long runs and fine detail — especially in multimetal varieties.

### How To Prepare a Deep-Etch Plate

Instead of negatives, the deep-etch process requires a flat made up of *right-reading positive images* on transparent backgrounds. Photographically-composed positive transparencies, or proofs, pulled on cellophane can be used, if the image is sufficiently opaque.

Fig. 388.   Pre-Etching a Plate (Courtesy Harris-Intertype Corp.)

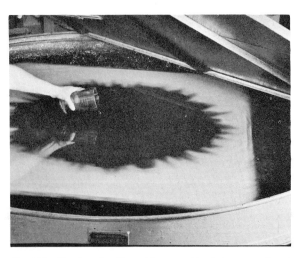

Fig. 389.   Coating the Plate (Courtesy Harris-Intertype Corp.)

For making deep-etch plates, it is best to purchase the needed chemicals and solutions from a chemical supply house. The following items should be on hand:

Pre-etching solution
Positive coating solution
Positive developer
Positive etching solution
Alcohol cleaner (anhydrous alcohol, free of water)
Positive lacquer
Deep-etch developing ink
Cellulose cleaning paper
Stop-out solution
Developing pad
Etching pad
Squeegee
Filtering cloth (for coating solution)
The positive (of the work to be reproduced)

NOTE: For deep-etch plates, use plates of a standard grain — #00 or finer. This grade will take a 133-line screen, or coarser. Grades #000 and #0000 are finer-grain plates. While zinc was once used, aluminum plates are now standard. Either new or freshly regrained plates can be used.

The steps of procedure in making the deep-etch plate are as follows:

(1) *Wash* the plate with running water.

(2) *Pre-etch,* applying pre-etch solution with wide paint brush for about one minute. Then flush with water. See Fig. 388.

(3) *Coat* the plate with positive deep-etch coating solution. Set the whirler at 40 to 50 rpm. Pour the coating solution from its container through a cheesecloth or flannel filter to remove all bubbles. Make a pool of coating solution in the center of the plate, and work toward the edges. Now increase the speed to 80 or 90 rpm, using a little heat. Too much heat may cause tough developing. Dry thoroughly. See Fig. 389.

(4) *Expose* in the vacuum printing frame with arc lights. Give the plate an exposure 25% to 50% longer than surface albumin plates.

(5) *Stop-out.* With an artist's brush, apply stop-out solution to all unwanted areas, such as dust spots, film edges and tape marks.

Use sufficient stop-out solution to avoid brush marks. Fan dry.

(6) *Develop* on a flat table trough, in a well-ventilated area. Rubber gloves should be worn to protect the hands. Pour the positive-developing solution on the plate, and spread with the developing pad over the entire surface, using a circular motion. Continue until bare printing areas are exposed and foaming action starts. Remove with squeegee, and coat again with developer. Squeegee again. Use about 4 ounces of developer for a 22″ x 28″ plate.

(7) *Etching.* Pour on the etching solution. Using the etching pad, spread out the etching solution, Fig. 390. Let this work in for 1½ minutes on that part of the image which has not taken the exposure (on the bare metal). Squeegee off.

(8) *Redeveloping.* Pour a little more developing solution over the plate, to guard against corrosion. Work it in with the developing pad. This neutralizes the etching solution. Squeegee off the plate.

(9) *Cleaning the plate.* Wipe off the plate with a pad of cellulose wiping paper staturated with anhydrous alcohol. Repeat three or four times. Be sure it is clean, and then dry thoroughly with a fan.

(10) *Lacquer.* Pour on a quantity of deep-etch positive lacquer, spreading it over the surface with a cloth pad. This gives a base

Fig. 390. Etching the Developed Plate (Courtesy Harris-Intertype Corp.)

for the developing ink which follows. Dry out the lacquer thoroughly. Then expose the *back* of the plate to the arc light for a minute or so.

(11) *Developing ink.* Pour developing ink on the plate and smooth out with a cloth pad over the entire plate, rubbing it down smooth and dry. Fan dry.

(12) *Developing.* Wash the plate with warm water and soft scrubbing brush in the sink, to remove the stencil from the non-printing areas of the plate. (The stencil is the light-hardened area). The image should now be .0002 to .0003 inches below the remaining or original plate surface level.

(13) *Desensitize.* Follow same procedure as for albumin surface plates.

(14) *Rinse* with running water.

(15) *Squeegee.*

(16) *Gum.*

(17) *Put the plate "under."* Wash out the image with turpentine, or press solvent, and apply asphaltum, Fig. 391.

## Multimetal Plates

Four varieties of multimetal plates were identified earlier. The specific techniques for making these special plates (which are capable of the longest possible runs) are beyond the scope of this book. If more information is desired, literature of the Graphic Arts Technical Foundation can be consulted.

Fig. 391. Applying Asphaltum (Courtesy Harris-Intertype Corp.)

## RELIEF PLATES FOR OFFSET

Relief plates are those plates which have an image area which is considerably higher ("in relief") than the non-printing area — enough so that no dampening solution is used on the press. Only the ink-form rollers are used, applying ink to the relief image on the plate. A firm ink-form roller generally is recommended. Printing with these plates is often referred to as "dry offset," "letterset", and "low relief" printing, and is not actually a form of lithography.

Since no water is needed on the press, a wider range of inks may be used, and problems with gummed papers are minimized. However, the image often has more image spread and less contrast than traditional lithographic plates.

Relief plates are generally .016" or more in thickness, necessitating sufficient plate-cylinder undercut for accommodation.

Several types of relief plates for offset-press use are: (1) the metal dry-offset plate, (2) the Kodak relief plate, and (3) the DuPont "Dycril" plate.

### Metal Dry-Offset Plate

The metal dry-offset plate is a single thickness (.016" or more), and is surface-sensitized. Zinc or magnesium metals can be used. It is exposed in contact with the stripped-up flat of negatives. The non-printing areas of the plate are then chemically etched about .008" to .010" below the level of the image area. Powderless (one-bite) etching machines simplify the etching process. The plates may be exposed and etched flat, then curved to fit the press or processed after curving for less distortion. Smaller plants usually have these plates made by a platemaking firm.

### Kodak Relief Plate

The Kodak relief plate as shown in Fig. 392 is a presensitized plate of .025" thickness, made up of a .010" flexible enameled steel base, .013" of modified (photopolymer) acetate, and a high-contrast silver-halide photosensitive emulsion.

The already-sensitized plate is exposed to the flat in a conventional vacuum frame, or on a step-and-repeat machine. Proper exposure produces a visible print-out image on the plate.

After exposure, the plate is immersed in an activator solution for 1½ minutes. This hardens (or "tans") the light-exposed gelatin in the emulsion layer, and simultaneously produces a black silver image which affords a "proof".

The unexposed, and thus unhardened, (non-image) areas of the emulsion are then washed off the plate by a warm-water spraying. The hardened portions of the emulsion (image areas) remain on the plate to act as a resistant to the solvents in the Kodak relief plate processor.

The plate is then dried and placed in the processor, where combined action of mild solvents and scrubbing with plush fabric removes the acetate unprotected by the hardened gelatin, leaving the printing image in further relief (usually about .010″ to .011″). The plate is now ready for the press.

## Dycril Photopolymer Relief Plates

DuPont Dycril photopolymer relief plates consist of a layer of photosensitive Dycril photopolymer (plastic) bonded to a backing of either metal or "Cronar"[5] polyester film base (Fig. 393).

Types 25 and 30 Dycril plates are .025″ and .031″, respectively, in total thickness, and both have a flexible steel base. The Type C plate has a total thickness of .017″, composed of a relief of .008″ and carried on a .007″ Cronar polyester film base.

### Processing a Type C Dycril Plate

Before processing, unexposed Type C Dycril plates must be protected from white light. During processing, gold fluorescent lighting should be used to illuminate the processing area.

The working (polymer) side of the unprocessed transparent plate must be determined by feel. The polymer side resists a sliding fingernail; the Cronar back is smooth and slick.

[5]DuPont's registered trademark

For exposure, either a rotary or a flat vacuum frame may be used. The polymer side of the plate is placed facing the exposure source, and the negative is placed over it in direct contact (Fig. 394). Vacuum is applied.

The plate is exposed (through the negative) to ultraviolet light. Where this light strikes the intended printing areas, the photopolymer becomes hardened and insoluble.

After exposure, the unexposed (soluble) areas of the photopolymer are washed away with a spray of dilute sodium hydroxide and water.

Excess water is then blown off the plate with compressed air. Final drying is accomplished conveniently by wrapping the plate (with the image side out) around a fiberboard tube, holding it with tape, rubber bands or staples. An example of a resulting plate is shown in Fig. 395.

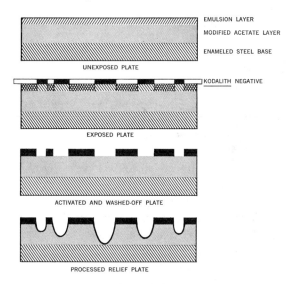

Fig. 392. Schematic Presentation of the Processing of the Kodak Relief Plate (Courtesy Eastman Kodak Co.)

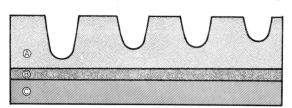

Fig. 393. Cross Section of Dycril Relief Plate. (A) Photosensitive layer (Dycril photopolymer), (B) Bonding layer, and (C) Metal or Cronar support.

Fig. 394. Preparing to Expose a Type C Dycril Plate on a Rotary Exposure Device. (Photopolymer side of plate is facing the negative.) (Courtesy E. I. DuPont de Nemours & Co.)

Fig. 395. Examining a Type C Dycril Plate over a Light Table (Courtesy E. I. DuPont de Nemours & Co.)

Recommended solvents for use with these plates are listed in the appendix of the Dycril Technical Manual.

## Questions

1. Explain what is meant by "two separate areas" of an offset plate. Why is this so?
2. Why is a plate grained?
3. How is graining done?
4. What is a "master"?
5. Of what materials are offset plates made?
6. Explain how, and why, a plate is gummed.
7. What is meant by "putting a plate under"?
8. Describe the care of a plate on the press.
9. What is gum arabic? How is a gum arabic solution made?
10. Tell what is meant by a surface plate. Name the main types of surface plates.
11. Describe a relief plate. By what other names is this kind of plate known?
12. What is meant by "step-and-repeat" work? What are its advantages?
13. In platemaking, why is a "step gray scale" used?
14. Describe the various methods of placing an image on a direct-image plate.
15. What is a presensitized plate?
16. Name the main classes of light-sensitive materials.

17. Describe two methods of exposing a presensitized plate.
18. What is meant by the terms "negative-working" and "positive-working" plates?
19. What is the difference between subtractive and additive plates?
20. Explain the theory of the diazo-coated surface plate.
21. Explain the convenience of a presensitized diazo-coated plate.
22. Explain the difference between the emulsion of photo-direct and contact-printed presensitized plates.
23. What are the two main ingredients in an albumin coating? Which is the sensitizer?
24. Explain the theory by which an image is produced on an Ektalith gelatin-silver-emulsion transfer plate.
25. How is an image created on an electronic-scanning facsimile plate?
26. Explain the xerographic dry photographic-electrostatic process of producing an image on a plate.
27. Describe a deep-etch plate. What are its advantages?
28. How is a relief image produced on a Kodak relief plate?
29. How is the relief image produced on the Type C Dycril plate?

## Problems and Projects

1. Prepare a 14° Baumé gum arabic solution. Label and store in an amber-colored bottle.
2. Dilute a portion of the 14° gum arabic solution to 7° or 8° Baumé. Label and store in an amber-colored bottle.
3. Report on the manufacture of sheet aluminum.
4. Prepare a direct-image plate. Include typing and drawing by hand in the plate image.
5. Place an image on a direct-image plate by imprinting with a letterpress form.
6. Prepare a presensitized plate.
7. Prepare a surface albumin plate-coating solution.
8. Make a surface albumin plate (aluminum), using the coating solution you have prepared.
9. Report on first aid for ammonium dichromate poisoning. Tell what the antidote is. Advise what should be kept in the shop for first aid in this case.
10. Make a report on "dermatitis" — an affliction which sometimes is associated with workers using bichromated chemicals. Tell what the symptoms are, what usually is done for it, and how best to avoid it.
11. Why is the name "Baumé" associated with the measuring of density?
12. Prepare a paper (cellulose-base) direct-image plate with coating solution. Use the solution you made in the shop or use a purchased coating solution.
13. Mix solutions for, and prepare, a wipe-on Diazo surface plate.
14. Prepare a plate by the Ektalith method.
15. Prepare a plate by the silver-diffusion transfer method.
16. Prepare a thermographic transfer plate.
17. Prepare a plate by the xerographic photo-electrostatic process.
18. Make a Kodak relief plate.
19. Make a Type C Dycril relief plate.
20. Make a deep-etch plate.
21. Make step-and-repeat exposures. Make the multiple exposures on the platemaker you have.

## New Words

1. acetate
2. additive coating
3. albumin
4. aluminum
5. ammonium-bichromate
6. asphaltum
7. automated
8. autoscreen
9. bichromated coatings
10. cellulose-base
11. cheesecloth
12. chemically
13. copiously
14. diazo
15. evaporate
16. explicitly
17. facsimile
18. ferric
19. grain
20. image-bearing
21. ink-receptive
22. ink-repellent
23. insoluble
24. interchangeable
25. intermediary
26. lacquer
27. multimetal
28. oxidation
29. photopolymer
30. photo-electrostatic
31. polyester
32. positive-working
33. presensitized
34. sandblasting
35. silver-halide
36. subdued
37. subtractive coating
38. thermographic
39. transparencies
40. turpentine
41. vacuum
42. water-receptive
43. whirler
44. xerography

# Offset

# Inks

Offset inks are compounded especially for use on offset presses. Never use letterpress inks, or inks intended for *stone* lithography, on offset presses.

## Requirements

Offset ink must be able to withstand the reaction of the press fountain solution which it encounters on the dampened offset plate. Ideally, the ink should not emulsify (absorb any of the fountain solution); neither should the ink break down and *combine with* the fountain solution in the clear areas of the plate on the press. Either of these situations would tend to impair the body, color or drying qualities of the ink, weaken the plate image or cause "scumming" (or ink-tinting) of the clear areas of the press plate and printed sheets.

Fig. 405. Ink Must Be Suited for the Work. The two inks above looked alike, but the left example soaked through the wrapper, marring the soap. (Courtesy Interchemical Corp., Printing Ink Div.)

The ink used on an offset press must be able to carry the full intended color and covering to the paper, despite the *split-film* action which occurs as the offset-press blanket picks up only a portion of the ink on the plate; and despite the necessary use of a comparatively soft rubber blanket in transferring the impression to the paper.

## Composition

Most offset inks consist of a *vehicle, pigments* and *modifiers.*

### Vehicle

Heat-treated linseed oil (referred to as "lithographic varnish") forms the body, or bulk, of the ink.

### Pigments

Pigments are the coloring materials. Offset inks usually employ pigments chemically manufactured from *coal tar* (a by-product in the manufacture of coke and fuel gas from coal). Pigments vary a great deal in cost; this difference is reflected in the prices of the various colors of inks.

### Modifiers

Modifiers are added to control the drying, viscosity, length, tack or other qualities of the ink — even including the *odor* of the ink, as when wrappers are printed for butter, bacon, etc.

## Manufacture

In addition to stock colors of ink, manufacturers will supply inks to match submitted color samples, as well as special inks for satisfactory printing on paper samples submitted. Advice on ink problems is generally available from the manufacturer's technical staff.

### Preparing Ingredients

All ingredients for inkmaking are inspected, tested and processed to meet the specifications of the laboratory technicians.

### Mixing

For each batch to be mixed, a formula-controlled quantity of each necessary ingredient is carefully weighed out and sent to the *blade mixers,* which blend the ingredients together.

### Grinding

After mixing, the ink is passed repeatedly through an "ink mill" where several smooth steel rollers grind the ingredients to the degree of fineness required.

### Testing

Each finished batch of ink is tested by the laboratory, under actual printing conditions, to insure that it meets specifications.

### Packaging

The final step before delivery is the packaging and labelling of the ink in convenient-size containers for the printer. Ink is packed in tubes, cans, drums and even delivered in tank-truck and tank-car loads.

## Color Mixing of Inks

Some color mixing (for small amounts of ink) may be done by the pressman if he has a knowledge of the results of mixing primary colors to achieve another color, or to get a lighter or darker shade or tint of the ink on hand.

A supply of yellow, red, blue, orange, green, purple, white and black will enable one to mix the usual colors needed.

Fig. 406. Ink Mixer
(Courtesy Interchemical Corp., Printing Ink Div.)

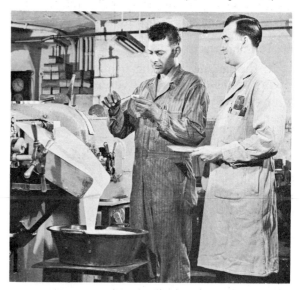

Fig. 407. Ink Mill
(Courtesy Interchemical Corp., Printing Ink Div.)

Fig. 408. Packaged Ink
(Courtesy Interchemical Corp., Printing Ink Div.)

In general, the "stronger" colors should be added sparingly to the "weaker" colors, and then thoroughly blended until the desired color is reached. Notably, small amounts of green or blue will have a great effect on white, etc. Cleanliness of the ink knife and the mixing slab are of primary importance. One should anticipate the amount of ink needed before mixing to the final color or shade.

For large amounts of colored ink, it is best to use stock colors of ink, or have the ink mixed to your specifications by the manufacturer. In this way, additional quantities and ink for re-runs can always be matched. Inks for all process printing (four-color halftones) are best purchased ready-mixed for the job.

## Ink Terminology

In the language of the inkmaker, the following terms describe the various properties of offset inks:

### Viscosity

Viscosity is the "resistance to flow." If ink flows readily, it has a "low" viscosity; if it is heavy-bodied, it has a "high" viscosity. Of necessity, offset inks generally have a high viscosity.

### Tack

Tack is a measure of "stickiness." Too much tack in offset ink reduces its "film-splitting" ability, and thus its effectiveness.

### Length

An ink may be "long" or "short." Test it by tapping the ink with a corner of the ink knife and attempting to draw it out into a long string. A good offset ink is generally long.

### Opacity

Opacity is the "hiding" or "covering" quality of an ink. An opaque ink will show in its true color when printed over another color of a previous run.

### Transparency

A "transparent" ink does not have great hiding power. It allows previously-printed colors to show through clearly. Many times this show-through is desired.

### Permanence or Fastness

"Permanent" or "fast" inks maintain their color and do not fade even though exposed to sunlight for long periods. They are especially suitable for signs and posters.

### Fugitive

A "fugitive" ink is one which tends to lose its color and fade when exposed for long periods to sunlight.

### Resistant

A "resistant" ink is so constituted by the manufacturer to withstand the action of gases, chemicals, heat, moisture, etc.

### Lakes

"Lakes" are body colors — not particularly strong colors.

### Toners

"Toners" are especially strong colors — highly concentrated. They are practically pure pigments ground in oil (linseed-oil varnish).

### Job Black

Job black is a black ink which is used for the regular run of ordinary jobs.

### Halftone Black

A finely-ground ink especially suited for reproducing finely-screened halftone work is called "halftone" black.

### Metallic Inks

Metallic inks are aluminum or bronze powder mixed in a suitable vehicle. Some color may be added. Such inks are difficult to run, and it is important that they be fresh.

### Water Colors

These colors produce flat effects. They contain no varnish.

## Storing Inks

When an opened can of ink is to be stored, flatten the top surface of the ink and pour a little varnish over it. This coat of varnish will prevent air from forming a skin on the ink.

If stored ink becomes thickened, mix in a little varnish to restore the consistency desired.

## Questions

1. Are letterpress inks recommended for offset use?
2. What are the special requirements of offset inks?
3. What are the usual ingredients of offset inks?
4. What is the function of the vehicle?
5. What is the function of the pigment?
6. What is the function of the modifiers?
7. Tell how ink is manufactured.
8. What is an ink mill?
9. Tell how small quantities of ink may be mixed in the shop when a certain color or tone is not available.
10. What is a "job black" ink?
11. What is an "opaque" ink?
12. What is a "transparent" ink?
13. What is a "long" ink?
14. How do you select from an ink catalog a good ink for posters which will be exposed to sunlight?

## Problems and Projects

1. Consult an ink catalog, and select for the shop a suitable assortment of black and colored inks for general use. Include the colors necessary for mixing and obtaining the usual colors needed.
2. Prepare (mix) a quantity of ink for a job of the color specified by the instructor.
3. Locate a film on inkmaking, and arrange for a showing in your school or shop.
4. Write for an ink catalog for your shop. Get one which shows the colors of inks.

## New Words

1. blended
2. bronze
3. comparatively
4. compounded
5. emulsify
6. formula
7. fugitive
8. ingredients
9. laboratory
10. linseed
11. metallic
12. modifier
13. opacity
14. permanent
15. pigment
16. reaction
17. resistant
18. specifications
19. technical
20. technicians
21. terminology
22. toner
23. varnish
24. vehicle
25. viscosity

# Papers and

# Bindery Work

Fine paper stock will improve a printing job, avoid aggravating press trouble and stand up well in the usage expected of the printed product.

## Requirements

Good offset papers have the proper affinity for ink (will not unduly absorb, nor repel, the ink). The surface of the paper must not soften under the action of the press dampening solution, lest it break down and give off coating particles which may dirty the ink and cause a change in the pH (acidity) of the fountain solution.

The paper must have a truly even (flat) surface to reproduce faithfully every dot of a halftone illustration. The surface must be free of fuzz or lint. Its finish must set off to best advantage the quality of the artwork, photography, composition and platemaking so that

Fig. 420. Hardwood Chips for the Digester — Note size (Courtesy S. D. Warren Co.)

the finished printing will be a source of pride for both the printer and the customer.

## Papermaking Pulps

All paper is made from pulp (the basic raw material reduced to fibers), plus the addition of ingredients for coloring, sizing, or to provide other desirable characteristics.

### Kinds of Pulps

Pulps in common use are:
(1) *mechanically-ground wood pulp*
(2) *old-paper pulp*
(3) *chemical wood pulp*
(4) *rag pulp*
(5) *cotton pulp.*

*Mechanically-ground wood pulp* is produced by grinding the entire log (except for the bark), until it is reduced to tiny particles. Nothing is wasted, but the resulting pulp has short fibers and paper made from it has low tear-strength. Fugitive substances which are not removed cause later discoloration, weakening and disintegration of the paper. This pulp is suited for handbills, newspapers and other items which are not permanent.

*Old-paper pulp* is made by returning used paper to a pulp state by a chemical cooking process, and then removing the old ink. Again, the fibers are reduced in length, which makes for a weak paper. Inferior old-paper pulp is used for box boards, cheaper papers, etc.; however, a good grade of paper can be made from the better grades of used-paper pulp.

*Chemical wood pulp* is made by cooking wood chips in a digester to remove lignin, gums, resins and other materials. This results in pure, long fibers which make a strong paper. Since about half the content of the original wood is eliminated in this process, the resulting paper is more expensive. Although this is a relatively new process, it is believed that paper made from chemical wood pulp is a "permanent" paper, since some of these papers over sixty years old are still in good condition. Four kinds of chemical wood pulp are described below:

(1) *Soda pulp* is made of wood of the beech, birch, maple, oak and poplar trees. The fibers of these woods separate quickly when cooked with caustic soda. The fibers are short, but the addition of some long-fiber pulp makes a fine book and coated paper.

(2) *Sulphite pulp* is a long-fiber pulp made from such evergreens as spruce, pine and hemlock. The wood chips are cooked in a liquor of lime and sulphuric acid, until the fibers are freed. The long fibers help make a strong paper.

(3) *Alpha-cellulose pulp* is obtained from coniferous woods by cooking the wood chips in sulphuric acid and then in caustic soda. It forms into a strong paper with good folding qualities. Bright in color, it is used in some bonds and decorative text papers.

Fig. 422. Washing Pulp (Courtesy S. D. Warren Co.)

Fig. 421. Digester (Courtesy S. D. Warren Co.)

Fig. 423. Pulp After Washing and Bleaching
(Courtesy S. D. Warren Co.)

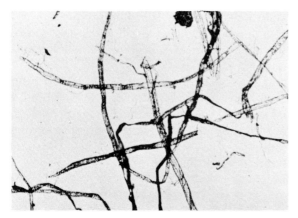

Fig. 424.  Magnified Soft Wood Sulphite Fibers (Courtesy Kimberly-Clark Corp.)

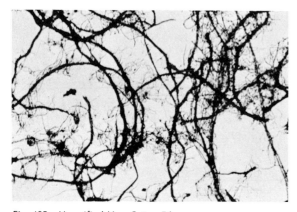

Fig. 425.  Magnified New Cotton Fibers (Courtesy Kimberly-Clark Corp.)

(4) *Sulphate pulp* is produced by cooking coniferous wood chips with caustic soda. It is used for kraft (brownish) paper; however, when refined and bleached, it makes a good book paper because of its long, strong fiber which makes a paper of high tear-test.

*Rag pulp* and *cotton pulp* make a good or poor paper, depending upon the amount of laundering the original rags were subjected to, and the amount of dye which has to be removed. New No. 1 white rags and new cotton make the finest pulps for permanent and strong bond paper, antique book paper and cover stock.

## Papermaking

An outline of the usual steps in the making of paper is given below:

### Reducing Materials to Fibers

Wood, old paper, cellulose and rags are reduced to fibers as previously explained.

### Beating

A many-bladed revolving drum, on an oval-shaped tub, beats the pulp each time the pulp is forced to travel beneath it. This roughens and frays the fibers so they may better cling together in the finished paper.

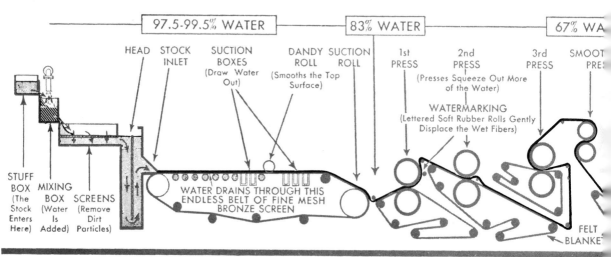

Fig. 426.  Diagram Showing How Paper Is Made on a Modern Fourdrinier Papermaking Machine (Courtesy Hammermill Paper Co.)

Beating is controlled to provide the desired strength, opacity, surface and bulk.

### Refining

A Jordan engine receives the pulp from the beater and gives it a further beating. This is the ultimate refinement of the pulp before it flows onto the paper machine.

### Sizing

Pulps for lithographic printing papers receive generous quantities of sizing materials in manufacture, so that the finished paper will not soften and shed any coating particles while on the offset press.

During press operation, the fountain solution tends to dampen the paper and weaken it. The pull of the ink on the offset press blanket may then tear off particles of weakened paper, and these particles may get into the ink and the fountain, thus causing scumming on the press.

The addition of sizing prevents writing inks from blurring by keeping the ink on the surface; it also provides a binder to hold down the surface fibers, which might tend to rise, making the surface fuzzy. A sized paper, too, keeps the offset ink on the surface, retaining its brilliance and density.

Fig. 427. The Beater (Courtesy S. D. Warren Co.)

Fig. 428. The Jordan Engine Further Refines the Pulp
(Courtesy S. D. Warren Co.)

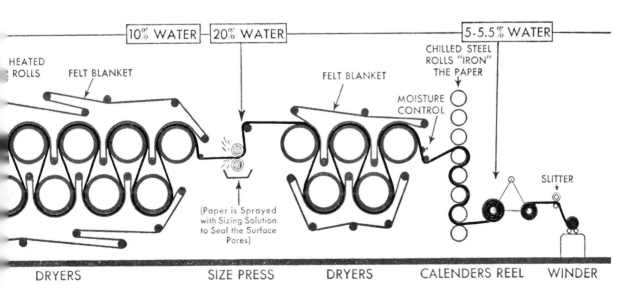

Fig. 429. Papermaking Machine Viewed from the Wet End
(Courtesy S. D. Warren Co.)

Fig. 430   Transfer of the Paper Web from the Wire at Left to
the Felts at Right (Courtesy S. D. Warren Co.)

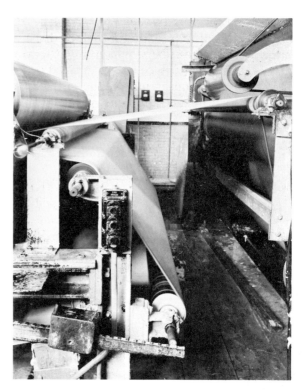

Fig. 431.  Paper Coming from the Wet Presses and Starting
Through the Smoothing Press
(Courtesy S. D. Warren Co.)

Fig. 432. Dry End of Papermaking Machine, Showing Paper Being Delivered and Wound Onto Rolls
(Courtesy S. D. Warren Co.)

Rosin is used as a sizing, if the sizing is added while the pulp is in the beaters. If the sizing is sprayed on the surface after the paper is made, starch is used.

### Loading

Clay (a natural earth product) is added to pulps which are intended for uncoated papers, while the pulp is still in the beaters. This improves opacity, makes for a smooth surface, provides a better affinity for ink and brightens the color of the paper.

### Forming the Paper

After beating and loading, the pulp flows into the "stuff chest" (a vat) on the wet end of the papermaking machine.

In a highly diluted (with water) form, the pulp is flowed onto an endless, traveling wire screen. While traveling at high speed, the screen is shaken from side to side, meshing the fibers together, and draining off much of the water. At this time, the partially-formed wet web of paper may be "watermarked" by a metal "dandy roller" which bears an etched design. The paper is then transferred to a felt blanket, which carries it through pressing and drying rolls to squeeze out the water and dry the paper. It is then wound into rolls on the "dry end" of the papermaking machine.

Fig. 433. Slitters Divide the Web into Rolls
(Courtesy S. D. Warren Co.)

Fig. 434. Calendering (Courtesy S. D. Warren Co.)

Fig. 435. Trimming the Paper (Courtesy S. D. Warren Co.)

### Calendering

Coated papers may be "calendered" after coating and drying. This is done in a separate machine, where the paper passes through a series of calender rollers which press and polish the paper.

### Packaging

Sheets are cut from the rolls, and trimmed; then inspected, counted, and wrapped.

## Some Common Paper Terms

### Ream

A *ream* is five hundred sheets of paper — often the amount packaged in common papers.

### Package

Sheets in a package vary with thickness of sheets — *e.g.*, 100 sheets of index bristol.

### Piece

Full sheets of paper, as they come from a packaged ream, are cut into press-size or job-size *pieces*.

### Sheet

Paper is purchased in full *sheets* and may be cut into job-sized pieces, but when it reaches the press, the former pieces are again called *sheets*. Thus: "Cut 2000 pieces for the job," but, "Feed a sheet through the press."

### Felt Side

The *felt side* is that surface which was next to the felt blanket on the papermaking machine. It is the better of the two sides (if distinguishable) of a sheet of paper. Use this side for printing, if there is a choice. The watermark is "readable" on the felt side of a sheet. Not all paper is watermarked, however.

### Wire Side

The *wire side* is that surface which was next to the screen on the papermaking machine. The screen markings (pattern) can be distinguished, on some papers, if a sheet is held horizontally toward the light. Also, when looking at the wire side, the watermark will appear reversed. If printing only one side of a sheet, don't use the wire side.

### Grain

The grain is determined by the direction of the fibers which make up the sheet. It runs either the long way or the short way of the sheet. Paper is stiffer *with* the grain than *across* the grain; consequently, the grain should run vertically in a pamphlet, book or show card.

The paper (especially bristols, covers, etc.) makes a smoother and longer lasting fold if the fold runs *with* the grain.

When purchasing paper, specify the direction of grain desired.

*Grain marking on wrapper.* The direction of grain may be stamped on the ream wrapper as "grain long" or "grain short." Sometimes the grain direction is indicated by underlining one of the dimensions on the label, such as: 17" x 22".

*Testing direction of grain.* If no label or wrapper markings are evident, the direction of grain may be tested in several ways:

(1) *Bending.* Hold the sheet by one edge, letting the opposite edge sag under its own weight. Repeat with an adjacent edge. The test producing the greater sag indicates the grain is running in the same direction as the edge being held in your hands.

(2) *Tearing.* Tear the paper half way across from one edge. Repeat with an adjacent edge. The paper usually tears with a cleaner and more even tear *with* the grain.

(3) *Folding.* Fold and crease sharply in one direction. Repeat at ninety degrees. The sharper and cleaner fold (or crease) will be *with* the grain.

(4) *Wetting.* Wet one side of a piece of paper (6" x 6", or so). Hold the paper flat on the palm with the wet side down. It will form into a roll. The direction of grain is parallel to the axis of the roll.

### Basis (Substance)

The weight, in pounds, of 500 sheets of a basic size of a particular kind of paper is known as its *basis weight.* For instance, the basic size of bond paper is 17" x 22". The label on a ream of 16-pound bond which is 17" x 22" would read "17 x 22 — 16." It might

also read "17 x 22 — 16 32/M," indicating the weight of a thousand sheets. Basis weight is related to the *thickness* of paper: 20-pound bond is thicker than 16-pound.

### Weight

The weight indicates the actual number of pounds per ream. Thus, the designation on the label of a ream of 16-pound bond, 17" x 28" would read: "17 x 28 — 20.5 41/M Sub. 16." This means that, although the sheets in this ream of paper are of 16-pound substance (bond is always 17" x 22" basic size), the actual weight is 20.5 pounds per ream, and 41 pounds per thousand sheets. It weighs more per ream because the sheets are larger than the standard size.

### Papercutting

For economy, paper should be bought in a size to fit the job, or to be cut for the job without excessive waste. If paper is already on hand, try to plan the job to fit the size of

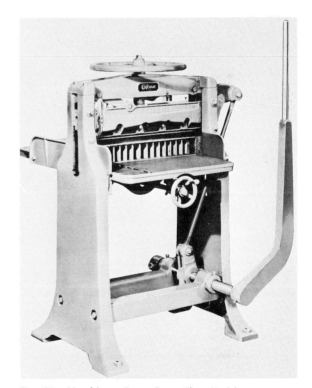

Fig. 436 . Hand-Lever Paper Cutter, Floor Model
(Courtesy Chandler & Price Co.)

the paper. Scrap, or waste, costs just as much per pound as the paper used.

In cutting paper, keep the blade sharp, and the cutter bed clean. Use a long-handled swab, faintly dampened with cedar oil, to brush off dust from the cutter blade and the bed. (This dust may cause scumming on the press, if it reaches the blanket.)

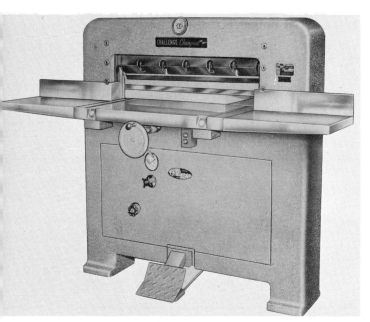

Fig. 437. Challenge "Champion" 30½" Power Paper Cutter
(Courtesy The Challenge Machinery Co.)

## Figuring Number of Pieces from a Sheet

To find the number of 6″ x 10″ pieces that can be obtained from a sheet, 22½″ x 28½″, figure as shown below, cancelling up and down:

$$\text{(a)} \quad \dfrac{\overset{3}{22\frac{1}{2}''} \times \overset{2}{28\frac{1}{2}''}}{6 \ \times \ 10} = 6 \qquad \text{(b)} \quad \dfrac{\overset{2}{22\frac{1}{2}''} \times \overset{4}{28\frac{1}{2}''}}{10 \ \times \ 6} = 8$$

Solution (b), on the right above results in eight pieces, two more than in (a). Eight pieces, therefore, is the better answer.

However, if there are large remainders when performing the division in the cancellations (as in the case of the above two solutions), it may be possible to draw the sizes of the pieces to be cut directly on the full sheet and secure a larger number of pieces per sheet. Study Fig. 438.

Fig. 438 shows that nine 6″ x 10″ pieces can be obtained from the same 22½″ x 28½″ sheet — one additional piece per sheet. This would be a considerable saving, if many sheets were to be cut.

The diagram method obviously is limited in use if it is required that the grain on all pieces run the same way.

Note carefully, in Fig. 438, that the first cut must, of necessity, be possible *as a straight line* across the entire width, or length, of the sheets — as line 'AB'.

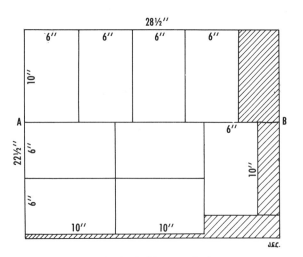

Fig. 438. Diagram Method of Figuring Stock

Fig. 439. Flat Cutting Operation on 84-Inch Cutter
(Courtesy Western Printing & Lithographing Co.)

## TABLE 8. SOME USEFUL PAPER INFORMATION*

| Kind | General Uses | Basic Size (inches) | Some Substance Weights (pounds) | Some Other Sizes Commonly Made (inches) |
|---|---|---|---|---|
| 1. Bond | Letterheads, documents, office forms | 17 x 22 | 9, 13, 16, 20, 24 | 17 x 28,  19 x 24, 22 x 34,  24 x 38 |
| 2. Onionskin | Makeready in pressroom, carbon copies, air mail | 17 x 22 | 7, 8, 9, 10 | 17 x 26,  17 x 28, 19 x 24,  22 x 34 |
| 3. Writing or Flat | Price books, statements, booklets, broadsides | 17 x 22 | 16, 20, 24 | 17 x 28,  19 x 24, 22 x 34,  24 x 38 |
| 4. Safety | Checks, drafts, notes | 17 x 22 | 24 | 17 x 28,  19 x 24 |
| 5. Ledger | Accounting and machine bookkeeping | 17 x 22 | 24, 28, 32, 36 | 17 x 28,  19 x 24, 22 x 34,  24 x 38 |
| 6. Index Bristol | Index cards, folders | 25½ x 30½ | 90, 110, 140, 170 | 20½ x 24¾, 22½ x 28½ |
| 7. Card Bristol | Postcards, tickets | 22½ x 28½ | 94 | |
| 8. Offset (Book) | Surface sized for general printing  Surface sized book for books and halftones  Calendered for halftones  Enameled for best (finest) halftones | 25 x 38 | 50, 60, 70, 80, 90, 100 | 17½ x 22½, 19 x 25, 23 x 29, 28 x 42, and multiples |
| 9. Opaque | Highly opaque for circulars with halftones | 17 x 22 | 16, 20, 24, 28, 32 | 17½ x 22½, 23 x 29, 23 x 35 |
| 10. Cover | Covers.  Enameled for covers with halftones | 20 x 26 | 50, 60, 65, 80 | 23 x 35,  26 x 40 |
| 11. Label | Labels.  Coated — for varnishing | 25 x 38 | 50, 60, 70 | |

* For complete listings, consult papermakers' catalogs.

It would be convenient, in the diagram shown (Fig. 438), to make all the cuts possible using the 10-inch setting on the cutter; then changing the setting to 6 inches for all the 6″ cuts. If trim is needed on all four sides of the pieces, it should be allowed on the diagram where needed.

## Controlling the Stretching and Shrinking of Paper

It is a fact that paper will tend to stretch when it absorbs moisture, and will shrink when it loses moisture. This stretching and shrinking occurs *mostly across the grain*, and *very little with the grain*. Consequently, on the press, the paper grain should run *parallel with the cylinders* (the direction of least shrinkage or stretching). This fact should be remembered in specifying the direction of grain when ordering paper. Since large offset plates are wider in the direction parallel with the cylinders, most offset papers should be ordered "grain long." The printer must often compromise and print short-grain stock in order that the finished job have the proper grain direction.

When a job is to be run through the press a second time, it sometimes happens that the paper has shrunk or stretched after the first run. To compensate for this stretching or shrinking on the second run, the image for the second press run can be *shortened* (to effect register) by transferring some of the packing from the blanket cylinder to the plate cylinder. To *lengthen* the image, transfer some packing from the plate cylinder to the blanket cylinder.

Only minor changes in register should be attempted in the manner described above, since greatly different cylinder diameters may cause undue plate-image wear and slurs.

Paper stock should be allowed to remain unprinted in the pressroom for "seasoning" until it reaches the same humidity or moisture content as the pressroom. If the paper is to be used for "register jobs" — such as two or more colors — the top and sides of the stacks of paper should be covered with polyethylene between runs.

Paper usually has a 6% moisture content when it is shipped from the mill. If a relative humidity of 50 to 55% is maintained in the shop, day and night continuously, and the paper stock allowed to condition to this, shrinking and stretching of the paper stock will be avoided or minimized.

## Bindery Operations

All work with sheets other than printing on them is classified as *bindery work*. This includes such operations as cutting, jogging, gathering sheets in sequence, folding, drilling or punching holes, padding, hand numbering, sewing, stapling, wire stitching, mechanical binding and wrapping and labeling packages. Some of these are illustrated here.

### Jogging

Jogging is handling sheets to make a neater, evenly piled stack. Usually it is necessary to *fan* a few sheets at a time (to get air between them) by holding one edge and flipping through them by moving the opposite edge back. Then the sheets are tapped on the edges until they are even. The operation is then re-

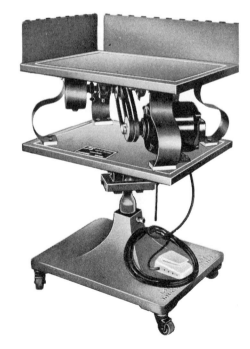

Fig. 440. Jogger (Courtesy Ilya Scheinker Inc.)

peated with the next few sheets. A mechanical jogger with a vibrating table makes this easier. See Fig. 440. A few sheets to be handled at once are called a *lift*. Sheets should not be jogged while ink is still wet.

### Plastic Binding

Catalogs, manuals, etc., printed on single sheets, may be bound conveniently into loose-leaf books by using plastic bindings, Fig. 441. The sheets must be put in order and then punched, as shown in Fig. 442. There are special fingers on the binding machine which open the backing strip so that the punched sheets can be inserted, Fig. 443.

### Gathering

Putting individual sheets or pages in order is called *gathering*. It can be done by laying stacks of each page in order along the edge of a table, and picking one sheet from each stack while walking past them. Checking that the right number of pages has been gathered is

called *collating*, although this term is often misused to also mean gathering. Staggered marks on the folded edge of a series of signatures (pages folded in a unit) which are used to check the order of the signatures are called *collating marks*. Fig. 444 shows an eight-station gathering machine in-line with an electric punch for plastic binding.

### Stapling and Stitching

Fig. 445 illustrates a *stapler*, which is loaded with U-shaped staples. The legs are available in various lengths to accommodate different thicknesses. If the machine makes its own staples from a coil of wire, it is known as a wire *stitcher*. Fig. 445 shows the stapler set up for *saddle-stitching* — that is, placing a staple (from the back side) in the center fold of a pamphlet or signature. If the *saddle* of the machine is tipped up to form a small, flat table, stitches can be placed along the edge of the pamphlet. This is called *side-stitching*.

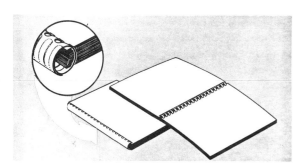

Fig. 441. Plastic Binding (Courtesy General Binding Corp.)

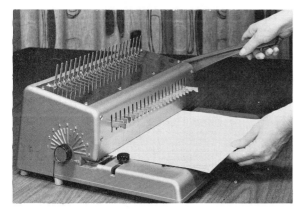

Fig. 442. Punching Sheets for Plastic Binding (Courtesy General Binding Corp.)

Fig. 443. Inserting Punched Sheets into Binding (Courtesy General Binding Corp.)

Fig. 444. Eight-Pocket Collator, Fitted with Automatic Electric Punch for Binding (Courtesy General Binding Corp.)

### Punching and Drilling Holes

Fig. 446 shows a paper drill, which makes holes by means of a rotating, sharpened, hollow tube. Some versions have three heads so that three holes are drilled at once. Drills can accommodate a lift of paper about ½″ high at a time.

Punches also make holes in paper. A punch has a solid rod-like piece which fits into a matching hole. Punches will take only a few sheets at a time.

### Folding

Sheets may be folded easily by hand. Simply take the near edge of the sheet, place it evenly on the far edge, and crease down the fold smartly across the sheet. A wooden or bone folder makes creasing the sheet much easier; the back of a comb or a ruler also can be used. Fig. 447 shows a folding machine which will make two successive folds in a sheet at right angles to each other, forming 8 pages out of the flat sheet. It is known as a buckle folder due to the manner in which it buckles the bended sheet in forming the fold. This machine also will score (make a crease across the sheet for later folding), slit a sheet into two pieces, and perforate (cut a row of small slots across the sheet), either with or without folding.

### Questions

1. What are the requirements of a good offset paper?
2. What may be the disadvantages in using a poor grade of paper (not made or adapted) for offset printing?
3. What kinds of pulps are in use today for papermaking?

Fig. 445.   Foot-Power Stapler — Flat and Saddleback (Courtesy Acme Staple Co.)

Fig. 446.   Paper Drilling Machine (Courtesy The Challenge Machinery Co.)

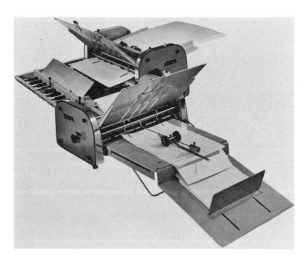

Fig. 447.   17⅛″ x 28″ Folding Machine (Courtesy The Challenge Machinery Co.)

4. Describe the making of pulp for newsprint paper.

5. Describe the paper products made from old papers.

6. Describe each of the pulps produced by the chemical cooking of wood chips.

7. What kind of paper is made of rags?

8. Name the main steps in the process of papermaking.

9. Why is sizing important for offset papers? What sizing materials are added to the paper?

10. What does loading contribute to the paper?

11. How many sheets of paper are there in a ream?

12. Name the two "sides" of a sheet of paper. Which is the preferred side for printing?

13. Tell how to test the grain direction of a sheet of paper.

14. How is the grain direction indicated on a wrapped ream or package of paper?

15. Explain what is meant by basis (or substance).

16. Explain the term "weight" as applied to paper.

17. What does 41/M mean on a ream of paper?

18. What is a "sheet" of paper? A "piece" of paper?

19. Make a list of the basic sizes of each of the papers listed on page 269.

## Problems and Projects

1. Locate a film on papermaking. Write to the paper mill arranging for a showing of the film. Write a report on the film.

2. Make a display of papermaking materials. Try to secure samples of papermaking ingredients and pulps. Include samples of various kinds of papers and photographs of the processes involved.

3. If possible, arrange for a visit to a nearby paper mill. Follow the standard procedure for field trips for your school. Decide what you wish to see before making the trip. Write a report on the trip.

4. Determine the felt and wire sides of several kinds of paper in the shop. Can you find the wire side of a sheet of calendered stock? Of bond? Of index bristol?

5. Determine the direction of grain on several different kinds of paper stock in the shop, especially bristols and covers. Use all the methods for testing grain described for papers. Test the heavier stock by folding and bending.

6. Figure how many pieces can be cut from the sheet sizes listed below. Use the formula method; if there is excessive waste, make a diagram to see if additional pieces can be obtained.

| Piece Size | Sheet Size | Sheet Size |
|---|---|---|
| 3 x 5 | 20½ x 24¾ | 22½ x 28½ |
| 5 x 8 | 17 x 22 | 17 x 28 |
| 8½ x 11 | 17 x 22 | 17 x 28 |
| 8 x 10 | 20 x 26 | 25 x 38 |

## New Words

| | | | |
|---|---|---|---|
| 1. | acidity | 21. | minimize |
| 2. | binder | 22. | parallel |
| 3. | calendering | 23. | particles |
| 4. | caustic | 24. | perforate |
| 5. | characteristics | 25. | permanent |
| 6. | collate | 26. | pH |
| 7. | coniferous | 27. | punch |
| 8. | diagram | 28. | reduction |
| 9. | digester | 29. | refinement |
| 10. | diluted | 30. | relative |
| 11. | dimension | 31. | requirements |
| 12. | discoloration | 32. | score |
| 13. | disintegration | 33. | sizing |
| 14. | drill | 34. | staple |
| 15. | fugitive | 35. | stitch |
| 16. | gather | 36. | substance |
| 17. | humidity | 37. | sulphate |
| 18. | jog | 38. | sulphite |
| 19. | a lift | 39. | watermark |
| 20. | liquor | | |

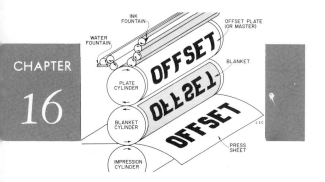

# Offset Press

# Fundamentals

Sheet-fed offset presses and duplicators all function in a similar manner, although different makes vary in minor details of construction, operating controls, nomenclature of parts, arrangement of cylinders and rollers, and in the feeding, registration and delivery sheets.

The term "offset duplicators" generally is used to refer to some of the smaller offset-printing presses. In this book, the term "offset press", in general, will include both presses

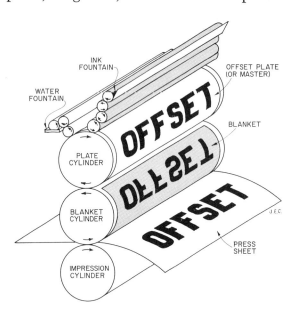

Fig. 449.  Basic Schematic Drawing of an Offset Press

[1]Press models referred to in this chapter are the products of the following firms: Multilith 1250 — Addressograph Multigraph Corporation; Fairchild-Davidson Duplicators — Fairchild-Davidson Division of Fairchild Camera and Instrument Corporation; ATF Chief 20 and 20A — American Type Founders Co., Inc.

and duplicators.[1] The same skills and understandings are required to do quality work with either type.

## Operation and General Nomenclature

The reader is asked first to review the theory of offset printing (page 3), and to study carefully Figs. 449 and 450A.

Fig. 450A illustrates, in schematic form, some basic components and nomenclature of a typical duplicator-size offset press. Note the six main "systems" or divisions: (1) the *dampening system;* (2) the *inking system;* (3) the *main printing unit;* (4) the *feeder* (usually vacuum operated); (5) the *register board* and *sheet controls;* and (6) the *delivery system.*

### Dampening System

In the dampening system, the dampening rollers apply a film of dampening solution to the surface of the offset plate (master) which is wrapped around the plate cylinder. This dampening solution adheres only to the clear areas of the plate — the image areas repel the dampening solution.

### Inking System

On the dampened plate, the ink rollers apply a film of ink, which adheres only to the image portions of the plate. The ink is repelled by the dampened areas of the plate.

This dampening and inking of the plate continues throughout the press run (carefully controlled by the operator), thus maintaining the non-printing areas of the plate clear and replenishing the ink on the plate image.

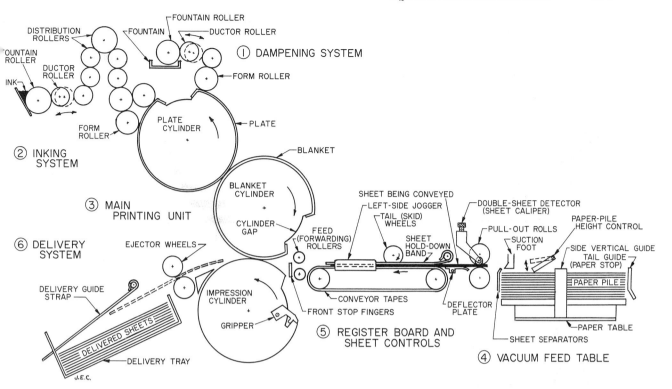

Fig. 450A. Schematic Cross Section of a Sheet-Fed, Single-Color Offset Duplicator, with Three Main Cylinders, and Conventional (Separate) Inking and Dampening Systems

## Main Printing Unit

In the main printing unit, the inked plate image is transferred to the surface of the blanket (on the blanket cylinder) when the plate cylinder and the blanket cylinder are brought into contact with each other.

The blanket image is then printed on the sheet of paper as it passes (under pressure) between the blanket and impression cylinders.

## Feeder Unit

Most feeders are air- and vacuum-operated. An air blast separates the top sheets causing them to float individually. The feed table maintains the paper pile at proper height so that the suction feet (suckers) can pick up the top sheet and pass it forward. Sheet separators hold back all but the top sheet, which is pulled off by the suction feet.

## Register Board and Sheet Controls

Each sheet that is carried forward by the sucker feet is passed to the pullout rolls and

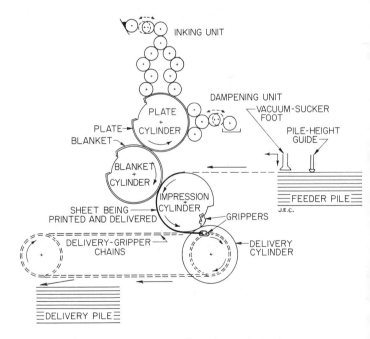

Fig. 450B. Schematic Cross Section of a Sheet-Fed, Single-Color Offset Press, Four-Main-Cylinder Design, Chain Delivery, and Conventional (Separate) Inking and Dampening Systems

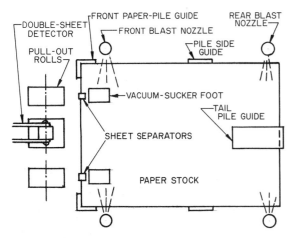

Fig. 451A. Vacuum-Feeder Set-Up (Top View). Paper pile is held in position by front, side, and tail pile guides. Front and rear blast nozzles direct streams of air to flutter the top sheets.

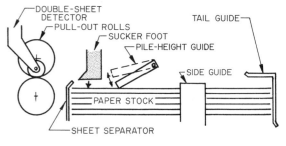

Fig. 451B. Vacuum-Feeder Set-Up (Side View). Sucker feet are in lowest position. Pile-height guide, rocking up and down, actuates mechanism to maintain pile height within lifting distance of sucker feet.

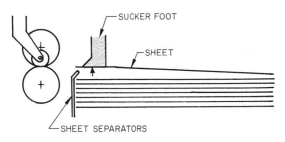

Fig. 451C. Sucker foot has descended and has picked up one sheet. In its upward travel, sheet is dragged across tips of sheet separators (combs), which help to hold back other sheets.

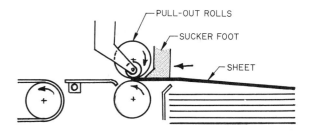

Fig. 451D. Sucker foot has traveled forward, delivering sheet between revolving pull-out rolls.

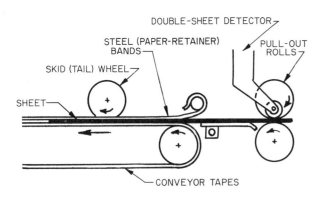

Fig. 451E. Pull-out rolls have passed paper through double-sheet detector, and on to the conveyor tapes, which propel sheet forward. Steel (paper-retainer) bands hold sheet to tapes. Skid (tail) wheels provide additional rotating pressure to traveling paper.

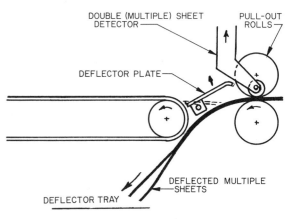

Fig. 451F. Any multiple sheets force double-sheet detector upward by the added thickness. This activates and opens the deflector plate, thus deflecting the double sheets downward into the deflector tray. Most larger presses simply have the feeder stop if detector trips.

# FEED TO DELIVERY

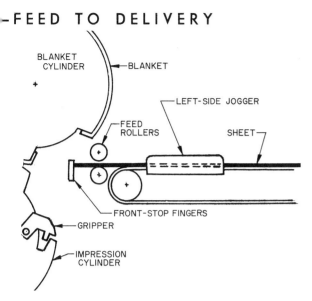

Fig. 451G. Having been conveyed down feeder table, sheet is stopped by the front-stop fingers, and is ready to be jogged. Note that the impression-cylinder grippers have opened.

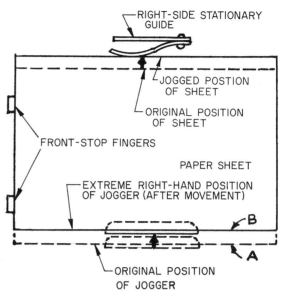

Fig. 451H. (View from Above). The momentarily-stopped sheet is jogged across the feed table (from "A" to "B") into registration position for printing. On some models, jogging side can be switched.

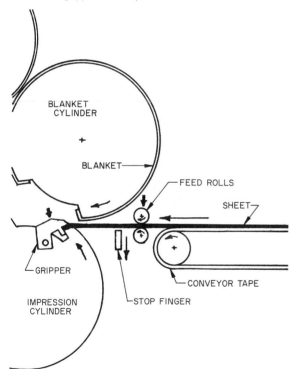

Fig. 451I. After sheet is jogged, stop fingers move downward, and feed rolls close on sheet, propelling it forward to grippers on the impression cylinder. Timing should be such that the sheet is buckled slightly to ensure positive positioning at the gripper.

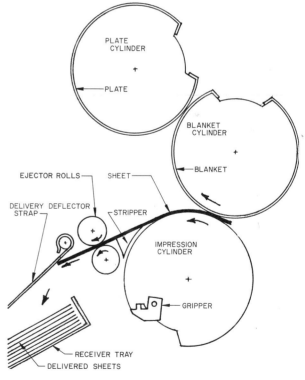

Fig. 451J. Impression-cylinder grippers have drawn sheet between blanket and impression cylinders, where sheet has been printed. Then, grippers open and strippers guide sheet between ejector rollers, which propel the sheet into the tray.

then is introduced to the caliper device (or multiple-sheet detector). This device will pass only one sheet without tripping. The sheet is then conveyed down the register table (or board) until it reaches the front-stop fingers. Stopped at this point, it is jogged across the table to a predetermined register position.

Next, the front stop fingers drop down and the sheet is fed to, and gripped by, the impression-cylinder grippers which carry it under impression (pressure) between the blanket and impression cylinders to receive the inked image from the blanket.

### Delivery System

On duplicators, the printed sheet may be ejected simply into a delivery tray. If the press is so equipped, the sheet may be gripped by the chain delivery grippers, which deliver the sheet into the receding stacker where it is jogged neatly. See Fig. 450B.

## Paper Feeding to Delivery

In the paper feeding-to-delivery cycle, each individual sheet is lifted from the paper pile, passed down the delivery table, jogged into position, printed, and then delivered and stacked. This action is illustrated in schematic detail in Figs. 451A through 451J.

## Some Basic Arrangements

Various arrangements of cylinder and roller systems are employed on different presses.

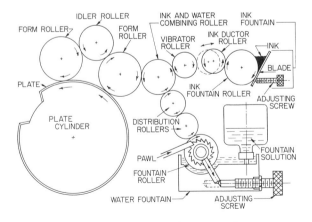

Fig. 452.  Combined Ink-and-Water (Dampening) System

### Conventional (Separate) Inking and Dampening System

In the conventional inking and dampening system, the ink and the dampener solution are applied to the plate surface by separate rollers. Refer again to Figs. 450A and 450B.

### Combined Inking and Dampening System

In the combined inking and dampening system, the ink and the dampener solution, although originating in separate fountains, are both fed through the same form roller[2] (or rollers) to the offset plate. See Fig. 452.

In this system, all the ink rollers first are allowed to ink up. Then the fountain solution is added to the water fountain, and all the rollers are allowed to operate. A film of dampener solution is transferred to the surface of the ink rollers (on the ink film). When the form rollers contact the premoistened plate surface, both the fountain solution and the ink are transferred. Adjustment controls on the fountains are provided to maintain proper ink-and-water balance for printing.

A slight "emulsification"[3] of the ink occurs when the fountain solution is applied over the

Fig. 453.  Gear-Driven Cylinders — Chief 20A Offset Press (Courtesy American Type Founders Co., Inc.)

[2]The term "form roller" refers to any roller in either the inking or dampening systems which contacts the offset plate during operation of the press.

[3]*Emulsification* (emulsifying), in presswork, generally indicates that some fountain solution is working into, and mixing with, the ink, so that its substance is diluted somewhat.

ink film on the rollers, but the amount is not objectionable. In fact, some ink emulsification takes place in the conventional system as well.

### Three-Main-Cylinder Design

The three-main-cylinder design employs the *plate, blanket* and *impression* cylinders. Refer again to Fig. 450A.

The offset plate is mounted on the plate cylinder. The plate image is transferred to the blanket surface which, in turn, transfers the image to the paper passing between the blanket and impression cylinders.

After printing, the paper is propelled forward by ejector wheels and the "squeeze-thrust" of the blanket and impression cylinders, to be deposited in the delivery pile or receiver.

To insure that the inked plate image deposits additional ink in *exactly* the same places on the blanket image during successive revolutions of the cylinders, both the plate and blanket cylinders must be virtually identical in diameter, their bearers (full diameter surface at each end) must be in contact, and they must be gear-driven to prevent slipping. See Fig. 453.

### Four-Main-Cylinder Design

In addition to the plate, blanket, and impression cylinders, a fourth cylinder may be used — the *delivery* (or transfer) cylinder. This cylinder, located beneath the impression cylinder, carries the gripper-equipped chains which control the printed sheet as it leaves the impression and blanket cylinders, starting it toward the delivery end of the press. Refer again to Fig. 450B.

### Two-Main-Cylinder Design

In the two-main-cylinder design, the double-sized upper cylinder contains two segments — the plate segment and the impression segment. The smaller, lower cylinder (the blanket drum) carries the blanket. See Fig. 454A.

The blanket drum is exactly half the circumference of the upper cylinder. Thus, for each single revolution of the upper cylinder, the blanket revolves twice. On the first revolution, the blanket contacts the plate segment; on the second, it contacts the impression segment.

When the plate segment and the blanket drum are opposite, the inked image of the plate contacts the rubber blanket. At this time, the image is transferred from the plate to the blanket (Fig. 454B).

As the duplicator continues to revolve and the plate segment returns to the dampening unit for replenishing, the blanket drum with its inked image begins its second revolution.

Just as the leading edge of the impression segment would contact the leading edge of the

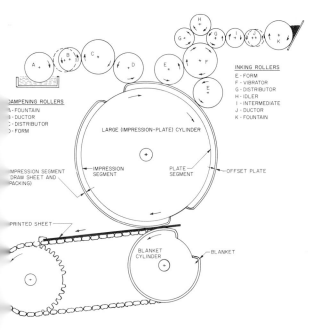

DAMPENING ROLLERS
A - FOUNTAIN
B - DUCTOR
C - DISTRIBUTOR
D - FORM

INKING ROLLERS
E - FORM
F - VIBRATOR
G - DISTRIBUTOR
H - IDLER
I - INTERMEDIATE
J - DUCTOR
K - FOUNTAIN

LARGE (IMPRESSION-PLATE) CYLINDER

IMPRESSION SEGMENT

PLATE SEGMENT

OFFSET PLATE

IMPRESSION SEGMENT DRAW SHEET AND PACKING)

PRINTED SHEET

BLANKET CYLINDER

BLANKET

Fig. 454A. Two-Main-Cylinder Design Used on Fairchild-Davidson Duplicators (Courtesy Fairchild-Davidson Division — Fairchild Camera and Instrument Corp.)

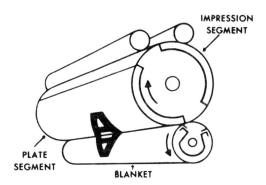

IMPRESSION SEGMENT

PLATE SEGMENT

BLANKET

Fig. 454B. Plate-to-Blanket Image Transfer (Courtesy Fairchild-Davidson Division — Fairchild Camera and Instrument Corp.)

blanket, a sheet of paper arrives and passes between the cylinders. The impression segment exerts a downward pressure, "offsetting" the blanket image onto the sheet (Fig. 454C). The printed sheet is then carried face upwards to the delivery end of the machine.

### Suction (Vacuum) Paper Feed

Sucker feet pick up the sheet of paper stock from the feeder pile by vacuum and pass it down the register table (or board), Fig. 455A. (See "Paper Feeding to Delivery", page 278).

### Friction Paper Feed

Rubber-covered, rotating wheels, in contact with the paper stock on the feeder table, propel the top sheet forward into the printing unit, Fig. 455B.

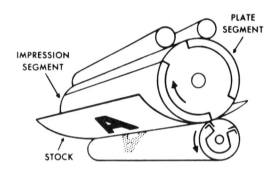

Fig. 454C.  Image Offset from Blanket to Sheet (Courtesy Fairchild-Davidson Division — Fairchild Camera and Instrument Corp.)

### Ejector Mechanism

The printed sheet, emerging from between the blanket and impression cylinders, is guided and propelled, in part, by ejector rolls (wheels) riding on the ejector ring shaft, Fig. 456A. The rolls are positioned just outside the rings so that the sheet is cupped upward at the center. This helps to keep the fore edge from buckling under as it is pushed out.

### Chain Delivery

The chain delivery uses gripper bars mounted across two endless chains which revolve between the delivery cylinder and the delivery end of the press. See Figs. 450B, 454A, and 456B.

The gripper bars, traveling around the delivery cylinder, grip the fore edge of the printed sheet when it is released from the impression-cylinder grippers and carry the sheet to, and deposit it in, the delivery pile. This positive delivery is better than the simpler ejector rolls for large sheets, thin paper, or high speeds.

### Receiver (Delivery) Tray

Without chain delivery, the printed sheets are merely ejected or dropped into a tray arrangement. In the tray, they may or may not be jogged into a neat pile. Capacity of the tray is about 500 sheets. Refer again to Fig. 456A.

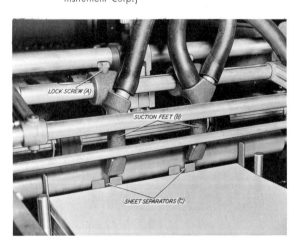

Fig. 455A.  Suction (Vacuum) Paper Feeder — Multilith 1250 (Courtesy Addressograph Multigraph Corp.)

Fig. 455B.  Friction Paper Feed — Multilith 85 (Courtesy Addressograph Multigraph Corp.)

### Receding Stacker

Chain-delivered, printed sheets are released into the stacker and jogged automatically. The stacker also recedes (lowers itself) automatically to accommodate a large quantity of printed sheets, as shown in Fig. 456B. The stacker platform may be equipped with wheels so that the printed sheets may be moved without rehandling (which may smudge the ink).

The stacker also may be equipped with an anti-offset spray which shoots a fine powder mist over each freshly printed sheet to prevent smudging and transfer of wet ink to the back side of the next sheet above. This undesirable offsetting from one sheet to another is often called "set-off" to distinguish it from the *offset* process. (See page 328.)

### The Dampening System

During the press operation, the dampening system feeds a controlled amount of fountain solution (dampener solution or water) from the fountain to the surface of the offset plate. See Fig. 457.

### Description

The capped bottle of prepared fountain solution is placed into its recess in the water fountain. (After the bottle is capped, it should be inverted to check that no water is leaking from it.) A valve in the bottle cap allows the fountain solution to escape and rise to its proper level in the fountain.

The fountain roller, partially submerged along its length in the fountain solution, rotates and carries on its surface a film of the fountain solution. Its rotation is activated by a pawl-

Fig. 456B. Chain Delivery with Receding Stacker — Multilith 1250 (Courtesy Addressograph Multigraph Corp.)

Fig. 456A. Ejector Mechanism and Delivery Tray with Automatic Jogger — Multilith 1250 (Courtesy Addressograph Multigraph Corp.)

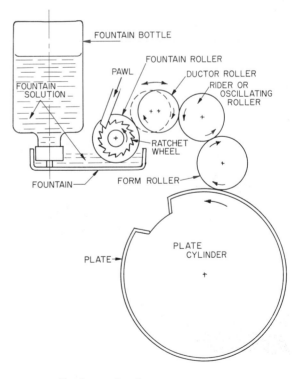

Fig. 457. The Dampening System

and-ratchet arrangement. By adjusting the stroke of the pawl, more, or less, solution can be fed.

A ductor roller, rocking to-and-fro, transfers the solution from the fountain roller to the dampener (rider, or oscillating) roller.

The rider roller, oscillating (vibrating) from end-to-end as it revolves, equalizes the coverage of fountain solution along its length, and finally transfers the fountain solution to the form roller and thence to the plate.

Commonly, the form roller and the ductor roller are encased in either a molleton (towel-like) cover or a paper (cellulose-base) cover. (See also "Combined Inking and Dampening System", page 278.)

### Controls

A knob on one end of the fountain roller can be turned by hand when it is desired to add large amounts of water quickly.

A ratchet-control lever may be set to provide the desired speed of rotation of the fountain roller during the press run.

A ductor-contact lever may be set to stop the action of the ductor roller, when it is desired to discontinue the flow of fountain solution to the form roller during press operation.

A form-roller control lever is used to lift the form roller from, or drop it into contact with, the plate.

Generally, a "night-latch" lever is provided to lift the rollers away from each other when

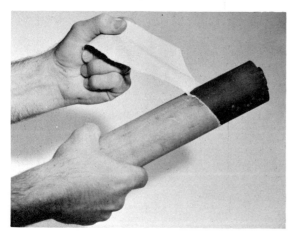

Fig. 458A.  Installing Dampening Sleeve, Step 1 — Tearing old sleeve from roller. (Courtesy 3M Co.)

press operation is stopped for any length of time. This prevents the formation of flat spots along the length of the rollers.

### Rollers

Dampening system rollers may be solid metal, solid rubber, or they may be covered. The latter increases the water-carrying capacity of the roller surface.

Fountain rollers generally are knurled solid metal, while ductor and form rollers generally are covered. Distributor rollers may be any of the three varieties.

Note: Combined ink-and-water systems may have *all* solid-rubber rollers.

Metal dampening rollers occasionally should be scoured with pumice and water, and then etched to resist ink attraction.

### Molleton Covers

Molleton-covered dampening rollers should be clean, the molleton evenly applied, and the rollers properly "set" (pressure setting) to deliver an even, continuous supply of moisture to the plate.

These rollers must be able to hold the floating scum or tint that collects on the face of all plates and prevent this scum from reaching the blanket and press sheet. The condition of the molleton covers, rather than their age or length of press service, should determine whether or not they need attention. Careful, constant care of dampening rollers is very necessary for quality work.

Dirty rollers should be removed from the press and washed first with solvent, then detergent and water. If they are excessively greasy or dirty, the covering should be replaced.

### Installing

Molleton covers may be purchased ready-cut for your press, in tubular or wrap-around strip form, or in continuous rolls of tubular material. For installation, the instructions supplied with the covers should be followed. In general, the following instructions apply to installation of tubular molleton covers:

Cut a length of molleton about two or three inches longer than the roller. Work the molleton over the roller end, being sure that any seam in the cover is not over a seam in the undercover. Slip the molleton a few inches along the roller as smoothly as possible, allowing ⅜ of an inch of the molleton to overhang the shoulder of the roller. Sew a drawcord in the end of the overhang; pull tight and knot this end.

Begin to stretch the remaining molleton along the length of the roller. Slightly-moistened hands or rubber gloves will help you get some "grab" on the molleton surface. Keep forcing the molleton along smoothly and tightly, starting near the first drawcord end. Uneven stretching may result in unequal diameters along the length. By gradually working the molleton along, it will lay smoothly the entire length, past the remaining shoulder.

Cut the molleton ⅜ inch past the shoulder, and tie and knot the second drawcord. With a damp sponge, smooth the finished roller in the direction of the nap. This helps it set smoothly and evenly.

### Fiber Covers

A dampening-roller sleeve of preformed synthetic fiber (a product of the 3M Company) may be used instead of cloth and paper dampening covers. Its seamless fiber design eliminates lint and the bulge of seams, and results in uniformity across the plate.

The sleeves are designed to be used with a matching dampening roller to insure maximum performance.

*Installation.* Installation of the 3M sleeve is performed in the three simple steps below:

(1) *Tear off the old sleeve.* When the sleeve needs changing, remove the dampening roller from the press, and peel off the moist, dirty sleeve (Fig. 458A). Clean the roller with a mild solvent, removing all ink or grease.

(2) *Slip on the new sleeve* (Fig. 458B). It should overhang evenly on both ends of the dampening roller. Since these sleeves are very sensitive to moisture, they should not be removed from the package until ready for use.

(3) *Moisten the sleeve* (Fig. 458C). Either water or fountain solution may be used. The sleeve will shrink skintight onto the dampening roller in sixty seconds. A run-in period is not required, nor is it necessary to reset the dampening-roller pressure after each sleeve change. However, the dampening roller should be replaced as it was before removal.

*Checking Pressure.* Pressure of the dampening roller to the plate should be checked after installation, and, if necessary, readjusted, using a 0.005″ gauge. (See "Dampener-Roller Pressure Settings", below.)

*Cleaning and Care.* Before starting the press run each day and before recommencing a press run after a shut-down of 30 minutes or longer, dampen the sleeve thoroughly with fountain solution. Failure to do this may cause ink to be transferred to the sleeve.

When the sleeve becomes dirty (or when going from a dark ink to a light ink), clean the roller sleeve with naptha or mild solvent, followed by fountain solution.

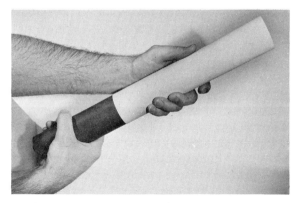

Fig. 458B. Installing Dampening Sleeve, Step 2 — Slipping seamless sleeve onto roller. (Courtesy 3M Co.)

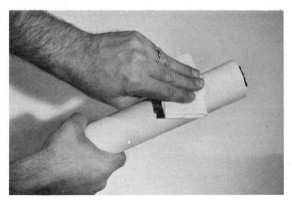

Fig. 458C. Installing Dampening Sleeve, Step 3 — Wetting the sleeve. (Courtesy 3M Co.)

## Dampener-Roller Pressure Settings

Newly-installed dampener covers may settle due to water and "roll-in" squeeze. They should be set for proper pressure first after they are installed, then after they have been run-in for a while against a plate on the press, and finally at a later time during the day. (This pressure check also should be made on all presses each morning before the press run.)

Specific press manufacturer's instructions should be followed for plate packing (if used), order of procedure, rollers to be checked, and pressure recommended. In general, the following procedure may be used to check dampening-roller settings:

(1) Prepare dampening system for operation. Test for dampness of form roller. Allow form roller to run-in against plate on plate cylinder for a minute or two. Then lift the form roller and *stop the press*. (Skill in testing the form roller for dampness comes with practice. Some operators test with the knuckle of a clenched finger. Ask your instructor to show you how he wants this tested.)

Fig. 459. Checking Pressure of Dampening Roller to Plate (Courtesy 3M Co.)

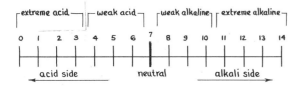

Fig. 460. pH Scale

(2) *With the press stopped*, place two strips of 20-pound bond paper (or 0.005"-thick acetate gauges) between the form roller and the plate, one strip near each end, as shown in Fig. 459.

Drop the form roller to "on" position.

(3) With one hand holding each test strip, pull toward your body with slow, uniform tension. You should feel a slight drag on both strips. If one strip pulls easier than the other or if there is too much (or too little) drag on both, adjust the roller on one end, or both, as indicated by the test procedure.

When pressures are satisfactory (still with the *press stopped*), drop the form roller to the plate and lift it — do this quickly! If you inspect the plate carefully, you should see a *dampened* line across its surface.

## Fountain (Dampening) Solution

The function of the offset press fountain solution is to furnish a mildly-acidic wetting agent to the offset plate surface during the press run, to keep the clear (non-printing) areas of the plate free of ink. This solution sometimes is referred to as the "water" or "dampener" solution.

### Preparing the Solution

Fountain solution generally is purchased in concentrated form and prepared as directed on the container. It is also well to check the plate manufacturer's recommendations and instructions for the particular plate being used.

Sometimes a quantity of gum arabic is added to the fountain solution. It is a mild etch and is slow to evaporate — two qualities which tend to keep the non-printing areas of the plate free of ink.

In making up the fountain solution, add the concentrate (acid constituent) in small amounts to the total volume of water required, and test for "pH." (The pH is the degree of alkalinity or acidity, as explained below.) If needed, add more of the acid constituent; then test again. Continue until the desired pH is reached.

Below is a formula for a concentrated fountain solution suitable for aluminum plates:

(1) Into ½ gallon of water, add:

9 ounces (Avoird) magnesium nitrate (or zinc nitrate)

1¾ ounces (Avoird) ammonium dichromate (Ammonium bichromate is the same chemical.)

⅝ ounce (liquid) phosphoric acid, 85%.

(2) Add water to make a total of 1 gallon.

To use the above in the press fountain, add 2 ounces (liquid) of this concentrate and 1 ounce (liquid) of gum arabic solution (14° Baumé) to one gallon of water.

## pH Values (Readings)

The chemical term "pH" means the *degree of alkalinity or acidity* of a solution. The pH of a solution is expressed as a numerical value, as shown on the scale in Fig. 460. A solution which has a pH value of 7.0 is regarded as neutral — neither acid nor alkaline.

As the readings decrease from 7 toward 0, they are increasingly acid; as they increase from 7 to 14, they are increasingly alkaline.

## Recommended pH Values

A fountain solution at pH 4.6 is recommended when running aluminum plates. For zinc plates, a solution at pH 3.8 should be used.

Test for pH of the fountain solution frequently during the press run, as it may change due to contact with the fountain metal, the rollers, the ink or the paper.

When the fountain solution has too high a pH value (low acidity), the non-printing areas of the plate tend to pick up ink. This is called "scumming." City water with high chlorine or mineral content may cause this. With too low a pH value (high acidity), the image areas will not pick up the ink properly.

## Determining the pH of the Solution

The pH of fountain solutions (and platemaking solutions) may be tested by use of lithographic pH test papers, as shown and explained in Figs. 461A through 461C. The specific pH value is printed above each color on the dispenser chart.

Strengthen, or weaken, the solution if it is desired to change the pH reading of the solution being tested.

NOTE: Only distilled water is neutral. Tap water has additives, so should be tested for pH.

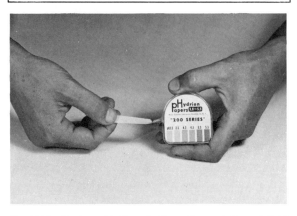

Fig. 461A. Testing pH, Step 1. Draw Out and Tear Off 2" Strip of Lithographic Test Paper (Courtesy Micro Essential Laboratory, Inc.)

Fig. 461B. Testing pH, Step 2. Dip Test Paper Into Solution or Water Fountain (Courtesy Micro Essential Laboratory, Inc.)

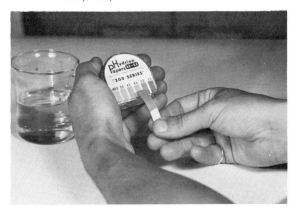

Fig. 461C. Testing pH, Step 3. Match Wet Color of Test Paper with Color Standard on Dispenser (Courtesy Micro Essential Laboratory. Inc.)

## The Inking System

The inking system provides a metered flow of well-distributed ink from the ink fountain to the offset plate during the operation of the press. See Fig. 462.

### Description

As the fountain roller revolves, a film of ink is drawn from the fountain, from between the fountain blade and the fountain roller. This adheres to the surface of the fountain roller. The ductor roller, rocking to-and-fro as it revolves, transfers this ink to the train of ink rollers, and from there to the form rollers, which deposit the ink on the offset-plate image.

### Controls

Note in Fig. 463A that a series of adjusting screws, or fountain "keys" (B), along the length of the fountain serve to move the fountain blade either in toward, or away from, the fountain roller (A). This provides easy control over the thickness of the film of ink which the fountain roller may draw from the fountain.

The ink coverage supplied to specific areas across the offset plate may be varied by adjusting the proper screws. It is important to make "tapered" adjustments with the keys. For example, if one or more screws are opened, say one-quarter turn, then the adjoining screws should be opened one-eighth turn, etc. (The blade is steel — not rubber!)

A pawl-and-ratchet arrangement, adjustable for length of stroke (lever C), drives the fountain roller and also governs the rotational speed of that roller.

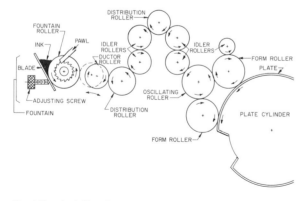

Fig. 462. An Inking System

The ductor roller is usually provided with an "on-off" lever to stop the addition of ink to the ink train while the press is operating.

The "on-off" lever of the form roller brings these rollers into contact with, or away from, the offset plate.

A night-latch lever is provided to lift the oscillating roller (and perhaps others) out of contact with the form rollers during extended shut-downs, to prevent the formation of flat spots on the rollers.

### Combined Inking-and-Dampening System
(See page 278.)

### Ink-Form-Roller Pressure Settings

With the ink unit prepared, and an old plate (or a "gummed" plate) on the press, test the contact of the form roller to the plate — *while the press is stopped!*

Drop the form rollers in full contact with the plate, and lift them off. There should be an inked line of uniform width, clear across the plate — about ⅛th inch in width (although some prefer ³⁄₁₆ths). (See Fig. 463B.)

Turn the handwheel to see the inked test lines on the plate. Perform this test several places along the plate.

If needed, adjust the roller settings, first for parallel (uniform width across the plate) and then to obtain the desired width. If the inking system has two form rollers, complete all adjustments on one before working on the second.

A uniformly *tapered* line across the plate indicates unequal pressure settings for the roller ends.

An *uneven* line indicates that the roller is worn unevenly and should be re-ground or replaced.

Specific press manufacturer's instructions should be followed for plate packing (if used) prior to testing, order of procedure, rollers to be checked, and width of line recommended.

### Care of Ink Rollers

Rollers that are properly cared for will add to the quality of the printed job, will cause less trouble on the press, and will give maximum service.

### Composition of Rollers

Offset press rollers commonly are made of natural rubber, synthetic rubber or compounded or vulcanized vegetable oils.

### Setting

Proper setting of the rollers minimizes friction and its resulting roller troubles. In general, the form rollers are set parallel to the plate cylinder, and are set for the clearance specified by the press manufacturer. When composition rollers are used, the setting should be checked occasionally during the run, as it may vary.

### Resurfacing

Rubber and vulcanized-oil rollers may be re-ground and buffed by the roller manufacturers to give a fresh surface and years of additional use.

### Washing Up

Proper wash-up will prolong the life of rollers. An accumulation of dried ink on the rollers should be avoided. Wash lengthwise of the roller, and avoid using too much pressure. Wash more frequently when using tacky inks or inks with driers or reducers. Stay away from strong solvents.

The *solvent* used for washing depends upon the local supply and your fire regulations. Kerosene is economical and fire-safe, but leaves an undesirable oily film. Most suppliers recommend a mineral spirit having a flash point (fire rating) similar to kerosene, but which dries quickly without leaving an oily residue and without harming rubber rollers and blankets. Leaded gasoline and chlorinated hydrocarbons (like carbon "tet") are poisonous and must be avoided. White gasoline and naptha are major fire hazards.

For a *complete periodic wash-up*, a lye bath may be used (about three ounces of household lye to a gallon of water). Wash the roller with a steel-wool pad dipped in the solution. Rub firmly to remove all ink film, but not hard enough to mark the roller. Keep the solution on the roller for no more than ten or twelve minutes. *Do not allow the lye solution to get on the hands — it will burn! Use rubber gloves.* Wash the roller with water or a water-dampened cloth to remove the lye before storing the roller on the rack.

In some plants, a warm-water bath with Lava soap is now replacing the lye method of cleaning. Place the roller in warm water, and wash with Lava soap, lengthwise of the roller. Be sure to rinse all traces of soap from the roller when finished. No brush or abrasive is necessary with this method, and the dangers common with the use of lye are avoided.

Fig. 463A. Ink Fountain, Fountain Adjusting Keys, Ink-Feed Control Lever, and Ink Rollers — Multilith 1250 (Courtesy Addressograph Multigraph Corp.)

Fig. 463B. Checking Ink Form Roller-to-Plate Contact on Multilith 1250 (Courtesy Addressograph Multigraph Corp.)

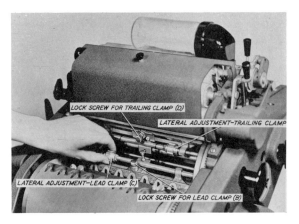

Fig. 464.  Plate (Master) Lateral Adjustment — Multilith 1250
(Courtesy Addressograph Multigraph Corp.)

Fig. 465A.  Attaching Serrated (Slotted) Master — Lead End —
on Multilith 1250. Note hooks "A" on plate-holding
device. (Courtesy Addressograph Multigraph
Corp.)

## Storing Rollers

All rollers should be carefully cleaned before being put away. Composition rollers should then be covered with a thin film of oil to seal them against changing weather conditions. Rubber and vulcanized-oil rollers need no special preparation other than the cleaning. All rollers should be stored in cabinets, rather than on open racks where they might be injured or pick up dirt. A vertical rack is preferred, as horizontal racking may produce sags in the rollers, unless they are rotated frequently. Regardless of how rollers are stored, they must have free air circulation.

## The Plate Cylinder

The smooth-metal plate cylinder has a longitudinal gap fitted with plate-clamping devices. These clamps may be for plates which have straight, pin-hole, slotted-hole (oval), or looped (serrated) ends.

On many presses, the style of plate clamp may be changed as desired.

Some plate-cylinder clamps are adjustable laterally (from side-to-side) to "twist" the plate slightly and, so, compensate for an image which is not placed squarely on the plate. (See Fig. 464.) If the lead clamp is moved to one side in twisting a plate, then the trail clamp must be moved a corresponding amount to the opposite side. Plate images that are badly tilted require a plate re-make.

Fig. 465B.  Attaching Serrated (Slotted) Master — Trailing End
— Multilith 1250 (Courtesy Addressograph Multigraph Corp.)

## Installing an Offset Plate

*Check that power is "off."* Handle the plate carefully, to avoid scratching one plate with the corner of another.

Clean the back of the plate and the plate cylinder. Wipe off the blanket. Check that the plate image is square.

If the plate differs from that just previously run, measure the thickness with micrometer calipers. A difference in thickness may call for new pressure checks on dampeners and ink-form rollers, plus a change in the total thickness of packing sheets.

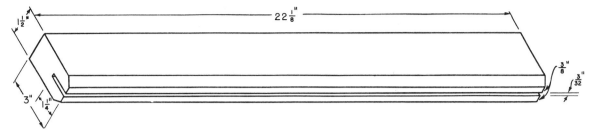

Fig. 466. Plate-Bending Jig — ATF Chief 20 Press (Courtesy American Type Founders Co., Inc.)    ers Co., Inc.)

If the plate cylinder calls for packing, see page 294.

*For the duplicators,* engage the leading end of the plate on (or in) the lead clamp, Fig. 465A. Holding the free end of the plate in the right hand, turn the handwheel, and draw the plate evenly around the cylinder, engaging the plate with the tail clamp, Fig. 465B.

Spring pressure is adequate for paper plates. Metal plates require that the plate-clamp draw-down screw be tightened, but not so much that the plate is torn.

Before installation, the ends of metal plates should be preformed (bent somewhat) with a plate-bending jig (Fig. 466).

*When installing a plate on presses larger than duplicators,* set the press impression "on". Check that ink rollers and water rollers are in "off" position. If the paper-feeding mechanism has an automatic trip, place a sheet of paper under it or otherwise arrange it so that the impression will not be thrown off when the cylinders are rotated (as would be the case, since no paper is being fed while the plate is being installed).

Bend the ends of the plate with the plate-bending jig.

Attach the leading end of the plate to the leading edge of the cylinder, catching ¼ to ½ inch of the leading edges of the packing sheets beyond the bend of the cylinder. The plate should be centered on the cylinder with the image facing the operator, Fig. 467A.

Turn the cylinder (against the pressure of the blanket cylinder) to draw the plate, and its packing, smoothly over the cylinder. Engage the tail end of the plate in the tail clamp of the cylinder, taking care not to tighten excessively and thus tear the plate, Fig. 467B.

Fig. 467A. Installing Plate on Cylinder — ATF Chief 20 Press (Courtesy American Type Founders Co., Inc.)

Fig. 467B. Fastening Plate on Cylinder — ATF Chief 20 Press (Courtesy American Type Founders Co., Inc.)

Rearrange the automatic trip on the press so it will again function (with no paper going through).

If it is necessary to twist the plate for register, refer to the press manufacturer's instructions.

### Removing an Offset Plate

At the end of a press run, run a few extra sheets through the press with impression "on", and ink and water rollers "off". This "runs down" the plate image (removes excess ink). Now *stop the press.*

Moisten a sponge with gum arabic solution[4], and wipe over the plate surface, turning the press handwheel so the entire plate can be reached. Wipe smooth and dry with a cheesecloth pad.

Release the tail end of the plate first, turning the press backward by hand. Then release the leading (gripper) edge. Prepare the plate for storage. (See page 220.)

## The Blanket Cylinder

Two blanket-clamping devices in the blanket-cylinder gap are provided for attaching the blanket to its cylinder. (See Figs. 468A

Fig. 468A. Attaching Blanket to Lead Clamp. (A) Blanket; (B) Lead clamp — Multilith 1250. (Courtesy Addressograph Multigraph Corp.)

[4]A diluted gum arabic solution of 7° or 8° Baumé is recommended for gumming a plate while it is on the press. For gumming a plate on the bench, a 14° Baumé gum arabic solution is recommended.

and 468B.) One of the clamping devices is fitted with a screw arrangement for drawing the blanket tightly around the cylinder. (See also: "Pressure Settings," page 292, and "Undercut-Cylinder Packings", page 294.)

### The Blanket

The blanket is made of a rubber-covered fabric. This relatively soft surface receives the inked image from the plate and transfers it to the printing paper which is pressed against the blanket by the impression cylinder. Since the impression cylinder is an unyielding steel surface, the character and quality of the impression depend upon the blanket surface.

### Preparing a New Blanket

Clean the powder from a new blanket by washing with press wash; scour with pumice if necessary. Inspect the surface for nicks and other imperfections. Low spots in the blanket prevent image transfer. These can be repaired by pasting layers of tissue on the back side under the low spot.

Measure the thickness of the blanket with a micrometer calipers, and record this measurement for future use in packing the blanket cylinder when using this particular blanket.

If necessary, lay the blanket on a clean, covered surface, and mark the two edges

Fig. 468B. Attaching Blanket to Trailing Clamp. (A) Trailing clamp; (B) Lock nut; (C) Tightening screw — Multilith 1250. (Courtesy Addressograph Multigraph Corp.)

which will be parallel with the blanket cylinder. Mark and punch the holes, and attach the mounting bars, as required.

Powder the surface of the blanket with a mixture of sulphur and French chalk (or prepared blanket dusting powder).

### Installing a New Blanket

Add packing sheets beneath the blanket, if called for in press manufacturer's instructions.

The forward edge of the blanket *and* the forward edges of the packing sheets should be fastened to the blanket cylinder. (Follow the instruction manual for your particular press.) Fastening the packing at the forward edge will keep it from creeping during operation of the press. If clamping screws are used, tighten all equally.

Turn the press over *by hand* to feed the blanket to the cylinder — be sure the packing is fed smoothly with the blanket, Fig. 469A. Attach the free end of the blanket to the cylinder. If tightening screws are used, tighten each equally. (See Fig. 469B.) Avoid stretching the blanket "dead" as this produces a hard, poor printing surface.

After a short run, a new blanket is apt to stretch, and should be retightened some.

### Care of Blankets

The life of the blanket and the quality of the printing can both be improved by following these suggestions:

(1) When the press is to be idle for several days, release the tension on the blanket.

(2) Check and correct the thickness of the packing occasionally to eliminate surface friction.

(3) Keep the blanket clean and powdered with sulphur and French chalk when not in use.

(4) Wash the blanket with water to remove gum solution or accumulation.

(5) Dissolve any dried ink on the blanket with press solvent, whether on the surface, edges, or back. Keep the blanket absolutely clean for the best presswork. Do not let fluids dry on the blanket — *wipe* the blanket clean and dry.

(6) Keep the blanket away from heat, especially away from the direct rays of the sun.

(7) Never use gasoline or combinations of turpentine and gasoline.

(8) Level any low spot on the blanket by pasting a patch of tissue or onionskin *under* the area with Sphinx or pressroom paste.

(9) When the blanket is too tacky to receive a good impression, treat it with carbon disulfide and sulphur powder.

(10) When the blanket is too glazed to receive a good impression, scour the surface with pumice and solvent, and then treat with a mixture of equal parts of powdered sulphur and soapstone (French chalk).

Fig. 469A. Installing Blanket on Blanket Cylinder — ATF Chief 20 Press (Courtesy American Type Founders Co., Inc.)

Fig. 469B. Adjusting Blanket Tension — ATF Chief 20 Press (Courtesy American Type Founders Co., Inc.)

(11) When the blanket is to be stored for a time, wash the surface thoroughly with press solvent and caustic soda or pumice. Powder it well with a half-and-half mixture of sulphur and French chalk. Then roll it so the printing surface is on the inside, to protect it.

(12) To prolong the life of the blanket, give it a rest occasionally. It is well to have extra blankets and rotate them periodically. Blankets might be used "progessively," that is, a new blanket could be used for the "fussiest" kind of work, and then, when it is worn some, it could be used for the general run of line work.

### The Impression Cylinder

A set of grippers, in the leading edge of the impression-cylinder gap, grips the forwarded sheet of paper and carries it between the impression cylinder and the blanket cylinder, transferring the blanket image to the paper. See Fig. 470. These grippers should *not* be adjusted to compensate for a "cocked" plate image.

### Pressure Checks (Settings)

In general, a number of pressure checks must be made to rollers and cylinders each day before the press is run. These checks also should be made when blanket, rollers, or roller coverings are replaced, when troubles develop

with the plate image, or when a plate or printing paper of different thickness is to be used. Specific press manufacturer's instructions should be followed. General instructions for sequence and procedure are given below. (See also Fig. 471.)

(1) *Dampener form roller-to-plate.* (See page 284.)

(2) *Ink form roller-to-plate.* (See page 286.)

(3) *Plate cylinder-to-blanket cylinder.* With a properly mounted, packed, and gummed plate on the press, start the press. See page 294 for plate packing. Keep dampener form rollers in "off" position. Drop ink rollers to "on" position, and allow the gummed plate to ink up over its entire surface. Now, *stop the press,* lifting the ink rollers to "off" position.

Bring the plate cylinder *fully* in contact with the blanket cylinder; then take the plate cylinder *out* of contact. Perform this test several times in different locations on the blanket.

Uniformly-inked lines, $\frac{3}{16}''$ wide, should appear across the blanket. (See Fig. 472.) If not, an adjustment must be made, first for *parallel,* then for *overall* pressure, if needed.

Fig. 470. Impression-Cylinder Gripper Fingers. (A) Stop plates; (B) Grippers — Multilith 1250. (Courtesy Addressograph Multigraph Corp.)

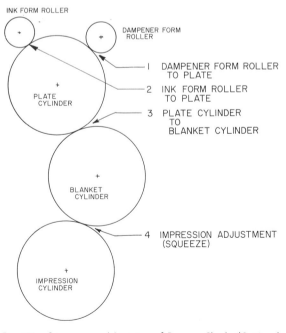

Fig. 471. Sequence and Location of Pressure Checks (Settings)

Some presses require a packing (using sheets of paper) beneath the blanket to arrive at proper printing pressure or to compensate for differences in thickness of blankets. (See page 294 and appropriate press manual.)

A second test can be made. Start the press (dampeners "off"), drop the ink rollers to "on", and ink up (roll up) the plate completely. With the press still in operation, allow the blanket to ink up *completely*. Any area of the blanket which will not "roll up" indicates a low spot. (See page 290 for underlaying a low spot.)

(4) *Impression adjustment (squeeze)*. Your press may have a compensating adjustment (spring-loaded impression, which will provide self-adjustment for variations in stock thickness. Otherwise, the pressure between the blanket cylinder and the impression cylinder should be adjusted to provide the correct "squeeze" for each different thickness of stock being run. Your press manufacturer's instructions should be followed. Two methods of testing are explained below.

a. *Ink-band test*. With a plate on the plate cylinder, start the press. Drop dampeners and then ink-form rollers, inking up the plate image in the usual manner. Bring the blanket cylinder into contact with the plate cylinder,

obtaining an inked image on the blanket. Now, *stop the press* (first lifting the ink rollers and dampeners).

Rotate the handwheel until the blanket image is over the solid part of the impression cylinder. Insert a sheet of the printing paper between the blanket and the impression cylinders. Bring the blanket cylinder into contact with the impression cylinder; then bring it away.

A ³⁄₁₆″-wide, uniformly-inked band of the image should appear across the paper. Adjust, if needed, first for parallel, then for width of the band.

NOTE: This "band" test may be performed also by contacting the printing paper with a blanket that has been completely covered with ink.

b. *Test strips*. With the press *stopped*, insert two 2″ x 8″ test strips of paper (of the printing stock) between the blanket and the impression cylinders, one strip near each end.

Adjust for *parallel* impression until a pull on each strip indicates the strips are held firmly

Fig. 472. Plate Cylinder to Blanket Cylinder (Master to Blanket) Ink Band Pressure Test. (A) Operating Control Handle; (B) Master Inked Completely; and (C) Ink Band — Multilith 1250. (Courtesy Addressograph Multigraph Corp.)

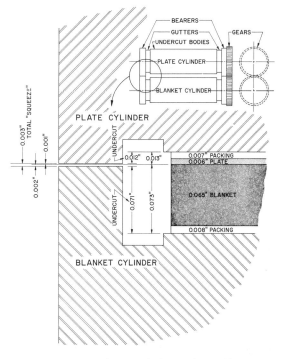

Fig. 473. Typical Undercut Cylinder Packings. Measurements used are illustrative only. Substitute the actual figures for your press.

between the cylinders. (Always begin this test from a setting *greater than* the thickness of the stock to be run.)

In general, to obtain a *uniform drag* on the two test strips, 0.003″ more squeeze should be added, either by adjustment or by addition of packing sheets.

## Undercut-Cylinder Packings

On larger presses, the bodies of the plate cylinder and the blanket cylinder are each "undercut" — that is, made smaller in diameter than the narrow band at each end (called "bearers"). When properly adjusted, the bearers maintain the two cylinders parallel to each other and at the correct "rolling off" level. See Fig. 473.

The amount that the cylinders are undercut below that of the bearers usually is stamped somewhere in the cylinder gutters, indicating in thousandths of an inch how much the cylinder body is undercut below the bearers *in radius*.

The undercut allows for adding packing sheets beneath the plate and blanket. This helps compensate for variations in thickness of plates and blankets, thus maintaining these two cylinders virtually equal in diameters. If one were larger, this tends to change the image size during transfer.

The total thickness of the packing sheets, plus the thickness of the blanket and the plate should equal 0.003″ *more* than the combined undercut of the two cylinders. This excess is called the "squeeze".

For example, in Fig. 473, a 0.071″ undercut blanket cylinder has added packing sheets totaling 0.008″ and a blanket 0.065″ thick. Together, these equal 0.002″ *more* than the undercut.

Similarly, 0.007″ of packing sheets has been added to the 0.006″ plate, totaling 0.001″ *more* than the 0.012″ undercut of the plate cylinder. These two excesses of packing total 0.003″ — the recommended "squeeze".

If, for any reason, more packing is added to one of the cylinders, the exact amount should be removed from the other. (See page 270.)

## Questions

1. Name the basic parts of an offset press. Briefly describe the function of each.
2. Explain in detail what happens to the paper stock from the time it is picked out of the feeder pile until it is delivered into the receiver or delivery unit.
3. Tell how the "combined" inking-and-dampening system operates.
4. In offset presswork, what does the term "emulsification" indicate?
5. How does the four-main-cylinder design of offset press differ from the three-main-cylinder design?
6. Explain the theory of operation of the two-main-cylinder design of offset press.
7. Tell how the fountain solution is transferred from the fountain to the plate surface.
8. Why do you suppose that coverings are used for dampener form rollers? Name two kinds.
9. Explain how to check the setting (pressure) of the dampener form roller (or rollers).
10. Explain the term "pH". How is it measured?
11. Tell how to prepare fountain solution from the concentrate.
12. What are the recommended pH values of fountain solution to be used with zinc plates and aluminum plates?
13. Describe the inking system.
14. Explain how to control the amount of ink that is fed to any area across the width of the plate.
15. Describe the test for proper pressure setting of ink form rollers.
16. How should ink rollers be stored?
17. Tell how to prepare and install a new blanket.
18. How should gum be removed from the blanket?
19. How is a low spot in a blanket corrected?
20. Describe the installation of a plate on a duplicator. On a large press.
21. What does "running down" a plate mean? Describe how this is done.

22. How is an offset plate removed from the press?
23. Describe how to check the pressure of the plate cylinder to blanket cylinder.
24. Describe one method of checking the impression adjustment.
25. What is meant by a cylinder "undercut"? Why is the undercut provided?

## Problems and Projects

1. For each of the different presses in your shop, make a schematic drawing of the roller systems, cylinder arrangement, and paper feeding-to-delivery components.
2. While your instructor demonstrates, observe the action and function of each of the press components.
3. Study thoroughly the press operator's manual for each of the presses suggested by your instructor.
4. Assist your instructor in applying new dampener covers.
5. Under your instructor's supervision, make the dampening-system pressure checks on the press he selects.
6. Prepare a given quantity of fountain solution for a given pH value.
7. Under the direction of your instructor, prepare and install a new blanket. Test and correct for any low spots.
8. Under the direction of your instructor, install and remove an offset plate.

9. Prepare a quantity of gum arabic solution of either 7° or 8° Baumé.
10. Assist your instructor in performing complete pressure checks on an offset press.
11. Assist your instructor in determining and installing proper packing for blanket and plate cylinders for a specific situation.

## New Words

| | | | |
|---|---|---|---|
| 1. | accumulation | 21. | impression |
| 2. | acidic | 22. | magnesium |
| 3. | acidity | 23. | micrometer |
| 4. | additive | 24. | mineral spirits |
| 5. | alkalinity | 25. | molleton |
| 6. | automatically | 26. | nitrate |
| 7. | Avoirdupois | 27. | nomenclature |
| 8. | Baumé | 28. | pawl-and-ratchet |
| 9. | caliper | 29. | phosphoric |
| 10. | carbon disulphide | 30. | pumice |
| 11. | cellulose | 31. | receding |
| 12. | circulation | 32. | replenishing |
| 13. | concentrated | 33. | revolution |
| 14. | constituent | 34. | segment |
| 15. | construction | 35. | separate |
| 16. | conventional | 36. | submerged |
| 17. | conveyed | 37. | synthetic |
| 18. | duplicator | 38. | thrust |
| 19. | emulsification | 39. | undercut |
| 20. | emulsifying | 40. | vulcanized |

# Offset Presswork

# Operations

For optimum results, it is most desirable that a qualified instructor demonstrate and teach the operation of the press. The instructions in this chapter apply, in general, to most duplicators and presses.[1]

## Preliminary Preparation

No press should be operated by any person until he has been thoroughly instructed in its safe operation, demonstrates that he understands its operation, and is specifically designated to operate that press. No unauthorized persons should "help" or experiment.

In addition, no adjustments to the press should be attempted by the student until he has received proper instruction and is judged competent by the instructor. The student should not hesitate to ask questions or to seek assistance or further instruction.

### Press Instruction Manuals

Operators' instruction manuals for the particular presses in the shop should be on hand and available to students.

### Personal Dress

Remove coats and sweaters. Roll shirt sleeves *above* the elbows. Remove or "tuck in" neckties. Remove jewelry such as rings and bracelets. Do not wear gloves or loose aprons.

### Items Needed

While the exact needs will vary with the situation, use the following as a suggestion.

[1]All photographs in this chapter courtesy Addressograph Multigraph Corporation.

10-quart enamel pail (half-filled with tepid water).

Cellulose sponge, approximately 2″ x 4″ x 4″ (for sponging the plate on the press).

Shallow bowl, about 4″ or 5″ diameter, with about 1″ of 7° Baumé gum solution (for gumming the plate on the press). (Use 14° Baumé gum for gumming the plate on the bench.)

Cheesecloth pads, about 4″ square.

Cotton wipes, about 4″ square.

Clean cotton wiping cloths.

Oil can with spout (hand oiler) filled with solvent. Label it "solvent" and use only for this purpose.

Pint- or quart-size safety can, filled with solvent.

(NOTE: See "Solvents", pages 287, 334.)

Ink knife, square end (or putty knife).

Screwdriver, Allen wrenches, open-end wrenches, socket wrenches, pliers, etc., to fit commonly-adjusted screws and nuts on the press being used. A tool panel is a handy way to keep tools accessible.

Roller-storage rack.

Cleaner sheets.

Roller-cleaning device.

Magnifier (tripod-base, linen-tester, or pocket-clip type).

Dampener gauges (acetate or paper strips, 0.005″ thick x 1″ wide x 8″ or more long).

Paper micrometers and blanket gage.

Newspaper sheets, cut half-page size.

In addition to the above, it is well to have on hand chemicals and supplies for storing and preserving specific plates.

A worktable should be provided for the pressman's use.

The proper fountain solution and ink supply should be available, according to the plates being run and the specifications for the inks to be used.

### Visual Inspection

Remove the fabric press covering. Examine the press carefully to see that all component parts are in place and that all settings and controls are in "off" position.

Install any fountains and rollers which may have been removed the previous day, first removing any protective gum coating (if so treated).

Remove any paper dust or lint from the feeder and register table.

Wipe off any dust from the blanket, cylinders and rollers with a cloth dampened in solvent.

### Turn By Hand

As an additional check to be certain there is no interference, turn the press by means of the handwheel for a revolution or two.

### Turn On the Press (Power Check)

If all is clear, turn on the power, allowing the press to revolve for a few times. Check that all parts are functioning correctly. If the speed selector is at other than the slowest speed, set it at this speed *while the press is operating.* Do not adjust the speed setting while the press is stopped.

### Lubrication

Lubricate the press daily before operation — *while the press is stopped!* Never attempt to lubricate a moving press.

Study the manufacturer's lubrication chart and locate each oil hole, grease fitting, and point of lubrication. These should be marked with red paint to make them prominent.

Begin at one point on the press and work your way around, filling each hole with No. 20 S.A.E. motor oil and wiping off the excess with a clean cloth. If any oil holes are on parts which rotate during operation, turn the press by hand so that these holes are on top, and then oil them. In this way, the oil will have a chance to work down to the bearing surfaces.

Once a week, lubricate the delivery and feeder drive chains with penetrating oil or a mixture of equal parts of kerosene and No. 20 S.A.E. motor oil. Use gear grease compound on all gears. Oil the motors sparingly, at this weekly lubrication. If the motors have grease fittings, add grease twice yearly, or every 1000 hours.

Occasionally, during the day when the press is stopped, check the main bearings. They should never be very warm. Lubricate if needed.

Check the recommended oil level in the vacuum-blower pump jars weekly (Fig. 474). This is generally No. 10 S. A. E. oil. Clean the air inlet holes.

### Check Specifications

Check the job specifications. Do you have the correct ink? Is the correct paper stock at hand, and cut to the correct size? Are the plates ready? What other "specs" are called for? If in doubt, consult your instructor.

### Setting Up for Operation

Assuming the preliminary preparation of the press as described above has been done, set up for operation as follows.

Fig. 474. Vacuum-Blower Pump. (A) Oil filler cap; (B) Gasket; (C) Filter elements; (D) Wing nut; (E) Glass jar; and (F) Pump bearing oil holes (Multilith 1250)

### Prepare the Ink Unit

Install the ink fountain and all rollers which may have been removed. If an ink-fountain liner is used, install it now. (See Fig. 475.)

Estimate how much ink is needed. It is better to start with too little ink on the rollers than too much. More can be added easily.

Turn the handwheel (or adjust press) so that the ink ductor roller is out of contact with the fountain roller.

Place the ink in the bottom of the fountain, forcing it from the tube and rotating the fountain roller by hand. Adjust "keys" (or fountain screws) so that an even film of ink is all along the fountain roller.

If the ink is in a can, first scrape and discard any scum from the top, using the ink knife. Then, with a rotary motion, pick up the ink with the knife, removing an even layer from the top of the ink in the can. Hold this "glob" down in the fountain against the roller, and turn the roller by hand, picking off the ink from the knife. Add more ink, if needed, in a different location; then work the ink along the length of the fountain with the knife.

Turn the night latch of the ink form roller to the "off" position, so that these rollers are in contact with other ink unit rollers, ready to operate.

Set the ink ductor roller "on", and turn the ratchet control for the ink fountain to "full on" position. (*Do not* set the form rollers to "on".)

Turn on the press, and when sufficient ink is on the rollers (just barely enough to begin to "hiss"), shut off the press. Set the ratchet control for the fountain roller to the usual running position, as determined by experience (usually a little less than the middle setting).

### Prepare the Water (Dampening) Unit

Install the water fountain, fountain roller, and all other water system rollers which may have been removed.

Fill the fountain bottle with the recommended solution. Invert the bottle to make sure no solution leaks out from between the cap and the bottle. Place the bottle in its recess in the fountain. Allow the solution to reach its level.

Turn the night latch for the dampener roller "off" (if any); this drops the rollers into operating position. The form roller remains "off", not contacting the plate.

Start the press, allowing the rollers to pick up moisture. Help the moisture along by rotating the fountain roller by hand. Some operators drip a little fountain solution on the oscillating roller from the corner of a sponge.

The dampener ductor roller may be pre-dampened as follows: With the press stopped, turn the handwheel to bring the ductor roller into contact with the fountain roller. Turn the fountain roller knob by hand, thus quickly transferring fountain solution from the fountain roller to the ductor roller, until the ductor roller is sufficiently dampened.

Stop the press when the form rollers are sufficiently damp, as determined from experience. Some operators extend a clenched fist, touching the form roller with the knuckle of one finger as the press revolves. Have your instructor show you. (Never use a finger tip!)

Fig. 475. Installing Ink-Fountain Liner. (A) Liner; (B) Blade assembly; (C) Fountain roller (Multilith 1250)

Fig. 476A. Vacuum Feeder and Paper Magazine (Multilith 1250)

Set the ratchet control for the fountain roller at its "normal" setting.

### Install the Plate

When performing pressure checks, use either the gummed plate to be used on the job or a test plate of the same thickness as the plate for the job.

Follow instructions given on page 288.

### Perform the Pressure Checks

Perform the pressure checks in this sequence:

1. Dampener form roller to plate. (See page 284.)
2. Ink form roller to plate. (See page 286.)
3. Plate cylinder to blanket cylinder. (See page 292.)
4. Impression adjustment (or squeeze). (See page 293.)

### Prepare the Feeder, Sheet Controls and Delivery

Setting up for the "paper cycle" (feeder, sheet controls and delivery) is greatly simplified if all jobs are laid out on the flat (1) so that the *printing sheet* (not necessarily the image) is always centered on the flat from left to right and (2) so that the leading edge of the sheet is always the same distance down from the leading edge of the flat.

*Feeder Set-Up.* A typical vacuum feeder is shown in Figs. 476A and 476B. The set-up is as follows:

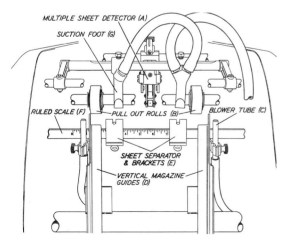

Fig. 476B. Vacuum Feeder and Paper Magazine, Showing Relative Positioning of Units (Multilith 1250)

(1) Cut a piece of heavy cardboard or binders board, ⅛" shorter and narrower than the stock to be run, and place this on the paper supports (Fig. 476A).

(2) Fold a sheet of the paper stock to be run in the center, and place it on the feeder platform, so the crease is ⅛" to the *left* of the center mark on the scale (Fig. 476B).

(3) Secure the left pile (magazine) guide $\frac{1}{32}$" from the paper (Fig. 476B).

(4) "Wind" or "fan" the paper in small lifts, and jog it neatly against the front and left pile guides (Fig. 476C).

Do not turn over any lift of paper unless you are instructed to do so. This is done sometimes if the paper tends to curl upward, or for backing up sheets (printing on the other side). Ordinarily, paper is cut and fed so that the felt side (usually the better side) is up. Also, any watermark on the paper should be right side up and readable when the front of sheets are printed. (See Chapter 15 for more information on paper.)

(5) Position and secure the right pile guide against the paper pile. This should not be a snug fit.

(6) Turn the press handwheel until the sucker feet are at their lowest point of travel; then raise the paper pile so that the top sheet is ¼" below the sucker feet.

(7) Position and secure the tail guide against the tail end of the paper pile so that it will not be struck by the rising paper platform when the last few sheets are fed.

(8) Position the sheet separator combs so they will provide a "combing" action to the

Fig. 476C. Loading the Paper Magazine (Multilith 1250)

vacuum-lifted sheet. Then position the vacuum feet directly above the sheet separators (Fig. 476D).

(9) Turn on the air pump. Adjust the blast to flutter the top few sheets, so the top sheet can be picked up by the sucker feet. Both blast and suction are increased as needed for heavier weights of stock.

(10) Check the vacuum, after positioning the sucker feet at their lowest point. The amount of suction should be just enough to lift one sheet and hold it. Usually this need not be changed.

(11) Adjust the pile-height governor so it just touches the top sheet when the sucker feet are at their lowest position and the top sheet is about ¼″ below the sucker feet. See Fig. 477. Check it by lowering the pile a bit to see if it will return to the proper height.

*Conveyor Board and Sheet Controls.* The conveyor board and sheet controls include the pullout roll and wheels, the sheet caliper (double-sheet detector), the conveyor tapes, the riders (steel balls or metal bands), front stops, side jogger, stationary side guide and forwarding rollers (Figs. 478 through 480).

(1) Cut a strip of paper from the stock to be run (about 2″ x 11″), and fold it about 4″ from the end. Holding the strip by the fold, insert it into the sheet caliper under the detector roll (part C of Fig. 478), so that the single thickness passes but the double thickness trips the mechanism (press running, feed vacuum on).

(2) Adjust the pullout rolls (Fig. 479) for light, equal traction, using two paper test strips — one for each wheel.

(3) Move the register board side guides out to the left and right (Fig. 480). Run a sheet down the board to the front stop fingers, and stop the press.

(4) Turn the handwheel until the left side guide (jogger) is in its extreme position towards the far side of the press. Loosen and move the left side guide over to just touch the sheet; then move it ⅛″ *more*, and secure it in position. (During press operation, this ⅛″ lateral movement is the jogging action.)

(5) Bring the right side guide (stationary guide) just to the right-hand edge of the paper, and secure in place.

If the stationary guide has a leaf spring, bring the guide over to the paper, then ⅟₃₂″ *more*, compressing the spring slightly. Secure in place.

Fig. 476D. Positioning of Suction Feet and Sheet Separators (Combs) (Multilith 1250)

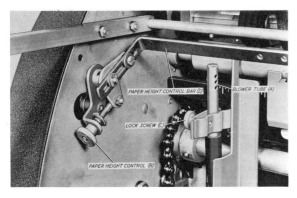

Fig. 477. Paper-Pile-Height (Governor) Control Bar (Multilith 1250)

Fig. 478. Multiple-Sheet Detector (Multilith 1250)

(6) See that the conveyor tapes are equidistant across the table under the paper. Position the hold-downs (rider balls or steel bands) over the two outside tapes.

(7) Set the rider wheels (speed or "skid" wheels) so that they are just off the trailing end of the sheet as the sheet meets the front guides (stop fingers), in jogging position.

*Delivery.* Set the delivery tray, jogger, or stacker for maximum width. (See Fig. 481.) Feed a sheet through. Turn the press by hand until the jogger is in closed position. Set the jogger, tray or stacker to this sheet position.

### Feeding Test Sheets

After the press has been set up and *before* the run is started, one or more test sheets should be run to determine if any adjustments are necessary to obtain most satisfactory results. No press run should be started until the test sheets are approved by the instructor or foreman.

With a proper press set-up, feed a test sheet as follows:

(1) Using sponge and water, wash off preservative from plate surface — or simply dampen the unpreserved plate. (Other plate dampening solution may be used if plate manufacturer so recommends.)

(2) Turn on press motor.

(3) Drop dampener form rollers, and allow press to turn several revolutions. *Do not stop press.*

(4) Drop ink form rollers, allowing plate image several revolutions to "roll up" (ink up).

(5) Bring plate in contact with blanket.

(6) Turn on blowers, and check for blast.

(7) Turn on feeder, adjust suction, and allow a sheet or two to be fed.

(8) Shut off feeder.

(9) Break contact between plate and blanket.

(10) Lift ink form rollers.

(11) Lift dampener form rollers.

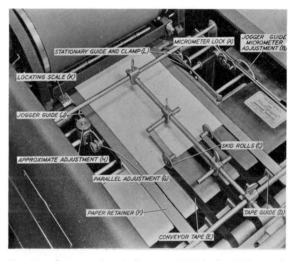

Fig. 480. Conveyor Board (Register Table) (Multilith 1250)

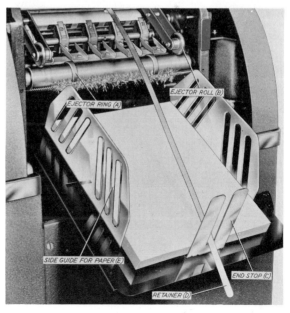

Fig. 481. Ejector Mechanism and Paper Receiver (Multilith 1250)

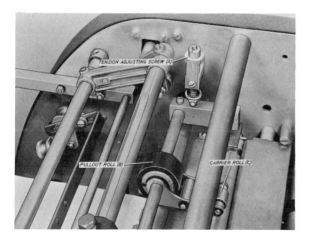

Fig. 479. Pullout Rolls—Left Side Shown (Multilith 1250)

(12) Stop the press.

(13) Gum the plate (if a metal plate). Remember to sponge off the gum when recommencing operation.

### Inspection of Test Sheet

These are some of the important points to inspect for on the test sheets:

(1) Is the ink coverage correct — not too heavy nor too light?

(2) Is the ink coverage consistent across the sheet?

(3) Are the clear areas free of ink?

(4) Is the entire image printing?

(5) Is the image square on the sheet?

(6) Is the image correctly placed laterally?

(7) Is the image correctly placed vertically?

(8) Is the overall impression satisfactory — not too light nor too heavy?

(9) In the halftones, are highlight dots visible and shadow dots unplugged?

### Adjustments

If the answer to any of the above questions is *no*, then adjustments for these printing deficiencies are necessary. Instructions for correcting some of these are described below. Corrections for other operating troubles are discussed in Chapter 19.

The operator should remain alert to detect printing troubles as they occur, so as to avoid

Fig. 482A. Vertical Positioning Control (Multilith 1250)

unnecessary waste of paper and time. Also, in making adjustments, as many corrections should be done at one time as possible.

*Obtaining Ink and Water Balance.* Ideally, the printed image should be dense and the non-printing areas clear.

Initially, start the run with a thin supply of image ink; then increase the supply gradually to obtain the desired density. Adjust the ink-fountain keys so that there is uniform inking of the image across the sheet.

If the clear areas tend to "scum" (show tones in the clear areas, Fig. 505), cut back some ink and increase the flow of water a bit; then increase the ink gradually. Water level should be just enough to prevent "scumming".

If the image is too light, increase the ink supply by small degrees. If the increase causes scum, add more water.

Obtaining proper ink and water balance is a matter of experience in using *just enough* moisture with the proper amount of ink to obtain a dense image. Too much initial moisture will invite the use of excess ink, leading to "mud" and troubles. (See Chapter 19.)

*Correcting Image Position on Sheet.* The test sheet may show that the image on the sheet must be moved laterally (to the left or right), vertically (up or down), or, possibly, straightened from a "cocked" position.

Whenever a position adjustment is made to a plate or plate cylinder, the image must be washed from the blanket, since, on most presses, the next test impression will be in a different place on the blanket.

(1) *Lateral Adjustment.* To move the image to the left or right on the printed sheet, reset the side jogger and the stationary guide on the feed board (Fig. 480). If necessary, make a minute adjustment of the jogger guide micrometer adjustment wheel. Large adjustments require repositioning the feed pile.

(2) *Cocked Image.* To straighten a "cocked" image (if not excessively crooked), adjust the leading and trailing plate clamp lateral adjusting screws, if the press is so equipped. Refer again to Fig. 464.

For straight-edge plates, release the plate from the trailing clamp, and then loosen and twist at the lead clamp. Tighten the plate again at the lead and trailing ends.

For a badly cocked image, have the plate remade.

(3) *Vertical Adjustment.* To make a vertical adjustment on some presses, move the plate around the plate cylinder by loosening the tension on the set of plate clamp screws at one end of the plate. Then tighten the plate clamp screws at the opposite end of the plate.

On many presses, the plate cylinder or the impression cylinder may be moved independently of its driving gears, so that, when moved, the plate image will print on the blanket either up or down from its previous location. See Figs. 482A and B. To make a vertical adjustment on this type of press, first turn the press *off.* Then locate and engage the vertical positioning control onto the plate cylinder lock screw. While it is still engaged, loosen the screw and rock the handwheel up or down to move the plate cylinder in relation to the plate cylinder gear. (See circled area in Fig. 482A.) Retighten the plate cylinder lock screw.

*Impression.* The impression check (impression cylinder to blanket cylinder, page 293) should have been performed prior to the running of the test sheets. Too little impression will result in too-light an image and, perhaps, missing highlight dots. Too heavy an impression will result in a "squashed-out" image — a spreading of individual highlight dots and a filling-in of halftone shadow areas and fine reverses.

On some presses, the impression is adjusted by means of a micrometer lever or handscrew, which moves the impression cylinder closer to or away from the blanket cylinder.

Refer to appropriate press manuals for details for your specific press. Your instructor will demonstrate the proper procedure to follow for the presses in your shop.

## Operating the Press

During the operation of the press, stop the press if something goes amiss which you cannot readily and understandably cope with. Ask for your instructor's help. Considerable paper can be wasted while you experiment.

If, for any reason, the press is stopped for more than a few seconds (while running a metal plate), gum the plate immediately. Sponge off with water before recommencing the run.

### Before the Run

Ask yourself these important questions before starting the run:

(1) Am I authorized to operate this press and make this run?

(2) Am I observing all personal safety precautions? (Pages 296, 331-338.)

(3) Are all supplies and equipment on hand? (Page 296.)

(4) Do I have the proper plate, paper stock, ink, as checked against the job specifications?

(5) Have I inspected the press — visually; turning over by hand; with power on?

(6) Has the press been lubricated?

### Preparation

Is the press prepared for operation?

(1) Ink unit prepared?

(2) Water unit prepared?

(3) Plate installed?

(4) All pressure checks completed?

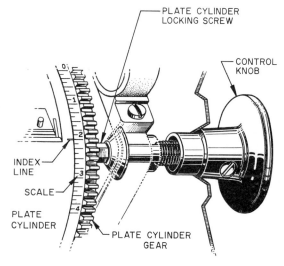

Fig. 482B. Vertical Positioning Control, Cut-Away View (Multi-lith 1250)

(5) Paper feeding and delivery system set-up okay?

(6) Test sheets okayed?

Now, set the counter to zero (all 9's, then trip once).

### Operation

Usually, plates are gummed when they arrive at the press. With the plate mounted and *the press stopped,* remove the gum from the plate with a sponge dipped in water. Be careful to wipe the entire plate, including the edges.

The usual procedure in the operation of the press follows:

*To begin a press run* (after dampening the plate):

1. Turn on press motor. (Always start the press at a slow speed, increasing the speed only when sheets are feeding satisfactorily and the test sheets have been okayed.)
2. Drop the dampener form rollers.[2]
3. Drop the ink form rollers.
4. Bring the plate into contact with the blanket.
5. Feed the sheets.

*To stop the run,* the procedure is reversed:

1. Shut off the feeder.
2. Break contact between the plate and the blanket.
3. Lift the ink form rollers.
4. Lift the dampener form rollers.
5. Stop the press.

During the press run, if minor adjustments are needed, stop feeding ink to the plate and break the contact between the plate and blanket to avoid piling up ink on the blanket.

*Points to Watch for During the Run:* Carefully read Chapter 19, "Offset Presswork Troubleshooting", for common troubles which may develop during the press run, and note

the remedies given for these. In addition, watch constantly for:

1. Sheet register.
2. Color and coverage of ink.
3. Level of fountain solution.
4. Amount of ink in fountain. (Keep ink worked from side to side with ink knife.)
5. Complete coverage of image on paper.
6. Clear areas picking up ink, or other evidence of clear area fouling up.
7. Level of paper pile in receiver.
8. Halftones plugging up or losing highlight areas.

It is well to keep handy an okayed test sheet for comparison from time to time with a sheet pulled from the press run, to be sure the printed sheets match throughout the job.

If registration gradually creeps vertically during the press run, stop the press. First check that the adjustment for vertical positioning of the image is secure; then check to see if the punched holes in the plate ends are being torn longer by the hooks on the plate cylinder.

It may be that (1) excessive pressure has been used in securing the plate to the press; (2) excessive moisture is being or has been used on the plate; (3) rollers or cylinders are exerting undue pressure; or (4) the run is too long for the type plate being used. The latter especially may be true with plates of a soft base.

### After Operation

At the end of the press run, lift the dampeners, lift the ink form rollers, "run down" the plate[3], break contact (blanket to plate), stop the feeder and stop the press. Gum the plate, and remove to the bench for preparation for storage or preservation (page 219).

Remove the printed sheets (being careful not to smudge wet ink); also remove any remaining sheets in the feeder and any sheets which may have been deflected.

---

[2]An alternate method, when "rolling up" a newly-installed plate is to first sponge off the plate, start the press, then drop the ink form rollers before the dampener form rollers. After the press revolves several times, dampener form rollers may be dropped. This allows the image to pick up ink coverage to protect it against possible effects of the dampening solution.

[3]"Run down" a plate: Removing much of the ink on the plate image (before gumming it) by feeding a dozen or so waste sheets through, with impression "on", but ink and water "off."

At the end of the day, prepare the press for shut-down, and proceed with "Press Wash-Up" as described below.

## Press Wash-Up

Assuming that the offset plate has been "run down", gummed and removed from the press, proceed to wash up the press as follows:

(1) *Turn all operating controls "off"*.

(2) *Remove paper stock* from the feeder and receiver tray or stacker; take out any deflected sheets from beneath the feed board.

(3) *Blanket*. Remove the image with a cloth dampened with solvent, being sure to clean the edges of the blanket. Wash the blanket with water to remove any dried gum, and again wash with solvent. Wipe dry with a clean cloth. (See "Solvents", page 287, 334.)

(4) *Water fountain*. Remove the fountain bottle. Drain off the water fountain and discard the solution.

Remove the fountain roller. Wash it with a pad moistened with fountain solution on which has been sprinkled a little FF pumice. Wipe first with a pad moistened with fountain solution, then with a dry pad. Place in rack. Keep fingers off surface of the roller.

Wipe the inside of the fountain tray with a clean cloth. If any scum is present, wipe it out with a water-wet pad and a little FF pumice. Then flush with water.

(5) *Other dampener rollers*. Remove molleton-covered ductor and form rollers and place in rack. If dirty, soak them for a few minutes in a detergent solution. Work out the ink by hand, squeezing in the direction of the nap, or roll on paper. Rinse thoroughly with clean water, and roll on clean paper to remove excess water. Place on rack for storage.

Rollers that are not covered should be washed with water and pad and dried. For extended shut-down, metal rollers should be gummed. (This must be washed off with water and pad before re-use.)

(6) *Gum Bowl and Water Pail*. Discard any gum that is left in the gum bowl. Rinse out the bowl and the sponge with warm water, and set on the bench.

Empty plate-dampening water pail. Flush out the sponge with warm water, and set on the bench. Wash out the pail with hand soap and warm water; rinse well; set on the bench.

(7) *Ink Fountain and Ductor*. Remove ink from the fountain with the ink knife, sliding the knife down between the blade and the roller and lifting out against the roller. Discard the ink.

Remove and discard the fountain liner, if one is used.

Lift off the fountain and remove as much ink as possible with the ink knife. Clean the fountain and the fountain roller with a cloth and solvent.

Clean the ductor roller with a cloth and solvent; remove from the press and set on the rack.

(8) *Ink Rollers*. The ink rollers may be cleaned (a) by hand, (b) with cleaner sheets, (c) with a roller-cleaning device, or (d) by a combination of these three methods.

(a) *By Hand*. Place all removable rollers on papers on the bench. Clean rollers with cloth and solvent, and place them in the rack.

Now, turning the press when necessary *by hand — your own hand —* clean all the remaining rollers, wiping side-to-side, and then holding the cloth against the roller ends as you turn the press. Be careful to get the ends clean.

Never clean rollers by hand when the press is in operation. The press *must be stopped*.

(b) *With Cleaner Sheet*. Cleaner sheets are made of blotting paper, Fig. 483. They are the same size and have the same ends as offset plates, and they are mounted on the plate cylinder in the same manner.

Fig. 483. Attaching a Cleaner Sheet (Multilith 1250)

Remove the dampener form rollers to avoid smudging them.

If press has a protective cover beneath the inking unit, see that it is lined with blotting paper, and set it in place.

With a cleaner sheet on the plate cylinder, start the press revolving at its slowest speed. Using a hand oiler (spouted oil can) filled with solvent, apply some solvent to the uppermost distribution roller (Fig. 484). Lower the spout of the oiler slowly to the roller, and feed the solvent slowly across the roller. Allow the press to revolve, thus working the solvent in.

After the ink has been softened by the solvent, drop the ink form rollers to the cleaner sheet as the press continues to operate.

Now feed some solvent to the left half of the rollers. When that is picked up by the cleaner sheet, feed some solvent to the right half of the rollers. Cleaning only half of the bank of rollers at a time prevents them from skidding.

When the cleaner sheet is dirty, lift the form rollers and stop the press. Replace with a clean sheet. Repeat the process and remove the second sheet. Since the sheets are dirty on only one side, they may be used for cleaning the press at another time (but in reverse order — start with the cleanest one).

With the press stopped, inspect all the rollers, especially the ends. Touch up by hand.

(c) *With Roller-Cleaning Device.* The roller-cleaning device is essentially a fixture with a rubber-bladed squeegee and a metal pan which attaches below the ink unit on the press. See Fig. 485. It has adjusting screws which bring the rubber blade into forced scraping contact with one of the ink rollers. To use the device, proceed as follows:

With the press *stopped*, attach the roller-cleaning device to the press. Bring the rubber blade into contact with the adjacent ink roller (for testing); then bring it away.

Start the press. Slowly apply press solvent to the uppermost distribution roller, along the top, and allow the solvent to work in.

While the press is still operating, adjust the cleaning device so its blade contacts the ink roller; then bring it in somewhat tighter.

As the blade squeegees off the ink-and-solvent mixture from the rollers, the metal pan catches the drippings. Apply a little more solvent to the left-hand half of the rollers, until they are clean. Then apply solvent to the right-hand half.

When the rollers appear clean (*i.e.,* dull and velvety), stop the press. Loosen the blade tension, and remove the metal pan. Drain and clean the pan as recommended by your instructor.

Remove the washing device from the press, clean it thoroughly and put it away.

While the press is stopped, inspect the rollers and clean off any remaining ink or solvent, especially on the roller ends. Carefully inspect for and remove any ink from press parts.

NOTE: For presses equipped with combination ink-and-water system, drain the water fountain, and remove and clean the ink fountain, the ink fountain roller, and the ink ductor roller. Then proceed to clean remaining rollers as above.

(9) *Replacing Rollers.* Make certain that all rollers, especially the form rollers, are replaced in the same holders from which they were removed. Check that their position has not been reversed, left-to-right. Often they are marked or numbered on the end toward the operator. Lubricate roller shafts and bearings as specified by the manufacturer. If rollers are to be left in the press overnight, set them in "night-latch" position.

Fig. 484. Applying Solvent to Uppermost Distribution Roller (Multilith 1250)

(10) *Final Check.* Examine the press carefully, and clean off any ink which may have been thrown or dropped to any part. Clean off any spots caused by fountain solution. Wipe all bright work, especially around the printing unit, with a clean cloth moistened with light machine oil.

Wipe ejector rollers and collars with oil and cloth, sliding them to one side to oil the shaft beneath.

Wipe the plate cylinder with solvent and cloth. Chrome-plated cylinders may be cleaned with special chrome cleaner. Using a dry cloth, wipe away any dust and lint from the feeder, register table, and jogger assemblies.

At least once a week (perhaps more often, and especially before extended shut-down) remove the blanket (see page 291) and wipe down the blanket cylinder with a pad moistened with machine oil. Over-generous use of fountain solution may work beneath the blanket and etch the metal cylinder.

If available, place the protective fabric cover over the press. Replace all tools on the tool panel, straighten the items on the work bench, and be sure all bottles are capped. Put all used cloths into the safety can. Discard unwanted ink, old cleaner sheets, etc. Pick up clutter from the floor, and then wash your hands thoroughly with soap and warm water, especially between the fingers.

*Roller Glaze.* Ink and fountain solution may tend to form a shiny, glossy accumulation on the surface of ink rollers. This "glaze" prevents the rollers from picking up ink.

Approximately once a week, remove the rollers and scrub them with a solvent-wet cloth on which has been sprinkled a little FF pumice. Commercial glaze removers also are available.

## Questions

1. When may a student operate (or assist in the operation of) an offset press in the shop?
2. What safety precautions as regards personal dress should be observed when operating an offset press?
3. What essential items should be provided at the press?
4. Describe the procedure for making a visual inspection of the press.
5. Describe the procedure for making a power check of the press.
6. When should the press speed be adjusted?
7. Explain the proper procedure for lubricating the press.
8. What is meant by "checking the specifications" for the job to be printed?
9. What is an ink-fountain liner? Why is it used?
10. How should ink be placed in the fountain?
11. Explain how to ink up the ink rollers.
12. How should the dampening system be prepared for operation?
13. What pressure checks should be made prior to operating the press?
14. Tell how to prepare the feeder set-up.
15. What sheet controls and conveyor-board settings must be made?
16. Tell how to feed test sheets.
17. What items should be checked on the printed test sheet?
18. How is an ink-and-water balance obtained?
19. Why must the blanket be washed (on most presses) when the image position is moved?
20. Name two methods of making a vertical adjustment of the image.
21. What are the usual steps to follow in commencing a press run?

Fig. 485. Roller-Cleaning Device (Multilith 1250)

22. What is the usual procedure in stopping the press?
23. What, especially, should be watched for during the run?
24. Outline the procedure for press wash-up.
25. What three methods may be employed for washing the ink rollers?
26. What is "roller glaze"? How is it removed?

## Problems and Projects

1. Lubricate an offset press, including the vacuum-blower pump, according to the manufacturer's lubrication instructions.
2. Secure from the manufacturer or distributor one or more operator's manuals for each of the offset presses in the shop.
3. Design and construct a tool panel for each press, so that the wrenches and other small tools needed for operation of that press may be mounted.
4. Under direction and supervision of your instructor, set up an offset press for operation.
5. Install and remove an offset plate.
6. Perform the necessary and recommended

pressure checks for the press assigned by your instructor.
7. Feed test sheets, and make necessary adjustments to the press so that the final test sheet is okayed by the instructor.
8. Prepare plates for storage after a run.
9. At the termination of a press run, wash up the press and prepare it for extended shutdown. On successive occasions, demonstrate all three methods of washing the ink rollers.
10. Make a storage rack for press rollers; make one for storing spare rollers, and one for use during press wash-up.

## New Words

1. authorized
2. conveyor
3. deficiencies
4. equidistant
5. interference
6. lateral
7. lubrication
8. magnifier
9. optimum
10. precautions
11. preliminary
12. recommended
13. revolutions
14. separator
15. specifications
16. sufficiently
17. troubleshooting
18. unauthorized

# Offset Presses
# and Duplicators

## 18

This chapter contains some additional information and illustrations on a number of specific offset presses and duplicators. Topics common to most presses and duplicators have been discussed in previous chapters, and, therefore, are omitted here.

It is assumed that the reader will have access to manufacturers' instruction and manuals, and will be helped and guided by his instructor.

## Multilith 1250

The Multilith 1250 is vacuum fed, has conventional inking and dampening systems, and is of the conventional three-main-cylinder design[1]. See Fig. 486 and 486A.

Earlier production models are equipped with separate operating controls for operating the Repelex (dampening) form roller, ink form rollers, and master-to-blanket contact (Fig. 486B). However, in recent models, a single-lever control operates these three functions, as shown in Fig. 486C.

Fig. 456B in Chapter 16 shows this model with chain delivery and receding stacker.

### Specifications

Minimum gripper margin is $\frac{5}{16}''$ at lead edge of paper. Recommended duplicating

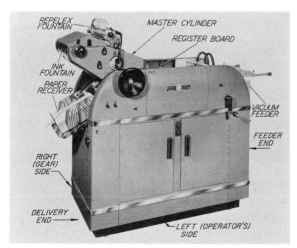

Fig. 486. Multilith 1250

[1]Multilith 1250 illustrations are reproduced by permission of the manufacturers, The Addressograph Multigraph Corporation.

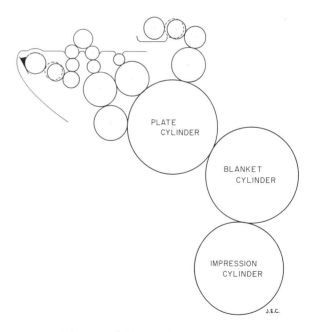

Fig. 486A. Schematic of Inking and Dampening Systems and Cylinder Arrangement for Multiliths 1250, 1250W, 1275 and 1275W

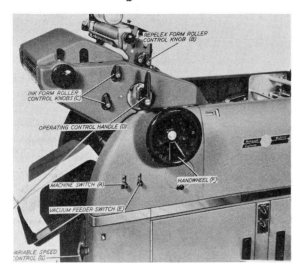

Fig. 486B. Multilith 1250 Equipped with Separate (Individual) Operating Controls

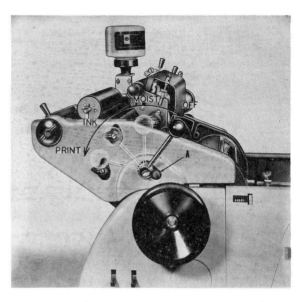

Fig. 486C. Multilith 1250 Single-Lever Operating Control

(image-printing) area is 9½″ x 13″. Recommended range for paper size is 3″ x 5″ to 11″ x 14″.

## Operating Procedure

*For models equipped with separate controls for dampening, inking and master-to-blanket contact:*

1. Prepare fountain unit.
2. Prepare ink unit.
3. Install master.
4. Adjust register board.
5. Adjust feeder.
6. Adjust receiver.
7. Moisten master.
8. Start duplicator.
9. Drop dampener form roller.
10. Drop ink form rollers.
11. Contact master to blanket.
12. Start vacuum feeder.

To stop the duplicator, reverse the sequence of the above steps.

*For models equipped with single-lever operating control:*

First, turn the Repelex (dampener) form roller knob and the ink form roller knobs to "on" position (one-quarter turn to the left), and leave them in this position while the press is operating.

1. Follow steps 1 through 8, above.
2. Move single-lever control to "moist".

3. Move single-lever control to "ink".
4. Move single-lever control to "print".
5. Start the vacuum feeder.

To stop the duplicator, reverse the sequence of the above steps.

## Pressure Adjustments

The following pressure checks should be performed in the order given.

*Repelex (Dampener) Form Roller.* Roller must be "run-in" and damp before testing. (All letters are keyed to Fig. 486D.)

(1) *Parallel Adjustment.* Place two 1″ strips of 20-pound paper between the Repelex (dampener) form roller and the master, as shown in Fig. 486D. Drop the form roller to the master. Test for equal pull on the paper strips. To adjust (only the left end is adjustable), loosen the set screw (B), and turn the eccentric bearing (F) *clockwise* to *decrease* tension on left end of roller (*counterclockwise* to *increase* tension). Tighten set screw.

(2) *Removing End Play.* Remove rider roller (above Repelex form roller) and turn Repelex form roller control knob to "off" position. Loosen set screw (B), press inward on eccentric bearing (F), and tighten set screw. Roller should revolve freely without end play.

(3) *Overall Pressure.* Using test strips, turn Repelex form roller knob to "on" position, and

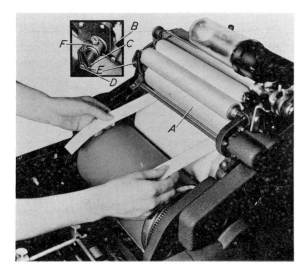

Fig. 486D. Adjusting Repelex (Dampener) Form Roller, Multilith 1250. (Guard is removed from rollers only for purpose of illustration.)

Fig. 486E. Ink-Band Test for Checking Ink Form Roller-to-Plate Contact, Multilith 1250

contact roller to master. Loosen set screw (C). With a screwdriver, turn eccentric shaft (D) *counterclockwise* until a fairly-strong pull is felt on the test strips. Then tighten set screw. Knob must point to left when form roller is contacting master.

*Ink Form Rollers.* The upper and lower ink form rollers are both tested and adjusted in the same manner — first one roller, then the other.

Ink rollers must be inked up and a dry master mounted on the plate cylinder. Ink form roller disengaging knob (night latch) must be in "off" position so ink form rollers will be able to contact the master.

Turn ink form roller control knob "on" momentarily, allowing roller to contact the master; then turn knob "off". The resulting ink line (or "bead") on master should be a uniform ⅛" to 3/16" width all the way across the master (Fig. 486E).

(1) *Overall Pressure.* (Keyed to Fig. 486E). Loosen set screw (A) in form roller control knob. With a screwdriver, turn eccentric shaft (B) *counterclockwise* to *increase* width of bead, and *clockwise* to *decrease* the width. Lock adjustment with set screw.

(2) *Parallel Adjustment.* (Keyed to Fig. 486F). Remove right side plate from ink unit. Disengaging cam (B) must be out of con-

Fig. 486F. Ink Form Roller Adjustments, Multilith 1250 (Right Cover Removed)

tact with eccentric bearing brackets. Loosen lock screw (A), and turn bearing (C) *clockwise* to *decrease* the width of right-hand end of contact line; *counterclockwise* to *increase* the right-hand end. (Only the right-hand end of the rollers is adjustable.) Then tighten the lock screw.

If the overall width of the test line is too great or too small, repeat the overall adjustment, as described above.

(3) *Removing End Play.* (Keyed to Fig. 486F). Turn disengaging cam (B) until it contacts eccentric bearing brackets. Loosen lock screw (A), and press inward on eccentric

bearing (C) until side play is eliminated, but roller is free to rotate easily on its shaft. Adjust both rollers. Recheck parallel adjustment.

*Master-to-Blanket Pressure* (For models *not* equipped with single-lever operating control). (Letters are keyed to Fig. 486G.)

With a dry test master on the cylinder, and the dampener form roller control knob in "off" position, completely ink up the master (B). Stop the duplicator.

Turn operating control handle (A) to "on" position (contacting the master with the blanket; then break the contact. The resulting inked line on the blanket should be a uniform ⅛″ to ³⁄₁₆″ width across the blanket (C).

To adjust pressure (Keyed to Fig. 486H), loosen clamp screw (C). Rotate disc (B), together with control handle (A), *counterclockwise* to *increase* contact pressure, or *clockwise* to *decrease* contact pressure. Then tighten clamp screw.

*Master-to-Blanket Pressure* (For models equipped with single-lever operating control).

To check pressure, mount a dry master on the cylinder. Do not dampen the master. Start the duplicator. Turn Repelex form roller knob "off". Turn ink form roller knobs "on". Then turn single-lever operating control to "ink" position, allowing master to completely ink up. Turn single-lever control "off", and stop the press.

With duplicator stationary, turn ink form roller knobs "off". Turn single-lever control to "print" position; then draw it away to "off" position. Inspect ink bead on blanket.

Adjust master-to-blanket pressure by moving single-lever control to "print" position. Then loosen lock bolt (part A of Fig. 486C) with T-wrench, and turn single-lever control *slightly* to *left* to *increase* pressure, or slightly to *right* to *decrease* pressure. Tighten lock bolt, and return lever to "off" position.

*Impression Adjustments.* Two adjustments for impression may be performed — (1) an *overall* adjustment, when changing from one thickness of stock to another; and (2) a *leveling* adjustment, to give the same impression on the left and right side of the sheet.

(1) *Overall Adjustment* (Keyed to Fig. 486I). When changing to a heavier stock, first loosen clamp screw (C). Turn micrometer screw (A) several turns clockwise to draw the impression cylinder away from the blanket cylinder. Using the handwheel, run a sheet of the paper to be used between the blanket and impression cylinders. Turn the micrometer screw *clockwise* (to *increase* pressure) by drawing the index finger over the top of the screw until it can no longer be turned in this manner. Then, with thumb and index finger, turn it another one-quarter turn. Tighten clamp screw.

Fig. 486G.  Plate Cylinder-to-Blanket Cylinder (Master-to-Blanket) Pressure Test, Multilith 1250

Fig. 486H.  Master-to-Blanket Pressure Adjustment, Multilith 1250

When changing to a lighter stock, it is not necessary first to bring the impression cylinder away from the blanket cylinder. Otherwise, proceed as in the above paragraph.

If test sheets show need for further impression adjustment, loosen the clamp screw, and turn the micrometer screw *clockwise* to *decrease* pressure, or *counterclockwise* to *increase* pressure. Then tighten the clamp screw.

(2) *Leveling the Impression Cylinder* (Keyed to Fig. 486J). A leveling adjustment is indicated when the blanket image is complete, yet the printed image on the sheet is distinct only along one side or is heavier on one side than the other.

To level the impression, remove register board side cover. Loosen lock screw (A), and move sector (B) *left* for *increasing* pressure, or *right* for *decreasing* pressure. Then tighten the lock screw. This adjustment affects only the *right* side of the sheet.

*Compensating Impression Device.* Instead of the impression-cylinder adjusting mechanism shown in Fig. 486I, your Multilith may be equipped with a *compensating impression device* as in Fig. 486K. This device permits the press to be operated either on *fixed impression* for any given weight of paper, or it may be set to operate on spring-controlled *compensating action*, which automatically adjusts the impression for varying thicknesses of paper (from job to job or from sheet to sheet). The following description of this device is keyed to Fig. 486K.

(1) *For Fixed (Constant) Pressure.* Revolve handwheel until compensating impression device is as shown in Fig. 486K. Loosen A, B and

C. Turn knurled adjusting disc (D) *clockwise* to *increase* pressure, or *counterclockwise* to *decrease* pressure. Then tighten A, B and C.

(2) *For Compensating Action (Pressure).* Adjustments a and b, below, are necessary, in this order:

(a) Entirely *remove* lock screw (C). Loosen Alemite fitting and screw (B). Then turn adjusting disc (D) *clockwise* to *increase* pressure, or *counterclockwise* to *decrease* pressure. Now tighten A and B.

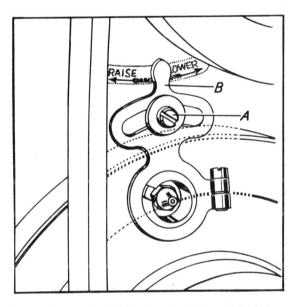

Fig. 486J. Impression-Cylinder Leveling Sector, Multilith 1250

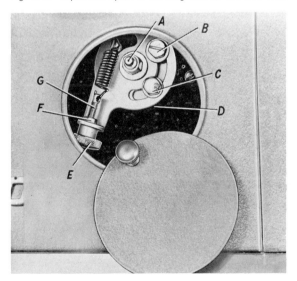

Fig. 486K. Compensating Impression Device, Multilith 1250

Fig. 486I. Impression-Cylinder Adjusting Sector, Multilith 1250

(b) To regulate the compensating pressure (after performing adjustment a, above), loosen locknut (F), and adjust knurled thumbscrew (E). Then tighten F. Normal setting is achieved when end of threaded screw (G) is flush with surface of knurled nut (E).

In adjusting for printing sets composed of heavy and light sheets, make adjustments a and b, above, to obtain clearest impression on the *lightest* sheet. (Correct impression automatically will be provided for the heavier sheets.)

NOTE: When cleaner sheets are to be used for cleaning ink rollers on presses equipped with single-lever control, first remove the Repelex (dampener) form roller to prevent it from picking up ink.

## Heidelberg Model KOR

The Model KOR Heidelberg is a single-color, sheet-fed rotary press equipped for both letterset and offset (Fig. 487).[2] Removable segments on the plate cylinder can be interchanged for either process. For letterset, only the inking-roller system is used — the dampening system is not used. For offset, naturally, both the inking and dampening systems are used.

Fig. 487. Heidelberg Offset or Letterset Press, Model KOR

[2]Model KOR illustrations are by permission of Heidelberg Eastern, Inc.

## Nomenclature

Fig. 487A shows the partial nomenclature and arrangement of some of the components of the Model KOR. Notice the almost-horizontal arrangement of cylinders, the feeding and delivery of sheets from the same end, and the fact that no tapes or friction devices are used in the paper-feeding mechanism.

## Specifications

Sheet size 15¾″ x 22½″ to 4¹⁵⁄₁₆″ x 5⅞″
Image area 15⅜″ x 22⅛″
Minimum gripper margin ²⁵⁄₆₄″

## Cylinder Packings for Offset

While offset plates up to .020″ in thickness may be used, recommended thicknesses are .010″ and .006″, in that order.

*Plate Cylinder.* Undercut is .016″. The thickness of the plate *plus* the packing should equal .020″ — *i.e.,* .004″ *above* the bearer. See Fig. 487B.

*Blanket Cylinder.* Undercut is .087″. The thickness of the blanket *plus* the packing should be .085″ — *i.e.,* .002″ *below* the bearers.

*Impression Cylinder.* Undercut is .047″. This cylinder may be packed with either a metal packing jacket plus packing sheets *or* a rubber blanket plus packing sheets. The total thickness of the sheet to be printed, *plus* the jacket or rubber blanket, *plus* the packing sheets should total .051″ — *i.e.,* .004″ *above* the bearers.

## Pressure Checks for Offset Printing

*Blanket-to-Impression Cylinder.* When packed as described above, the pressure be-

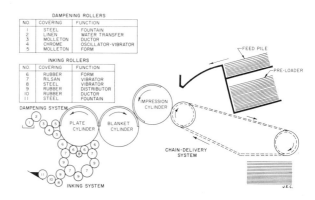

Fig. 487A. Schematic Cross Section, Model KOR

tween the blanket and impression cylinders normally should be .002″. However, for very rough or grained papers, a pressure of .004″ is recommended.

*Ink Form Rollers-to-Plate.* Adjust so ink form rollers make an ink-band width of ⅛″ across the plate.

*Dampener Form Rollers-to-Plate.* Set for slight resistance to pull when using .004″ steel-band test strips.

While test strips may be used, it is preferable to set the dampeners while the press *is running.* For this, the correct setting is achieved when the journal boxes for the dampener form rollers lift slightly as the dampeners contact the revolving plate.

### For Different Thicknesses of Stock

To compensate for variations in thickness of stock to be run, adjust the impression cylinder to the blanket cylinder. Do not change the distance between the plate and blanket cylinders.

### Changing the Printing (Image) Length

The recommended procedure for changing the length of the printing image (to achieve register) is to start with the pressure settings and packings as above. Then, increase or decrease the packing on the impression cylinder. Compensate for this change by increasing or decreasing the distance between the impression and blanket cylinders a like amount.

NOTE: For register jobs, the grain of the paper should always be parallel to the axis of the cylinders.

### Settings for Letterset

For printing by letterset, the offset plate sheet is removed from the plate cylinder and is replaced with the letterset plate shell, Fig. 487C. Only the inking system is used. It is also recommended that a *wrap-around* letterpress plate be used.

The blanket and impression cylinders are packed the same as for offset, as described above.

The wrap-around plate shell (for letterset) has an undercut of .040″. The total thickness of the wrap-around letterpress plate, *plus* the

packing, should equal .044″ — *i.e.,* .004″ *above* the bearer.

If any underlay is necessary, it should be placed under the wrap-around plate. Onionskin or tissue should be used, never chemical or powder makeready.

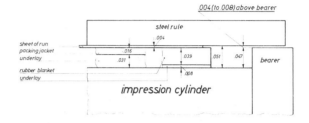

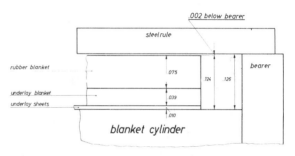

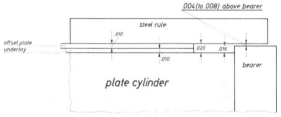

Fig. 487B. Cylinder Packing for Offset When Using Bearer Contact, Model KOR. All dimensions are given in thousandths of an inch.

Fig. 487C. Interchanging the Plate Shell for Dry Offset, Model KOR

Other features of the Heidelberg Model KOR are shown in Figs. 487D and E.

## ATF Chief 20A

The American Type Founders Chief 20A offset press is a single-color, sheet-fed, four-main-cylinder offset press, with conventional inking and dampening system.[3] It is equipped with vacuum feeder, chain delivery and receding stacker. See Figs. 488A through C.

Fig. 487D. Single-Lever Operating Control, Model KOR Heidelberg — "Run," "Paper," "Impression"

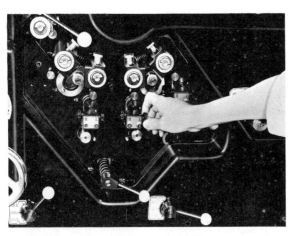

Fig. 487E. Micrometer Control of Rollers from Operator's Side of Press, Model KOR.

[3]ATF Chief 20A illustrations are by permission of American Type Founders Co., Inc.

## Specifications

The range for the printing sheet size is from 8″ x 10″ minimum to 14″ x 20″ maximum.

Fig. 488A. ATF Chief 20A

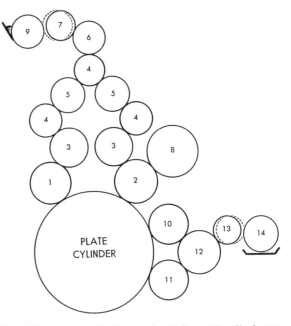

Fig. 488B. Inking and Dampening Rollers, ATF Chief 20A. **Inking Rollers:** 1 & 2 Form Rollers; 3 & 5 Vibrator Rollers; 4 Distributor Rollers; 6 Rider Roller; 7 Ductor Roller; 8 Auxiliary Vibrator Roller; 9 Fountain Roller; **Dampening Rollers:** 10 & 11 Form Rollers; 12 Vibrator Roller; 13 Ductor Roller; 14 Fountain Roller.

Maximum printing area is 13½″ x 19½″, with a gripper bite of ³⁄₁₆″ to ⁵⁄₁₆″.

The blanket cylinder is undercut .071″. The undercut of the plate cylinder is .012″.

## Whitin-Manufactured Offset Duplicators — Ditto 215; ATF Chief 15; Itek 11.15

Instructions and illustrations in this section apply equally to the Whitin-manufactured offset duplicators marketed as ATF Chief 15, Ditto 215, and Itek 11.15.[4]

### Description

Figs. 489A, 489B, and 490 show the nomenclature and location of the operating controls. The duplicators have a gripper margin adjustable from ³⁄₁₆″ to ⁵⁄₁₆″, an image area of 9¾″ x 13¼″, and will accommodate paper stock from 3″ x 5″ to 11″ x 15″.

The duplicators employ conventional (separate) inking and dampening systems (Fig. 491); also, they have a single-lever moisture-ink control lever (Fig. 492).

### Feeder Table Components

Figs. 493A, B, C, D and 494A and B show the feeder table components set up for a run.

Fig. 488C. View of Feeder Components, ATF Chief 20A

[4]Distributors of the above-mentioned duplicators are:
"Ditto 215" — Ditto, Inc.
"ATF Chief 15" — American Type Founders Co., Inc.
"Itek 11.15" — Itek Business Products
Illustrations are by courtesy of Ditto, Inc.

To adjust the double-sheet detector, start up both motors. While feeding the sheets, loosen the lock nut, and turn the sheet detector thumb-

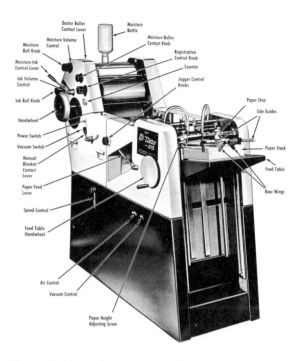

Fig. 489A. Nomenclature and Controls—From Feeder End

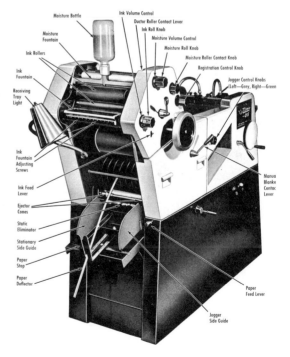

Fig. 489B. Nomenclature and Controls—From Receiver End

screw counterclockwise, until single sheets are ejected. Then turn clockwise slightly, until the ejector does not trip on a single sheet. Tighten the lock nut.

### Feed Board

The feed board may be set to jog left, right, or both left and right, since the duplicator is equipped with two joggers. See Fig. 494A. Both joggers are set into motion while the press is running.

To set the left-hand jogger into motion, hold the right jogger with your left hand, and pull it toward you. At the same time, with your right hand, move the jogger-selector lever back toward the feeder, Fig. 494B.

To set the right-hand jogger into motion, hold the left jogger with your left hand and push it away from you, as you move the jogger-selector lever into its forward position, toward the delivery end of the press.

To set both joggers into action (for running small sheets), move the jogger-selector lever

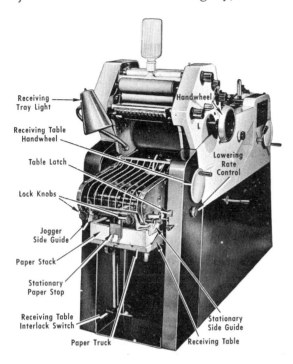

Fig. 490. Duplicator Equipped with Chain Delivery and Receding Stacker

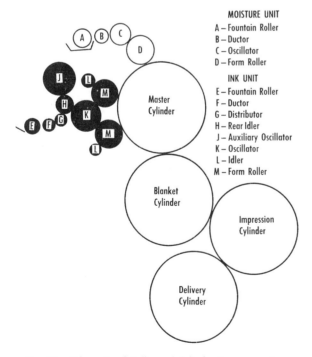

MOISTURE UNIT
A – Fountain Roller
B – Ductor
C – Oscillator
D – Form Roller

INK UNIT
E – Fountain Roller
F – Ductor
G – Distributor
H – Rear Idler
J – Auxiliary Oscillator
K – Oscillator
L – Idler
M – Form Roller

Fig. 491. Schematic of Roller and Cylinder Arrangement

Fig. 492. Moisture-Ink Control Lever. Position 1—dampener form roller and ink form rollers "off"; Position 2—dampener form roller "on," and ink form rollers "off"; Position 3—dampener form roller and ink form rollers "on."

into its center position. For accurate side register, the feather on the idle jogger should be lowered (by pressing on its front part), and the feather on the jogger being used should be raised (by pressing on its back part). Refer again to Fig. 494B.

The jogger control knobs, as previously shown in Fig. 489A, move the paper joggers,

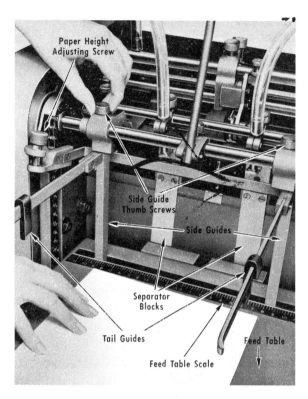

Fig. 493A. Feed Table Components

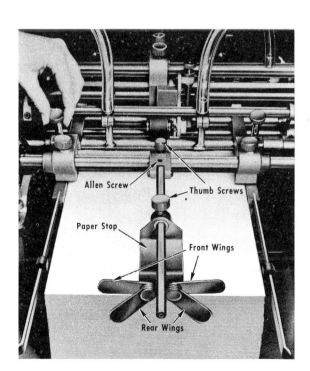

Fig. 493B. Paper Table Set-Up Components

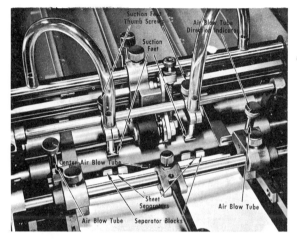

Fig. 493C. Sheet Suction and Blast Components

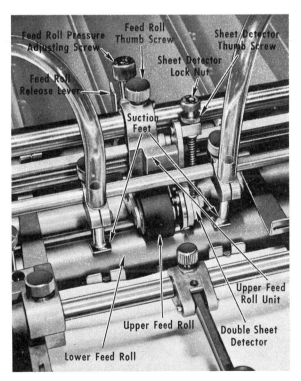

Fig. 493D. Sheet Detector and Feed Roll Components

ball races and tapes, all at the same time, towards or away from the center of the feed board. These knobs should be turned only when the duplicator is operating, except for initial jogger positioning.

## A. B. Dick and Related Presses

The A. B. Dick Models 320 and 330 are table-model offset duplicators with friction feeders, and (like all A. B. Dick offset duplicators) they have combined ink and dampener units. See Figs. 495A and 495B.

The Models 350 and 360 are floor models with suction feeders and more rollers. See Figs. 496A and 496B. These duplicators are more compact than many competing models because of the elimination of the long conveyor board. Sheets are transferred directly from the feeder pile to the feed rolls.

The MGD Models 20 and 22 are quite similar in construction and operation to the larger A. B. Dick duplicators, except that they are much wider and the sheet size is enlarged to 14″ x 20″ or 17½″ x 22½″. See Figs. 497A and 497B.

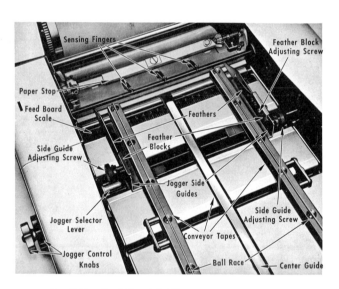

Fig. 494A.  Feed Board Set-Up

Fig. 495A.  A.B. Dick Model 330 Offset Duplicator (Courtesy A.B. Dick Co.)

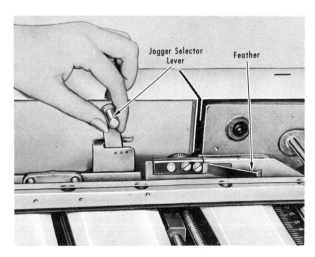

Fig. 494B.  Jogger-Selector Lever and Feather

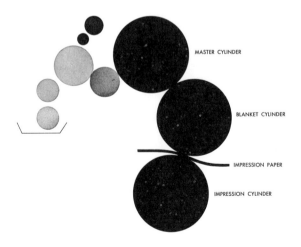

Fig. 495B.  A.B. Dick Model 330, Arrangement of Ink-Water (Aquamatic) System and Cylinders (Courtesy A.B. Dick Co.)

## Fairchild-Davidson Dualiths

The Davidson press (Fig. 498) features the two-cylinder principle explained earlier. If the impression segment of the main cylinder is replaced with a lithographic plate (wrong reading for printing directly against the paper), both sides of the sheet can be printed in one pass. The press can also be equipped for printing from rubber relief plates and for embossing.

## Selected Other Models

Various other models of duplicators and presses are shown in Figs. 499 through 502B.

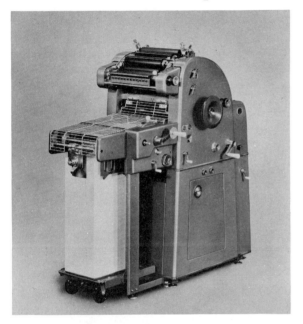

Fig. 496A.  A.B. Dick Model 350 Offset Duplicator with Chain Delivery and Receding Stacker (Courtesy A.B. Dick Co.)

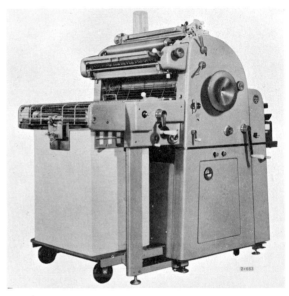

Fig. 497A.  MGD Offset Duplicators 20 and 22 (Courtesy Miehle Co., Division of Miehle-Goss-Dexter, Inc.)

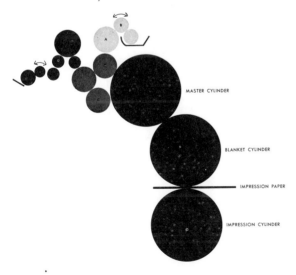

Fig. 496B.  A.B. Dick Model 350, Arrangement of Ink-Water (Aquamatic) System and Cylinders (Courtesy A.B. Dick Co.)

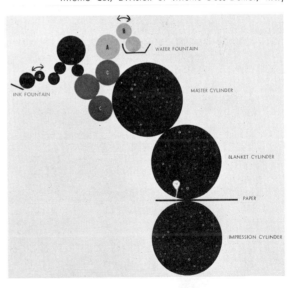

Fig. 497B.  MGD Offset Duplicators 20 and 22—Diagram of Cylinders and Rollers. (A) Water oscillating roller; (B) Water fountain ductor roller; (C) Form rollers; and (D) Ink ductor roller. (Courtesy The Miehle Co., Division of Miehle-Goss-Dexter, Inc.)

Fig. 498. Fairchild-Davidson Dualith 400 (Courtesy Davidson Division of Fairchild Camera and Instrument Corp.)

Fig. 499. Multilith 1275. In one pass through the machine, a sheet is printed on both sides in the same color or different colors, or one side may be printed in two colors. (Courtesy Addressograph Multigraph Corp.)

Fig. 500. Royal Zenith 14 x 20, Single-Color Offset Duplicator (Courtesy Royal Zenith Corp.)

Fig. 501. Mailänder Flatbed Offset Press. This press can be used as a proof press and for printing on tin, wood, plastic, glass and all thicknesses of board and paper. (Courtesy HCM Corp.)

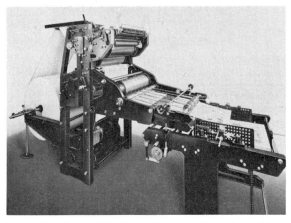

Fig. 502A. Gazette "Compact" Web Perfecting Press (Courtesy Gazette Offset Americana)

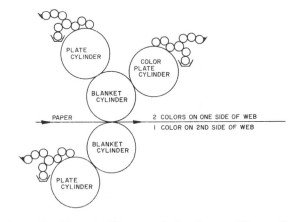

Fig. 502B. Schematic Diagram of the Gazette "Compact". This is an example of a blanket-to-blanket perfector, a web-fed press equipped with a sheeter, as well as two color units which print from a single blanket cylinder, and combined ink-and-water systems.

# Offset Presswork
# Troubleshooting

It is far better to prevent trouble than to try to correct it. The press operator should obtain a copy of the manufacturer's instruction manual for the press, and should study it and the press until he is familiar with the press parts, their functions, and lubrication.

Initially, the press should be properly installed, and then maintained in good operating condition. If proper attention is given to the preparation of the offset plates, ink and water fountain preparation and balance, and preparation and maintenance of the press, the troubles described may never appear.

Use the following series of illustrations* as a handy guide to the quick identification and elimination of many common troubles which may occur during the press run. Additional information on these, and other common troubles and their probable causes and remedies is listed in tabular form on the following pages.

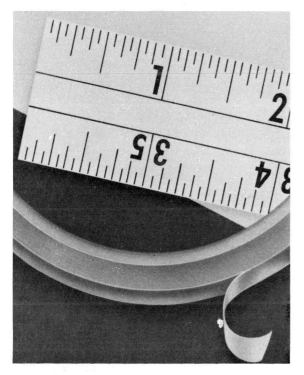

Fig. 503. **You're Okay!** Good copy has . . . crisp, dark lines and solids . . . a clean background . . . clear halftones, screens and reverses . . . good registration . . . and each sheet dries completely.

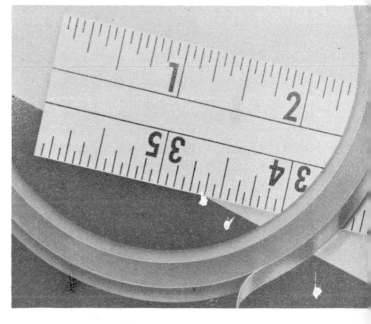

Fig. 504. **Gray, Washed Out?** . . . too much moisture . . . not enough ink . . . incorrect ink- or dampener-form-roller pressure, or both . . . incorrect plate-to-blanket pressure . . . incorrect impression-to-blanket pressure.

*3M Company photos by courtesy of Minnesota Mining and Manufacturing Company.

Fig. 505. **Scumming** (Background Dirty)?...too much ink... not enough moisture... dirty dampener roll covers ... dampener covers tied too tightly on ends.

Fig. 507. **Too Dark** (Halftones and Fine Reverses Fill In and Sheet Dries Slowly)?... too much ink... too much impression-to-blanket pressure.

Fig. 506. **Both - Scumming** (Dirty Background) **and Gray, Washed-Out Copy?**... glazed ink rollers... glazed blanket... too much ink-form-roller pressure ... too much dampener-form-roller pressure.

Fig. 508. **Weak Spots?** ... incorrect plate-to-blanket pressure ... incorrect impression-to-blanket pressure... low spot in blanket... "blind" image caused by dried gum, strong fountain solution, or glazed blanket.

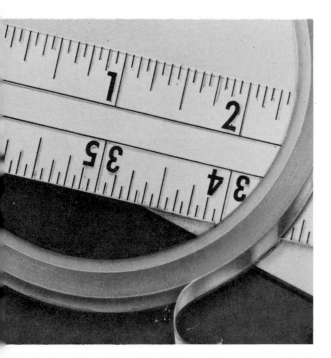

Fig. 509. **Blurred Copy** (Double Image)? . . . too much ink . . . loose blanket . . . torn plate anchor . . . not enough plate-to-blanket pressure . . . incorrect impression-to-blanket pressure.

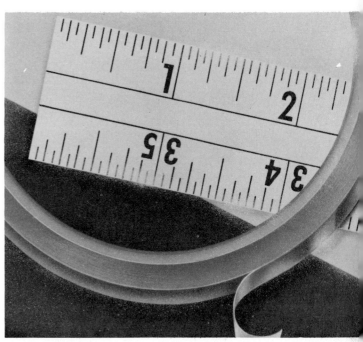

Fig. 511. **Image Breaks Down While Plate is Running?** . . . too much form-roller pressure (ink or dampener) . . . too much plate-to-blanket pressure . . . fountain solution too strong . . . or end play.

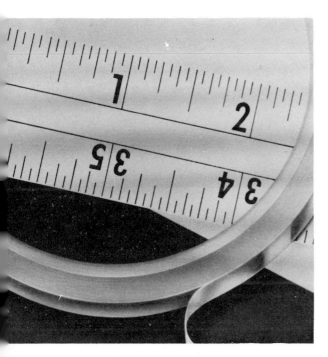

Fig. 510. **Streaks?** . . . incorrect ink-form-roller pressure . . . incorrect dampener-form-roller pressure . . . incorrect plate-to-blanket pressure . . . incorrect impression-to-blanket pressure . . . improper ink . . . loose blanket.

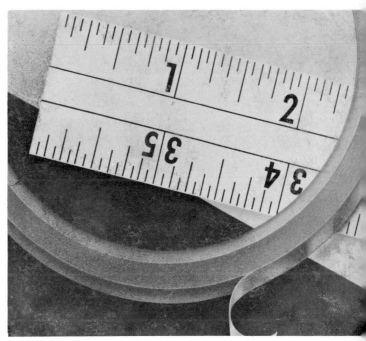

Fig. 512. **Uneven Printing?** . . . incorrect ink distribution . . . incorrect parallel pressure (heavy on one end and light on the other) on: dampener form rollers, ink form rollers, plate-to-blanket, or impression-to-blanket.

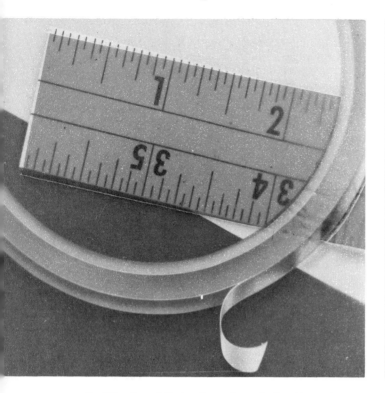

Fig. 513. **Out of Register?** . . . loose feeder side guide . . . loose plate . . . incorrect feed-roll pressure.

Fig. 514. **What? No Image at All?** . . . not enough ink-form-roller pressure . . . not enough plate-to-blanket pressure . . . **not enough impression-to-blanket** pressure . . . too much moisture . . . glazed blanket . . . glazed ink rollers.

## Scumming

"Scumming" is evidenced by the plate picking up ink in the clear areas, and transferring this ink to the clear areas of the sheet.

| Probable Cause | Remedy |
|---|---|
| 1. Clear areas of plate not etched properly — cannot repel the ink. | 1. Re-etch the plate, or make a new plate. |
| 2. Too little fountain solution. | 2. Increase flow of fountain solution. |
| 3. Dampener form rollers not parallel, or set too far from plate cylinder. | 3. Set according to instruction manual. Make new plate if damaged, or re-etch the plate. |
| 4. Dirty dampener rollers. | 4. Clean or replace the dampener rollers. Check the pH of fountain solution. Feed less ink. Replace ink, if emulsified. |
| 5. Unevenly applied molleton cover on dampener roller. | 5. Even out; recover if necessary. |
| 6. Dampener roller not parallel with the plate. | 6. Re-set according to instruction book. Make new plate, if damaged. |
| 7. Dampener roller dragging or bouncing on plate. | 7. Re-set according to instruction book. Make new plate, if damaged. |
| 8. Fountain solution too strong or too weak. | 8. Maintain at recommended pH. |

9. Plate and blanket cylinders not properly packed.
10. Flattened form rollers.
11. Plate not perfectly concentric with cylinder.
12. Skidding form roller.

13. Too much ink during make-ready.
14. Loose blanket.
15. Oxidation on plate.
16. Over-developed plate.
17. Residual coating solution on plate.

9. Set according to instruction manual.

10. Replace rollers.
11. Take up slack. Make new plate if the image is damaged.
12. Maintain proper contact between the rollers and their riders.
13. Cut down on ink, and re-etch the plate.
14. Take up the slack.
15. Re-etch, or make a new plate.
16. Make new plate.
17. Make new plate.

## Tinting

"Tinting" appears as a uniform, light-colored tint over the entire sheet of paper.

| Probable Cause | Remedy |
| --- | --- |
| 1. Poor (weak) varnish in ink. | 1. Replace with better ink. |
| 2. Breakdown of pigment particles in the ink. | 2. Ink may be at fault. Notify the ink manufacturer. May need reformulated ink. |
| 3. Fountain solution. | 3. Check pH. Check mixing procedure used. Replace with a different fountain solution. |
| 4. Paper coating particles getting into fountain solution. | 4. Replace the fountain solution. |
| 5. Acid getting into ink from an improperly washed-out plate. | 5. Wash up press. Replace ink. Re-process the plate. |

## Filling Up

"Filling up" is evidenced on the printed sheet and plate by the type matter and half-tones filling in with ink.

| Probable Cause | Remedy |
| --- | --- |
| 1. Dust from dull-finished or soft papers. | 1. Dust off each sheet of paper before using. Use a better paper stock. |
| 2. Ink is too tacky. | 2. Add thin varnish, or a non-pick compound. |
| 3. Too much ink. | 3. Adjust the ink fountain. |
| 4. Lack of coloring matter in ink. | 4. Add transparent white ink to the ink in the fountain. |

## Piling

"Piling" occurs when the ink builds up, or "piles," on the plate or blanket, or on both.

| Probable Cause | Remedy |
| --- | --- |
| 1. Pigment is not "carried" by the vehicle. | 1. Add a #3 or #4 varnish to the ink. |
| 2. Ink has not been sufficiently ground. | 2. Same as above. |
| 3. Ink is over-pigmented. | 3. Same as above. |

## Set-Off

"Set-off" is a term which indicates that the obverse (other side) of the paper is picking up an image from the sheet below it in the stacker.

| Probable Cause | Remedy |
|---|---|
| 1. Excessive ink. | 1. Reduce the fountain setting, or use an anti-offset device. |
| 2. Ink lacks a drier. | 2. Add a drier. Use an anti-offset device. |

## Vanishing

"Vanishing" is the gradual disappearance of some lines and some halftone dots from the plate image.

| Probable Cause | Remedy |
|---|---|
| 1. Friction of the form rollers. | 1. Readjust the form rollers. |
| 2. Chemical action of certain inks. | 2. Add a little stearic acid to the ink. |

## Sticking

The sheets may stick together in the stacker, or delivery pile. The sheets tear when pulled apart.

| Probable Cause | Remedy |
|---|---|
| 1. Ink is being run too heavily. | 1. Feed less ink. Use an anti-offset device. |
| 2. Too much drier in the ink. | 2. Use less drier. Use an anti-offset device. |
| 3. Paper stock won't absorb the ink. | 3. Try a different ink. Run less ink. Use an anti-offset device. Remove the sheets from delivery end in small lifts. Use another kind of paper. |
| 4. Relative humidity is too high. | 4. Maintain relative humidity. Add drier to the ink. |
| 5. Moisture content of the paper is too high. | 5. Condition paper before using. Adding drier may help. |
| 6. Paper surface too acid. | 6. Add drier to the ink. |

## Picking

"Picking" is evidenced when "hickies" (black spots) appear in the blank areas of the printed image, and white spots appear in the solid areas.

| Probable Cause | Remedy |
|---|---|
| 1. Ink is too tacky. It pulls off particles of paper coating. These stick to plate, blanket and ink rollers. | 1. Reduce tack. Add a thin-bodied varnish, or a non-pick compound. |
| 2. Paper stock is too "linty." | 2. Clean up press. Use a different paper stock. |
| 3. Stock is poorly coated. | 3. Same as above. |

## Roller Stripping

When there is uneven printing of the image, it may be caused by bare sections on the rollers.

| Probable Cause | Remedy |
|---|---|
| 1. Fountain solution is too strong. It is getting into the ink. | 1. Check pH of fountain solution. Replace if too strong. |
| 2. Ink rollers are glazed. | 2. Remove the glaze with pumice and water. Wipe clean; then wash with solvent. |

## Spraying

The ink may spray over the press, especially at high temperatures.

| Probable Cause | Remedy |
|---|---|
| 1. If dots appear on press parts, ink is too thin. | 1. Add mixing white, and heavy varnish. Use a heavier ink. |
| 2. If little ink lines appear on press parts, ink is too thick. | 2. Add thin varnish. |
| 3. Too much ink being fed. | 3. Adjust fountain for less ink. |
| 4. Ink rollers set too lightly. | 4. Re-set ink rollers. |
| 5. Ink rollers too hard. | 5. Replace rollers. |
| 6. Ink rollers swollen. | 6. Use a more volatile press wash. Re-set the rollers. |
| 7. Ink rollers too soft. | 7. Replace the rollers. |

## Mottling

"Mottling" occurs as a muddy image on the paper. The ink does not cover evenly.

| Probable Cause | Remedy |
|---|---|
| 1. Too much reducer in the ink. | 1. Add heavy varnish, liquid glass or magnesia to the ink. |

## Gray Type

| Probable Cause | Remedy |
|---|---|
| 1. Too little pressure. | 1. Increase pressure. |
| 2. Too much water. | 2. Decrease water. |
| 3. Starved for ink. | 3. Increase ink. |

## Chalking

"Chalking" is evidenced by the ink on the paper turning dry and powdery. It falls off the sheet as dust.

| Probable Cause | Remedy |
|---|---|
| 1. Lack of sufficient binder in the ink. | 1. Add heavy varnish or drier to the ink. |

## Running

The ink is said to "run" if it penetrates through the paper stock.

| Probable Cause | Remedy |
| --- | --- |
| 1. Varnish in ink is too thin. | 1. Add mixing white, or replace the ink. |

## Questions

1. Describe the appearance of good, acceptable printed copies.
2. What are some of the causes of gray, washed-out printed copies?
3. What is "scumming"? What conditions might bring it about?
4. What is the effect on halftones and fine reverses in the printed copies when running too much ink or when there is too much impression-to-blanket pressure?
5. By inspection of the printed sheets, how can it be determined that there are possible low spots in the blanket?
6. What might cause blurred copies?
7. What causes streaks in printed sheets?
8. What might cause an image to break down while the plate is running?
9. Name some causes of uneven printing.
10. Why might the press be printing out-of-register?
11. Why might the image be extremely light, or not printing at all?
12. Describe "tinting". What might cause this?
13. How can "piling" be detected? What is the remedy?
14. Describe "set-off". Give a remedy for it.
15. What is "picking"? Describe the remedies.
16. Tell how to overcome "spraying"?
17. What compensations can be made for ink "running"?
18. What trouble might develop if the ink rollers become "glazed"?

## Problems and Projects

1. Obtain a copy of the press instruction manual. Read it thoroughly.

2. Check the manufacturer's recommendations for the installation of the press.

3. Check the manufacturer's recommendations for the adjustments of the press parts. With the instructor's approval, make any adjustments which are needed.

4. During your actual operation of the press, consult with the instructor about any problems which arise in the actual printing of the sheets. See if you can offer the solutions for the difficulties.

## New Words

| | |
| --- | --- |
| 1. concentric | 10. pigmented |
| 2. disappearance | 11. preparation |
| 3. familiar | 12. pumice |
| 4. glazed | 13. residual |
| 5. maintenance | 14. stearic |
| 6. make-ready | 15. transferring |
| 7. mottling | 16. transparent |
| 8. oxidation | 17. troubleshooting |
| 9. particles | 18. volatile |

## Shop Safety

Because of the chemicals and equipment used in photo-offset lithography, there are certain situations in which serious injury may result. To avoid injury and to minimize the effects of accidents, a continuous program of shop safety should be followed.

In all work in the shop, remember that the safety of yourself and your fellow workers comes first. Naturally, the valuable shop equipment should be protected against damage, but that is secondary to personal safety.

### General Safety Precautions

A standard operating plan should be worked out for the shop so that, in case of injury, the students, instructor and other school personnel know exactly what should be done and what assistance is available and can be offered. This plan should be posted in the shop, and all should become familiar with it.

A complete first-aid kit (unlocked) should be available in the shop. This kit should contain instructions for the use of the first-aid materials for the most common accidents. It should be assembled by the school or plant physician, who should instruct the personnel in its use.

Should an accident occur, one person should be sent to phone for assistance, while another is sent immediately on foot. The results of their calls should be reported as soon as they return. The injured person never should be left alone, nor sent alone anywhere, no matter how slight the injury.

*Every* injury, no matter how slight, must be referred to the school or plant medical office.

A person never should work alone in the shop, nor in the darkroom. *Nor* should persons engage in shopwork when the medical personnel are not on duty in the building, nor when the telephone line to outside is not functioning. This may be over-cautious — but it is safest.

### Shop Layout

The thought for safety should be uppermost when planning and equipping a shop; otherwise, hazards may be built in.

The room itself should be of ample size, with adequate lighting and ventilation. It should be free of posts or columns which prevent supervision of the entire room and all personnel.

Floors should be smooth and un-waxed. A non-skid abrasive paint may be applied to the floor areas about presses and other machinery. The floor in the darkroom should be of a non-electrical-conductive type, and a built-in floor drain should be provided. Absolutely necessary for the darkroom, also, is a strong intake air fan, and, if doors are used, light-tight louvers are needed to insure good exhaust of fumes.

Entrance doors to the shop should be extra-wide double doors, to admit machinery and cartons without manhandling.

No electrical conduits or other wire raceways should be permitted *on* the floor. Underfloor raceways, if possible, should be installed — otherwise, overhead.

Electrical outlets to machines, tables, etc. should be located under the items. Sufficient floor and wall outlets should be provided so that extension cords need not be used.

Wash-up and other working sinks should be provided in such locations and number as convenient for the workers. Hot and cold water, paper towels and suitable hand cleaners should be in constant supply.

Arrangement of equipment should follow straight-line patterns, with ample aisle space between rows to allow the passage of stock carts and drying racks while workers are at their stations. Machinery should be arranged or protected so that no projecting arms, gauges, etc. will injure workers or passersby.

Provision should be made for orderly storage of coats, lunches, books, etc., to keep these from littering the work areas.

Where feasible, equipment should be anchored to the floor or to the workbench tops.

Storage rooms should be provided for paper stock, supplies, etc. Storeroom shelving should not exceed six feet in height. Large or heavy items should not be stored above the shelving tops, since these might fall off and cause injury. Heavy or breakable items should be stored on the floor beneath the shelves, or on the lowest shelves. A stepladder should be provided for reaching the high items, if needed, so that a chair or box is never used as a substitute.

A telephone in the shop is a must — for summoning assistance in case of accident or for reporting a fire.

Tote carts and drying racks should be provided to transport paper stock and heavy items about the shop.

Push brooms, counter dusters (brushes), dust pans and a mop should be provided to encourage shop cleanliness. A sufficient number of covered, metal trash barrels should be conveniently located near the paper cutter, presses, folder, sinks, etc.

## Safety Tour

New classes or personnel should be conducted on a safety tour as one of the first items of business. The tour should include a visit to each location which might present a possibility of injury, and items which are provided for cleanliness, first aid and safety should be pointed out.

On this trip, the instructor should indicate the inherent dangers of the papercutter, presses, arc lights, folder, etc. Likewise, he should point out the locations of master switch, panic buttons, fire alarm, fire extinguishers, etc. He should emphasize the necessity of turning on the lights when working on machinery, working at stations, or entering storerooms (except where the process prohibits this).

## Personal Conduct

No "horseplay" of any kind can be permitted — no "joking" about a machine, no tossing of an item to another person, no splashing of water, etc. Such conduct engenders unsafe habits and is likely to cause serious injury. Unsafe conduct and practices by a student always should be promptly corrected; if they persist, the worker should be barred permanently from the shop for protection of himself and others.

## Permissions

It should be clearly understood that no person is to mix any solutions, handle any chemicals or operate or adjust any equipment unless he has first been thoroughly instructed in its use and dangers and then is judged competent in its use by the instructor. Even then, permission of the instructor must be obtained in each instance.

## Personal Cleanliness

Wash thoroughly with hot water and soap after handling chemicals and solvents — especially before eating lunch. Wash well between the fingers, and wash your face, ears and neck.

Keep your fingers away from your mouth and eyes, and never form the habit of eating while working — you may be eating a little solvent or chemicals each time. The effects of many chemicals (such as lead or carbon "tet") are cumulative over a lifetime.

Change clothing which becomes splashed with chemicals or solvent, or which has become soiled with ink, solvent, etc.

## Eyes and Face

Never mix solutions near your eyes and face. Keep them at arm's length. Especially when removing the snap top of a metal container, hold the container on the bench at arm's length, with the face and eyes averted (turned away), to prevent accidental "gushing" of the contents into the face and eyes.

At all times when mixing or pouring chemicals, wear approved safety glasses. These glasses should be provided individually or by (and remain in) the school or shop, *one pair for each student or worker,* plus a cabinet to facilitate storage and sterilization.

Mask-type goggles are available commercially for persons with prescription glasses to be worn *over* these glasses. Also organizations selling safety glasses will make up attractive prescription safety glasses at a nominal charge for those students who wish to purchase them. These are intended for everyday general use, and they eliminate the need for the mask-type goggles.

## Fire Safety

Never smoke in the shop proper or in the darkroom.

Fire extinguishers for extinguishing gasoline, oil and electrical fires should be furnished as specified by the fire marshal as to type, quantity, and location in the shop. These extinguishers should be inspected and serviced at the required intervals.

At the start of a term or school year, it is a good plan to arrange for an actual demonstration — outdoors — of the use of the fire extinguishers.

All personnel should know the location of the building fire alarm and how it is used. They also should know how to telephone in a fire alarm.

Periodic fire drills should be scheduled and practiced so that all become used to the procedure and quickly shut down equipment, close windows, and, after filing out of a room, close the doors behind them.

Only those cleaning liquids permitted and approved by the fire marshal should be permitted in the shop — and, then, only in such quantity and in such containers as approved by him.

All-metal containers, with both self-closing top and leg supports, should be provided as the *only receptacles* in which to place cloths which have been used with oils or type- or press-cleaning solvent. The building custodian should be consulted for the proper disposal method of the used cloths and any dirty press solvents.

Oil and papers should not be allowed to accumulate on the floor about and beneath any equipment. Spilled liquids of all kinds should be wiped up immediately.

When pouring solvents, oil, etc. from a large container into a smaller container, first place the smaller container in the sink, then pour. This avoids spilling the liquid on the bench, counter or floor.

## Deliveries

Newly-delivered crates, cases, etc. should be placed out of the travel lanes, and they should be unpacked with care. Attention should be paid to withdrawing all nails from boards and properly and promptly disposing of all packing materials. The floor area should be kept clean.

Machinery and heavy items should be moved and installed by the supplier's agents or the building superintendent's staff.

Crates of supplies, or bundles or skids of paper, should be opened on the floor, as delivered; individual reams or small "lifts" of paper or individual items should be picked out and stored on shelves. Never "show off" by attempting to lift heavy items. This is asking for serious injury.

The instructor should demonstrate how to do "leg lifting," *i.e.,* lifting with the leg muscles, rather than the back muscles. He should re-emphasize *not lifting heavy items.*

## Chemicals

Store chemicals on the lowest shelves in their cabinets or racks so that if they fall, spill or drip, they will then do the least damage.

When making solutions, wear safety glasses — and pour the *chemical into the water — never pour the water into the chemical.* (In this latter situation, a violent reaction may occur!) Note, in published formulas, the ingredients are added in the order in which they appear in the formula.

Label every container into which any chemical preparation is to be placed. If it is a poisonous substance, be certain to plainly mark it "POISON". If a container has no label, be suspicious of its contents — bring it to the instructor.

Whenever chemicals and solutions are not being used, return them to the chemical cabinet and *lock* the cabinet.

In handling graduates and jars, extend the little finger underneath the glassware so it won't slip out of your hand. Place containers toward the back of the countertop — not near the front where they might be knocked over or off.

Wear rubber gloves when the hands must come into contact with irritants which might cause "dermatitis" (skin infection). Some of these irritants are: bichromates (used in coating solutions), etching solutions, cyanides, developers, solvents, and strong cleansers such as lye and gasoline. If any skin blisters or other skin conditions develop, seek a physician's advice.

Never use a food or drink container for mixing, weighing, or storing chemicals. Accidental poisoning might result.

Wear a rubber apron to keep chemicals from staining your clothing and possibly reaching your skin.

When mixing or weighing chemicals, keep the fumes and rising dust from entering your nostrils, mouth and eyes. Don't mix or weigh chemicals in the darkroom unless there is a strong exhaust fan in operation.

Occasionally, it is necessary to smell a chemical solution in order to identify it. When this is necessary, be careful to take a "wee" sniff — avoid a full nosefull!

With chemicals, *never guess. Ask questions.* Ignorance can be excused, but not injury!

### Solvents

There are many safe commercial solvents for removing ink from type and from offset press rollers, ink fountain, plates and blankets. Use only those which your fire marshal approves from samples you submit to him.

If possible, avoid using gasoline (flammable and explosive), benzene and toluene (toxic and flammable), and turpentine (toxic).

Kerosene is relatively safe, with a flash point* of about 140°, but is slow-drying and has low solvent power.

Carbon tetrachloride is non-flammable, but its vapors are toxic. It can irritate the skin and eyes. If heated, it can form *phosgene* — a deadly gas!

Solvents are available which are non-flammable (or have a high flash point — at least 100° or more), are non-toxic, non-irritating to the skin, have a high solvent power, and are non-injurious to rollers and blankets.

Good, safe solvents tend to be expensive, but expense should be secondary to prevention of fire and health hazards. If ratings of a solvent are not available, check its fire safety, toxicity and flash-point rating with your fire marshal.

A crude, but useful, test for fire-safety (but not toxicity) of a solvent is performed as follows: wipe a steel-top table clean; dip a ½″ x 4″ strip of paper into the solvent (half way); remove the can of solvent safely away, then place the solvent-wet paper on the table; touch a lighted match to the wet paper. If the wet paper lights readily, this writer considers the solvent unsafe — not for use in his shop; if the wet paper first must be dried by the match before it will burn, then the solvent is considered safe. (Follow up with a test and ratings by the fire marshal.)

Adequate room ventilation is a must when using solvents. For example, if a pint of solvent is used in washing a press, a good part of that pint is evaporated into the air for you to breathe (or cause a fire). This is a serious matter, since it may be, at the least, a daily occurrence.

### Electrical

A main disconnect switch (master switch) should be provided so that, when "pulled", all

---

*"Flash-point" refers to the lowest temperature at which a substance will give off vapors which will support combustion. For example: white gasoline has a flash-point rating of 0° F. This means that at a temperature as low as 0° F., gasoline vapors are so highly dangerous that they will ignite or support combustion.

power to machinery, appliances and outlets will be disconnected. This will insure that when the shop is closed down, all power is "off".

A sufficient number of "panic buttons" (emergency disconnect switches) should be installed at strategic locations throughout the shop. Thus, in event of an emergency, any person may "hit the panic button", shutting off all power.

It is both convenient and safe to have a disconnect switch at each piece of machinery or equipment. Such a switch may be locked in the "off" position when desired, to prevent use of the equipment or to prevent anyone from turning on the equipment when another is working on it. It is safest to open the disconnect switch before attempting machine repairs, installing carbons, etc.

Damaged or frayed electric cords, plugs, switches, etc. should be promptly replaced — or kept from use until replaced.

Wherever feasible, a red pilot light can be installed on equipment, in a prominent location, to show that the item is under power. This is especially desirable for film or print dryers or any item with heaters.

All electrical wiring — lighting, power and appliance cords — should be inspected by the local electrical inspecting authority, to see that it conforms to existing regulations and to make sure that all equipment is adequately grounded.

All convenience outlet wiring and plugs should be converted (if not so already) to the three-prong, "U-ground" type — to accommodate the 3-pronged plugs and cords now in use. (This is better than using the "3-wire adapters" in the plugs.)

All appliances with a two-pronged plug and two-wire cord should be rewired with a three-wire cord and 3-pronged plug. The extra prong and wire insures that a "ground" connection is automatically provided when the appliance is plugged in, eliminating accidental electrical shock from defective equipment.

If possible, equipment should never be located so close to sinks or water pipes that it is possible to touch both at the same time.

## Operating Equipment

Before working on or operating any machinery, the worker should remove his coat and roll all sleeves above the elbows. He should remove (or, tuck in) his necktie, and remove all jewelry from his fingers, wrists and neck. No gloves should be worn by the operator of a machine.

No person should operate any machine until (1) he has been taught personally (by the instructor) the operation of that machine, (2) he proves by demonstration that he is capable of safe operation of that machine, and (3) he has the instructor's permission in each instance to operate that machine.

No person who has been authorized to operate a machine should allow any other person to "take a turn" at operating that machine or to make any adjustment to that machine.

Persons observing the operation of a machine must keep back, out of the operator's way, so as not to impede his operation or control of that machine. In addition, the observer must keep his hands *off the machine* and *out of the machine*.

Machinery must be operated in the manner and at the speed demonstrated by the instructor. Only those adjustments authorized by the instructor should be performed — and, then, only in the manner demonstrated by the instructor. If faster speeds are considered safe for that operator, the instructor will so authorize.

The floor and aisle about a machine must be kept free of oil, paper or other debris, to prevent persons slipping or falling.

A complete and accessible file should be kept of all service manuals, instruction manuals, parts lists and lubrication manuals or charts for each piece of equipment in the shop. Personnel should be made to feel free to consult and study these items so as to better understand each piece of equipment and the manufacturer's recommended methods of operation, adjustment, repair and lubrication.

### Offset Presses

One person should be designated by the instructor as the operator of the press. If an assistant is appointed by the instructor, that person must keep his hands *off* the switches, handwheel and controls, and only perform those functions directed by the operator of the press. When changing a blanket, installing a plate, adjusting for register, setting up feeder or delivery, *only the operator* should touch the machine — otherwise, someone might cause a movement of the machine and catch the operator's hands! Unauthorized persons should keep at a distance from the machine — hands off!

The press should not be operated at any time without the cylinder guard in place.

The operator should operate the press at the speed designated by the instructor. (There is a dangerous tendency for immature people to "see how fast it will go".)

The press should be lubricated, and the rollers and fountain, plate and blanket washed *only when the press is stopped.* The instructor may demonstrate the use of the roller-cleaning device which is used on a press in motion, but this must be used only under his supervision.

With a press in motion, it is easy and *disastrous* to get your fingers, a cloth, or a tool caught in the cylinder gaps, between rollers, or in other moving parts.

There are certain tests and adjustments which are made while the press is in motion. These will be demonstrated by the instructor, who then will check the operator's performance of these. Only after the instructor's approval should they be performed on a moving press.

Even though the press is stopped, tools, cloths or oil cans should not be placed on any part of the machine. They may be forgotten when the press is started and will fall into the machine. A press cabinet or bench should be provided near the press for these items.

For extensive repairs, or when the press is not in shape to be run, the disconnect switch should be pulled and locked "open."

### Stripping Tables

Don't use the stripping table as a depository for school books, lunches, or other items, or as a workbench. Above all, don't lean on it heavily, since the glass top might crash in, inflicting serious injury.

Cut films slowly and carefully, keeping thumb and fingers back from the guiding edge of the straightedge or triangle, to avoid injury.

When through with the knife, blade, or other sharp tool, place it in storage, to keep it from "playful" and irresponsible persons.

Only the instructor should remove the glass table top. A large sheet of glass can cause serious injury if it breaks.

### Folding Machine

Keep your hands away from swiftly-moving paper edges. Keep from putting your fingers into the rollers, and keep others away from the machine. Make all adjustments and set-ups only in the manner demonstrated by the instructor.

### Card Cutter (or Film Cutter)

The card cutter is strictly a one-man device. It is most dangerous since it is easy, on this device, to slice off a thumb! Keep fingers and thumb back from cutting edge, and lock blade in "down" position when through using it.

An L-shaped guard (1″ wide x 5″ high) can be fashioned of metal and installed along the bed, next to the knife edge and raised from the bed with a washer or two at each end. This will prove most effective in keeping fingers away from the knife, yet will allow paper and film to be slid under the guard for cutting.

### Paper Cutter

Only one person, designated by the instructor, should operate the cutter at one time. No one else should be allowed to be within reach of the machine. This is a must, since the cutting action is swift, and amputation easily can result. Particularly, do not allow another person to assist in holding the paper stock — if you are having difficulties, call the instructor.

The cutter blade (knife) should be removed and installed *only* by the instructor or an approved workman. Watch how he does it, and observe that the extra knife (or the removed knife) is always bolted into its cover guard to prevent accident, *except* when it is being transported to or from the machine. Before transporting the knife, thread two of the cap screws into the threaded holes at opposite ends of the knife to serve to grip the knife securely.

Form the habit of using only a wooden ruler or yardstick at the cutter, and keep these and all other items *off* the cutter table.

While operating the cutter, if you must talk to a person or look elsewhere, first step away from the machine.

During the entire cutting operation, keep your eyes on the knife and keep both hands on the controls! Your instructor will show you how much of a "lift" of paper can be comfortably cut at one time.

*Absolutely never* attempt to "beat" or circumvent the safety devices by adapting the controls to be operated with one hand. This is a sure invitation to cutting off one of your hands!

When using a lever cutter, keep both hands on the lever during the entire stroke down and during the entire return of the lever to its extreme "up" resting position. (A lever cutter should be fitted with a two-hand safety control lever.) When through using the cutter, run the clamp all the way down.

With both the power- and lever-operated cutters, when through using them, place a large (2″ x 4″) block of wood — the length of the bed — in front of the knife on the bed of the machine, to keep prying fingers out.

In handling the paper, never slide your hands along the edges since they can cut like a razor! Likewise, never experiment with testing the sharpness of the knife by running your finger along the edge — you certainly will be cut!

Remember: with the paper cutter, an accident usually means *complete amputation of fingers or hands* — be sure to observe all safety rules.

### Exposure Devices
The lights (lamps) in cameras and platemakers run at high temperatures. Let them cool off before trying to change them. Because of the high voltage and exposed electrical parts in some platemakers, always disconnect the platemaker by pulling out the plug before attempting to change carbons or lamps or to make repairs to the underneath mechanism.

Avoid a "blast" of light in the eyes from any exposure device, since this may temporarily impair your vision. *Never, never* look directly at the light of the arc lights! This could cause serious and *permanent* damage to the eyes. It's a good idea to look away when turning on arc lights.

### Stapler (Stitcher)
Operate slowly enough so that you keep your fingers out of the open throat of the machine — so that you don't staple your fingers.

Don't allow another person to touch the machine or its controls when you are loading, setting up or operating the stapler.

### Paper Drill
Expect the drill to be hot when you remove it, and use suitable precautions to keep from burning your fingers.

Don't allow another person near the controls when you are setting up or operating the drill. (Somebody could drill through your hand!)

Keep fingers away from the drill head when drilling. Pull the plug when setting in a new drill or attachments. When finished, remove the drill or attachments to keep the curious from injury.

### Small Tools

More serious cuts, punctures and skinned knuckles are caused by improper use of small tools than by that of power tools and machines.

To avoid dangerous consequences of improvising, the proper common tools should be provided for repairs, adjustments, unpacking, uncrating, etc. The list should include, in part, a claw hammer, ball peen hammer, machinist's vise secured to bench, drift punches, center punch, several types and sizes of screwdrivers, Allen wrenches, open-end wrenches, box wrenches, socket wrenches, tin snips, punches, knives, etc. Other tools should be purchased as the need arises, so that the proper tool, in the proper size, is always available.

Instruction in the proper use of hand tools should be given. Here are some points to remember: (1) Wrenches preferably should be pulled; if pushed, keep the hand open, palm forward, to avoid skinning knuckles. (2) Two hands should be used on a screwdriver — one on the handle and one at the blade end, to keep it from jumping out and stabbing oneself or others. (3) In passing a sharp, or pointed, tool to another person, offer it in a vertical position, point down, so the person may grasp it by the handle. (4) If an edged or sharp tool is dropped, don't try to catch it — let it fall. (5) Never rest an oil can (hand oiler) on the floor, a chair, or bench top — this is an invitation to injury; store it on a shelf beneath the bench top. (6) In lubricating a machine, hold a cloth next to the oil hole to wipe any excess oil which might otherwise drip onto the floor or other parts of the machine. (7) Wear goggles (safety glasses) when hammering or chipping on metal.

## Safeguard

As a member of an organized personnel system, you are bound morally and legally to be reasonably prudent in maintaining safe working conditions.

If any unsafe conditions exist, or if any are brought to your attention, take immediate steps to eliminate or correct them. Where necessary, requisition safe repair, replacement or installation, and keep a carbon copy of that requisition as a safeguard against possible charges of negligence.

Keep a copy of any accident report, together with names of witnesses, dates, circumstances, etc.

## Questions

1. What is the prime object of a program of shop safety?
2. In case of serious accident, why are two persons designated to summon assistance? Why would only one be insufficient?
3. State one reason why an injured person should never be left alone. Why he should never be sent alone to the medical center.
4. Why is it dangerous for a person to work in the shop when alone? When the medical center personnel are not on duty?
5. What danger is there in having an electrical conduit (pipe) on the floor from the wall to a machine?
6. What danger is there in storing heavy items on top of the shelving in the storerooms?
7. What danger is there in using a chair or a box for a ladder?
8. Whose permission must be obtained before mixing chemicals or operating any machine? Why?
9. What happens, or should happen, to a person in the shop who indulges in horseplay?
10. Why is smoking prohibited in the shop and darkroom?
11. What eye-protection measures should be observed when mixing chemicals?
12. What kind of a container is considered the only safe container for oily or dirty type-cleaning and press-cleaning cloths?
13. What danger is there in allowing oil or papers on the floor?
14. What is meant by "leg lifting"?
15. Why should chemicals be stored on the lowest shelves?
16. How would you turn in a fire alarm in your building?
17. What substances in your shop might cause dermatitis?
18. How do you avoid, or minimize, the chances of contracting dermatitis?
19. Name four liquids which are unsafe to use as press solvents.
20. What is meant by "the flash point" of a substance?
21. What is a "panic button"? When should it be used? By whom?
22. What precautions as to personal dress should be observed before operating any machinery? Why?
23. What are the conditions of instruction, demonstration and permission which must be observed before a person may operate a machine?
24. What dangers are present for the operator when an unauthorized person touches or leans on the machine or its controls? What dangers are present for him?

25. List eleven safety rules which must be observed when using paper cutters.
26. What serious injury may be expected if the safety precautions for the paper cutter are not observed?
27. In mixing solutions, why must the acid (chemical) be poured *into* (added to) the water?
28. List the recommendations for personal cleanliness.
29. What danger is there in looking at a lighted arc lamp?

## Problems and Projects

1. With the help of the instructor and the school administration, develop a standard procedure in case of an accident in the shop. Have this plan printed up and copies posted in the shop near the first-aid kit, telephone and near possible sources of accident.
2. Plan and print up lists of safety rules for each machine or area. Post these conspicuously.
3. Working with the school or shop physician, compile a first-aid kit for the shop. Requisition the needed items. Mount the kit when it is available. (This should *not* be locked.)
4. Develop first-aid procedures for each kind of accident which might occur in the shop, such as burns, electrical shock, cuts (bleeding), poisoning, etc. Work in cooperation with a physician. Print these procedures for distribution, with a copy at the first-aid kit.
5. Plan a "first aid" day when you and your classmates demonstrate first-aid procedures for each type of accident possible in your shop. If feasible, invite the school or plant physician to be present.
6. Work up a plan of procedure to follow in case of fire in your shop. Print up the procedure, and post copies conspicuously. Discuss this procedure in a class session.
7. Invite the fire marshal to talk to your group on fire-drill procedure, how to report fires, how to prevent fires, and the proper use of fire extinguishers.
8. Develop and initiate a "fire and safety foreman" system, in which each person has that responsibility for a period of time.
9. List items and situations which should be checked daily by the "fire and safety foreman."
10. Requisition any items needed in the shop to promote fire and personal safety. Ask your instructor's advice. Keep a carbon copy.
11. Invite the local electrical inspection authority to your shop to inspect the power and lighting wiring, including all appliances and equipment.
12. Prepare and process a requisition for electrical work to be done to comply with any recommendations of the electrical inspector. Keep a carbon copy.

## New Words

1. benzene
2. carbon tetrachloride
3. circumstances
4. combustion
5. conduit
6. cyanide
7. depository
8. dermatitis
9. disastrous
10. explosive
11. extinguisher
12. feasible
13. flammable
14. frayed
15. goggles
16. grounded
17. hazard
18. irritant
19. negligence
20. phosgene
21. prescription
22. prudent
23. receptacle
24. safety
25. strategic
26. toluene
27. toxic
28. vapors
29. ventilation

# Legal Restrictions

# on Copying

Because photo lithography utilizes in many cases the photographic copying of existing printed work for the preparation of plates for reproductions, it should be understood that there are certain legal restrictions as to what may or may not be reproduced.

It is impossible, in this book, to give an all-inclusive treatment of this legal problem. If there is any doubt as to the legality of copying any matter, it may be best to seek legal advice on the specific problem. Some general observations on the subject of copying are given here.

## Copyrighted Materials

A copyright is a form of protection given by the law of the United States to the authors of literary, dramatic, musical, artistic and other similar works. The owner of the copyright has the exclusive right to copy his work, and to sell or distribute copies of his work.

### The Copyright Notice

As a general rule, the copyright notice should consist of three elements:

(1) The word "Copyright", the abbreviation "Copr.", or the symbol "©".

(2) The name of the copyright owner.

(3) The year date of publication.

The above three elements should appear together on the copies as "Copyright John Doe 1967". Normally, for a book, this notice appears on the page following the title page. In other works, the symbol "©" may be ac-

companied by the owner's initials, monogram, mark or symbol, if his name appears elsewhere on the work.

### What May Be Copyrighted

Among others, the following items may be copyrighted: books, pamphlets, catalogs, leaflets, cards, single pages, tabular matter, newspapers, magazines, bulletins, maps, drawings, paintings, photographs, musical compositions, greeting cards, labels, picture postcards, film strips and motion pictures.

### What May Not Be Copyrighted

In general, these items are not eligible for copyright: time cards, graph paper, calendars, account books, diaries, height and weight charts, tape measures, rulers, schedules of sporting events, names, titles, slogans, familiar symbols, familiar designs and mere listing of contents or ingredients.

### Duration of Copyright

The first statutory copyright runs for twenty-eight years, beginning with the date the work is published with the notice of copyright. A copyright may be renewed for a second term of twenty-eight years, providing an application for renewal is made to the Copyright Office (Library of Congress) and duly registered with that office during the last year of the original twenty-eight year term, which is measured from the exact date on which the original copyright began.

### Common-Law Literary Property

Unpublished maps, books, photographs and other works are protected by state laws against copying. This protection begins when the works are created and ends when the works are published for sale or distribution (even free distribution).

### Permission for Reproduction

If the owner of the copyright can be ascertained, permission *in writing* should be secured from him before copying is done. This permission should indicate the nature and extent of the copying to be done, the exact title or designation of the work from which the copying is to be done, and the purpose to which the reproduced copies are to be put — whether for sale, schoolroom use, free distribution, textbook, etc.

If there is any doubt whatsoever as to whether or not a work is copyrighted, the safest and most courteous method of procedure is to write the owner and request the permission outlined above. In most cases the authors of the work involved will make satisfactory arrangements, and are often very happy to cooperate. If permission is granted, the copied work should carry a courtesy or credit line (as specified by the author or copyright owner of the work) acknowledging the source of the material.

A pamphlet edition of the law, Bulletin No. 14, "The Copyright Law of the United States of America," is available from the Copyright Office, Library of Congress, Washington 25, D.C., for $0.25.

## Photographs for Advertising

Any photographs which show clearly recognizable faces of persons cannot be used for advertising purposes without first obtaining written consent from the persons involved. If minors are concerned, permission must be obtained from their legal guardians. To do otherwise may result in a claim of invasion of privacy and a demand for reparations from the parties concerned.

## Counterfeiting

Any request for printing or photographing, in part or whole, or the supplying of materials for any work which may violate or seem to violate any part or the entirety of any of the regulations quoted below should be reported at once to the Federal Bureau of Investigation and the Treasury Department Secret Service for clarification and investigation. If the proposed work is legally permissible, you will be so informed; if it is illegal, you will be far better off having had no part of its execution. Never proceed on the assumption that something similar to what is requested has been publicly distributed with permission. Prior violations may have gone unnoticed, unknown or be under investigation at the time.

### U.S. Code of Law, Title 18, Sec. 474. Plates or Stones for Counterfeiting Obligations or Securities

"Whoever, having control, custody or possession of any plate, stone or other thing, or any part thereof, from which has been printed, or which may be prepared by direction of the Secretary of the Treasury for the purpose of printing, any obligation or other security of the United States, uses such plate, stone, or other thing, or any part thereof, or knowingly suffers the same to be used for the purpose of printing any such or similar obligation or other security, or any part thereof, except as may be printed for the use of the United States by order of the proper officer thereof; or

"Whoever makes or executes any plate, stone or other thing in the likeness of any plate designated for the printing of such obligation or other security; or

"Whoever sells any such plate, stone or other thing, or brings into the United States any such plate, stone or other thing, except under the direction of the Secretary of the Treasury or other proper officer, or with any other intent, in either case, that such plate, stone or other thing be used for the printing of the obligations or other securities of the United States; or

"Whoever has in his control, custody, or possession any plate, stone, or other thing in any manner made after or in the similitude of any plate, stone or other thing, from which any such obligation or other security has been printed, with intent to use such plate, stone or other thing, or to suffer the same to be used in forging or counterfeiting any such obligation or other security, or any part thereof; or

"Whoever has in his possession or custody, except under authority from the Secretary of the Treasury or other proper officer, any obligation or other security made or executed, in whole or in part, after the similitude of any obligation or other security issued under the authority of the United States, with intent to sell or otherwise use the same; or

"Whoever prints, photographs or in any other manner makes or executes any engraving, photograph, print or impression in the likeness of any such obligation or other security, or any part thereof, or sells any such engraving, photograph, print or impression, except to the United States or brings into the United States, any such engraving, photograph, print or impression, except by direction of some proper officer of the United States; or

"Whoever has or retains in his control or possession, after a distinctive paper has been adopted by the Secretary of the Treasury for the obligations and other securities of the United States, any similar paper adapted to the making of any such obligation or other security, except under the authority of the Secretary of the Treasury or some other proper officer of the United States —

"Shall be fined not more than $5,000 or imprisoned not more than fifteen years, or both."

## U.S. Code of Laws, Title 18, Section 475 (as amended). Imitating Obligations or Securities; Advertisements

"Whoever designs, engraves, prints, makes or executes, or utters, issues, distributes, circulates or uses any business or professional card, notice, placard, circular, handbill or advertisement in the likeness or similitude of any obligation or security of the United States issued under or authorized by any Act of Congress or writes, prints or otherwise impresses upon or attaches to any such instrument, obligation or security, or any coin of the United States, any business or professional card, notice or advertisement, or any notice of advertisement whatever, shall be fined not more than $500."

## U.S. Savings Bonds

Reproductions of U.S. Savings Bonds or Savings Stamps may not be made in any form except for publicity purposes in connection with a campaign for the sale of such bonds and stamps. The illustrations of Savings Stamps for these campaigns must be less than three-quarters, or more than one and one-half, in linear dimensions, of each part of such stamps.

## U.S. Coins

Public Law 79, 82nd Congress, approved July 16, 1951, removed the restrictions on photographing and printing illustrations of United States coins. These are now permitted.

## U.S. and Foreign Postage Stamps

United States and foreign postage stamps may be reproduced in black and white (not colors) providing the following regulations are observed:

(1) Regulations of the Secretary of the Treasury, as may at any time be in force, must be followed. Seek current rulings.

(2) Reproductions of cancelled and un-cancelled United States postage stamps (including stamped envelopes and postage cards) are permitted for philatelic (stamp collecting) purposes in articles, books, albums, journals, newspapers and advertising literature of legitimate stamp dealers. These illustrations must be of a size less than three-quarters or more than one and one-half, in linear dimension, of each part of such stamp. If only a portion of stamp is shown to clarify a detail, that portion must be at least four times as large as the corresponding portion on the original U.S. stamp.

(3) Foreign revenue stamps may be reproduced in black and white if the plates are so defaced as to indicate that the illustrations are not adapted or intended for use as stamps.

(4) Foreign postage stamps may be reproduced in black and white for philatelic purposes.

## Miscellaneous Documents

The following group of items may not be reproduced in photographic or printed form:

(1) Drivers' licenses

(2) Amateur radio operators' licenses

(3) Classified government documents, maps, photographs, drawings and publications

(4) Draft registration cards

(5) Badges, identification cards, passes or insignia carried by members of Federal Departments and Bureaus; such as F.B.I., Treasury, Army, etc., or of similar branches of state and local law enforcement officials.

## Offensive and Obscene Material

Refuse to print or aid otherwise in the printing or publication of any literature, drawings or photographs which may be offensive, immoral or detrimental to our form of government, its officials, our accepted moral code or to any group of people because of their race or religious beliefs.

Remember — almost every invention in the graphic arts industry, from its very beginnings, had its inception in the need to further our methods of communication for the cause of religion, education and liberty. Printers have always been men of the highest integrity and skill, admired in every community.

## Questions

1. Can you photograph and reproduce anything you please? Explain.

2. What is a "copyright"?

3. Where does the copyright notice normally appear in a book?

4. What privileges does the copyright owner enjoy?

5. For how long does the original copyright run?

6. How can a copyright be renewed?

7. What is common-law literary property?

8. When is common-law literary property no longer protected by state law?

9. Tell how you would go about securing permission to reproduce copyrighted material, and how you would credit its source.

10. What are the prohibitions on reproducing paper money?

11. What does "in the similitude" mean in the law (Title 18)?

12. Besides the prohibition on the actual printing of United States money (currency), what finer restrictions are there?

13. What regulations are there concerning the printing of illustrations of U. S. Savings Bonds and Savings Stamps?

14. Are you allowed to print illustrations of coins? Explain.

15. Tell under what conditions illustrations of United States postage stamps may be printed.

16. List some miscellaneous documents which may not be printed.

## Problems and Projects

1. Secure a copy of the copyright laws for your shop library.
2. Secure copies of the laws concerning the reproduction of money, coins, stamps, documents, etc., for your shop library.
3. Arrange with your instructor to invite a speaker from the Treasury Department to speak to the class or school assembly concerning counterfeiting.
4. Make up a small display showing permissible forms of reproductions of U. S. postage stamps for philatelic purposes.
5. Make up a small display of forms of copyright notice. Label each to indicate any unusual items. Include an illustration, if you can, which carries a credit line.
6. List some inventions in the graphic arts which were primarily developed for the dissemination of religious literature.

## New Words

1. abbreviation
2. advertising
3. ascertained
4. calendars
5. clarification
6. classified
7. copyright
8. counterfeit
9. courteous
10. custody
11. distinctive
12. duration
13. exclusive
14. forging
15. guardian
16. invasion
17. legal
18. legitimate
19. literary
20. monogram
21. obligation
22. obscene
23. philatelic
24. placard
25. publication
26. reparations
27. restrictions
28. security
29. similitude
30. symbol
31. violate

# Appendices

APPENDIX *1*

# The Use and Care of Drawing Instruments*

A knowledge of the correct use of drawing instruments will enable one to become more proficient in laying out work, making additions to line work and in producing ruled forms for originals. It should be noted that the following directions are directed toward right-handed students; left-handed students must reverse these directions (substituting left for right and *vice versa*).

## Fastening Paper Squarely

Drawing, goldenrod and layout paper should be fastened squarely and smoothly on the board or other surface. Place the T square over the paper, holding it firmly against the left-hand edge of the table or board and line up the lower edge of the paper so it is parallel with the upper edge of the T square. Tape the upper left-hand corner of the paper to the table or board. Then draw the paper smoothly and tightly to the lower right-hand corner, and tape it there. Now smooth out the paper from the center to the upper right-hand corner and fasten with tape. Smooth the paper from the center to the lower left-hand corner and tape that corner. The paper should now be taut and smooth.

Remember to use the same T square for all future work on this same sheet of paper. Always hold the T square against the same left-hand edge as was used in fastening and squaring the paper.

## Drawing Pencils

The various grades of drawing pencils are from softest to hardest: 7B, 6B, 5B, 4B, 3B, 2B, B, HB, F, H, 2H, 3H, 4H, 5H, 6H, 7H, 8H, and 9H. Grade 7B is the softest and blackest:

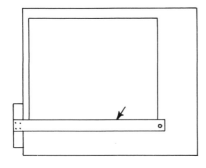

Fig. 515. Line Up Bottom Edge of Paper with Upper Edge of T Square Blade

* Illustrations and adaptation of text from "Use and Care of Drawing Instruments," published by Eugene Dietzgen Co., New York. Reproduced by permission.

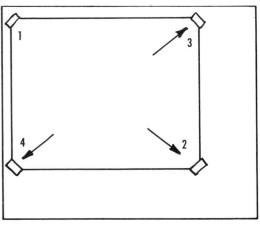

Fig. 516. Correct Order of Taping Paper to Table

9H is the hardest grade. The B grades are used primarily for sketching and artwork; H and 2H are preferred for lettering; 2H and harder are used for mechanical drawings.

To sharpen a pencil, remove the wood with a pocket knife or draftman's pencil sharpener until about ¼ inch of the lead is exposed. Do not point the lead with a knife; use a sand-paper pencil pointer or a draftsman's pencil pointer. A flat chisel-shaped point (Fig. 517-B) is preferred by some draftsmen for drawing straight lines. A conical-shaped point (Fig. 517-A) is used for sketching, and lettering.

In ruling lines, the pencil should be held in a nearly vertical position, inclined slightly to the direction in which the line is being drawn.

## T Square

The T square is used for drawing horizontal lines, and also as a guide for triangles in drawing vertical and inclined lines. It may be made of wood or metal. When placed on the drawing board or table, the head should be held firmly against the left edge of the board. Sliding the T square head along this edge affords a means of drawing parallel lines. Always use the left hand on the head of the square to move the T square, leaving the right hand free to manipulate the pencils and instruments. Only the upper edge, called the "working edge" of the T square is used.

(Left-handed workers use the right-hand edge of the board for the T square, making all lines with the left hand.)

When ruling lines with the pen and pencil, draw the lines from left to right, and from bottom to top of paper.

## Triangles

The triangles are used for drawing vertical and inclined lines. The most commonly used triangles are the 45 and 30-60 degree triangles. The 45 degree triangle has angles of 45, 45, and 90 degrees; the 30-60 degree triangle has angles of 30, 60, and 90 degrees.

They are generally made of plastic or steel. Figs. 522 and 523 show how two triangles are used in combination with the T square for drawing lines and angles of various degrees.

Fig. 517. Conical and Chisel Points on Drawing Pencils

Fig. 518. Wood T Square

Fig. 519. Steel T Square (Adjustable Head)

Fig. 520. Ruling Horizontal Lines

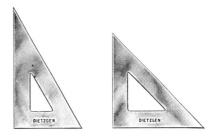
Fig. 521. Left–30°; Right–45°

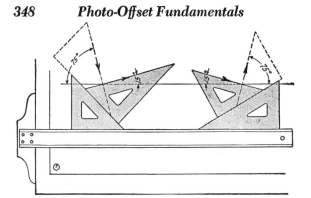

Fig. 522.  Using Two Triangles in Combination with the T Square

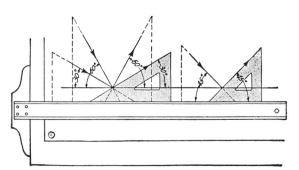

Fig. 523.  Using Two Triangles in Combination with the T Square

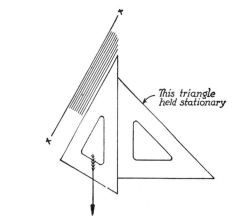

Fig. 524.  Drawing Lines Parallel to a Given Line Without Aid of the T Square

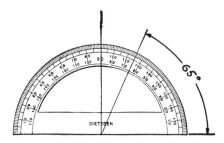

Fig. 525.  How to Use the Protractor

To draw parallel lines at odd angles or to a given line without the aid of a T square (Fig. 524), the edge of one triangle is placed at the desired angle or upon the given line XX. The other triangle is placed against the edge of the first triangle, on which it slides. The guiding triangle should be held firmly with the thumb, third and fourth fingers, sliding the other triangle with the first and second fingers.

## Protractor

The protractor is an instrument used in laying off angles that are not included in the triangles. They are generally made semi-circular in shape with a center mark on the straight edge indicating the center of the circle. When laying out angles with the protractor, place its straight edge on the line with its center mark at the point in the line from which the angle is to be drawn or measured (Fig. 525). Next, find the given angle on the outer edge of the protractor and mark the paper at the point exactly opposite this division. Remove the protractor and draw a straight line through the point just found and the point on which the center of the protractor rested. This gives the required angle.

## Rules and Scales

Beveled-edge metal or wood scales and rules are used for laying off distances and measuring. The beveled edge permits marking on the paper exactly opposite the division marks on the scale or ruler. If a thick-edged scale or rule is used, hold it up on its edge so its division marks will be touching the paper.

Fig. 526.  Beveled-Edge Rule

Fig. 527.  Architect's Scale

Remember to use a finely pointed pencil to mark off distances.

If a reduction or enlargement is being drawn, use the architect's scale shown in Fig. 527. A drawing which is either smaller or larger than the object and still retains the same relative proportion is said to be "drawn to scale." The scale of a drawing is expressed as so many inches to the foot: ½ size is 6 inches to the foot; ¼ size is 3 inches to the foot, etc.

Engineer's scales are available which are used to draw to scale when the drawing is to be $\frac{1}{10}$, $\frac{1}{20}$, $\frac{1}{50}$, or $\frac{1}{100}$ the size of the object.

## Compasses

The compasses (Fig. 528) are used for drawing circles. There are several detachable parts: the pencil part, the pen part, the lengthening bar and sometimes the divider part.

The needle point should be so adjusted that it extends about $\frac{1}{64}$ inch beyond the pen point (Fig. 529).

The pencil part should be fitted with a hard (4H or 6H) lead, sharpened to a chisel point with the bevel on the outside. Adjust the lead so it is about $\frac{1}{64}$ inch shorter than the needle.

The pen part is inked by inserting ink between its nibs with the quill end of the ink bottle stopper (Fig. 530). A deposit of ink about $\frac{3}{16}$ inch high is enough for a filling.

The lengthening bar is used for lengthening one leg of the compasses (Fig. 531) so that large circles may be drawn. The shank

of the bar is fastened into the socket of the compasses leg, and the pen or pencil part is fastened into the socket of the bar.

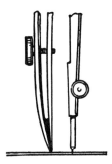

Fig. 529. Adjustment of Compasses Needle Point

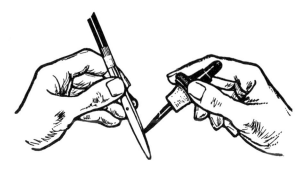

Fig. 530. Filling the Pen

Fig. 531. Use of Compasses with Lengthening Bar

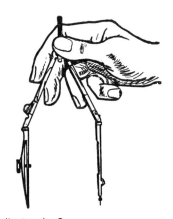

Fig. 532. Adjusting the Compasses

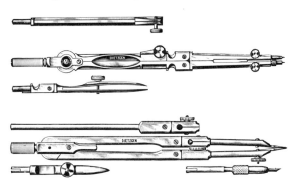

Fig. 528. The Compasses

The compasses are opened with one hand, pressing the thumb and second finger between the legs. This will permit its being held in correct position for easy adjustment

Fig. 533. Drawing a Circle with the Compasses

Fig. 534. Using the Dividers to Divide a Line into a Given Number of Parts

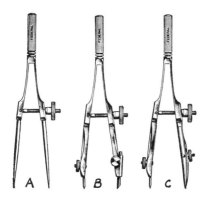

Fig. 535. Bow Instruments: a., Bow Dividers; b., Bow Pencil; c., Bow Pen

with the thumb and forefinger on the outside and the second and third finger on the inside, as shown in Fig. 532.

When the legs are adjusted to the proper radius, the hand is raised to the handle and the circle is drawn with a sweeping motion of the compasses, rolling the handle between the thumb and forefinger and inclining it slightly in the direction the line is drawn (Fig. 533). Circles larger than three inches in diameter should be drawn with the lower parts of the legs nearly perpendicular to the paper, as shown in Fig. 533.

## Dividers

The dividers are similar to compasses, except that both legs are pointed and neither leg has joints. They are used for transferring scaled dimensions. They are also used for dividing a line into a number of equal parts.

To divide a line into a given number of parts — for example, five — estimate the first division and step this division off lightly along the line, holding the dividers vertically by the handle and turning the instrument first in one direction and then in the other (Fig. 534). If the last division falls short, open the dividers one-fifth of the remaining distance, and re-step the line. If the last division is over, close the dividers one-fifth of the excess distance and try again.

Where a number of small divisions are to be made, it is better to use the bow dividers. This instrument has a screw adjustment which permits a finer setting.

## Bow Instruments

The bow instruments include: the bow pencil, the bow pen, and the bow dividers. They are used in the same manner as the compasses and dividers, except that their use is confined to small dimensions. They are somewhat similar in design, except that the legs have a spring joint or head and are set by means of an adjusting screw.

In changing the setting of bow instruments, much time is saved and much wear and tear on threads are avoided by releasing the pressure of the spring against the nut (Fig. 536). Press the legs together between the thumb and forefinger of the left hand and spin the nut in or out as desired with the other hand.

Small changes in adjustment are best made with the right hand, keeping the needle point in the paper. Hold the instrument with the forefinger on top of the handle, raise the remaining instrument leg slightly and adjust the screw with the thumb and second finger.

If there is a tendency for the needle point to lift from the paper when drawing small circles, extend the needle point slightly.

## Ruling Pen

The ruling pen is used for inking all lines, other than circles. The blades, or nibs, of the pen should be of equal length, slightly sharp and when viewed from the front should have oval-shaped points (Fig. 537). Place ink between the points with an ordinary writing pen or the quill point of the ink bottle stopper. Be careful not to get ink on the outside of the nibs. Fill to a height of ³⁄₁₆ inch — more ink than this is likely to run too rapidly from the pen and blot on account of its weight. (See Fig. 530.)

Hold the pen as shown in Fig. 538. The adjusting screw should be away from the body with the handle resting against the first finger. The thumb and first finger are held in such a position as to be handy for turning the adjusting screw.

When ruling lines, hold the pen in a nearly-vertical position against the T square, straightedge or triangle, with the points of the pen parallel to the edge and the handle inclined slightly to the right. The pen is thus guided by the straightedge, bearing just enough against the edge to guide its direction. The line is drawn with a free arm movement, the hand resting on the tips of the third and fourth fingers and keeping the angle of inclination of the pen constant. When nearing the end of the line, hold the hand firm and draw the pen toward the end of the line with

the fingers only. As the end of the line is reached, lift the pen quickly from the paper with the first and second fingers.

Fig. 536.  Release Tension when Adjusting Bow Instruments

Fig. 537.  Correctly Shaped Ruling Pen Nibs

Fig. 538.  How to Hold and Use the Ruling Pen

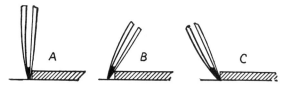

Fig. 539.  Angles of Ruling Pen Against Straightedge: A, Correct; B and C, wrong.

Both nibs of the pen should always touch the paper to obtain a clear-cut line as in Fig. 539-A. If the point of the pen is inclined out from the straightedge (Fig. 539-B), only the near nib will touch, and a ragged line will result. If the pen is inclined toward the straightedge, the ink will run under the straightedge, thus making a blotted line. (See Fig. 539-C.)

Clean the pen frequently during use by inserting the point of a cloth between the nibs, rotating the pen so the cloth is wrapped once around the pen. Squeeze the nibs together lightly, while drawing the cloth lightly through the nibs. Do not change the adjustment of the pen to do this.

If the ink refuses to flow from the pen because it has dried at the extreme point of the nibs, squeeze the nibs together gently and

Fig. 540. Sharpening the Ruling Pen

touch them to a scrap of paper. This generally will remove the dried ink.

When through using the pen, insert a cloth through the nibs, rotate the pen so the cloth is wrapped around the pen and withdraw the pen through the roll of cloth while squeezing the nibs together gently. Repeat with the cloth slightly dampened with water. Then repeat with a dry cloth. Adjust so the nibs are wide apart, thus retaining the spring.

### Sharpening a Ruling Pen (or Pen Part)

If the nibs become dull and flat through use, adjust them so they touch together, and sharpen them to an oval shape as shown in Fig. 537. Use an oilstone. Hold the pen as when drawing lines, and draw the pen in a pendulum fashion, starting the stroke at about 30 degrees to the stone and swinging over until it reaches the same angle on the opposite side. When both nibs are of equal length and an oval shape is obtained, open the nibs and sharpen each to a keen edge. Never sharpen the inside edges of the nibs. The pen should not be sharp enough to cut the paper, but it should produce the finest of hairlines.

## Converting Fractions, Decimals, and Percentages

A value which is more or less than a whole number may be expressed as a *fraction,* a *decimal* or a *percentage*. For example: one-half inch may be written as:

    a.  a fraction — ½ — which is read as "one-half"

    b.  a decimal — .50 — which is read as "fifty-hundredths"

              .5 — which is read as "five tenths"

    c.  a percentage — 50% — which is read as "fifty per cent"

To change a fraction to a decimal, divide the numerator (top number) by the denominator (bottom number). For example:

    a.  $\frac{1}{3} = 3\overline{)1.000}^{\,.333} = .333$, or .33⅓

    b.  $\frac{1}{5} = 5\overline{)1.00}^{\,.20} = .20$, or .2

    c.  $1\frac{1}{2} = \frac{3}{2} = 2\overline{)3.00}^{\,1.50} = 1.50$, or 1.5

To change a decimal to a percentage, multiply by 100. For example:

    a.  .6 × 100 = 60., or 60 per cent

    b.  1.5 × 100 = 150., or 150 per cent

    c.  2.0 × 100 = 200., or 200 per cent

    d.  1.35 × 100 = 135., or 135 per cent

To change a fraction to a percentage, first change the fraction to a decimal, then multiply by 100. For example:

    a.  $\frac{2}{3} = 3\overline{)2.000}^{\,.666} = .666$ (or .66⅔)

          .666 × 100 = 66.6, or 66⅔ per cent

    b.  $\frac{2}{5} = 5\overline{)2.00}^{\,.40} = .40$ (or .4)

          .4 × 100 = 40, or 40 per cent

    c.  $2\frac{1}{2} = \frac{5}{2} = 2\overline{)5.0}^{\,2.5} = 2.5$

          2.5 × 100 = 250, or 250 per cent

APPENDIX *3*

## Decimal Equivalents — Parts of an Inch, Point System

By Sixty-Fourths

| | | |
|---|---|---|
| 1/64 | | .01563 |
| | 1/32 | .03125 |
| 3/64 | | .04688 |
| | 1/16 | .0625 |
| 5/64 | | .07813 |
| | 3/32 | .09375 |
| 7/64 | | .10938 |
| | 1/8 | .125 |
| 9/64 | | .14063 |
| | 5/32 | .15625 |
| 11/64 | | .17188 |
| | 3/16 | .1875 |
| 13/64 | | .20313 |
| | 7/32 | .21875 |
| 15/64 | | .23438 |
| | 1/4 | .250 |
| 17/64 | | .26563 |
| | 9/32 | .28125 |
| 19/64 | | .29688 |
| | 5/16 | .3125 |
| 21/64 | | .32813 |
| | 11/32 | .34375 |
| 23/64 | | .35938 |
| | 3/8 | .375 |
| 25/64 | | .39063 |
| | 13/32 | .40625 |
| 27/64 | | .42188 |
| | 7/16 | .4375 |
| 29/64 | | .45313 |
| | 15/32 | .46875 |
| 31/64 | | .48438 |
| | 1/2 | .500 |

| | | |
|---|---|---|
| 33/64 | | .51563 |
| | 17/32 | .53125 |
| 35/64 | | .54688 |
| | 9/16 | .5625 |
| 37/64 | | .57813 |
| | 19/32 | .59375 |
| 39/64 | | .60938 |
| | 5/8 | .625 |
| 41/64 | | .64063 |
| | 21/32 | .65625 |
| 43/64 | | .67188 |
| | 11/16 | .6875 |
| 45/64 | | .70313 |
| | 23/32 | .71875 |
| 47/64 | | .73438 |
| | 3/4 | .750 |
| 49/64 | | .76563 |
| | 25/32 | .78125 |
| 51/64 | | .79688 |
| | 13/16 | .8125 |
| 53/64 | | .82813 |
| | 27/32 | .84375 |
| 55/64 | | .85938 |
| | 7/8 | .875 |
| 57/64 | | .89063 |
| | 29/32 | .90625 |
| 59/64 | | .92188 |
| | 15/16 | .9375 |
| 61/64 | | .95313 |
| | 31/32 | .96875 |
| 63/64 | | .98438 |

## By Selected Twelfths

| | |
|---|---|
| 1/12 | .083333 |
| 1/6 | .166667 |
| 1/3 | .333333 |
| 5/12 | .416667 |
| 7/12 | .583333 |
| 2/3 | .666667 |
| 5/6 | .833333 |
| 12/12 | 1.00 |

## By Fifths

| | |
|---|---|
| 1/5 | .20 |
| 2/5 | .40 |
| 3/5 | .60 |
| 4/5 | .80 |
| 5/5 | 1.00 |

## By American Point System

| | |
|---|---|
| 1 Pica Em | .16600 |
| 6 Picas | .99600 |
| 1 Point | .01383 |
| 72 Points | .99600 |
| Type-high | .91860 |

## By Didot (French) Point System

| | |
|---|---|
| 1 Cicero Em | .17800 |
| 6 Cicero Ems | 1.06800 |
| 1 Point (Corps) | .01483 |
| 12 Points | .17800 |

APPENDIX 4

## How to Read the Micrometer Calipers

The micrometer calipers (sometimes called a "micrometer", and very popularly called a 'mike") is a precision measuring tool designed to indicate measurements in *thousandths* of

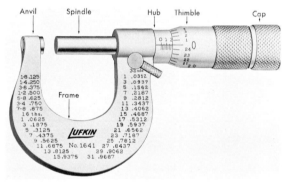

Fig. 555. Micrometer Nomenclature (Courtesy Lufkin Rule Co.)

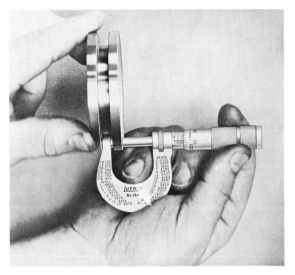

Fig. 556. Measuring With a Micrometer
(Courtesy Lufkin Rule Co.)

an inch. If the micrometer is provided with "vernier" markings on its hub, measurements can be made to the *ten-thousandth* part of an inch.

Fig. 555 indicates the nomenclature of a standard micrometer.

### Reading Thousandths

Hold the mike in the right hand (as shown in Fig. 556), the frame resting on the palm of the hand, and held there by the third finger.

With the left hand, hold the object to be measured between the anvil and the spindle. Rotate the thimble clockwise with the thumb and index finger of the right hand until the anvil and spindle gently contact the object. *Do not exert force* — make a gentle contact.

Read the measurement by counting each exposed full division on the hub as 25 thousandths, and adding to that the number of divisions indicated on the thimble scale.

In Fig. 557, the measurement of .154″ (or 154 thousandths) is obtained since there are six full divisions exposed on the hub and four divisions on the thimble — 6 × 25 = 150 — 150 plus 4 = 154 thousandths.

Often, in the shop, a sum such as .154 (one hundred fifty-four thousandths) is expressed as "point one five four."

Note that each complete revolution of the thimble will move the thimble horizontally along the hub 25 thousandths of an inch, or one full division on the hub. Each fourth division mark on the hub is marked with a figure: *1* for one hundred thousandths, *2* for two hundred thousandths, etc. This aids in reading large measurements.

When the mike is used for measuring the thickness of plates or paper which is less than 25 thousandths thick, the reading is taken directly from the thimble. A division mark on the hub will not be exposed until the thimble is turned 25 thousandths, or more, from the closed position; most plates and paper will measure less than this.

## Testing Your "Feel" or "Touch"

Holding the mike as described, close your eyes and bring the spindle up to the anvil with a gentle contact. Open your eyes and read the mike. Is it zero? Repeat this procedure until you learn *by feel* just how much gentle contact is required to produce a zero reading. Use this same feel or touch in all micrometer measuring.

Some micrometers are equipped with a spindle or ratchet cap, which permits only a uniform pressure to be exerted in all measuring. After the spindle and anvil contact the piece being measured, excess pressure on the spindle screw results only in clicking the ratchet.

## Reading to Ten-Thousandths

It is possible to measure to the ten-thousandth part of an inch if your micrometer hub is provided with vernier markings above the hub scale as shown in Fig. 558.

In Fig. 558, the reading is .1546″ (fifteen hundred and forty-six ten-thousandths of an inch.) It is obtained by reading .154 in the usual manner: six hub divisions of 25 equal .150, and four divisions on the thimble added to the .150 equal .154″. Since the sixth line on the vernier scale is the line which coincides with a line on the thimble, place a 6 after the .154 to make it read .1546″ (or 1546 ten-thousandths of an inch).

The reading obtained above (.1546″) is often referred to as *1546 tenths*, meaning to mechanics: "ten-thousandths."

## Recording Measurements

When recording (writing down) measurements taken with the micrometer, be sure to include the decimal point and any zeros. For example:

a. Three thousandths is written as . .003
b. Ten thousandths as ........... .010
c. Twenty-five thousandths as.... .025
d. One hundred and five
   thousandths as ............. .105
e. One hundred and twenty-five
   thousandths as ............. .125
f. Twelve hundred and twenty-five
   ten-thousandths as ........... .1225
g. One thousand and five ten-
   thousandths as ............. .1005

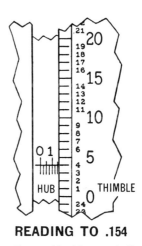

**READING TO .154**

Fig. 557.  Reading Thousandths (Courtesy Lufkin Rule Co.)

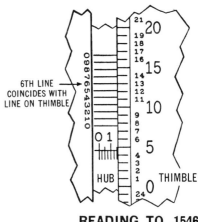

**READING TO .1546**

Fig. 558.  Reading Ten-Thousandths (Courtesy Lufkin Rule Co.)

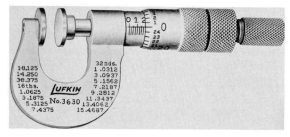

Fig. 559.  Paper Gage Micrometer (Courtesy Lufkin Rule Co.)

## Paper Gage Micrometers

Paper, rubber blankets and other soft materials may be more accurately measured with the paper gage micrometer shown in Fig. 559. This mike has extra-wide faces on the anvil and spindle to prevent undue compression of the material being measured.

# Weights and Measures

### Avoirdupois Weight

$$27^{11}\!/_{32} \text{ grains } = 1 \text{ dram}$$
$$16 \text{ drams } = 1 \text{ ounce}$$
$$16 \text{ ounces } = 1 \text{ pound}$$
$$7000 \text{ grains } = 1 \text{ pound}$$

### Metric Weight

$$10 \text{ decigrams} = 1 \text{ gram}$$
$$10 \text{ grams} \quad = 1 \text{ dekogram}$$

### Emergency Weights

| Coin (New) | Weight in Grains |
|---|---|
| Dime | 40 |
| Cent | 50 |
| Nickel | 80 |
| Quarter | 100 |
| Half-dollar | 200 |
| Silver dollar | 400 |

### Liquid Measure

$$4 \text{ ounces} = 1 \text{ gill}$$
$$4 \text{ gills} \quad = 1 \text{ pint (16 ounces)}$$
$$2 \text{ pints} \quad = 1 \text{ quart (32 ounces)}$$
$$4 \text{ quarts} \quad = 1 \text{ gallon (128 ounces)}$$
$$1 \text{ liter} \quad = 1.06 \text{ quarts (32.92 ounces)}$$
$$3785 \text{ cubic centimeters} = 1 \text{ gallon}$$
$$231 \text{ cubic inches} = 1 \text{ gallon}$$

### Time

$$60 \text{ seconds} = 1 \text{ minute}$$
$$60 \text{ minutes} = 1 \text{ hour}$$

### Circular Measure

$$60 \text{ seconds } (60'') = 1 \text{ minute } (1')$$
$$60 \text{ minutes } (60') = 1 \text{ degree}(1°)$$
$$90 \text{ degrees } (90°) = \text{ right angle}$$
$$360 \text{ degrees } (360°) = \text{ complete circle}$$

### Linear Measure

$$12 \text{ inches } (12'') = 1 \text{ foot } (1'\text{-}0'')$$
$$36 \text{ inches} \quad = 1 \text{ yard}$$
$$1 \text{ millimeter} \quad = .03937 \text{ inches}$$
$$10 \text{ millimeters} \quad = 1 \text{ centimeter}$$
$$10 \text{ centimeters} \quad = 1 \text{ decimeter}$$
$$10 \text{ decimeters} \quad = 1 \text{ meter (39.37 inches)}$$

# Conversion Factors

| | | | |
|---|---|---|---|
| Centimeters | × 0.3937 | = | Inches |
| Centimeters | × 10 | = | Millimeters |
| Degrees (of an angle) | × 60 | = | Minutes |
| Gallons | × 3.785 | = | Liters |
| Gallons | × 8 | = | Pints |
| Gallons | × 4 | = | Quarts |
| Gallons | × 128 | = | Ounces (liquid) |
| Gallons | × 3785 | = | Cubic centimeters |
| Grams | × 0.03527 | = | Ounces (avoirdupois) |
| Grams | × 15.432 | = | Grains |
| | | | |
| Inches | × 2.540 | = | Centimeters |
| Liters | × 0.2642 | = | Gallons |
| Liters | × 1.057 | = | Quarts |
| Liters | × 2.113 | = | Pints |
| Millimeters | × 0.1 | = | Centimeters |
| Millimeters | × 0.03937 | = | Inches |
| Ounces (avoirdupois) | × 0.0625 | = | Pounds |
| Ounces (avoirdupois) | × 28.35 | = | Grams |
| Ounces (liquid) | × 0.02957 | = | Liters |
| Pounds | × 16 | = | Ounces (avoirdupois) |
| Pounds | × 256 | = | Drams |
| Pounds | × 7000 | = | Grains |

To convert Degrees Centigrade to Degrees Fahrenheit, multiply by 9/5 and add 32.

To convert Degrees Fahrenheit to Degrees Centigrade, subtract 32 and multiply by 5/9.

APPENDIX *7*

# Humidity

Humidity is moisture in the air. When the humidity is at a low level, the air is dry and will absorb moisture from any surrounding exposed materials which contain more moisture than the air itself.

When the humidity is at a high level, the air is damp, and it will give off moisture which will be absorbed by any surrounding exposed materials which contain less moisture than the air.

## 100% Humidity

When the air contains all the moisture it can absorb, the saturation point, or 100% humidity, has been achieved.

At 100% humidity, the amount of water contained in a cubic foot of air will vary according to the temperature, as follows:

| 1 cu. ft. of air at | can hold a maximum of |
|---|---|
| 20 degrees F. . . . . | 1.24 grains of water* |
| 32 degrees F. . . . . | 2.12 grains of water |
| 40 degrees F. . . . . | 2.87 grains of water |
| 55 degrees F. . . . . | 4.89 grains of water |
| 70 degrees F. . . . . | 8.05 grains of water |
| 80 degrees F. . . . . | 11.08 grains of water |

*7,000 grains equals 1 pound of water

The warmer the air, the more water it can contain per cubic foot.

## Relative Humidity

The air about us is not always at the saturation point, or 100% humidity. Some days the air is dry, and sometimes it is damp.

If, on a certain day (whatever the temperature may be), the air contains 80% of the total amount of moisture it could possibly contain, it is said that *the relative humidity is 80%*. Relative humidity, then, is a comparison (at a particular temperature) between the actual amount of moisture in the air and the amount it could possibly hold.

Generally speaking, humans feel comfortable when the relative humidity is about 50%.

## Measuring Relative Humidity

Relative humidity is read directly from the dial of a direct-reading relative humidity indicator, or is determined by the use of a wet-and-dry-bulb thermometer.

### Direct Reading Indicator

Moisture-bearing air, entering the openings in the indicator case, causes a hygroscopic element to lengthen and activate the indicator pointer which then points to a position on the dial scale, indicating the percentage of relative humidity.

### Wet-and-Dry-Bulb Thermometer

The wet-and-dry-bulb thermometer actually consists of two accurate thermometers. The bulb of one thermometer is exposed to the air as usual (this is the dry-bulb thermometer); the bulb of the other is wrapped with a wick whose free end is submerged in

**361**

a vial of distilled water (this is the wet-bulb thermometer).

Evaporation of water from the wick on the wet-bulb thermometer causes it always to read at a lower temperature than the dry-bulb thermometer.

Fig. 575. Direct-Reading Relative Humidity Indicator (Courtesy Abbeon Supply Co.)

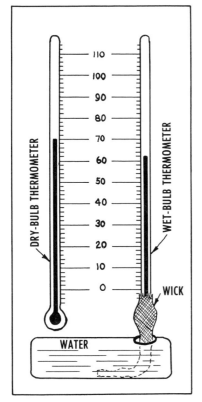

Fig. 576. Wet-and-Dry-Bulb Thermometer

To calculate relative humidity with the wet-and-dry-bulb thermometer, fan the wet-bulb thermometer vigorously until the reading no longer recedes. Read the temperatures on both the wet and the dry thermometers. Subtract the lower reading from the higher reading, arriving at a difference between the two. Finally, consulting a relative humidity table, read across on the line of figures opposite the dry-bulb reading to a point directly below the figure representing difference between the readings. This will indicate the relative humidity.

For example, assume that the difference between the two thermometer readings is eight degrees and the dry-bulb reading is 70°. Using the table below, and reading across from the dry-bulb reading of 70° to the column headed by eight degrees difference, the indicated relative humidity is read as 64%.

## Control of Relative Humidity

Extreme variations in relative humidity in the lithographic shop may cause inconsistencies in platemaking, press operation, drying of inks, static electricity and stretching and shrinking of paper stock (especially across the grain.)

If possible, a system of air conditioning or humidifiers should be employed to maintain the relative humidity at 50% to 55% with a temperature of 70°. This is an average for the small one- or two-room shop.

### Table 5
#### Relative Humidity
Difference between Wet- and Dry-Bulb Therometers

| Dry-bulb thermometer reading | 7 | 8 | 9 | 10 | 11 | 12 | 13 |
|---|---|---|---|---|---|---|---|
| 62 | 64 | 59 | 54 | 50 | 45 | 41 | 37 |
| 64 | 65 | 60 | 56 | 51 | 47 | 43 | 38 |
| 66 | 66 | 61 | 57 | 53 | 48 | 44 | 40 |
| 68 | 67 | 62 | 58 | 54 | 50 | 46 | 42 |
| 70 | 68 | 64 | 59 | 55 | 51 | 48 | 44 |
| 72 | 69 | 65 | 61 | 57 | 53 | 49 | 46 |
| 74 | 70 | 66 | 62 | 58 | 54 | 51 | 47 |
| 76 | 70 | 67 | 63 | 59 | 55 | 52 | 48 |
| 78 | 71 | 67 | 64 | 60 | 57 | 53 | 50 |

APPENDIX 8

# Albumin Plate Coating

This section is included for those who wish to make their own light-sensitive solution for coating plates. It also explains how to prepare, expose, develop and use the traditional albumin plate for photo-offset lithography.

The albumin coating remains one of the easiest light-sensitive coatings to prepare from simple chemicals. The solution can be used for either whirler-coated offset plates or for a wipe-on coating (requiring no expensive equipment or regraining of metal plates). It can also be the basis for some interesting experimental uses in the school laboratory, where the student needs a light-sensitive coating for such operations as etching nameplates in aluminum sheet using a photographic resist.

A general description of albumin plates was given in Chapter 13, "Platemaking," on page 237.

## How to Make an Albumin Plate-Coating Solution

The albumin coating solution consists of two parts:

(1) *the albumin solution*
(2) *the ammonium-dichromate[1] stock solution*

These solutions are prepared separately the day before the plates are to be coated. The

[1]*Ammonium-dichromate* and *ammonium-bichromate* are the same. This substance, if taken internally, is a deadly poison.

The addition of the ammonium-dichromate renders the coating solution light-sensitive.

two are combined, as described later, into one solution when the plates are ready to be coated.

### The Albumin Solution

The albumin solution is prepared by measuring out separately:

2¼ ounces (avoirdupois) of edible egg albumin scales

11 ounces (liquid) of water (Use a 32-ounce graduate.)

Cut several thicknesses of cheesecloth to make a pad about 9 inches in diameter. Place the albumin on the center of the pad, turn up the edges and tie with string at the top. Suspend this "sack" of albumin flakes in the water of the graduate so that the albumin is below the surface of the water (but not touching the bottom). Tie the string to a stick across the top of the graduate to maintain this level, much the same as in Fig. 335, page 221. Cover with paper, and let stand overnight.

### The Ammonium-Dichromate Stock Solution

The ammonium-dichromate stock solution is prepared by measuring out:

1 ounce (avoirdupois) of ammonium dichromate (granular)

4 ounces (liquid) of water.

Pour the dichromate into the water. Cover the graduate with a piece of paper, and let stand overnight. Label this container "Poison." Avoid undue contact with the crystals, and wash your hands thoroughly when you are through. Return the jar of dichromate crystals (grains) to the chemical cabinet, and *lock the cabinet.*

### Mixing the Coating Solution

After the albumin solution and the ammonium-dichromate stock solution have been allowed to stand overnight, the two solutions must be combined to make the *coating solution.*

Secure two clean, quart-size, amber-colored bottles. Label one "Coating Solution", and the other "Ammonium-Dichromate Stock Solution — Poison." Date each label.

Stir the dichromate solution. Then filter it through a water-wet cotton pad into a hydrometer jar. Take a hydrometer reading; add water slowly until the solution has a density of 14.2° Bé (Baumé).[2] Pour this into the bottle marked "Ammonium-Dichromate Stock Solution — Poison."

Lift the sack of albumin scales out of the water, hold it above the graduate, and allow it to drain. *Do not squeeze it.* Discard the sack, or wash it out to use again. Take a hydrometer reading to the closest .1° Baumé. Using the left-hand column in Table 4, locate this reading; read directly across to the right-hand column. The figure there indicates how many ounces of the albumin solution is needed for the coating solution. Measure out the indicated quantity and pour it into the bottle marked "Coating Solution." Discard the remainder of the albumin solution.

Measure out 2½ ounces of the ammonium-dichromate stock solution and add it to the albumin solution in the bottle marked "Coating Solution." Now add sufficient water to bring the volume of coating solution to 20 liquid ounces. The coating solution is now ready for use. (The remainder of the ammonium-dichromate stock solution may be stored out of the light for future use.)

Addition of ammonium hydroxide (mixed with five parts of water) to the coating solution will slow the sensitivity of the plate coating. Add it slowly, and add only enough to bring the pH to 7.6. (See page 284 for explanation of pH.)

While the above described coating solution may keep satisfactorily in a cool place for several days, it may be better to make it up fresh the day it is to be used.

### Suggestions

Directly after use, thoroughly wash out all graduates, hydrometers and jars which have been used. Place them upside down on their racks to drain and dry.

To avoid accidental poisoning, label each container having ammonium dichromate in it as "Poison." Keep these containers (and their solutions) away from access by unauthorized persons.

Avoid breathing the dust which might arise when weighing or mixing dry chemicals.

After handling chemicals, especially those used in making the coating solution, wash hands thoroughly with hot water and soap — give particular attention to washing between the fingers.

## How to Prepare an Albumin Metal Plate Using a Whirler

Following are the main steps in the preparation of the traditional albumin plate on zinc or aluminum using a plate whirler:

(1) Wash the plate
(2) Counter-etch
(3) Coat
(4) Expose behind the flat
(5) Develop

[2]To take a hydrometer reading, hold the empty hydrometer jar horizontally and slide the float to the bottom of the jar. Now, holding the jar upright, pour the liquid slowly into the jar until the float is raised from the bottom and floats freely in the liquid. The marking on the float scale at the top of the liquid indicates the specific gravity of the liquid.

Antoine Baumé (1728-1804), after whom the Baumé (pronounced Bow-may') system of measurement is named, was a French chemist who designed two hydrometers in which the graduations are equally spaced along their length (or scale). One hydrometer is used for liquids *lighter* than water; the other — the hydrometer used extensively in lithography — is used for liquids *heavier* than water. This latter hydrometer, referred to here as the Baumé hydrometer, sinks to 0° in pure water, and to 15° in a 15% salt solution. Baumé readings may be converted to approximate specific gravity readings by the formula: Specific gravity = 144 ÷ (144 — Baumé reading).

(6) Desensitize
(7) Gum
(8) Preserve (with asphaltum).

The above assumes that the plate is purchased ready-grained. Each of the above steps is discussed in detail below.

## Wash

Place the metal plate, grained side up, on the slanted wooden rack in the platemaking

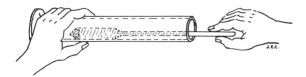

Fig. 580. Slide the Float Horizontally to the Bottom of the Hydrometer Jar

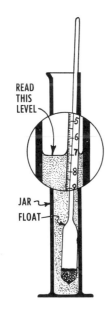

READ THIS LEVEL

JAR
FLOAT

Fig. 581. Taking a Reading with Baumé Hydrometer and Jar

Fig. 582. Scrubbing the Plate

sink. Allow water to run on it while scrubbing the plate with a soft scrubbing brush.

### Counter-Etch

Counter-etching removes surface dirt and oxidation. Drain excess water from the plate; then flush the plate with four to six ounces of the counter-etching solution (as explained in note below). Spread the solution over the plate with a soft, nylon paint brush, working the solution across and up and down for about half a minute. Then flush the plate with running water.

### Table 3
#### Amount of Albumin Solution to use in Preparing the Coating Solution[3]

| Degrees Baumé of Albumin Solution (at 76° F.) | Amount of Albumin Solution to Use (in liquid ounces) |
|---|---|
| 5.1 | 11⅝ |
| 5.2 | 11⅜ |
| 5.3 | 11¼ |
| 5.4 | 11 |
| 5.5 | 10¾ |
| 5.6 | 10⅝ |
| 5.7 | 10⅜ |
| 5.8 | 10⅛ |
| 5.9 | 10 |
| 6.0 | 9⅞ |
| 6.1 | 9⅝ |
| 6.2 | 9½ |
| 6.3 | 9⅜ |
| 6.4 | 9⅛ |
| 6.5 | 9 |
| 6.6 | 8⅞ |
| 6.7 | 8¾ |
| 6.8 | 8⅝ |
| 6.9 | 8½ |
| 7.0 | 8⅜ |
| 7.1 | 8¼ |
| 7.2 | 8 |
| 7.3 | 7⅞ |
| 7.4 | 7¾ |
| 7.5 | 7⅝ |
| 7.6 | 7½ |

[3]Adapted from "Offset Albumin Plate Making", by Joseph W. Mazzaferri. Courtesy of Graphic Arts Technical Foundation, Inc.

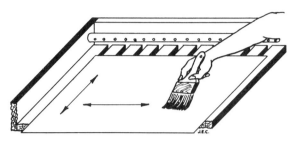

Fig. 583. Counter-Etching the Plate

Fig. 585. Cover the Mouth of the Graduate with Several Layers of Cheesecloth when Pouring the Coating Solution

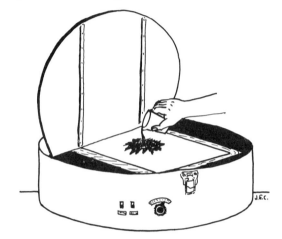

Fig. 584. Coating the Plate in the Whirler

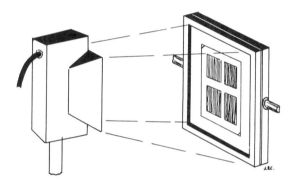

Fig. 586. Exposing the Plate

NOTE: Counter-etching formulas for metal plates are as follows: For *aluminum* plates add 4 liquid ounces of nitric acid (or 4 liquid ounces of phosphoric acid) to one gallon of water; keep in a glass container.

For *zinc* plates, add one liquid ounce of hydrochloric acid C.P., or 4 ounces of acetic acid, to one gallon of water. (Do not use muriatic acid.) Keep in a glass container.

Use the counter-etch brush only for the counter-etch solution.

### Coat

Immediately after counter-etching, place the plate (still wet) in the whirler. Clamp the plate in place, allow the whirler to rotate at 50 to 60 rpm, and flush off the plate with running water.

Turn on a little heat in the whirler, and allow the plate to whirl until it becomes velvety-smooth, but not completely dry.

Pour a quantity of coating solution (about 4 ounces for the average small plate) into a

beaker or graduate. Avoid pouring in such a way as to cause bubbles. Cover the mouth of the container with a couple of layers of cheesecloth to act as a filter. With the plate wet and still whirling, hold the solution container at the center of the plate close to the surface and carefully pour the solution on the plate, working from the center to the outside of the plate.

After coating, continue to whirl until the coating is dry. Then continue whirling a few more minutes to insure dryness and to acclimate the plate coating to the room humidity. Protect the plate against exposure to much light, since it is now light-sensitive.

### Expose

Tape the flat containing the negatives to the coated metal plate at two diagonally opposite corners. The negatives must be in *readable* form. Then place the assembly in the vacuum printing frame, lock it in place, and draw the air out of the frame.

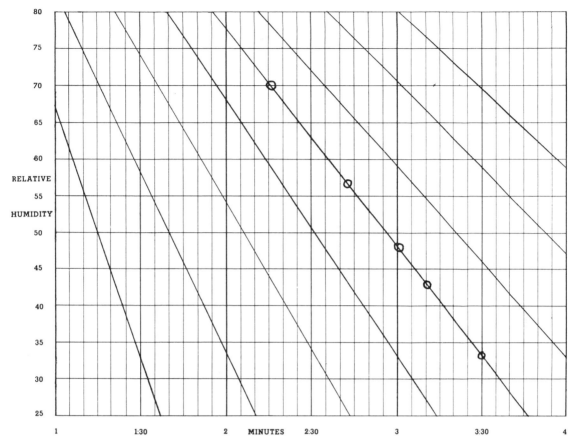

Fig. 587. Exposure Chart for Albumin Plates

Turn on the arc light and make the exposure. The length of exposure is determined beforehand experimentally in the shop, and a careful record kept so that a plate may be successfully exposed with consistently good results. Record for each exposure the relative humidity in the room and the length of the exposure. Plot a chart with the satisfactory results of these two measurements, so that for any reading of relative humidity a satisfactory exposure may be duplicated. See Fig. 587. Expose to obtain a developed Step 6 on a gray scale image.

### Develop

Remove the plate from the printing frame and separate it from the attached flat. Place the plate, exposed side up, on a flat table which is covered with newspapers for protection.

Fig. 588. Step Gray Scale (Screened for Reproduction)

Pour a small amount of developing ink on the center of the plate. With a pad of clean, soft cloth, rub the ink briskly and evenly over the image area of the plate. Rub until the ink is thin and dry. (Developing ink makes the image visible and, at the same time, the greasy nature of the ink makes the image ink-receptive when the plate is on the press.)

Subject the entire inked plate to lukewarm running water and allow it to soak until the developing ink starts to float off the non-printing areas of the plate. Rub the plate surface (still under running water) very gently with a pad of clean cloth, removing all traces of the developing ink from the clear portions of the plate and leaving only the image area. Avoid continued use of a dirty pad of cloth —

Fig. 589. Pouring a Small Quantity of Developing Ink on Center of Plate

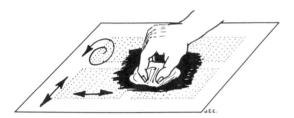

Fig. 590. Coating the Image with Developing Ink

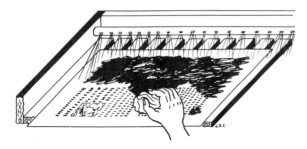

Fig. 591. Developing the Plate Under Running Water

keep turning the pad so you use a clean portion. This prevents rubbing ink into unwanted areas.

The plate may be placed for a few minutes in a tray containing a solution of one or two ounces of bicarbonate of soda to a gallon of water. This helps remove all traces of developing ink. Flush thoroughly under running water in the sink to remove all traces of the baking soda.

### Desensitize

There may yet be tiny traces of scum clinging to the plate. Desensitizing (etching) removes these traces from the non-printing areas of the plate.

Place the plate in a tray and pour over it a solution of:

Gum arabic solution at
  14° Baumé . . . . . . . . . . . .32 ounces
Ammonium dichromate
  stock solution . . . . . . . . . . .1½ ounces
Phosphoric acid (85% syrupy)   ¾ ounce

Let this solution remain for a few minutes; then flush off thoroughly with water. Let it drain, but not dry.

### Gum

With a clean sponge, wet the entire plate surface with gum arabic solution. Take a pad of clean, dry cheesecloth and rub the gum briskly and evenly up and down and across the plate. Rub the gum to a thin, hard finish, free of streaks. Fan the plate dry.

NOTE: The plate may now be mounted on the press. However, if the plate is to be stored for any length of time, apply asphaltum to the image area, as described in the following step.

### Asphaltum

Remove the developing ink from the image on the gummed plate with a little solvent (turpentine, or press-cleaning solvent) and give the plate a thin coating of asphaltum. Rub this thin and dry. Asphaltum prevents the image ink from drying out when the plate is to be stored for a lengthy period. The greasy asphaltum forms a non-drying film on the image area. This step is sometimes referred to as "putting the plate under."

Also, if the plate is to be printed in any color other than black, it is advisable to gum the plate, wash out the developing ink and replace the ink with asphaltum. When the plate is on the press, the gum and asphaltum coatings will sponge off easily with water, leaving the clean image to accept the colored ink.

### Care on the Press

Attach the plate on the plate cylinder of the press. When the press is ready to run, wash the asphaltum and gum from the plate with a clean sponge dipped in water.

If the press run is interrupted for more than a few seconds, the plate is likely to lose water. Oxidation then will attack the plate, causing it to "scum". Prevent this by immediately applying a coating of gum arabic with the sponge, and rubbing it smooth and dry. Gum arabic also protects the plate surface from ink smudges and dirt.

When ready to resume the press run, sponge off the gum with water.

At the end of the press run, gum the plate, remove it from the press, wash out the ink, apply asphaltum and store the plate for reuse.

For re-running a stored plate, attach it to the press, sponge off with water and start the press.

### How to Prepare a Wipe-On Albumin Paper Plate

The following directions are for applying an albumin coating to the surface of a paper (direct-image) plate — rendering it a sensitized plate for exposure to a stripped-up flat.

Although presensitized plates and commercial coating solutions are available, the student will benefit from the experience of preparing a few plates himself, using the albumin coating solution he has prepared himself. The wipe-on technique requires a minimum of equipment and expense.

It is suggested that a rather heavy paper (or plastic-coated) long-run plate be used for this work.

The uncoated plates need not be protected from light, but should be kept in their container in a clean place to protect against dust and dirt. Prepare the plate in subdued light as follows:

### Wash

Wash off the surface of the plate with a swab of clean cotton wet with water.

### Coat

In the center of the plate, pour a spot of albumin coating solution the size of a silver dollar. Spread this coating solution quickly and evenly over the entire surface, using a clean cotton swab. Rub lengthwise and sidewise. When the coating is a bit tacky, but not dry, repeat. Give three coats.

### Dry

Place the coated plate in the drying compartment of the exposure box. Apply heat and forced air for about three minutes.

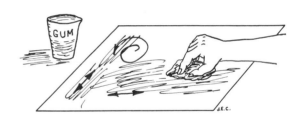

Fig. 592. Gumming the Plate

Fig. 593. Drying the Plate

Fig. 594. Wipe Plate with Cotton Pad (Moistened in Water and Wrung Out)

Fig. 595. Pour on a Spot of Coating Solution as Large as a Silver Dollar

Fig. 596. With a Folded Pad of Cheesecloth, Wipe Coating Solution Lengthwise and Sidewise. Apply and wipe down for a total of 3 times.

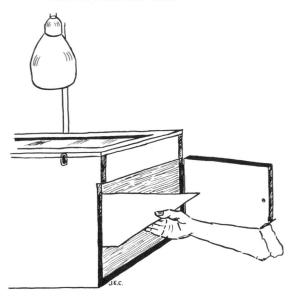

Fig. 597. Place Sensitized Plate in Drying Compartment

### Expose

Remove the plate from the heating compartment, and place it coated side up on the printing frame bed. Place the flat over the plate with the corners of one fastened to the other with small pieces of tape.

As you look down on the flat, the negatives should be "readable." Clamp the printing frame cover down, adjust the light so it is directly over the center of the image, and expose for about five minutes. This time may be varied as needed to produce a solid Step 6 on the gray scale.

### Develop

Remove the plate and place it on a paper-protected table top. Pour a 1½-inch spot of developing ink in the center of the plate, and quickly and briskly rub the ink over the image. Cover the entire image, and rub until dry and thin.

Dry the plate for one minute in the drying compartment of the exposure box.

Place the plate in a trough of running water (but not directly under the faucet stream) and let it soak. When the ink has loosened, remove it with gentle strokes of a swab of cotton. Avoid using ink-saturated cotton — turn it over, or get more cotton.

Rinse the plate and let it drip.

### Gum

Place the still-wet plate on a paper-covered table. Apply gum arabic solution with a clean sponge. Using a clean cheesecloth pad, rub the gum sidewise and lengthwise to a thin, hard coating, free of streaks. Hold the plate before a fan to dry it. The plate may now be used on the press, or put away for future use.

### Storing the Plate

To store the plate for extended periods, wash out the image on the gummed plate with a little turpentine or press solvent. Pour a small spot (1½ inches) of asphaltum on the center of the plate, and rub thin and dry with a pad of clean cheesecloth.

### Care on the Press

Paper plates are cared for on the press in the same manner as metal plates.

Fig. 598. Tape the Flat with the Image Readable to the Plate (Coated Side Up)

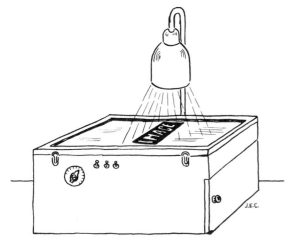

Fig. 599. Expose the Plate Under the Flat

Fig. 600. Apply Developing Ink Sparingly, and Wipe Over Image Area; Rub Dry and Even

Fig. 601. Let Cool, Running Water Flow Over Plate for at Least One Minute; then, Gently Wipe Off Developing Ink with a Clean Cotton Pad. Renew pad if it gets dirty.

Fig. 602. Lift Plate by a Corner and Let it Drip Off Excess Water. Moisten a clean sponge with gum and rub over entire plate, both up and down and across; smooth, flat and dry.

Fig. 603. Pour on a Spot of Asphaltum as Large as a Silver Dollar. Wipe briskly, evenly and dry, using a cheese-cloth pad.

## The Shop Library

It is suggested that a library be maintained as a part of the lithographic laboratory, so that the students can refer to sources of information as the need arises. While many books on printing can be found in school or public libraries, textbooks, instruction manuals, and data books should be more readily accessible.

A companion text to *Photo-Offset Fundamentals* warrants mention here since it augments the specialized content found in this book, by emphasizing basic typography, platen presswork, and the related units of a general and historical nature:

*Cleeton, Glen U., Charles W. Pitkin, and Raymond L. Cornwell,* **General Printing.** *Bloomington, Illinois: McKnight & McKnight Publishing Company, 1963. 221 pp.*

# Bibliography

The following is a selected list of recent books for additional reading and study. Books are included for several levels of advancement.

Allen, Edward M., *Harper's Dictionary of the Graphic Arts.* New York: Harper & Row, 1963. 295 pp.
A recent alphabetical listing of terms.

Arnold, Edmond C., *Ink on Paper.* New York: Harper and Row, 1963. 323 pp.
The story of printing — the art preservative of all arts — from the written alphabet to descriptions of modern printing processes. For the beginner, the artist, the journalist, or any other desiring an overview rather than specifics.

Birren, Faber, *Color: From Ancient Mysticism to Modern Science.* New Hyde Park, N. Y.: University Books, 1962. 338 pp.
Color traditions and the contributions of art and science to its use.

Graphic Arts Technical Foundation (formerly Lithographic Technical Foundation), 4615 Forbes Ave., Pittsburgh, Pa. 15213.
This organization publishes an extensive list of textbooks on all phases of lithography. A teacher may join the GATF for a nominal fee, allowing him or his school to purchase publications at the member price (only 30% of the list price). Write for latest information. Titles (with code numbers) which have been useful as school references are listed here.
*Textbooks:* 503 Line Photography, 508 Halftone Photography, 509 Color Separation — Photography, 510/11 Tone and Color Correcting, 507 Offset Stripping — Black and White, 512 Color Stripping, 515 Photo-Composing, 518 Contact Printing, 502/4 Platemaking, 505/6 Press Operating—Sheetfed Presses, 513 Advanced Pressmanship—Sheetfed Presses, 501 Offset Press Troubles—Sheetfed Presses, 401 Chemistry of Lithography, 402 The Science of Physics in Lithography, 407 Survey of Lithography.
*Bulletins:* 215 The Sensitivity Guide, 308 What the Lithographer Should Know About Paper, 310 What the Lithographer Should Know About Ink, 320 GATF Color Chart Bulletin, 321 Instruments for Quality Control.

Kodak Handbooks, Data books, and other publications. Rochester, N. Y.: Eastman Kodak Co.
Titles (with code numbers) useful in graphic arts are listed here. Some pamphlets are available free of charge.
*Handbooks:* Kodak Graphic Arts Handbook, Kodak Industrial Handbook (these include a number of the pamphlets below and matching loose-leaf binders are available to hold the other pamphlets).
*Pamphlets or Sheets:* B-3 Kodak Wratten Filters for Scientific and Technical Use, E-29 Condensed Data: Kodak Color Films, E-47 Three-Color Separation Prints from Color Negatives with Resisto Rapid Pan Paper, E-59 Notes on Practical Densitometry, E-74 Color as Seen and Photographed, G-1 Kodak Photographic Papers, J-1 Processing Chemicals and Formulas, J-24 Stabilization — What, Why and How, K-13 Darkroom Design and Construction, L-5 Index to Kodak Technical Information, M-1 Copying, P-21 Kodalith Autoscreen Ortho Film, P-79 Introduction to Photofabrication Using Photosensitive Resists, Q-1 Basic Photography for the Graphic Arts, Q-2 Kodak Graphic Arts Films and Plates, Q-6A Color Correction with Tri-Mask Film, Q-7 Basic Color for the Graphic Arts, Q-11 Formulas for the

Graphic Arts, Q-12A How to Use the Kodak Graphic Arts Exposure Computer, Q-18 Line Effects from Photographs by the Kodak Tone-Line Process, Q-21 Kodak Contact Screens — Types and Applications, Q-23 How to Use Autopositive Materials, Q-25 Kodak Photo Resist for Making Photolithographic Printing Plates, Q-27 Film and Filter Combinations for Photographing Color in Black-and-White, Q-28 Photography for the Printer, Q-30 Exposure-Development Adjustment Charts, Q-31 Angle Indicator (for Kodak Contact Screens), Q-104 Small Lens Openings Destroy Image Sharpness, Q-105 Filter Control of Screen Positives Made with the Magenta Contact Screen, Q-109 Camera-Back Masking with Silver Masks, Q-110 Density Measurement of Halftones, Q-111 Halftone Negatives for Powderless Etching Processes, Q-114 Kodak Direct-Screen Color-Separation Method, Q-118 Color Proofing for Pre-Press Proofs with Kodak Ektacolor Paper, Q-119 The New Light Sources (Quartz-Iodine and Xenon), T-11 A Yearbook — The Picture Way, T-13 Improving Pictures in School Publications, T-38 How to Make and Use a Pinhole Camera, T-51 How to Organize a Camera Club, T-56 Designing a Photo Course.

Kosloff, Albert, *Photographic Screen Process Printing.* Cincinnati: Signs of the Times Publishing Co., 1962. 235 pp.

Explains the principles, and the types of photo stencils. Some equipment and supplies are the same as required for photo-offset lithography.

Jayne, John J., *Small Printing Plant Management.* Chicago: Graphic Arts Monthly, 1965. 144 pp.

Covers estimating, selling, supervision of production, inventory control and other management functions.

Larson, Louis M., *Industrial Printing Inks.* New York: Reinhold Publishing Co., 1962.

A text for ink makers and a reference book for printers.

Lasky, Joseph, *Proofreading and Copy-Preparation.* New York: Mentor Press, 1954. 656 pp.

The most authoritative book on this subject. Includes a history of the art, the marks and how to use them, and guides for checking copy and proofs for grammar, punctuation, spelling and word division.

Lee, Marshall, *Bookmaking: The Illustrated Guide to Design and Production.* New York: R. R. Bowker Co., 1965. 416 pp.

The design profession; a good summary of printing processes and materials; analyzing, designing, and costing a new book.

Maurello, S. Ralph, *Complete Airbrush Book.* New York: Tudor Publishing Co., 1954.

How-to instruction for beginners or artists alike.

Maurello, S. Ralph, *How to Do Paste-Ups and Mechanicals.* New York: Tudor Publishing Co., 1960. 160 pp.

Well illustrated and complete; by an experienced teacher of this important area of photo reproduction.

Neblette, C. B., *Photography: Its Materials and Processes.* Princeton, New Jersey: D. Van Nostrand and Co., Inc., 1962. 6th edition.

A college text with a storehouse of information on general photography.

*Pocket Encyclopedia of Paper & Graphic Arts Terms.* Kaukauna, Wisconsin: Thomas Printing & Publishing Co., Ltd., 1960.

Definitions of printing terms with an emphasis on papers.

*Pocket Pal for Printers, Estimators, and Advertising Production Managers.* New York: International Paper Co. 131 pp.

Good, brief survey of history, processes, materials, terms. Revised frequently.

*Production Yearbook.* New York: Colton Press, Inc. Annual editions of approximately 600 pages.

Reference book on art, photography, photoengraving, duplicate relief plates, paper, printing processes, mailing, typography.

Shapiro, Charles (ed.), *The Lithographers Manual,* Soderstrom Edition. Pittsburgh: The Graphic Arts Technical Foundation, Inc., 1966. 560 pp.

Comprehensive coverage by 38 experts, well illustrated and indexed. The former two-volume edition has been updated and consolidated into one very usable reference book.

Tinker, Miles A., *Bases of Effective Reading.* Minneapolis: Univ. of Minnesota Press, 1965.

An authoritative work on legibility of types, sizes, tones and various arrangement, based on extensive research evidence.

Turnbull, Arthur T., and Russell N. Baird, *The Graphics of Communication.* New York: Holt, Rinehart and Winston, 1964. 342 pp.

Emphasis is on using typography, layout and design to get the message through. Some information on production processes.

Updike, Daniel B., *Printing Types: Their History, Forms, and Uses.* Harvard University Press, 3rd ed., 1962. 2 vols. 618 pp.

Comprehensive background of alphabet and printing.

# Index

Acetate —
  as common film base, 111
  proofs on, 34
Acetic acid —
  in counter etch, 366
  in stop bath, 191
Acidity, pH, 285
Additive color theory, 160
Additive offset plates, 231
Adhesive pre-printed type, 52
Advertising, photographs in, 341
Advertising men, work of, 20
Agfacopy platemaking, 243
Albumin plate coating, 363-371
Alkalinity, pH, 285
Alpha-cellulose pulp, 261
Alphatype, type machine, 89
Aluminum plates, 12, 219, 230, 366
Ammonium-dichromate, 273, 334, 363
Angstrom units, light, 155
Anti-halation film backing, 111
Anti-offset spray, press, 281
Aperture, see Camera, diaphragm
Apparent color, 159
Apron, rubber, 334
Arc lights, 117, 145
  color of, 158
Archer, Frederick Scott, 14
Architect's scale, 348
Arithmetic progression, 136
Art forms of man, 12
Artists, commercial, 24
  on printing staff, 20
Artwork, drawing, 49
  see also Copy
Artype, adhesive type, 52
ATF Typesetters, 85
Autopositive film described, 204
Autoscreen film, 133, 204
  using, 151, 200
Avoirdupois weight, 359
Azo paper for contacting, 197

Back, camera (rear case), 118
Balance, ink-water, 4, 302
Balls, on Cronapress conversion film, 45
  on press register board, 276, 301

Baumé, Antoine, 364
Baumé hydrometer scales, 364
Bavarian limestone, 8, 9
Beating, papermaking, 262
Bellows, camera, 118-120
Bellows extension, 119, 120
Bending jig plate, 289
Bennett, Charles, 15
Bibliography, 373
  for color separation, 180
  file of machine manuals, 335
Bindery work, 270-272
Bindery workers, 23
Blanket cylinder, 3-6, 290-292, 294
  blanket, 290
  development of, 12
Blast nozzles, press, 276
Block out heading on photo, 104
Blueline proofs, 202
Blue-sensitive film, 142, 167
Bonds, securities, printing, 342
Borders, tape type, 53
Bow instruments, using, 350
Brady, Mathew, 13, 15
Brightness, color value, 157
Brightype conversion method, 46
Brownline proofs, 202
Bump, highlight, 144, 146, 148

Calendering, paper, 266
California job case, 38
Caliper, double sheet detector, 278
Camera parts —
  back, rear case, 118
  basic settings, 122
  bellows, 118
  checking focus, 122
  copy board, 117
  enlargements, reductions, 122
  flashing lamp, 117, 143, 146
  focusing controls, 118
  glass-screen device, 118
  image formation in, 109
  lens care, 116
  lens construction, 113
  lens and its parts, 114
  lighting, 117, 119
  lights affected by voltage, 158

  parts named, 112, 113
  shutter, 115
Cameraless( reflex) photocopying, 199
Cameramen, work of, 21
Cameras (types) —
  for color separating, 180
Consolidated 31", (illus), 111
  copying, 112
  darkroom type, 112
  gallery type, 112
  historical models, 13-16
  horizontal type, 111
  Itek Project-A-Lith (illus), 236
  projection type (enlarger), xiv, 180
  Robertson 320, horizontal (illus), 22, 113
  Robertson Electricon (illus), 249
  Robertson 432 vertical (illus), 112
  Robertson 480, (illus), 111
  vertical type, 112
  Xerox 4, horizontal (illus), 22
Camerawork —
  Autoscreen film, using, 151
  color, process, separating, 180-187
  colors, copying or dropping, 126
  contact screen, angling, 180
  constant-aperture exposures, 121
  constant-time exposures, 122
  copy, preparing for camera, 99-108
  copyboard, loading, 122
  darkroom camera procedures, 125
  densitometer to check lighting, 139
  duotones, shooting, 152, 178
  eliminating "hot spots", 119, 120
  enlargement, determining exposure, 122
  focusing for 100%, 119
  gallery camera procedures, 126
  halftones, determining exposures, 144
  halftones, screening, 143, 147
  halftone negative, evaluating, 149
  halftone prints, copying dot for dot, 149
  halftone prints, rescreening, 150
  line copy, determining exposure, 120
  line copy procedure, 124

Carbon arc lights, 117, 145
Carbon tetrachloride, 287, 334
Care of equipment, 335
  camera lens, 116
  camera lights, 117
  cleaning camera copy glass, 117
  of contact halftone screen, 144
  *see also* Specific machines
Cellophane, proofs on, 34
Chalking, remedying on run, 329
Character count of type, 30
Character generation, 91
  *see also* Type composition
Chart —
  2-color overprints possible, 163
  4-color overprints possible, 164
Chart-Pak tape, 53
Checkerboard dot pattern, 131, 149
Chemical printing, Senefelder's, 9
Chemicals, safety rules, 333
Chemical-wood pulp, 261
Chokes and spreads, 199
Chroma, of colors, 157
Circular measure, angles, 359
Clay, in paper pulp, 265
Cleaner sheet, ink, 305
Clip art, 50
*Cogoli* (pronounced *Cog-o-li*), John, v
Coins, in illustrations, 342
Cold type —
  classifications, 33
  mechanical, 48
  photographic, *see* Phototypesetting
Collating, 271
Collodion wet negative plates, 14
Collotype, screenless tones by, 129
Colophon, 386
Color and light —
  additive color, lights, 160
  color temperature, 158
  complementary hues, 160
  defined, 155
  dimensions of color, 156
  holding or dropping on film, 126
  iridescent, from diffraction, 159
  lighting, affects color, 158
  "minus" filter colors, 162
  mixing colored lights, 160
  mixing pigments, 161
  Munsell notation, 157
  neutrals — black and white, 166
  pigments absorb some wavelengths, 159
  primary hues, 160
  by reflection, 159
  refraction, 156
  spectrophotometer, 159
  spectrum, 156
  subtractive color, inks, 161
  by transmission, 159
  wavelengths, 155
  wheel, circular arrangements, 156
Color, classes for reproduction, 99, 155
Color film —
  balance for lighting, 159, 169
  basic structure, 167

negative color film, 168
  reversal color film, positive, 170
Color-Key —
  color proofs, 186, 203
  direct from repro, 43
Color printing, flat —
  chart, 2-color overprints, 163
  chart, 4-color overprints, 164
  color from paper, 175
  duotones, 178
  from duplicate negatives, 176
  fake color, 179
  filter separations, line copy, 178
  Key-line art, 177
  multiple exposures on blue lines, 203
  opaque ink, action of, 163
  overlays for color, 177
  ruby film, hand cut, 176
  using a single color, 175
  Template masking, 175, 176
  use of tint screens, 178
  transparent ink, action of, 162
Color printing, process —
  bibliography, 180
  black ink, in color printing, 171
  color correction, 162, 173-174
  direct separation, 171, 174
  electronic scanning, 173
  guides for, 182
  halftone screens for, 180
  indirect separation, 174, 175
  overprinting process inks, 170
  photographic masking, 173
  press-run sequence, 173
  procedures, 180
  reflection curves, process inks, 162
  separation filters, function of, 162
  separation filter ratios, table, 184
  separation methods, 171, 174
  "short run" or "pleasing" color, 173
  trapping of wet inks, 174
Combination photoprints (neg.-pos.), 199
Combs, sheet separators, 276
Common-law literary property, 341
Compasses, drawing with, 349
Complementary colors, 160
Composing stick —
  for Fototype, 52
  for hand-set type, 38
  for Ludlow mats, 42
Composition houses, 24
Composition of type, *see* Type
Compositors, work of, 20
Comprehensive layout, 28
Computer, exposure guide, 144
Computers, in typesetting, 64, 70, 85, 88, 91
Contact films, named and described, 204
Contact halftone screen, 16, 134, 135
  *see also* Halftone screens

Contact photoprinting, 194-204
  blank areas, masking, 201
  combinations, negative-positive, 199
  dot gain, 196, 197
  on duplicating film, 198
  equipment for, 195
  film positives, making, 197
  lettering on halftones, 201
  negatives from negatives, 198
  negatives from positives, 198
  on orange Color-Key, 43
  outline letters, making, 200
  positive prints, making, 197
  positives from negatives, 197
  positives from positives, 198
  proofs, 202
  reflex copying, 199
  registering multiple exposures, 202
  reverse prints, making, 197
  screening line work, 202
  screening tone copy off camera, 200
  spreads and chokes, 199
  supplies for, 203
  surprinting, lettering, 201
  test strip, exposing, 195
  thin-base film, using, 198, 203
Control-tape —
  Alphatype, 89
  ATF Typesetter, 86, 88
  code, 7-channel, 68
  Friden Justowriter, 68
  Intertype Fotomatic, 81
  Linofilm 12-level code, 82
  magnetic, 89, 91
  Monotype, 39, 78
  Teletypesetter (TTS), 90
Conversion, type to film —
  Brightype, 46
  Color-Key, orange, 43
  Cronapress, 45
  instant negative, 44
  proofs of relief forms, 34
Conversion factors, mathematical, 360
Conveyer board, *see* Register board
Copperplate engraving, 2
  press adapted for lithography, 10
  reproduced by stone lithography, 9
  Senefelder adapts, 8
Copy —
  classes of, for camera, 99
  classes of, examples, 109, 129, 155
  clip art, 50
  in color, holding or dropping, 126
  for color printing, 171
  combination line and tone, 104
  contrast of tones, judging, 138
  densitometer, for tones and colors, 140
  hand lettering, artwork, 49
  Key-line art, 177
  line copy, identifying, 109
  line copy, preparing, 101
  marked for composition, 27
  marks for, 94-96

overlays for color, 177
preparing for camera, 99-108
reprinting existing prints, 48
reverses, preparing for, 101
ruby film, cut for color, 176
Copy preparation workers, 21
Copy holder, proofreading, 94
Copy writers, work of, 20
Copyboard, camera, 117
Copyboard extension, camera, 119, 120
Copyfitting techniques, 29
Copying camera (illus), 112
Copying colors on film, 126
Copyreading (editing) marks, 94-96
Copyright law, 340
Correction fluid, Senefelder's, 8
Corrections, composition —
  Fotosetter line corrector, 80
  on hand lettering, 49
  Linofilm Corrector, 84
  Linotype, Intertype, 42
  by merging computer tapes, 91
  Monotype, 40
  typing, 55
Corrections, reproduction —
  in halftone exposure, 149
  on surface plates, 249
  on presensitized plates, 236
  of presswork problems, 302, 323-330
  in printing color negatives, 169
  in process color printing, 173
Counter-etching plate, 365
Counterfeiting, 341
Cronapress, conversion method, 45
Cropping photographs, 102
Currier and Ives, lithoprints, 11
*Currier, Nathaniel*, 11
Cylinder unit (offset press) —
  basic function, 3, 5, 275
  blanket cylinder, 290
  delivery (fourth) cylinder, 279
  four-cylinder design, 279
  gear drive, 278
  impression cylinder, 292
  plate cylinder, 288
  pressure settings, 292
  three-cylinder design, 279
  two-cylinder design, 279
  undercut-cylinder packings, 294

*Daguerre, Louis Jaques Mende,* 13
Daguerreotype, 13
Dampening in stone lithography, 9
Dampening system, 274, 281
  automatic controls (illus), xiv
  cleaning up, 305
  combined with inking, 278
  conventional (separate), 278
  preparing for work, 298
  rollers, 282
  sleeves, 3M, 283
  solution, preparing, 284
  water fountain, 5

Darkroom —
  camera installation in, 112
  floor plan, 189
  safelights, 189, 203
  ventilation, 190, 331
Darkroom procedures, 189-207
  printing operations listed, 194
  *see also* Contact Photoprinting,
    Developing, Enlarging, Exposing,
    Proofing
Decimal equivalents, 354
Decimals, converting, 353
Deep-etch plates, 222, 250
Deflector, double-sheets, 276
Delivery system, press, 277-278, 280
  anti-offset spray, 281
  chain delivery, 280
  delivery cylinder, 279
  ejector rolls, duplicators, 280
  receeding stacker, 281
  tray, 280
  types of arrangements, 280
Deliveries, lifting dangers, 333
Demonstrations (experiments) —
  best *f*-number of lens, 121
  camera basic exposure, 120
  camera set-up and lighting, 119
  color separation, direct, 184
  color separation, indirect, 185
  grain of paper, determining, 267
  halftone test exposure, 145
  image formation in camera, 109
  image transfer, offset press, 6
  offset process on proof press, 6
  posterization, 129
  press systems, 274-278
  printing a color chart, 166
  spectrum from a prism, 156
  testing angled contact screen, 181
Densitometers, kinds and uses, 139
Densitometry, 135-143
  density range, 138, 145, 147
  density vs. opacity, 136
  equivalent factors, table, 137
  gray scale and density, 137
  halftone dot and density, 137
  reflectance, percentage, 136
  sensitometry, 135, 140
  transmittance, percentage, 136
Density —
  black ink, use in color, 171
  key points for fake color, 179
  Log E curves, film, 140
  range, 138, 145, 147
Dermatitis, skin blisters, 334
Detector, double-sheet, 276
Developing film (basic), 189-194
  Autoscreen film, 151
  basic techniques, three, 193
  chemical action of baths, 190
  critical step for varying copy, 124
  halftone negative, 146
  preparing solutions, 191
  processing times, 193
  solutions commonly stocked, 205

still, to lower contrast, 144
  tray order, 190
  under- and over-, examples, 192
Developing (special processes) —
  an albumin plate, 367
  blueline and brownline proofs, 202
  Color-Key film, 44, 187
  continuous developing unit, Typro, 76
  negative, color film, 168
  photostabilization process, 72
  presensitized plates, 233-236
  of reversal color film, 170
Diacritical workings (accents), 95
Diagonal method of scaling copy, 99
Diaphragm, of lens, 114, 115
Diazochrome proofs, 186, 203
Diazo-type materials, 229
Dido (French) point system, 355
Differential spacing, 66
  *see also* Proportional spacing
Diffraction as source of color, 159
Digester, paper, 261
Direct-image plates, 4, 57, 226
Distortion, in lenses, 114
Distribution, Linotype mats, 41
Dividers, using, 350
Doctor blade, gravure, 2
Documents, restrictions on printing, 343
Dollar volume, commercial printing, 1
Doric lettering tool, 50
Dot-for-dot copying of halftones, 149
Dot gain, controlling, 149, 196, 197
Dot structures, *see* Halftone
Drawing tools, and use, 346-352
Drilling holes in paper, 272
Drop-out halftones, 138
Dry offset, relief offset, 222, 252, 315
Dummy, in layout planning, 31
Duotones, 152, 178
Duplicating films, named, 204
Duplicators, office units, 18, 24
Dycril photopolymer plates, 253
Dye parent and coupler, 167, 229

*Eastman, George,* 15
Ejector, on press, *see* Delivery
Ektalith platemaking, 240
Electrical safety, 334
Electronic scanning, 244
Electronic typesetting, vii, 91
Electrostatic process, 245
Elipsis ( . . . ), 95
Em, defined, 82
Em and en quads, 38
Emulsification, on press, 278
Emulsion, of film, 110, 111
End play, rollers, cylinders, 310-314
Engraving, steel or copperplate, 2
Enlargement, computing, 99
Enlarger, color separation (illus), xiv, 171, 180
  halftone prints from negatives, 200
Equivalents, measures, 359
Estimating space for copy, 29

Estimators and price quotations, 20
Etch proofs, (repros), 33
Excess density range, 138, 145, 147
Executive functions of a company, 20
Executive, IBM typewriter, 59
Experiments, *see* Demonstrations
Exposure —
  albumin plates, 367
  Autoscreen film, 150
  blueline, brownline, proofs, 202
  blue lines, multiple tones, 203
  Brightype conversion method, 46
  camera, determining, 120
  Color-Key, orange contacts, 44
  Color-Key, proofs, 187
  color separation, determining, 183
  constant-aperture system, camera,
    121
  constant-time system, camera, 122
  densitometer to determine, 139
  in direct color separation, 173, 183
  effect of filters, 162
  effect of f-number on time, 121
  Graphic Arts Exposure Computer,
    143
  halftone procedure, 144, 145, 147
  highlight bump, 144, 146, 148
  offset plates, 223
  presensitized plates, 232
  safety rules, 337
  shadow flash, halftone, 144-149
  test strip, photoprinting, 195
  time factors for enlargement, table,
    123
  under and over, examples, 192
  variables, camera, 120
f-numbers, 115
  *see also* Camera or Diaphragm
Fairchild-Morisawa typesetter, 75
Fake color, art for, 179
Family, of type, 37
Fan, iris control, 115
Fan, ventilation, 334
Fastness, of ink, 258
Fat and skinny photoprints, 199
Feed board, *see* Register board
Feed rolls, press, 277
Feeder unit, press, 275
  friction-roller type, 280
  operation, step by step, 276
  register board, 275
  setting up, 299
  suction type, 276, 280
Feeders and press helpers, 23
Felt side of paper, 266
Filling up, on sheet, 327
Film —
  basic description, 111
  characteristic curves, 140
  color types, 166
  contrast of, 141
  cutting and loading camera, 118,
    126
  film speed index, 142
  gamma, 141
  handling in total darkness, 182

holder, camera, 118
  monochromatic color sensitivity,
    140-141, 166
  thin base, use in contacting, 197
Film positive, making, 197
Films—
  Autopositive, 198
  blue-sensitive types, 142
  color negative, 168
  color types, structures of, 167
  direct duplicating, 198
  examples, described, 143, 203
  orthochromatic types, 142
  panchromatic types, 142
  prescreened (Autoscreen), 133
  ruby film, hand cut, 176
  thin-base type, 111
Filter factors, 127
Filter slot, lens, 116
Filters —
  basic action, 159, 161
  camera, 127
  contrast control, magenta screen,
    144
  minus colors, 162
  for process color, 171
  separating line copy, 178
  separation, effect of, 162
  separation, ratios for, table, 184
Fire safety, 333
Fire and solvents, 287, 334
First aid, 331
Fitting copy to an area, 29
Fixer, photographic, 191
Flashing lamp, camera, 117, 143, 146
Flash-point of solvents, 334
Flat —
  layout and stripping, 208-217
  masking for flat-color separation,
    176
  *see also* Stripping
Flat-color printing, *see* Color print-
  ing, flat
Flopping image L to R, 194, 198
Focal length of lens, 114
Focus, camera, 110, 114
Folding machine, 24, 272
Fonts, of type, 35, 37
Formulas —
  for camera settings, 122
  exposure factor, enlargement, 122
  lighting distance and time, 122, 224
  opacity, 136
  for reproduction size, 100, 122
Fotosetter, 21, 79
Fototype letters, 52
Foundry type, 35
Fountain, dampening, 5, 281
Fountain, ink, 5, 286
Fourdrinier paper machine, 262-265
Fractions, converting, 353
French chalk, for blanket, 291
Friction feed, duplicator, 280
Friden Justowriter, 68
Friden Typro, 76
Fugitive, ink color, 258

Galley, type storage, 38
Gamma, of film, 141
Gasoline, as press wash, 287, 334
GATF, 156
  color chart, 166
  color diagrams, 156
  dot gain scale, slur gauge, 196
  research, xiv
Gathering sheets, 271
Geometric progression, 136
Gestefax facsimile scanner, 245
Gevaert (Agfa) platemaking, 243
Glass halftone screen, 133
Glass plates, photographic, 14
Glasses, safety, 333
Goldenrod sheets, stripping, 208
Grain, offset plates, 218, 251
Grain, of paper, 267
Graphic Arts Technical Foundation,
  156
  *see also* GATF
Graver tool, 2
Gravure printing, 1
Gray —
  as neutral color, 166
  screen percentages shown, 104
  tones and density scale, 136
Gray scales —
  based on density, 137
  in color separation, 183
  developing method, 193
  in platemaking, 225, 232
Grease, *see* Lubrication
Grinding, of litho stones, 10
Grippers, on press, 277, 292
  allowing for, in stripping, 210
Ground glass, camera, 118, 119, 125
Grounding electrical equipment, 335
Ground-wood pulp, 260
Guides and patches for color, 183
Gum arabic, 220, 296
*Gutenberg, Johann,* 90

Halation, 211
Halftone black ink, 258
Halftone screens —
  angles for colors, 134, 171, 180
  angling, how to achieve, 181
  angling, sizes after, 182
  in color charts, 163-166
  contact type, 16, 134
  early forms, 16
  eliminating moire in rescreening,
    150
  glass screen holder, camera, 118
  glass type, 16, 133
  methods of screening, 16, 132, 200
  off-camera screening, 200
  for process color, 180
  rulings and uses, 103, 105, 130,
    133
  rulings, counting, 133
  rulings, determining, 104
Halftones, 129-154
  background, subduing, 107
  basic procedure for making, 143

controlling contrast, ways of, 144
copy for, 98, 129
copying dot for dot, 48, 102, 149
cropping copy, 102
density range, 138, 146
determining exposures, 145
dot values, 131, 132
drop-out type of, 139
duotones, 178
effect of paper reflectability, 131
flashing, light set-up, 145
flat screen tints, 104
negative, evaluation of, 146, 149
negative dots vs. printed ones, 131
by Xerox process, 248
*see also* Color printing, process,
    Halftone screens, Screen tints
Headliner, type machine, 73
Hermes electric typewriter, 58
High-key photographs, 138
Highlight areas, halftone, 131
Highlight bump exposure, 144, 146,
    148
History of lithography, 8
Horizontal cameras, 111
Hot-type classifications, 33
    *see also* Type
Hue, colors, 157
Humidity, measuring, 361
Hydrochloric acid, in counter etch,
    366
Hydrometer, reading, 364
Hygrometer, 362
Hypo, photographic, 191

IBM Executive typewriter, 59
IBM Selectrics, 63, 64, 65
Illusion of tones, 129, 130
Image gain, 149, 196
    on contacting films, 198
    from improper press impression, 303
    lengthened image on cylinder, 270
    spreading intentionally, 199
Image transfer on press, 5, 270, 275
Impact (typewriter) composition,
    54-70
    care of machines, 57
    on direct-image masters, 57, 227
    Friden Justowriter, 68
    general procedures, 54
    Hermes Ambassador, 58
    IBM Executive, 59
    IBM Selectrics, 63
    interchangeable type bars, 58, 65
    Marginator attachment, 55
    on mechanical negatives, 57
    proportional spacing, 54, 62
    Remington electric, 57
    summary of refinements, 69
    Typit interchangeable bars, 65
    Underwood Raphael, 61
    variations in type face, 56, 69
Imposing multiple pages, 214
Impression cylinder, 3, 5, 277, 292
Incandescent bulbs, 117, 145, 158
Indicators, color separation, 183

Infinity, lens focus, 114
Ink drawings for copy, 49
Inking, hand leather roller, 9
Inking system, 274, 286-288
    cleaner sheets, 305
    combined with dampening, 278
    conventional (separate), 278
    fountain, 5, 275, 286
    **glaze, removing, 307**
    **ink band test, 286**
    roller-cleaning device, 306
    setting up for work, 298
    washing up, 305
Inks, 256-259
    as absorber of light, 131
    color mixing theory, 161
    composition of, 256
    densitometer, to check, 140
    manufacture of, 257
    mixing colors, 257
    problems on press, 323-330
    process, color reflectance, 162
    removing from can, 298
    requirements for offset, 256
    research in (illus), xiv
    specifying color, 158
    storing, 258
    terminology, 258
    transparent or opaque action, 162
    transparent overlaps, 161
    trapping, color printing, 174
Ink-water balance, 4, 302
Inspection, developing method, 193
Instant Negative, type conversion, 44
Instantype, 54
Intaglio printing methods, 2
Intertype, 40
Intertype Fotosetter, Fotomatic, 79
Iris control, camera, 115
*Ives, James,* 11

Job black ink, 258
Job planning, layout, 26
Jogger —
    press delivery, 280, 281
    register board, press, 277
    vibrating table type, 270
Jogging paper by hand, 270
Jordon, paper beater, 263
Justification of type lines —
    computerized, from "idiot" tape,
        65, 70
    for hand-set type, 38
    Intertype Fotosetter system, 79, 80
    Justowriter system, 68, 69
    Linofilm system, 82
    Linotype system, 41
    placement of extra spacing, 61
    proportional spacing typewriter,
        60, 61
    on Protype, 72
    of standard typewriters, 54
    summary for impact machines, 69
    Varityper system, 67
Justowriter, Friden, 68

Kelvin ( °K), color temperature, 158
Kerning, in typesetting, 83
Kerosene, as press wash, 287, 334
Keyboards —
    Alphatype, 89
    ATF Typesetter, 85, 88
    Harris Fototronic, vii
    Linofilm, 82
    Linotype Intertype, 21, 40
    Monotype, 39
Key-line art for color, 177
Kodabromide paper for contacting,
    197
Kodak relief plate, 252
Kodalith films, listed and described,
    203

Lake colors of ink, 258
*Lanston, Tolbert,* 90
Latent image, 110, 131
    color, 168
Lateral reversal, flopping image, 198
    *see also* Mirrored image
Lava soap, on ink rollers, 287
Layout —
    of California job case, 38
    of copy for printing, 26-31
    of flat, 210
    imposing multiple pages, 215
    rough to comprehensive, 28
    of shop for safety, 331
    table, 209
Layout men, work of, 20, 26
Lazy Susan, printing frame, 200
Leads, for spacing type, 38
Learning printing, 92
Left-handed students, 346, 347
Legal restrictions, copying, 340-343
Legibility, reverses on gray tones, 105
Length, of ink, 258
Lens —
    ATF Typesetter optics, 87
    of camera, 113
    Intertype photosetter, 81
    Monophoto, 78
Lens care, 116
Leroy lettering tool, 50
Letterguide scriber, 50
Lettering copy by hand, 49
Lettering on halftones, making, 201
Lettering pens, 49
Letterpress printing, 1
Letterset, dry offset, 222, 252, 315
Levy halftone screen, 133
Lifting, dangers of, 333
Ligature, 95
Light, *see* Color and light, Densi-
    tometry
Light sensitivities —
    albumin and potassium iodide, 14
    bichromated, 228, 237, 363
    characteristic curve, 140
    collodion - silver nitrate, 14
    color sensitivity, 141, 166
    diazo, 167, 186, 229, 238
    electronic scanning, 244

Ferric (iron), 202, 229
fixing with hypo, 14
on layers of color film, 168
photo-electrostatic, 229, 245
photopolymer, 229
silver salts, 12-15, 116, 190, 228, 240, 243
thermographic, 229
Lights —
camera, 117
for color separation, 180
color temperature of, 158
for contact printing, 195
set up for shadow flash, 145
types compared, 117
voltage drop, effect on, 158
Limestone, in lithography, 8, 9
Line, measure for wood type, 43
Line casting, typesetting, 40
Line copy, 98, 109
Line copy shot as halftone (illus), 99
Line gauge, 35, 37
Line photography, 109-128
results on tone copy, 129, 130
Line-up table, 209
Linen tester, magnifier, 126
Lines —
halftone screens, 103, 105, 130, 133
ruling or scribing, 102
Linofilm, type machine, 81
Linotron, type machine, 85
Linotypes, 21, 40
Lithographic camera, *see* Camera
Lithography, 8
*see also* Offset
Litho-type films, 141
Logarithms, 136
Log-exposure curves, film, 140
Low-key photographs, 138
Lubrication, press, 297
Ludlow, 42
Lye, for ink removal, 287

Magazine, Linotype matrices, 41
Magenta contact screens, 134, 144
Magnifiers, 126
Maintenance workers, 20
Make up, of type for repro, 34
Map work, color separating, 178
Marginator, for typewriters, 55
Master, offset, *see* Plate
Matrices and type masters —
Alphatype, 90
ATF Typesetter, 88
electronic video impulses, 91
Fotosetter Fotomat, 79
lettering stencils, 50
Linofilm font grid, 82
Linotype, Intertype, 41
Ludlow, 42
Monophoto film matrix, 77
Monotype, 39
Measures, equivalent, 354, 359
Measuring units, printers' math, 35, 37, 43, 355
Mechanical, pasted-up for camera, 48

Mechanical negatives, 57
Medalist paper for contacting, 197
*Mergenthaler, Ottmar,* 90
Metallic inks, 258
Metric measure of wave length, 155
Metric system, 359, 360
Micrometer, using, 356
Microscope, pocket magnifier, 126
Millimicrons (m$\mu$), 155
"Minus" filter colors, 162
Mirrored image, 5, 35
achieving in stone lithography, 9
contact printing to produce, 194, 198
at ground glass of camera, 109
in image transfer on press, 5
Mitered borders, 53
Mitterer lithographic press, 10
Modifiers, in ink, 256
Moire, 150
Molleton roller covers, 282
Monophoto, type machine, 27
Monotype, 39
Morisawa Photo Typesetter, 75
*Morse, Samuel F. B.,* 13
Mottling, remedying, 329
Multi-metal offset plates, 223
Munsell color notation, 157

Negatives —
continuous tones unprintable on press, 131
Cronapress type conversion, 44
duplicating, 197
film dots vs. printed ones, 131, 132
halftone, basic density range, 146
halftone evaluation, 149
identifying emulsion side, 110
Instant Negative, conversion, 44
invention of, 13-16
line, 109
for making a positive print, 197
opaquing, 211
by orange Color-Key contact, 44
positioning in flat, 211
using duplicates for colors, 176
Negative-working offset plates, 230
Newton's rings, 159
*Niepce, Claude Felix,* 14
Night-latch, roller, 282
Nodal point, of lens, 114

Obscene material, printing, 343
Office workers, 20
Offset plates, *see* Plate or master, Platemaking
Offset press, *see* Press
Offset principle developed, 12
Offset printing —
compared to other processes, 1-3
divisions of work, 20
first photographic halftones, 16
history, 8
synonyms for, 3
workers by departments, 20
Offset spray, press delivery, 281

Oil, *see* Lubrication
Opacity, 135
of ink, 258
Opaque ink, structure, 163
Opaquing negative, 211
Orthochromatic films, 142, 167
Overlays for color art, 177
Overprints (surprints), 104

Packing, on cylinders, 270, 288, 294
Page makeup —
before reproduction proofing, 34
Linofilm Composer, 85
Panchromatic films, 142, 167
Panic button, electrical, 335
Pantograph engraver, 2
Papers, 260-270
colored stock for interest, 175
densitometer to check opacity, 140
drawing paper, fastening, 346
goldenrod for stripping, 208
grain, determining, 267
handling safely, 337
loading with clay, 265
manufacturing process, 262
moisture content, 270
paper micrometer, 358
for photoprinting, 197, 204
printing requirements for, 260
problems on press, 328-330
pulp, kinds of, 260
as reflector of light, 131
research in (illus), xiv
"sheet" vs. "piece", 266
shrinking and stretching, 270
sides of, 266
table of kinds, sizes, weights, 269
terms, 266
watermark, aligning, 299
weight and substance, 267
Paper cutters, 23, 24
safety rules, 336
workmen, 23
Papercutting, 267, 270
calculations for, 268
Parallel lines, drawing, 348
Paste up, or mechanical, 48
Pen, technical fountain, 49
Pencils, drawing, 346
Percentages —
converting, 353
reproduction size, 101
tones of gray, 105
Perfecting, presses, 322
Perforating, on folder, 272
Permission, reproduction, 341
pH scale and tests, 284
Photo-composing, *see* Platemaking, step-and-repeat
Photo-direct platemakers, 225, 237
Photoelectric densitometer, 139
Photoelectric image scanning, 244
Photographs —
judging contrast of, 138
model release for, 341
Photographers, on printing staff, 20

Photography —
   basic theory, 109
   early attempts, 12
   latent image, 110, 131
   for line copy, 109-128
   for screenless tone reproduction,
      129
   use in Civil War, 15
   *see also* Camera, Exposure, Film
      Developing, Light Sensitivities,
      Negatives, Positives
Photon, type machine, 85
Photo-offset lithography, *see* Offset
Photoprinting, *see* Contact photo-
      printing, or Enlarging
Photoprints, making, 197
Photostabilization development, 72
Photo-typesetting —
   Alphatype, 89
   ATF Typesetters, 85
   for creating wiring diagrams, 85
   Friden Typro, 76
   Intertype Fotosetter, 79
   Linofilm, 81
   Linotron, electronic unit, 85
   Monophoto, 77
   Morisawa Photo Typesetter, 85
   Photon, 85
   photostabilization development, 72
   Photo-Typositor, 75
   Protype, 72
   RCA Videocomp electronic unit, 85
   StripPrinter, 73
   summary, 90
Pica, unit of measure, 35, 37, 355
Pigments —
   in ink, 256
   why colored, 159, 161
Pile guides, press, 276
Pile-height guide, 276
Piling, on press sheet, 327
Planographic printing method, 3
Plastic binding, 271
Plate cylinder, 3, 5, 288
Plate engraving, 2
Plate whirler, using, 366
Platemakers, work of, 23
Platemaking, 218-255, 363-371
   Agfacopy method, 243
   albumin, making, 363-371
   basic procedure, 223
   corrections, surface plates, 236, 249
   deep-etch type, 250
   A. B. Dick silver-difusion type, 243
   direct-image types, 226
   Dycril Type C type, 253
   "E" and "L" plates, processing, 233
   Ektalith method, 240
   exposure, determining, 224, 232
   exposure devices, 223
   gelatin-silver-emulsion type, 240
   Gevaert silver-diffusion type, 243
   in GPO (illus), 22
   gray scale, use of, 232
   gum solution, making, 221
   gumming, and putting under, 219

"K" plates, processing, 233, 236
   overview of, 4
   presensitized plates by Ektalith,
      242
   "R" plates, processing, 233, 234
   register pins, using, 202, 226
   "S" plates, processing, 233, 235
   sensitivity guide, gray scale, 225
   silver-diffusion transfer type, 243
   step-and-repeat work, 23, 225
   thermographic transfer type, 244
   wipe-on coating, applying, 238, 369
Plates and masters —
   albumin type, 237
   care of, 219
   characteristics, 218
   common surface types, 4
   deep-etch type, 222, 250
   direct image, 4, 57, 226
   dry-offset metal plate, 252
   Dycril relief plate, 253
   by electronic scanning, 244
   graining zinc plates (illus), 22
   image vs. clear area, 4
   inking process, 4, 5
   invention of, 12
   Kodak relief plate, 252
   development of metal types, 12
   "master", use of term, 219
   multimetal types, 222, 252
   photo-direct type, 237
   presensitized types, 228, 231
   relief types for offset, 222, 252
   Senefelder's stone substitutes, 11
   surface type, 222
   transfer type, 239
   types classified, 221
   wipe-on type, 238
   Xerox, 245
Plugging, halftone dots, 149
Point, unit of measure, 35, 355
Poisons, precautions, 334
Polyester, as a film base, 111
Positives —
   from Brightype conversion, 46
   intermediate, for reverses, 101
   from orange Color-Key, 43
   photoprint, making, 197
Positive-working, offset plates, 230
Postage stamps, reproducing, 342
Posterization, 129, 130
Pre-printed type, 51
Prescreened film, 149, 150
Presensitized offset plates, 228
   negative-, positive-working, 230
   subtractive, additive coatings, 231
Press parts, 274-295
   automatic dampener control, xiv
   basic systems, 3, 5, 274
   blanket cylinder, blanket, 290
   combined inking-dampening, 278
   cylinder (printing) unit, 275
   dampening solution, 284
   dampening system, 274, 281
   feeder unit, 275
   grippers, 292

impression cylinder, 292
   inking system, 274, 286
   offset principle developed, 12
   register board, 280
   sheet travel through, 276
Presses and duplicators —
   American Newspaper Publishers
      (illus), xiv
   ATF Chief 15, 317-320
   ATF Chief 20A, 5, 274, 278, 316,
      317
   brands, controls, 309-322
   Cottrell 4-over-4 web, 18
   Cottrell web book press (illus), xi
   Cottrell web newspaper press
      (illus), xiv
   A. B. Dick models, 320-321
   Ditto, 215, 317-320
   Fairchild-Davidson, 274, 279, 322
   first powered litho press, 11
   Gazette web, 322
   Harris 5-color electrostatic printer
      (illus), xiv
   Harris 6-color (illus), ii
   Harris 25 x 38 2-color (illus), 17
   Harris 4-color (illus), 17
   Heidelberg KOR, 314-316
   Itek 11.15, 317-320
   lithographic, primitive, 10
   Mailänder flat bed, 322
   MGD 20 and 22, 321
   Multilith 1250, 18, 274-313
   Multilith 1275, 322
   Multilith 2024 (illus), 16
   Royal Zenith, 322
   Schriber continuous-forms press
      (illus), xi
   Whitin-types, 317-320
Pressmen, work of, 23
Pressure adjustments, 310-314
   dampening roller, 284
   impression (squeeze), 293
   ink rollers, 286
   plate to blanket, 292, 294
Presswork —
   adjustments, *see also* Press parts
   basic sequence for a run, 296-307
   blanket, preparing, 290
   check points, test sheets, 302-303
   controlling image length, 270
   cylinder packing, 270, 288, 294
   dampening roller, setting, 284
   dampening sleeves, installing, 283
   dampening solution, preparing, 284
   dampening unit, preparing, 298
   defective prints, analyzed, 323-326
   ending run, 304
   feeder, setting up, 299
   filling up, remedying, 327
   gumming plate, 290
   image position, adjusting, 302
   impression (squeeze) adjustment,
      293
   ink rollers, setting, 287
   ink rollers, washing, 287
   ink unit, preparing, 298

inspection of press, 297
items needed, 296
job specifications, checking, 297
Molleton covers, installing, 282
packing the cylinders, 270, 288, 294
picking, remedying, 328
piling, remedying, 327
plate, installing, 288
plate, removing, 290
plate-to-blanket, setting, 292
preliminary preparation, 296
pressure checks, 292, 310-314
pressure checks, sequence, 299
running down plate, 290
safety rules, 335
scumming, remedying, 326
set off, remedying, 328
setting up for work, 297
start-stop sequence, 301, 304
test sheets, feeding, 301
tinting, remedying, 327
troubleshooting, 323-331
twisting the plate, 288
washing up, 305
Primary colors, 160
Printers units of measure, 35, 37, 43, 355
Process camera, *see* Camera
Process color, *see* Color printing process
Processes for commercial printing, 1
dollar volumes of each, 3
engraving (intaglio), 3
gravure (intaglio), 2
letterpress (relief), 1
offset, (planographic), 3-7
screen process (stencil), 2
Processing film, *see* Developing
Proofing type, procedure, 22, 38
Proofpress, offset demonstration, 6
Proofreaders, work of, 20
Proofreading, 94-97
marking techniques, 97
marks for, 95, 96
the reader and the marker, 94, 96
typewritten camera copy, 94
Proofs —
Color Key, 186, 203
colored coating solutions, 203
Diazochrome transparencies, 186, 203
on direct-image plates, 227, 228
of hot type, 94
kinds of, 94
orange Color-Key conversion, 43
photographic bluelines, 202
of phototype, 94
revision sequence, 94
ruling on, 102
Watercotes, 203
Proportional rule or wheel, 100
Proportional spacing, typewriter, 54, 59, 64, 66, 68, 69
Protractor, 348
Protype, 72
Pull out rolls, 276

Pulsed xenon lights, 117
Punching holes, 272
Punctuation marks, names of, 96
Purples, as non-spectrum color, 156
Putting plate under, 368

Quads and spaces for type, 38
Quality control —
densitometer, uses of, 139
halftone negative evaluation, 149
image gain control, 196
on press, 297, 302, 304
*see also* Corrections, Proofreading, Sensitivity guide, Color guides, Color correction, Exposure computer
Quartz-iodine lighting, 117
Query, on proof, 96, 97

Radiation temperature, color, 158
Rag pulp, 262
Rainbow, cause of, 159
Rapidograph pen, 49
RCA Videocomp, type machine, 85
Readable, right reading, 5, 210
Ream, of paper, 266
Reduction, computing, 99, 101
Reflectance, light percentage, 136
Reflection, opaque pigments, 160
*see also* Light
Reflection copy, color printing, 171
Reflection curves, process inks, 162
Reflection density, 138
Reflection of light, 156
Reflex photocopying, 199
Refraction, refractive index, 156, 162
Register board, press, 275, 277, 300
Register pins, buttons, 183, 202, 226
Relative humidity, measuring, 361
Relief offset plates, 222, 252
Relief printing, letterpress, 1
Remington electric typewriter, 57
Reprinting existing prints, 48
Reproduction of color, *see* Color
Reproduction proofs (repros), 33
Instant Negative conversion, 44
on Scotchprint, 34
type spaced before proofing, 34
Rescreening halftone prints, 150
Research in graphic arts, xiv
Reservoir pen, 49
Resistant, ink term, 258
Resonance, color explanation, 159
Retoucher, on printing staff, 20
Reversal, (L to R), 5, 9, 109, 194, 198
Reverses (tones) —
copy for, 101
legibility on tones of gray, 105
photoprint, contacting, 197
type, on photo, 104
Revised (second) proof, 94
Revolution, printing techniques, xiv, 92
Ribbon, controller, *see* Control tape
Right reading, 5, 210

Right-reading image on offset negatives, 210
Rochester Institute of Technology, xiv
Roller-cleaning (ink) device, 306
Rollers, dampening, 282
Rollers, ink, 287, 305
Rosin, as paper sizing, 265
Rotogravure printing, 1, 2
Rough layout, 26, 27, 28
Rubber gloves, 334
*Rubel, Ira,* 12
Rub-off lettering, 53
Ruby-film, hand cut, 176
Rules and scales, drawing, 348
Ruling lines on proof, 102
Ruling pen, using, sharpening, 351

Saddle stitching, 271
Safety, 331-339
blades, cutter, 336
at card (film) cutter, 336
chemicals, 333
deliveries, lifting, 333
dressing for work, 332, 335
electrical, 334
around equipment, general rules, 335
at exposure devices, 337
eyes and face, 332
fan, ventilation, 334
fire precautions, 333
first aid, 331
flash-point, defined, 334
at folding machine, 336
general precautions, 331
grounding electrical equipment, 335
legal responsibilities, 338
at offset press, 296, 303, 335
orientation tour for, 332
at paper cutter, 336
at paper drill, 337
permissions, 332
personal cleanliness, toxicity, 332
personal conduct, 332
poisons, 334
presswork, 296, 303, 335
rubber gloves, 334
safety glasses, 333
shop layout for, 331
solvents, 287, 334
at stapler or stitcher, 337
at stripping tables, 336
with tools, 337
Sales functions of a company, 20
Scale, darkroom, beam type, 190
Scales, drawing, 348
Scaling copy for size, 99
Scaling —
diagonal-line method, 99
formula method, 100
proportional rule, 100
specifying percentage, 101
wheel for, 100
Scoring sheets on folder, 272
Scotch print, proofing on, 34
Scraper presses, lithographic, 10

Screen printing (silk screen), 2
Screen tints, 104, 178
  in color charts, 163-166
Screenless printing process, 129
Scribing lines on negatives, 102, 213
Scumming, on press, 285, 326
Selectric, IBM typewriter, 63
*Senefelder, Alois,* 8
Sensitivity guide —
  adjusting camera exposure, 124-125
  appearance on film, 121
  camera type, 120
  critical step table, camera copy, 124
  developing method, 121, 124, 194
  in platemaking, 225
Sensitometry, 135, 140
Separation, *see* Color printing, process
Set-off, press delivery, 281
  remedying, 328
Shading sheets, adhesive type, 106
Shadow area dots, 131
"Sheets" vs. "piece" of paper, 266
Shipping department workers, 23
Shortstop, film developing, 191
Shutter, camera, 115
Side-stitching, 271
Silhouette, photographic, 13
Silk screen printing, 2
Silverprint proofs, 202
Sizing, paper pulp, 263
Sizing copy, *see* Scaling
Sketches for layout, 27
Slide rule, for scaling, 101
Slitting sheets on folder, 272
Slugs, linecast type, 40
  type spacing, 38
Slur gauge, 196
Soda pulp, 261
Solvents, 287, 334
Spaceband, Linotype, 41
Spaces and quads for type, 38
Spectrophotometer, 159
Spectrum, 156
Speed of typesetters, 90
Speedball pens, 50
Spreads and chokes, 199
Squeegee, silk screen, 2
Stapling, 271
Stay-flat, adhesive film holder, 118
Steelplate engraving, 2
Stencil printing method, 2
Step-and-Repeat, 215, 225
Sticky-back film holder, 118
Stitching, 271
Stock room workers, 23
Stone lithography, 8, 9
  applications of, 11
  modern supplies for, 12
  stones for, 9
Stopbath, developing, 191
StripPrinter, type machine, 73
**Stripping, ink band tests, 292**
Stripping —
  for color, 175-180, 216
  combinations, positive and reverse, 215

cutting windows, 213
equipment and supplies for, 208
the flat, 208-217
gripper allowance, 210
imposing multiple pages, 214
masks to separate flat color, 176
positioning negatives, 211
preparing for, 210
reference marks, 213
safety rules, 336
scribing lines, 213
step-and-repeat work, 215, 225
workers, x, 21, 22
Subtractive color theory, 161
Subtractive offset plates, 231
Sucker feet, 276
Sulphate pulp, 262
Sulphite pulp, 261
Sulphur, on blanket, 291
Supply houses for graphic arts, 24
Surface offset plates, 222, 226
Surprinting, 104, 201, 215
Systems office work, plates for, 226

T square, 347
Tab-type letters, 52
Tack, of ink, 258
*Talbot, Henry,* 16
*Talbot, William,* 13
Tape —
  preprinted borders, 53
  for stripping, 209
  *see also* Control tape
Teletypesetter (TTS), 90
Temperature conversion (F-C), 360
Template masking division for color,
  176
Templates, lettering, 49, 50
Thermo-Fax platemaking, 244
Thin-base film, use of, 111, 198, 203
Thumb-nail sketch, 27
Time-temperature, developing method,
  193
Tint screens, 104, 106, 178
Tinting on sheet, 327
Toners, ink colors, 258
Tones, continuous gradation, 129
  *see also* Halftone, Densitometry
Tones, reproducing, 99, 129
Tools for shop, 297, 337
Training for printing, 92
Transfer type, 53
Transmission density, 138
Transmittance, light percentage, 136
Transparency opening, camera, 117,
  180
Transparent colors, 160, 162, 258
Transparent copy, color printing, 171
Trays, developing, 190
Triangles, drawing, 347
Tri-Mask Guide, color, 182
Tungsten lights, *see* Incandescent
Tusche, "correction fluid", 8
Type —
  body sizes, 29
  display, 28

indicating on layout, 28
  tracing card for layout, 28
Type composition —
  adhesive preprinted type, 52
  Alphatype, 89
  ATF Typesetter, 85
  borders, tape type, 53
  Brightype conversion method, 46
  California job case layout, 38
  cold type methods, 33
  Color-Key conversion method, 43
  Cronapress conversion method, 45
  enlargement-reduction dangers, 34
  font, family, 35, 37
  foundry type, 35, 37
  Friden Justowriter, 68
  Friden Typro, 76
  hand lettered, 49
  hot type methods, 33
  Instant Negative, conversion, 44
  Intertype Fotosetter, 79
  justifying lines, 38
  leads and slugs for space, 38
  Linofilm, 81
  Linotron, electronic unit, 85
  Linotype, Intertype, 40
  Ludlow, 42
  marks on copy or proofs, 95, 96
  metal type, use of, 33
  Monophoto, 77
  Monotype, 39
  Morisawa Photo Typesetter, 85
  numerical size confusing, 35
  photographic display, 71
  photographic text, 77
  Photon, 85
  pre-printed type, 51
  proofing procedure, 38
  proofreading, 94-97
  Protype, 72
  series, of type sizes, 36
  size designation, 35
  spaces and quads, 38
  spacing terms, 95
  specimen books, 28, 35, 36
  specimens, 54, 56, 59, 62, 63, 65,
    66
  Strip Printer, 73
  summary of methods, 90
  Tab-type individual letters, 52
  transfer (rub-off) type, 53
  typewriter, 54-70, *see also*
    Impact
  variations in face, 95
  VariTyper, 65
  wood type, 43

Type designer (illus), vi
Type makeup (illus), 21
Type masters, *see* Matrices
Type-high, 35, 355
Typesetting, hand (illus), 21
Typesetting services, 24
Typewriter composition, *see* Impact
Typing a direct-image plate, 227
Typing manuscript to copyfit, 30

Typit interchangeable typewriter bars, 65
Typography, learning the art, 92
Typro, phototype machine, 76

Underlay, blanket patch, 290, 291
Underwood Raphael typewriter, 61
Unreadable, wrong-reading, 5

Vacuum back, camera, 118
Vacuum frame, 194, 195, 223
Value, of colors, 157
Varigraph lettering tool, 50
VariTyper composing machine, 65
Vehicle, ink, 256
Velox paper for contacting, 197
Vertical cameras, 112

Videocomp, electronic type machine, 85
Virgule, ( / ), 95, 97
Viscosity, of ink, 258
Visible spectrum, 156
    *see also* Color
Visual densitometer, 139
Voltage control, for lights, 158

Water, press, *see* Dampening
Water colors, ink, 258
Water fountain, *see* Dampening
Waterhouse stops, 116
Water-ink balance, 4
Watermark, aligning for run, 299
Wave lengths, color, electromagnetic, 156

Weighting and thinning, photoprints, 199
Weight-measure equivalents, 359
Wet photographic plates, 14
Wet-dry-bulb thermometer, 362
Wipe-on plates, 238, 369
Wire side, of paper, 266
Wood type, 43
Workers in offset printing, 20
Wrattan Filter numbers, 127, 184
Wrong-reading, unreadable, 5, 35

Xenon lighting, 117, 145
Xerography, 245

Zinc plates, 12, 219, 237

# Colophon

Since *Photo-Offset Fundamentals* is a product of offset printing, both inside and out, the production details may have special interest.

TYPOGRAPHY:      *Basic Type Face* — Caledonia, designed by William A. Dwiggins
                           11/12, 18 picas, for straight matter
                           8/10, for footnotes and tables
                           8/9, for index
                           9/11, for bibliography and colophon
                           11/12 Bold, for running heads and folios
                  *Contrasting Face* — Vogue, by Intertype
                           14/18 Extra Bold, for chapter titles
                           12/14 Bold, for main heads
                           10/12 Bold, for subheads
                           8/10 Light, for figure legends
                      *Featured Face* — Kennerley, designed by Frederick W. Goudy
                           30 point, handset, on opening pages

COMPOSITION:    Hand keyboarded on Intertypes at Loheide-Caswell Typographers of Peoria, made up into pages, conversion by repro proofs.

IMPOSITION:    Page repros positioned 8-up for 16-page signatures, blocks for windows, ruling, and other artwork added.

PHOTOGRAPHY:    4-up negatives on Kodalith Ortho Type 3 film, shot on a Robertson 31-inch Jupiter camera with Xenon lighting. Halftones shot on thin-base film with a 133-line gray contact screen having an elliptical dot. Duplicate negatives or positives contacted on DuPont Contact Reversal film or on Kodalith Contact film.

STRIPPING:    Film assembled on Carlson plastic masking sheets, registered with pins. Byrum screen tints added.

PLATEMAKING:    Type "K" and "S" 25" x 38" 3M plates exposed to a 140-ampere arc.

PRESSWORK:    Runs split between a Harris LUM 2-color press and a Miller TP-38 2-color-*or*-perfector press. Color progression: Y-C, M-Bk.

COVER:    Designed (with the title page) by H. Harris Howeler. Type photoset by Warwick Typographers of St. Louis. Lithographed in red and black on white cloth, by Rand McNally & Company of Chicago. Two plastic over-coatings.

BINDING:    Smyth-sewn in 32-page units with one 16 inserted in another, except for the first and last 16's (which incorporate special muslin reinforcement for the end sheets) and a pair of 24's (which have an 8-page insert for positioning color signatures efficiently). Bound by Rand McNally, to meet all specifications recommended by the Book Manufacturers Institute.